unit (amu): 1 amu $= 1.6604 \times 10^{-27}$ kg. The atomic mass of carb[illegible] because it is the average of the different isotopes naturally present in carbon. (For artificially produced elements, the approximate atomic mass of the most stable isotope is given in brackets.)

V	VI	VII	VIII			0
						2 He 4.0026
7 N 14.0067	8 O 15.9994	9 F 18.9984				10 Ne 20.183
15 P 30.9738	16 S 32.064	17 Cl 35.453				18 A 39.948
23 V 50.942	24 Cr 51.996	25 Mn 54.9380	26 Fe 55.847	27 Co 58.9332	28 Ni 58.71	
33 As 74.9216	34 Se 78.96	35 Br 79.909				36 Kr 83.80
41 Nb 92.906	42 Mo 95.94	43 Tc [99]	44 Ru 101.07	45 Rh 102.905	46 Pd 106.4	
51 Sb 121.75	52 Te 127.60	53 I 126.9044				54 Xe 131.30
73 Ta 180.948	74 W 183.85	75 Re 186.2	76 Os 190.2	77 Ir 192.2	78 Pt 195.09	
83 Bi 208.980	84 Po [210]	85 At [210]				86 Rn [222]

63 Eu 151.96	64 Gd 157.25	65 Tb 158.924	66 Dy 162.50	67 Ho 164.930	68 Er 167.26	69 Tm 168.934	70 Yb 173.04	71 Lu 174.97
95 Am [243]	96 Cm [245]	97 Bk [249]	98 Cf [249]	99 Es [253]	100 Fm [255]	101 Md [256]	102 No	103

Constant	Symbol	Value
Bohr magneton	μ_B	9.2732×10^{-24} J T^{-1}
Avogadro constant	N_A	6.0225×10^{23} mol^{-1}
Boltzmann constant	k	1.3805×10^{-23} J °K^{-1}
Gas constant	R	8.3143 J °K^{-1} mol^{-1}
Ideal gas normal volume (STP)	V_0	2.2414×10^{-2} m^3 mol^{-1}
Faraday constant	F	9.6487×10^4 C mol^{-1}
Coulomb constant	K_e	8.9874×10^9 N m^2 C^{-2}
Vacuum permittivity	ϵ_0	8.8544×10^{-12} N^{-1} m^{-2} C^2
Magnetic constant	K_m	1.0000×10^{-7} m kg C^{-2}
Vacuum permeability	μ_0	1.3566×10^{-6} m kg C^{-2}
Gravitational constant	γ	6.670×10^{-11} N m^2 kg^{-2}
Acceleration of gravity at sea level and at equator	g	9.7805 m s^{-2}

Numerical constants: $\pi = 3.1416$; $e = 2.7183$; $\sqrt{2} = 1.4142$; $\sqrt{3} = 1.7320$

FUNDAMENTAL UNIVERSITY PHYSICS

VOLUME I

MECHANICS

FUNDAMENTAL

ADDISON-WESLEY PUBLISHING COMPANY

UNIVERSITY PHYSICS

VOLUME I

MECHANICS

MARCELO ALONSO

Department of Scientific Affairs, Organization of American States

EDWARD J. FINN

Department of Physics, Georgetown University

READING, MASSACHUSETTS · PALO ALTO · LONDON · DON MILLS, ONTARIO

This book is in the

ADDISON-WESLEY SERIES IN PHYSICS

Consulting editor

DAVID LAZARUS

 Library of Congress Catalog Card Number 66-10828.

FOREWORD

Physics is a fundamental science which has a profound influence on all the other sciences. Therefore, not only must physics majors and engineering students have a thorough understanding of its fundamental ideas, but anyone who plans a career in science (including students majoring in biology, chemistry, and mathematics) must have this same understanding.

The primary purpose of the general physics course (and perhaps the only reason it is in the curriculum) is to give the student a unified view of physics. This should be done without bringing in too many details, but by analyzing the basic principles, their implications, and their limitations. The student will learn specific applications in the more specialized courses that follow. Thus this book presents what we believe are the fundamental ideas that constitute the core of today's physics. We gave careful consideration to the recommendations of the Commission on College Physics in selecting the subject matter and its method of presentation.

Until recently, physics has been taught as if it were a conglomeration of several sciences, more or less related, but without any real unifying point of view. The traditional division into (the "science" of) mechanics, heat, sound, optics, electromagnetism, and modern physics no longer has any justification. We have departed from this traditional approach. Instead, we follow a logical and unified presentation, emphasizing the conservation laws, the concepts of fields and waves, and the atomic view of matter. The special theory of relativity is used extensively throughout the text as one of the guiding principles that must be met by any physical theory.

The subject matter has been divided into five parts: (1) Mechanics, (2) Interactions and Fields, (3) Waves, (4) Quantum Physics, and (5) Statistical Physics. We start with mechanics, in order to set up the fundamental principles needed to describe the motions we observe around us. Then, since all phenomena in nature are the result of interactions, and these interactions are analyzed in terms of fields, in Part 2 we consider the kinds of interactions we understand best: gravitational and electromagnetic interactions, which are the interactions responsible for most of the macroscopic phenomena we observe. We discuss electromagnetism in considerable detail, concluding with the formulation of Maxwell's equations. In Part 3 we discuss wave phenomena as a consequence of the field concept. It is in this part that we have included much of the material usually covered under the headings of acoustics and optics. The emphasis, however, has been placed on electromagnetic waves as a natural extension of Maxwell's equations. In Part 4 we analyze the structure of matter—that is, atoms, molecules, nuclei, and fundamental particles—an analysis preceded by the necessary background in quantum mechanics. Finally, in Part 5, we talk about the properties of matter in bulk. First we present the principles of statistical mechanics, and apply them to some simple, but fundamental, cases. We discuss thermodynamics from the point of view of statistical mechanics, and conclude with a chapter on the thermal properties of matter, showing how the principles of statistical mechanics and of thermodynamics are applied.

This text is novel not only in its approach but also in its content, since we have included some fundamental topics not found in most general physics texts and deleted others that are traditional. The mathematics used can be found in any standard textbook on calculus. We assume that the student has had a minimal introduction to calculus and is taking a concurrent course in the subject. Many applications of fundamental principles, as well as a few more advanced topics, appear in the form of worked-out examples. These may be discussed at the instructor's convenience or proposed on a selective basis, thus allowing a greater flexibility in organizing the course.

The curricula for all sciences are under great pressure to incorporate new subjects that are becoming more relevant. We expect that this book will relieve this pressure by raising the level of the student's understanding of physical concepts and his ability to manipulate the corresponding mathematical relations. This will permit many intermediate courses presently offered in the undergraduate curriculum to be upgraded. The traditional undergraduate courses in mechanics, electromagnetism, and modern physics will benefit most from this upgrading. Thus the student will finish his undergraduate career at a higher level of knowledge than formerly—an important benefit for those who terminate their formal education at this point. Also there will now be room for newer and more exciting courses at the graduate level. This same trend is found in the more recent basic textbooks in other sciences for freshman and sophomore courses.

The text is designed for a three-semester course. It may also be used in those schools in which a two-semester general physics course is followed by a one-semester course in modern physics, thus offering a more unified presentation over the three semesters. For convenience the text has been divided into three volumes, each roughly corresponding to a semester. Volume I treats mechanics and the gravitational interaction. Volume II deals with electromagnetic interactions and waves, essentially covering the subjects of electromagnetism and optics. Quantum and statistical physics, including thermodynamics, are covered in Volume III. Although the three volumes are closely related and form a unified text, each one can be considered as a self-contained introductory text. In particular, Volumes I and II together are the equivalent of a two-semester general physics course, covering nonquantum physics.

We hope that this text will assist progressive physics instructors who are constantly struggling to improve the courses they teach. We also hope that it will stimulate the many students who deserve a presentation of physics which is more mature than that of the traditional course.

We want to express our gratitude to all those who, because of their assistance and encouragement, have made the completion of this work possible. We recognize our distinguished colleagues, in particular Professors D. Lazarus and H. S. Robertson, who read the original manuscript; their criticism and comments helped to correct and improve many aspects of the text. We are also grateful for the ability and dedication of the staff of Addison-Wesley. Last, but not least, we sincerely thank our wives, who have so patiently stood by us.

Washington, D.C.
June 1966

M.A.
E.J.F.

NOTE TO THE INSTRUCTOR

To assist the instructor in setting up his course, we present a brief outline of this volume and some suggestions concerning the important concepts in each chapter. As indicated in the foreword, this physics course has been developed in an integrated form so that the student quickly recognizes the few basic ideas on which physics is based (for example, the conservation laws, and the fact that physical phenomena can be reduced to interactions between fundamental particles). The student should recognize that to become a physicist or an engineer he must attain a clear understanding of these ideas and develop the ability to manipulate them.

The basic subject matter forms the body of the text. Many worked-out examples have been included in each chapter; some are simple numerical applications of the theory being discussed, while others are either actual extensions of the theory or mathematical derivations. It is recommended that in his first reading of a chapter the student be advised to omit *all* examples. Then, on the second reading, he should look into the examples chosen by the instructor. In this way the student will grasp the basic ideas separate from their applications or extensions.

There is a problem section at the end of each chapter. Some of them are more difficult than the average general physics problem and others are extremely simple. They are arranged in an order that roughly corresponds to the sections of the chapter, with a few more difficult problems at the end. The large number of varied problems gives the instructor more freedom of choice in matching problems with his own students' abilities.

We suggest that the instructor establish a reserve shelf based on the reference material listed at the end of each chapter, and encourage the student to use it so that he may develop the habit of checking source material, getting more than one interpretation of a topic, and acquiring historical information about physics.

The present volume is designed to cover the first semester. (However, Chapter 13 *can* be postponed until the second semester.) We have suggested as a guide, on the basis of our own experience, the number of lecture hours needed to comfortably cover the material. The time listed (43 lecture hours) does not include recitation or testing time. A brief comment on each chapter follows.

Chapter 1. *Introduction* (1 hour)

This chapter is designed to give the student a preliminary insight into the science he is about to study; hence he should read it carefully. A brief classroom discussion should be organized by the instructor.

Chapter 2. *Measurement and Units* (1 hour)

Following the recommendations of the commission on Symbols, Units, and Nomenclature of IUPAP, we have adhered to the MKSC system of units. Whenever we introduce a new MKSC unit in later chapters, we give its equivalent in the cgs and the British systems. The problems in this chapter are designed to give the student a feeling of the "large" and the "small."

Chapter 3. *Vectors* (3 hours)

The basic ideas of vector algebra are introduced and illustrated by problems in kinematics. Sections 3.8, 3.9, and 3.10 may be postponed until these concepts are needed for the first time in the text. Because of its limited physical motivation, the chapter may be a difficult one for the student. The teacher should, however, impress on him the necessity for vector notation, and seek to enliven the lectures with physical examples.

Chapter 4. *Forces* ($2\frac{1}{2}$ hours)

We put this chapter early in the book for several reasons. First, it provides a familiar application of vectors. Second, it allows time for the student to learn some basic calculus before embarking on the study of kinematics. Third, it permits an uninterrupted development of mechanics in Chapters 5 through 12. For courses in which this material is not required, this chapter can be omitted, with the exception of Sections 4.3 (torque) and 4.8 (center of mass). If desired, the chapter could be assigned after Section 7.6, but we do not recommend this procedure.

PART 1. MECHANICS

In Chapters 5 through 12, the text develops the major concepts of classical and relativistic mechanics. We first discuss, as a simplification, the mechanics of a single particle, but we cover many-particle systems in great detail. We emphasize the distinction between the ideal single-particle system and the real many-particle system.

Chapter 5. *Kinematics* ($3\frac{1}{2}$ hours)

This chapter must be covered in depth, and entirely. The student must understand the vector nature of velocity and acceleration and their relations to the path. The instructor should stress that, when the time rate of change of a vector is computed, one must consider both the changes in magnitude *and* in direction. The calculus required for this chapter is relatively simple. If the instructor wishes, he can postpone Section 5.11 and discuss it just before Section 7.14.

Chapter 6. *Relative Motion* (4 hours)

We consider relative motion from a kinematical point of view. This chapter precedes the one on dynamics, so that the student grasps the importance of frames of reference.

Sections 6.4 and 6.5 (on rotational frames) may be omitted and Sections 6.6 and 6.7 (on relativistic frames) may be postponed (if desired) until Chapter 11.

Chapter 7. *Dynamics of a Particle* (4 hours)

This is one of the more important chapters, and the student should digest it thoroughly. The principle of conservation of momentum is given more relevance than the relation $F = ma$. The limitations of the laws of motion and the concepts of interactions and forces must be analyzed very carefully.

Chapter 8. *Work and Energy* (3 hours)

This chapter is, in a sense, an extension of Chapter 7, and must also be understood thoroughly. Section 8.10 (central forces) may be omitted or postponed until Chapter 13. The more important ideas are the concepts of energy and the conservation of energy for a single particle. We introduce the virial theorem for a particle here, because this theorem is being used more and more extensively in both physics and chemistry.

Chapter 9. *Dynamics of a System of Particles* (5 hours)

For simplicity, most of the results are derived for two particles and then, by similarity, these results are extended to an arbitrary number of particles. We introduce the concepts of temperature, heat, and pressure as convenient statistical concepts to describe the behavior of systems composed of a very large number of particles. This allows us to use these concepts throughout the rest of the book. The equation of state of a gas is derived from the virial theorem because this more clearly reveals the role of internal forces; a more traditional approach is also presented in Example 9.17. The chapter closes with a section on fluid motion that may be omitted if desired.

Chapter 10. *Dynamics of a Rigid Body* ($3\frac{1}{2}$ hours)

Great emphasis should be placed on the precession of angular momentum under an applied torque. The section on gyroscopic motion is also important, since the ideas developed are used many times.

Chapter 11. *High-Energy Dynamics* ($3\frac{1}{2}$ hours)

This is essentially a chapter on relativistic dynamics, emphasizing the concepts of system velocity (or C-frame) and of the Lorentz transformation of energy and momentum. This is naturally an important chapter in today's physics.

Chapter 12. *Oscillatory Motion* (5 hours)

Simple harmonic motion is first presented kinematically and then dynamically. This chapter can either be discussed in its entirety at this time (end of first semester) or limited to the first few sections only, deferring the remaining sections until they are required for later chapters. We recommend the first alternative. The first semester could be concluded with this chapter.

PART 2. INTERACTIONS AND FIELDS

This part is dedicated to a study of gravitational and electromagnetic interactions, which are discussed in Chapters 13 through 17. Here we stress the concept of a field as a useful tool for physics. Since we realize that many instructors like to discuss gravitation during the first semester and immediately after completing mechanics, we have included Chapter 13 in this volume, reserving the study of the electromagnetic interaction (Chapters 14 through 17) for the second semester and Volume II.

Chapter 13. *Gravitational Interaction* (4 hours)

This is a brief account of gravitation, which illustrates the application of mechanics to a particular interaction. It also serves to introduce the student to the concept of field. The chapter is written in such a way that it ties in, in a natural way, with the discussion of electromagnetic interaction in Volume II. Sections 13.5 and 13.7 may be omitted without loss of continuity. Section 13.8 provides a brief account of the ideas of the theory of general relativity.

NOTE TO THE STUDENT

This is a book about the fundamentals of physics written for students majoring in science or engineering. The concepts and ideas you learn from it will, in all probability, become part of your professional life and your way of thinking. The better you understand them, the easier the rest of your undergraduate and graduate education will be.

The course in physics that you are about to begin is naturally more advanced than your high-school physics course. You must be prepared to tackle numerous difficult puzzles. To grasp the laws and techniques of physics may be, at times, a slow and painful process. Before you enter those regions of physics that appeal to your imagination, you must master other, less appealing, but very fundamental ones, without which you cannot use or understand physics properly.

You should keep two main objectives before you while taking this course. First: become thoroughly familiar with the handful of basic laws and principles that constitute the core of physics. Second: develop the ability to manipulate these ideas and apply them to concrete situations; in other words, to think and act as a physicist. You can achieve the first objective mainly by reading and re-reading those sections in large print in the text. To help you attain the second objective, there are many worked-out examples, in small print, throughout the text, and there are the homework problems at the end of each chapter. We strongly recommend that you first read the main text and, once you are acquainted with it, proceed with those examples and problems assigned by the instructor. The examples either illustrate an application of the theory to a concrete situation, or extend the theory by considering new aspects of the problem discussed. Sometimes they provide some justification for the theory.

The problems at the end of each chapter vary in degree of difficulty. They range from the very simple to the complex. In general, it is a good idea to try to solve a problem in a symbolic or algebraic form first, and insert numerical values only at the end. If you cannot solve an assigned problem in a reasonable time, lay the problem aside and make a second attempt later. For those few problems that refuse to yield a solution, you should seek help. One source of self-help that will teach you the *method* of problem-solving is the book *How to Solve It* (second edition), by G. Polya (Garden City, N. Y.: Doubleday, 1957).

Physics is a quantitative science, which requires mathematics for the expression of its ideas. All the mathematics used in this book can be found in a standard calculus text, and you should consult such a text whenever you do not understand a mathematical derivation. But by no means should you feel discouraged by a mathematical difficulty; in case of mathematical trouble, consult your instructor or a more advanced student. For the physical scientist and engineer, mathematics is a tool, and is second in importance to understanding the physical ideas. For your convenience, some of the most useful mathematical relations are listed in an appendix at the end of the book.

All physical calculations must be carried out using a consistent set of units. In this book the MKSC system is used. Since it differs from the British system, you may find it unfamiliar at first. However, it requires very little effort to become acquainted with it. Also, this is the system officially approved for scientific work and used by the United States National Bureau of Standards in its publications. Be extremely careful to check the consistency of the units in all your calculations. Also, it is a good idea to use a slide rule from the start; the three-place accuracy of even the simplest slide rule will save you many hours of computation. In some instances, however, a slide rule may not provide the required accuracy.

A selected list of references is given at the end of each chapter. Consult them as often as possible. Some will help you to grasp the idea of physics as an evolving science, while others will amplify material in the text. In particular, you will find the book by Holton and Roller, *Foundations of Modern Physics* (Reading, Mass.: Addison-Wesley, 1958) particularly useful for information about the evolution of ideas in physics.

CONTENTS

PART 1 MECHANICS

Chapter 5 Kinematics

Chapter 6 Relative Motion

Chapter 7 Dynamics of a Particle

Chapter 8 Work and Energy

Chapter 9 Dynamics of a System of Particles

The Parts of all homogeneal hard Bodies which fully touch one another, stick together very strongly. And for explaining how this may be, some have invented hooked Atoms. . . . I had rather infer from their Cohesion, that their Particles attract one another by some Force, which in immediate Contact is exceeding strong, and reaches not far from the Particles with any sensible Effect. . . . There are therefore Agents in Nature able to make the Particles of Bodies stick together by very strong Attractions. And it is the Business of experimental Philosophy to find them out.

Optiks, BOOK 3, QUERY 31 (1703), NEWTON

1
INTRODUCTION

Studying physics is an exciting and challenging adventure. To be a professional physicist is even more exciting. Perhaps it is one of the most pleasing activities of the human intellect since, in the authors' opinion, nothing appeals more to the mind than learning about the world we live in and unraveling the secrets of nature.

It may seem unnecessary at this point to tell the student what physics is about, why it is so challenging and interesting, or what its methods are, since he already has some familiarity with this science. However, precisely because of his familiarity with physics, it is desirable to analyze and review the objectives and methods of this science before embarking on its study at a somewhat higher level. That is what we shall briefly do in this chapter.

1.1 What Is Physics?

The word *physics* comes from a Greek term meaning *nature*, and therefore physics should be a science dedicated to the study of all natural phenomena. In fact, until early in the nineteenth century physics was understood in this broad sense, and it was called "natural philosophy." However, during the nineteenth century and until very recently, physics was restricted to the study of a more limited group of phenomena, designated by the name of *physical phenomena* and loosely defined as processes in which the *nature* of the participating substances does not change. This somewhat awkward definition of physics has been gradually discarded, returning to the broader and more fundamental concept of previous times. Accordingly, we may say that *physics is a science whose objective is to study the components of matter and their mutual interactions. In terms of these interactions the scientist explains the properties of matter in bulk, as well as the other natural phenomena we observe.*

As he progresses through this course, the student will witness the way this program is developed from basic and general principles and applied to the understanding of a large variety of physical phenomena, apparently unrelated but obeying the same fundamental laws. Once these great principles are clearly understood the student will be able to attack new problems with great economy of thought and effort.

1.2 The Classical Branches of Physics

Man, having an inquiring mind, has always had a great curiosity about how nature works. At the beginning his only sources of information were his senses, and therefore he classified the phenomena he observed according to the way he sensed them. *Light* was related to the act of vision and *optics* was developed as a more or less independent science associated with this act. *Sound* was related to the act of hearing and *acoustics* developed as a correlative science. *Heat* was related to another kind of physical sensation, and for many years the study of heat (called *thermodynamics*) was yet another autonomous branch of physics. *Motion*, of course, is the most common of all directly observed phenomena, and the science of motion, *mechanics*, developed earlier than any other branch of physics. The motion of the planets caused by their gravitational interactions, as well as the free fall of bodies, was very nicely explained by the laws of mechanics; therefore *gravitation* was traditionally discussed as a chapter of mechanics. *Electromagnetism*, not being directly related to any sensory experience—in spite of being responsible for most of them—did not appear as an organized branch of physics until the nineteenth century.

So physics in the nineteenth century appeared to be divided into a few (called *classical*) sciences or branches: mechanics, heat, sound, optics, and electromagnetism, with little or no connection between them, although mechanics was, quite properly, the guiding principle for all of them. And physics was so taught to students until very recently. Lately a new branch, called *modern physics*, which covers the developments of twentieth-century physics, has been added to these "classical" branches.

The "classical" branches of physics are, and will continue to be, very important fields of specialization and professional activity, but it no longer makes sense to study the fundamentals of physics in such a compartmentalized manner. The very same set of phenomena included under electromagnetism and modern physics have produced a new trend of thought that looks at physical phenomena from a unified and more logical point of view, and this is one of the great achievements of the twentieth century. This unified presentation of physics calls for a reappraisal of classical physics from a *modern* point of view—not a division of physics into *classical* and *modern*. There will always be a *modern physics* in the sense that there will be contemporary physics being developed in one's time. This modern physics will require at each instant a revision and a reevaluation of previous ideas and principles. *Classical* and *modern* physics are to be integrated at each stage into a single body of knowledge. Physics will always be a whole that must be considered in a consistent and logical way.

1.3 Our View of the Universe

At present we consider matter to be composed of a handful of fundamental (or elementary) particles and all bodies, both living and inert, to be made up of different groupings or arrangements of such particles. Three of these fundamental particles are especially important because of their presence in many common phenomena: *electrons*, *protons*, and *neutrons*.

There are a few other fundamental particles (some physicists think there are too many!) but they have a transient life, being continuously created and destroyed (and thus are termed unstable), and apparently they do not participate directly in most of the phenomena we observe around us (Fig. 1–1). Their existence is made manifest only by means of rather elaborate observational techniques, and their role in the general scheme is not yet completely understood. Some of these, such as the *pion*, are vital because of the role they play in the interactions between protons and neutrons. Fundamental particle research is of great importance today in obtaining some clue to the structure of the universe.

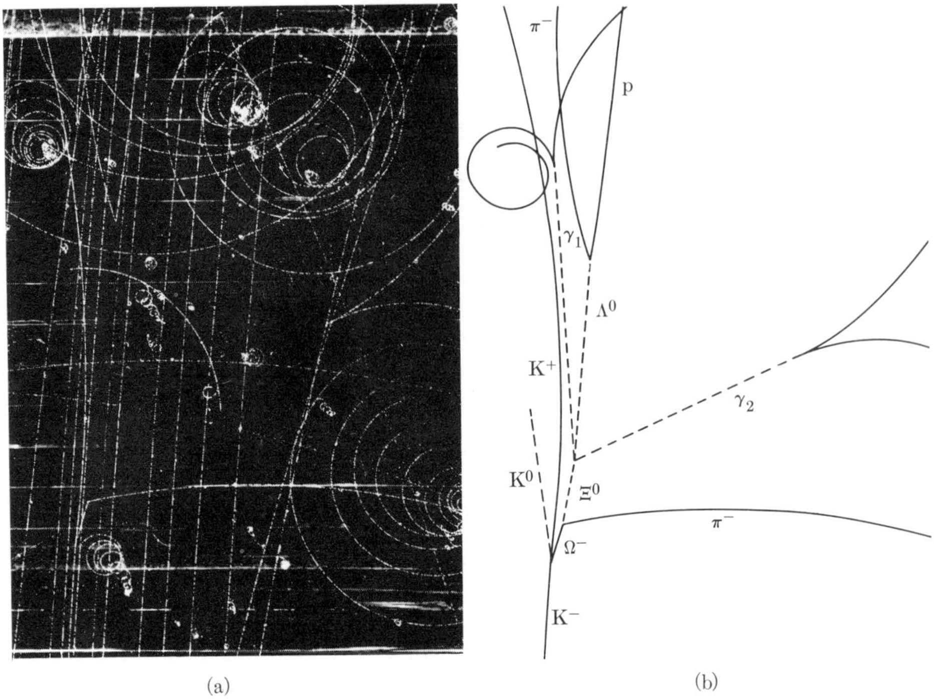

Fig. 1–1. (a) Fundamental particle tracks in 80-inch (2 m) liquid-hydrogen bubble chamber, which is placed in a strong magnetic field that forces the charged particles to follow curved paths. These tracks are analyzed, and from the analyses the properties of the different particles are derived. This photograph, taken in 1964, is historic. It provided the first evidence of the existence of the omega minus (Ω^-) particle, which had previously been predicted on a theoretical basis. (b) The line diagram shows the more important events registered in the photograph. The Ω^- track is the short line near the bottom of the picture. The particles corresponding to the other tracks are also identified. (Photograph courtesy Brookhaven National Laboratory.)

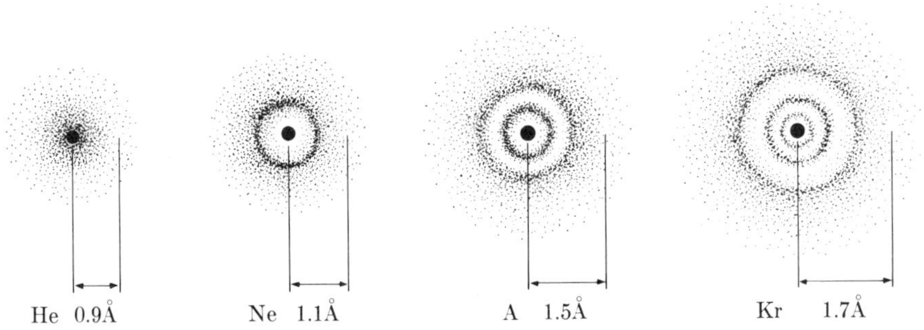

Fig. 1–2. Arrangements of electrons around the nucleus in some simple atoms (helium, He; neon, Ne; argon A; krypton, Kr). Since electrons do not follow well-defined paths, the dark regions are those more likely to be occupied by the electrons (1 Å = 1 angstrom = 10^{-10} m).

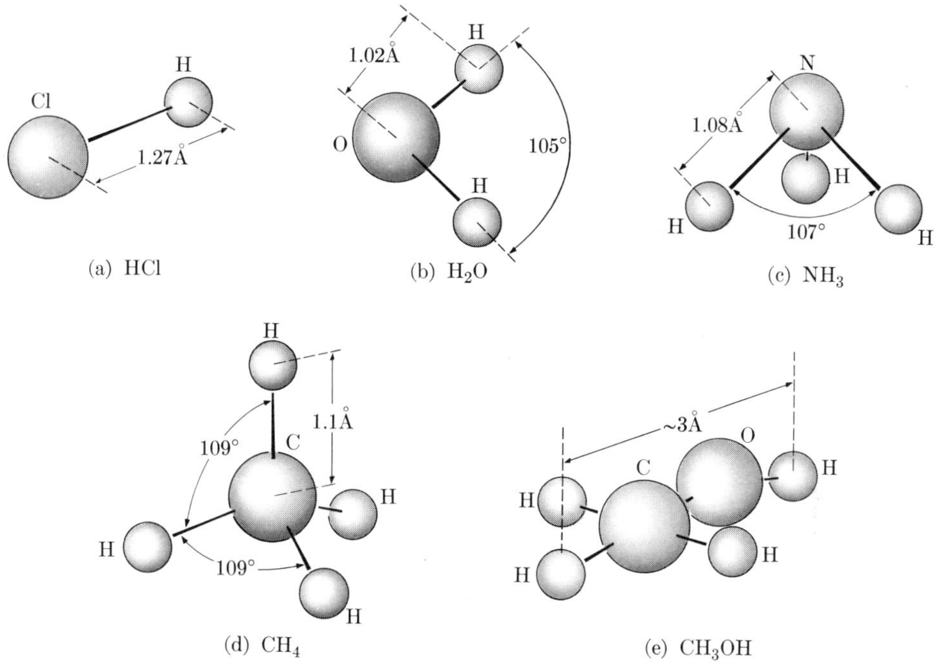

Fig. 1–3. Some relatively simple molecules. The inner electrons remain attached to the respective atoms, but the outer ones either move in the space between two atoms or more or less freely over the molecule (1 Å = 1 angstrom = 10^{-10} m).

Using an oversimplified language, we may say that the three particles, electron, proton, and neutron, are present in well-defined groups called *atoms*, with the protons and neutrons clustered in a very small central region called the *nucleus* (Fig. 1–2). About 104 distinct "species" of atoms have been recognized (see Table A–1), but there are about 1300 different "varieties" of atoms, called *isotopes*. Atoms in turn form other aggregates called *molecules*, of which several thousands of different kinds are known to exist. The number of different molecules seems to be extremely large, since more and more new molecules are synthesized every day in chemical laboratories. Some molecules contain just a few atoms, such as hydrochloric acid [whose molecules are formed of one atom of hydrogen and one atom of chlorine (Fig. 1–3)], while others may have as many as several hundred atoms, such as the proteins, enzymes, and the nucleic acids [DNA and RNA (Fig. 1–4)] or some organic polymers such as polyethylene or polyvinylchloride (PVC). Finally, molecules group together forming bodies (or matter in bulk), appearing to us as solids, liquids, or gases* (Fig. 1–5) although this classification or division is not a rigid one.

* Another state of matter is the *plasma*, consisting of a gaseous mixture of positive and negative ions (or charged particles). Most of the matter in the universe is in the form of a plasma.

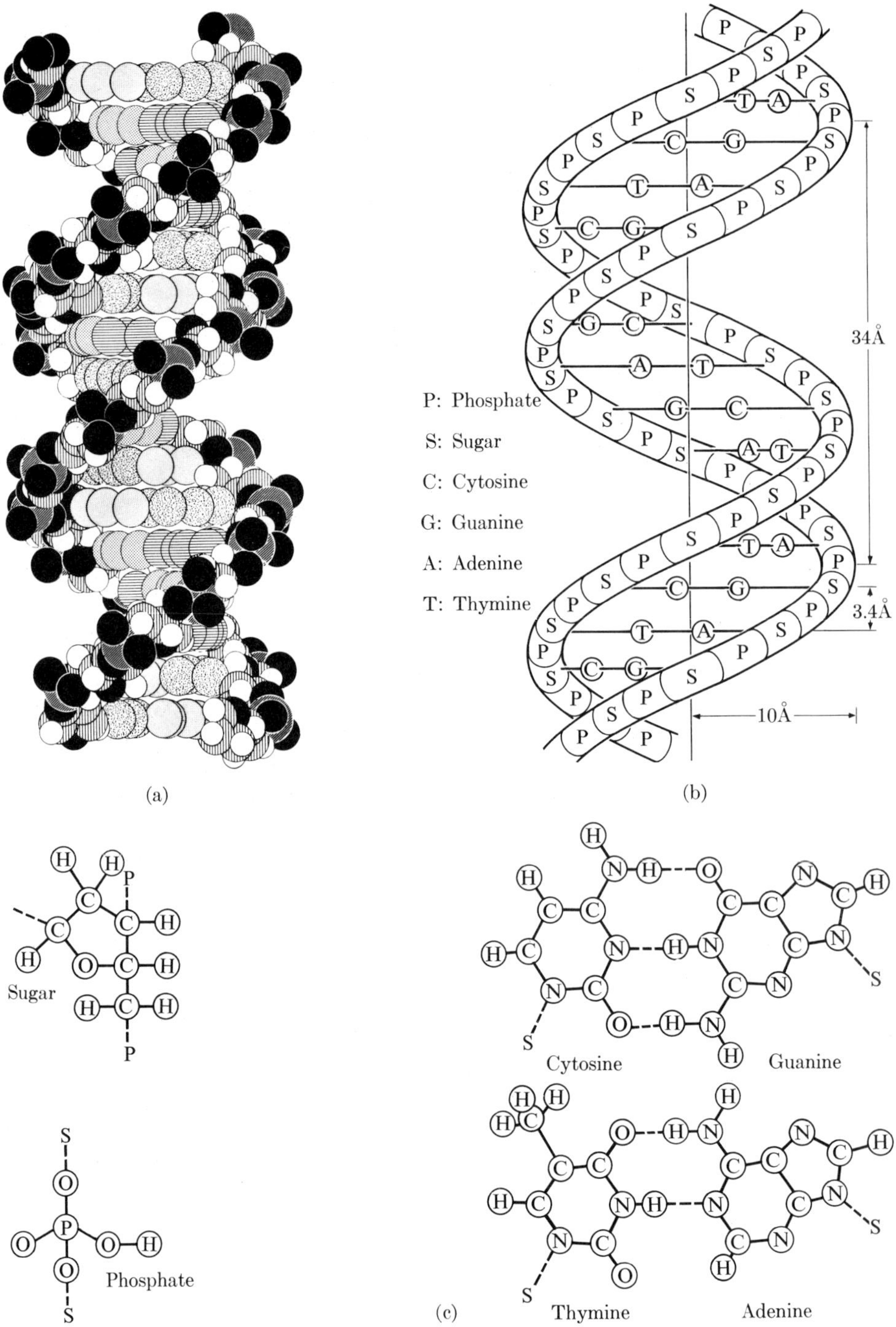
P: Phosphate
S: Sugar
C: Cytosine
G: Guanine
A: Adenine
T: Thymine
34Å
3.4Å
10Å
(a)
(b)
Sugar
Phosphate
Cytosine
Guanine
Thymine
Adenine
(c)

Figure 1–4

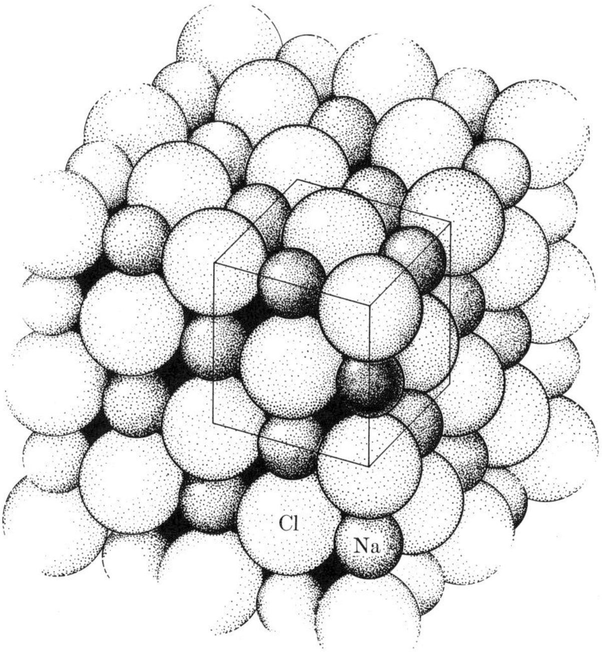

Fig. 1–5. Crystal structure of sodium chloride. The atoms are arranged in a regular geometric form that extends over a relatively large volume. This structure is reflected in the external appearance of the macroscopic crystals.

A particularly important kind of body is the living body or *living matter*, also designated *protoplasm*, in which molecules appear in a highly organized pattern and exhibit properties and functions that are apparently distinct from those of inert matter. The human body, which is the most developed of all living bodies, is composed of about 10^{28} atoms; most of these are carbon, hydrogen, oxygen, and nitrogen atoms.

The solar system is an aggregate of several huge bodies called planets, which rotate about a star, called the sun. One of the planets is our earth, which contains about 10^{51} atoms. The sun is composed of about 10^{57} atoms. The solar system

---

Fig. 1–4. Crick-Watson model of desoxyribonucleic acid (DNA). One of the two nucleic acids involved in the composition of a chromosome, DNA carries genetic information, and is one of the best-studied giant molecules. X-ray diffraction has shown that it consists of two antiparallel helices composed of a sequence of sugar (S) and phosphate (P) groups. The sugar, called desoxyribose, contains five carbon atoms. The two helices are interlocked by pairs of hydrogen-bonded base groups. One pair is formed by two substances called adenine and thymine (A-T) and the other by cytosine and guanine (C-G). The genetic code of the DNA molecule depends on the sequence or ordering of each base pair. These base pairs are like rungs along a helical stepladder, each rung being about 11 angstroms long. The pitch of each helix is about 34 angstroms, and its overall diameter is about 18 angstroms (1 angstrom $= 10^{-10}$ m).

in turn is a small part of a large aggregate of stars which form a galaxy called the Milky Way, composed of about 10^{11} stars or 10^{70} atoms and having a disk shape, with a diameter of about 10^{21} m or about 100,000 light years, and a maximum thickness of about 10^{20} m. Many galaxies similar to ours have been observed (Fig. 1–6), the closest being about two million light years or 2×10^{22} m from us. The universe may contain about 10^{20} stars grouped in about 10^{10} galaxies and containing a total of about 10^{80} atoms in a region whose radius is of the order of 10^{26} m or 10^{10} light years.

Some natural questions come to our mind. Why and how are electrons, protons, and neutrons bound together to form atoms? Why and how are atoms bound together to form molecules? Why and how are molecules bound together to form bodies? How does it happen that matter aggregates itself in size from small dust particles to huge planets, from bacteria to this marvelous creature called man? We may answer these fundamental questions, in principle, by introducing the notion of *interactions*. We say that the particles in an atom interact among themselves in such a way as to produce a stable configuration. Atoms in turn interact to produce molecules, and molecules interact to form bodies. Matter in bulk also exhibits certain obvious interactions, such as gravitation.

This concept of interaction is not new. We are not promulgating a radical new doctrine, or overthrowing long-established concepts. We have merely changed and adapted the wording used to describe the makeup of the universe, as a result of the many years of investigation since 300 B.C., when Aristotle, in his *De Caelo*, said, "They [atoms] move in the void and catching each other up jostle together, and some recoil in any direction that may chance, and others become entangled with one another in varying degrees, according to the symmetry of their shapes and sizes and positions and order, and they remain together; and thus the coming into being of composite things is effected." We may compare Aristotle's wording with that of the Nobel laureate T. D. Lee, who, in 1965, said:* "The purpose of science is to seek for that simple set of fundamental principles through which all known facts are understood and new results predicted. Since all matter is composed of the same fundamental units, the ultimate foundation of all natural sciences must be based on the laws governing the behavior of these elementary particles."

It is the primary objective of the physicist to disclose the various interactions of matter; mainly, these are gravitational, electromagnetic and nuclear interactions. The physicist then tries to express them in a quantitative way, for which mathematics is required. Finally he attempts to formulate general rules about the behavior of matter in bulk—behavior which results from these fundamental interactions. A description of the behavior of matter in bulk is, by necessity, statistical in nature, since it involves a tremendously large number of molecules, whose individual motions are impossible to follow in detail. For example, in a raindrop there may be as many as 10^{20} water molecules.

---

* *Nature of Matter—Purposes of High Energy Physics*, Luke C. L. Yuan, editor. New York: Brookhaven National Laboratory, 1965.

Fig. 1–6. Great Nebula in Andromeda, also called M-31. The nearest of the large regular galaxies, it is still about 2,500,000 light years or 2.5×10^{22} m from the solar system. Its diameter is about 125,000 light years or 10^{21} m, and it contains more than 10^{11} stars. (Photograph courtesy Mount Wilson and Palomar Observatories.)

Physics covers a tremendous range of magnitudes, going from lengths of the order of 10^{-15} m and masses of the order of 10^{-31} kg (corresponding to a single particle such as the electron), up to—and far beyond—lengths of the order of 10^{9} m and masses of the order of 10^{30} kg (corresponding to bodies in our solar system). Although the basic laws are all the same, the way the laws are expressed and the types of approximation made depend on the particular range of magnitudes in which one is working.

1.4 The Relation of Physics to Other Sciences

We indicated in Section 1.1, and we may say again, that the objective of physics is to enable us to understand the basic components of matter and their mutual interactions, and thus to explain natural phenomena, including the properties of matter in bulk. From this statement we can see that physics is the most fundamental of all natural sciences. Chemistry deals basically with one particular aspect of this ambitious program: the application of the laws of physics to the formation of molecules and the different practical means of transforming certain molecules into others. And biology must lean very heavily on physics and chemistry to explain the processes occurring in living bodies. The application of the principles of physics and chemistry to practical problems, in research and development as well as in professional practice, has given rise to the different branches of engineering. Modern engineering practice and research would be impossible without a sound understanding of the fundamental ideas of the natural sciences.

But physics is important not just because it provides the basic conceptual and theoretical framework on which the other natural sciences are founded. From the practical point of view, it is important because it provides techniques which can be used in almost any area of pure or applied research. The astronomer requires optical, spectroscopic, and radio techniques. The geologist uses gravimetric, acoustic, nuclear, and mechanical methods in his research. The same may be said of the oceanographer, the meteorologist, the seismologist, etc. A modern hospital is equipped with laboratories in which the most sophisticated of physical techniques are used. In summary, hardly any activity of research, including such fields as archaeology, paleontology, history, and art, can proceed without the use of modern physical techniques. This gives the physicist the gratifying feeling that he is not only advancing our body of knowledge about nature, but contributing to the social progress of mankind.

1.5 The Experimental Method

In order to fulfill its objective, physics, as well as all natural sciences both pure and applied, depends on *observation* and *experimentation.* Observation consists in a careful and critical examination of a phenomenon by noting and analyzing the different factors and circumstances that appear to influence it. Unfortunately, the conditions under which phenomena occur naturally rarely offer enough variation and flexibility. In some cases they occur only infrequently so that analyzing them is a difficult and slow process. For that reason experimentation is necessary. Experimentation consists in the observation of a phenomenon under prearranged and carefully controlled conditions. Thus the scientist can vary the conditions at his will, making it easier to disclose how they affect the process. Without experimentation modern science would never have achieved the advances it has. This is why laboratories are so essential to the scientist.

To emphasize this point, Fig. 1–7 shows the research reactor of the Oak Ridge National Laboratory. Note that the space surrounding the reactor is crowded with experimental equipment. Some of this equipment may be used by physicists to learn more about nuclear properties or to make a structural analysis of materials.

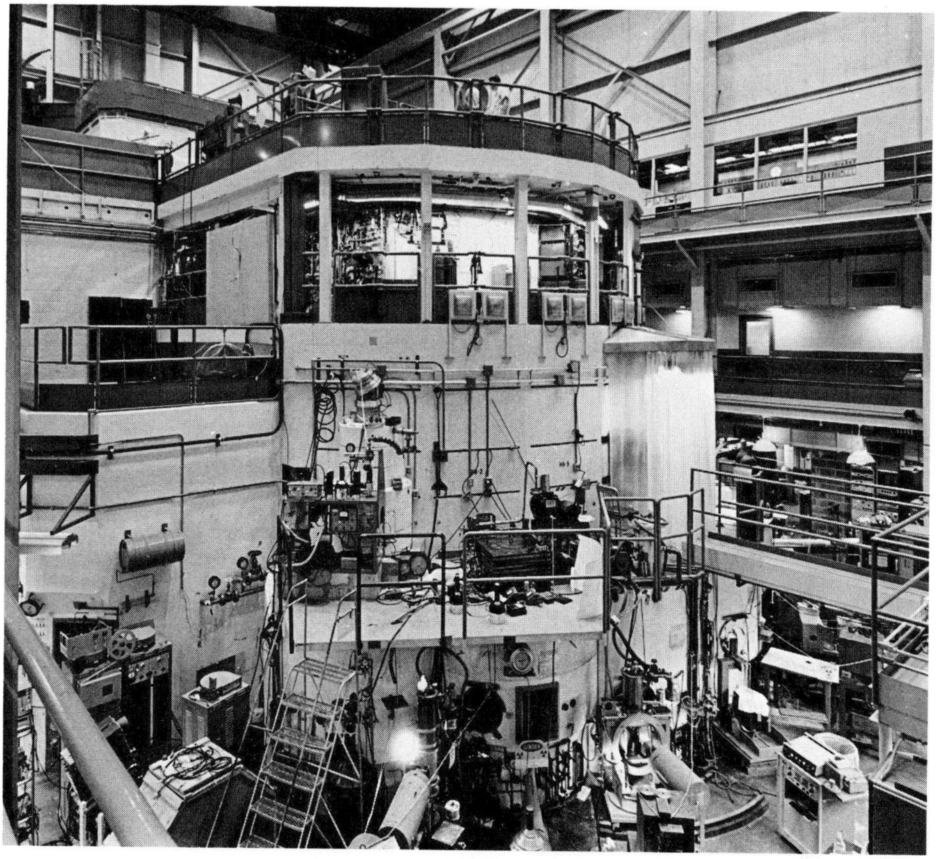

Fig. 1–7. The Oak Ridge National Laboratory research nuclear reactor, which is being used in a great variety of fundamental research. (Photograph courtesy of ORNL.)

Other apparatus may be used to prepare radioactive materials for applications in chemistry, medicine, biology, agriculture, or engineering. A group of biophysicists using some of the above equipment may be experimenting on the effects of radiation on biological specimens, while another group of scientists may be using the same equipment to study effects of radiation on different kinds of material. It is suggested that the student pay a visit to a modern research laboratory so that he may have a more personal feeling for the role of experimentation in science.

Of course, experimentation is not the only tool a physicist has. From the known facts a scientist may infer new knowledge in a *theoretical* way. By theoretical we mean that the physicist proposes a *model* of the physical situation he is studying. Using relations previously established, he applies logical and deductive reasoning to the model. Ordinarily he works out his reasoning by means of mathematical techniques. The end result may be the prediction of some phenomenon not yet observed or the verification of the relations among several processes. The knowledge a physicist acquires by theoretical means is in turn used by other scientists

Fig. 1–8. General view of CERN (European Organization for Nuclear Research), founded in 1954. Although it is a cooperative enterprise among European governments (Austria, Belgium, Denmark, Federal Republic of Germany, France, Greece, Italy, Netherlands, Norway, Spain, Sweden, Switzerland, and the United Kingdom), the United States also participates actively. Located at Meyrin, Switzerland, on the Swiss–French border, CERN has the best facilities for nuclear research in Western Europe, such as a 600-Mev synchro-cyclotron, a 28-Gev proton synchrotron (whose magnet lies underground along the circular structure), and a 2-m liquid-hydrogen bubble chamber. CERN's personnel (about 2000) comes from all the member countries, and its annual budget is close to $30,000,000. (Photograph courtesy of CERN.)

to perform new experiments for checking the model itself, or to determine its limitations and failures. The theoretician then revises and modifies his model so that it will agree with the new information. It is this interwoven relation between experimentation and theory that allows science to progress steadily and on solid ground.

Although in the old days a scientist could work in a more or less isolated fashion (and such was the case for Galileo, Newton, Huygens and others), modern science, because of its complexity, is mainly the result of teamwork, in which theoreticians and experimentalists work and think together. And by "together," we do not necessarily imply physical coincidence at the same place. Modern means of communication facilitate rapid exchange of ideas. Physicists several hundred miles apart, and from different nationalities, may work jointly, collaborating on a common research project (Fig. 1–8). This fact applies not only to physics, but to almost any science, and thereby demonstrates the universal value of science, which reaches beyond all kinds of human barriers. It may be hoped that science, through this type of cooperation, will assist in increasing understanding among men.

References

1. "Truth in Physics," P. Schmidt, *Am. J. Phys.* **28,** 24 (1960)
2. "Nature of Physics and Its Relation to Other Sciences," G. P. Thompson, *Am. J. Phys.* **28,** 187 (1960)
3. "'Empty' Space," H. van de Hulst, *Scientific American*, November 1955, page 72
4. "Some Reflections on Science and the Humanities," J. Ashmore, *Physics Today*, November 1963, page 46
5. "American Physics Comes of Age," J. Van Vleck, *Physics Today*, June 1964, page 21
6. "Science and Public Policy," E. Daddario, *Physics Today*, January 1965, page 23
7. "Physics and Biology," W. A. Rosenblith, *Physics Today*, January 1966, page 23
8. *Atoms and the Universe* (second edition), by G. Jones, J. Rotblat, and G. Whitrow. New York: Scribner's, 1963
9. *The Excitement of Science*, by J. R. Platt. Boston: Houghton Mifflin, 1962
10. *The Feynman Lectures on Physics*, Volume I, by R. Feynman, R. Leighton, and M. Sands. Reading, Mass.: Addison-Wesley, 1963, Chapters 1, 2, and 3
11. *Foundations of Modern Physical Science*, by G. Holton and D. H. D. Roller. Reading, Mass.: Addison-Wesley, 1958, Chapters 8, 12, 14, and 15

2 MEASUREMENT AND UNITS

2.1 Introduction

The observation of a phenomenon is in general incomplete unless it results in *quantitative* information. Obtaining such information requires the *measurement* of a physical property, and thus measurement constitutes a good part of the daily routine of the experimental physicist. Lord Kelvin said that our knowledge is satisfactory only when we can express it in terms of numbers. Although this assertion is perhaps exaggerated, it expresses a philosophy which a physicist must keep in mind at all times in his research. But, as we indicated in Chapter 1, the expression of a physical property in terms of numbers requires not only that we use mathematics to show the relations between the different quantities, but also that we be able to manipulate these relations. This is why mathematics is the language of physics; without mathematics it is impossible to understand physical phenomena, either from a theoretical or experimental viewpoint. Mathematics is the tool of the physicist; it must be manipulated with skill and thoroughness so that its use furthers instead of hinders his work.

In this chapter we shall not only define the units necessary to express the results of a measurement, but also we shall discuss a number of topics (all of which are important) that appear again and again throughout the book. These are density, the plane angle, the solid angle, significant figures, and the process of analyzing experimental data.

2.2 Measurement

Measurement is a technique by means of which we attach a number to a physical property as a result of comparing it with a similar, standard, quantity that has been adopted as a *unit*. Most measurements performed in the laboratory reduce essentially to the measurement of a length. By using this measurement (and certain conventions expressed by formulas), we obtain the desired quantity. When he measures something, the physicist must take great care to produce the minimum possible disturbance of the system that is under observation. For example, when we measure the temperature of a body, we place it in contact with a thermometer. But when we place the two together, some energy or "heat" is exchanged between the body and the thermometer, resulting in a slight change in the temperature of the body, thus affecting the very quantity we wanted to measure. In addition, all measurements are affected by some degree of *experimental error* because of the inevitable imperfections in the measuring device, or the limitations imposed by our senses (vision and hearing) which must record the information. Therefore, a physicist designs his measuring technique so that the disturbance of the quantity measured is smaller than his experimental error. In general, this is always possible when we are measuring quantities in the macroscopic range (i.e., in bodies composed of a large number of molecules), because then all we have to do is to use a measuring device that produces a disturbance smaller, by several orders of magnitude, than the quantity measured. Thus whatever the disturbance produced, it is negligible compared with the experimental error. In other cases the amount of disturbance can be estimated and the measured value corrected.

The situation, however, is quite different when we are measuring individual atomic properties, such as the motion of an electron. Now we do not have the option of using a measuring device that produces an interaction smaller than the quantity to be measured, because we do not have a device that small. The disturbance introduced is of the same order of magnitude as the quantity to be measured and it may not be possible even to estimate or account for it. Therefore a distinction must be made between the measurement of macroscopic quantities and of atomic quantities. We shall require a special theoretical structure when we deal with atomic quantities. The technique will not be discussed at this time; it is called *quantum mechanics.*

Another important requirement is that the definitions of physical quantities must be *operational,* in the sense that they must indicate explicitly or implicitly how to measure the quantity that is defined. For example, to say that velocity is an expression of the rate at which a body moves is not an operational definition of velocity, but to say that *velocity is the distance moved divided by the time* is an operational definition of velocity.

2.3 Fundamental Quantities and Units

Before we measure something, we must first select a unit for each quantity to be measured. For purposes of measurement, there are fundamental and derived quantities and units. The physicist recognizes four fundamental independent quantities: *length, mass, time,* and *charge.**

Length is a primary concept and is a notion we all acquire naturally; it is useless to attempt to give a definition of it. So is time. Mass and charge, however, are not that intuitive. The concept of mass will be analyzed in detail in Chapters 7 and 13. Let us say here only that mass is a coefficient, characteristic of each particle, that determines the particle's behavior when it interacts with other particles as well as the strength of its gravitational interactions.

Similarly, charge, which will be discussed in detail in Chapter 14, is another coefficient, characteristic of each particle, that determines the strength of its electromagnetic interaction with other particles. There may exist other coefficients characterizing other interactions between particles, but so far they have not been identified, and no additional fundamental quantities seem to be required at present.

Mass can also be defined operationally using the principle of the equal arm balance (Fig. 2–1); that is, a symmetric balance supported at its center O. Two bodies C and C' are said to have equal masses when, with one mass placed on each pan, the balance remains in equilibrium. Experimentally it is verified that if the balance is in equilibrium at one place on the earth, it remains in equilibrium when

* By this we do not mean that there are no other "fundamental" quantities in physics; however, the other quantities are such that they can be expressed as some combination of these four, or else they do not require a special unit for their expression.

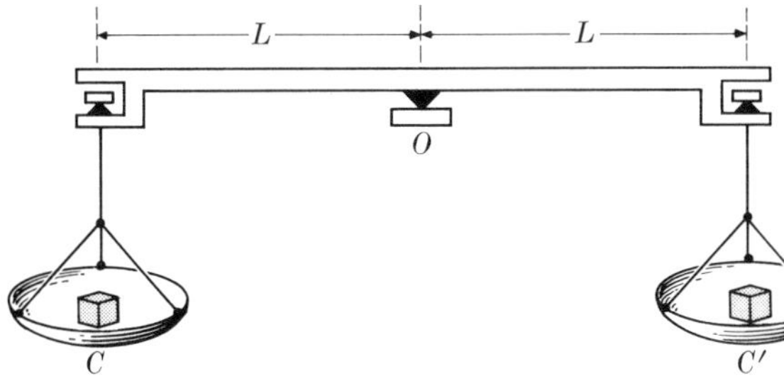

Fig. 2–1. Equal arm balance for comparing the masses of two bodies.

placed anywhere else. Therefore, the equality of mass is a property of the bodies, independent of the place where they are compared. If C' is composed of standard units, the mass of C can be obtained as a multiple of the standard mass. The mass obtained this way is really the gravitational mass (Chapter 13). But in Chapter 7 we shall see a means for comparing masses dynamically. Mass obtained dynamically is called *inertial mass*. No difference has been found between the two methods of measuring mass, as will be discussed in Chapter 13.

With a few exceptions, all other quantities used thus far in physics can be related to these four quantities by their definitions, expressed as mathematical relations involving length, mass, time, and charge. The units of all these derived quantities are in turn expressed in terms of the units of the four fundamental quantities by means of these defining relations. Therefore it is only necessary to agree on the units for the four fundamental quantities in order to have a consistent system of units. Physicists have agreed (at the Eleventh General Conference on Weights and Measures, held in Paris in 1960) to use the MKSC system of units, and this is what we shall adhere to in this book. The initials stand for *meter, kilogram, second,* and *coulomb*. Their definitions are as follows:

Meter, abbreviated m, is the unit of length. It is equal to 1,650,763.73 wavelengths of the electromagnetic radiation emitted by the isotope ^{86}Kr in its transition between states $2p_{10}$ and $5d_5$. Those two symbols refer to particular physical states of the krypton atom. The radiation emitted can easily be identified because it appears as a red line on a spectrogram.

Kilogram, abbreviated kg, is the unit of mass. It is defined as the mass of the *international kilogram*, a platinum block kept at the International Bureau of Weights and Measures in Sèvres, near Paris. For all practical purposes it is equal to the mass of 10^{-3} m^3 of distilled water at 4°C. The mass of 1 m^3 of water is thus 10^3 kg. A volume of 10^{-3} m^3 is called one *liter*. By analogy with the meter, we could associate the kilogram with an atomic property by saying that it is equal to the mass of 5.0188×10^{25} atoms of the isotope ^{12}C. In fact, this is the criterion adopted in defining the international scale of atomic masses.

Second, abbreviated s, is the unit of time. It is defined according to the International Astronomical Union as 1/31,556,925.975 of the duration of the tropical year 1900. The tropical year is defined as the time interval between two successive passages of the earth through the vernal equinox, which takes place approximately on March 21st each year (Fig. 2–2). It may also be defined as 1/86,400 of the mean solar day, which is the time interval between two successive passages of a point on the earth in front of the sun, averaged over one year. But this definition has the drawback that, because of tidal action, the period of the earth's rotation is decreasing gradually, and therefore this unit should also be changing gradually. For that reason a particular year, 1900, was arbitrarily chosen.

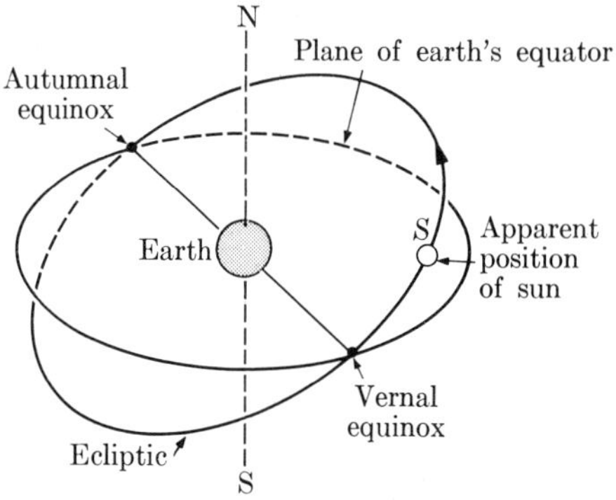

Fig. 2–2. Definition of the tropical year.

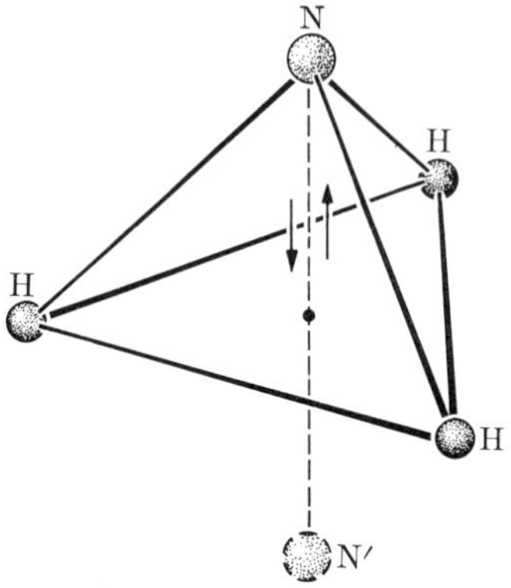

Fig. 2–3. Oscillation of the nitrogen atom between two symmetric positions in the ammonia molecule.

The unit of time could also be related to an atomic property, as has been done with the unit of length, resulting in what are called *atomic clocks*. For example, the molecule of ammonia (NH_3) has a pyramidal structure, with the three H atoms in the base and the N atom at the vertex (Fig. 2–3). But obviously there is a symmetric position, N′, for the nitrogen atom at the same distance from the H-H-H plane but on the opposite side. The N atom may oscillate between these two positions of equilibrium with a fixed period. The second may then be defined as the time required for the N atom to make 2.387×10^{10} such oscillations. The first atomic clock, based on this principle, was built at the National Bureau of Standards in 1948. Since then other substances have been tried as atomic clocks. However, no international agreement has yet been reached for an atomic standard of time, although it seems that there is a general consensus toward the adoption of such a definition of the unit of time.*

Coulomb, abbreviated C, is the unit of electric charge. Its precise and official definition will be given in Chapter 14, but at this moment we may say that it is equal in absolute value to the negative charge contained in 6.2418×10^{18} electrons, or to the positive charge in an equal number of protons.

---

* In October 1964, the International Committee on Weights and Measures temporarily based the international time interval on a particular atomic transition of the ^{133}Cs atom. The second is thus *temporarily* defined as the time required for the oscillator which forces cesium atoms to perform the stated transition to oscillate 9,192,631,770 times.

Note: Strictly speaking, in addition to the meter, the kilogram, and the second, the fourth unit adopted at the Eleventh Conference was the *ampere* (instead of the coulomb) as a unit of electric current. The coulomb is thus defined as the amount of electric charge that passes through a section of a conductor during one second when the current is one ampere. The reason for choosing the ampere is that a current is more easily established as a standard. Our decision to use the coulomb is based mainly on our wish to express the more fundamental character of electric charge, without departing essentially from the recommendations of the Eleventh Conference. The MKSA is the International System of units, designated by the symbol SI.

The meter and the kilogram are units originally introduced during the French revolution, when the French government decided to establish a rational system of units, known since then as the *metric system*, to supplant the chaotic and varied units in use at that time. The meter was at first defined as "the ten-millionth (10^{-7}) part of a quadrant of a terrestrial meridian." For that purpose an arc of a meridian was carefully measured—an operation that took several years—and a standard platinum bar measuring one meter was fabricated and kept under controlled conditions at 0°C at the International Bureau of Weights and Measures, at Sèvres. Later measurements indicated that the standard bar was shorter by 1.8×10^{-4} m than the ten-millionth part of the quadrant of a meridian, and it was decided to adopt the length of the bar as the standard meter without further reference to the earth meridian. Duplicates of the standard meter exist in many countries. However, the convenience of having a standard of more permanent character and easy availability at any laboratory was recognized. For that reason the red line of ^{86}Kr was chosen.

For mass, the unit chosen by the French was the *gram*, abbreviated g, defined as the mass of one cubic centimeter (1 cm $= 10^{-2}$ m $= 0.3937$ in. and 1 cm$^3 =$ 10^{-6} m^3) of distilled water at 4°C. This temperature was chosen because it is the temperature at which the density of water is a maximum. The kilogram is then equal to 10^3 grams. A platinum block, having a mass of one kilogram, was built. Later on it was decided to adopt this block as the standard kilogram without further reference to the water.

Before the MKSC system was adopted, another system was very popular in scientific work: the *cgs system*, in which the unit of length is the centimeter, the unit of mass is the gram, and the unit of time is the second. No definite unit of charge had been assigned to this system, although two were used: the statcoulomb and the abcoulomb, equal respectively to $\frac{1}{3} \times 10^{-9}$ C and 10 C. The cgs system is gradually being replaced in scientific and practical work by the MKSC system.

In many English-speaking countries another system of units is widely used in practical and engineering applications. The unit of length is the *foot*, abbreviated ft, the unit of mass is the *pound*, abbreviated lb, and the unit of time is again the *second*. The equivalent metric units are:

1 foot = 0.3048 m	1 m = 3.281 ft
1 pound = 0.4536 kg	1 kg = 2.205 lb

TABLE 2–1 Prefixes for Powers of Ten

Magnitude	Prefix	Symbol
10^{-18}	atto-	a
10^{-15}	femto-	f
10^{-12}	pico-	p
10^{-9}	nano-	n
10^{-6}	micro-	μ
10^{-3}	milli-	m
10^{-2}	centi-	c
10^{-1}	deci-	d
$10^{0} = 1$	Fundamental unit	
10	deca-	D
10^{2}	hecto-	H
10^{3}	kilo-	k (or K)
10^{6}	mega-	M
10^{9}	giga-	G
10^{12}	tera-	T

It is expected that eventually only the MKSC system will be used throughout the world for scientific, engineering, and household measurements.

For practical reasons multiples and submultiples of the fundamental and derived units have been introduced as powers of ten. They are designated with a prefix, according to the scheme given in Table 2–1.

2.4 Density

The density of a body is defined as its mass per unit volume. So a body having a mass m and a volume V has a density of

$$\rho = \frac{m}{V}. \tag{2.1}$$

Density is expressed in kg m^{-3}. Obviously the density of water is

$$\rho = 10^3 \text{ kg m}^{-3} \qquad (\text{or } 1 \text{ g cm}^{-3} \text{ and } 62.4 \text{ lb ft}^{-3}).$$

Density, as defined in Eq. (2.1), is applicable only to homogeneous bodies; i.e., bodies having the same composition or structure throughout their volume. Otherwise, it gives the *average* density of the body. For a heterogeneous body, the density varies from one place to another. To obtain the density at a particular place, the mass dm, contained in a small (or infinitesimal) volume dV located around the point, is measured. Then one applies Eq. (2.1), which now becomes

$$\rho = \frac{dm}{dV}. \tag{2.2}$$

TABLE 2–2 Densities (Relative to Water)

Solids		Liquids		Gases	
Iron	7.86	Water (4°C)	1.000	Air	1.2922×10^{-3}
Ice	0.917	Mercury	13.59	Hydrogen	8.988×10^{-5}
Magnesium	1.74	Ethyl alcohol	0.791	Oxygen	1.42904×10^{-3}
Aluminum	2.70	Gasoline	0.67	Nitrogen	1.25055×10^{-3}
Uranium	18.7	Air (−147°C)	0.92	Helium	1.7847×10^{-4}

Since density is a statistical concept, the volume dV, to have any physical meaning, must be of such a size as to contain a large number of molecules.

Another useful concept is *relative density*. If ρ_1 and ρ_2 are the densities of two different substances, their relative density is

$$\rho_{21} = \frac{\rho_2}{\rho_1}. \tag{2.3}$$

It is not expressed in any unit because it is a relative quantity; i.e., the quotient of two quantities of the same kind. It is customary to express relative densities with respect to water as a reference. In Table 2–2 we give the densities of several substances relative to water. The numerical values are given at standard temperature and pressure (STP: 0°C and 1 atm), unless otherwise noted.

2.5 Plane Angles

There are two systems for measuring plane angles: *degrees* and *radians*. It is the second that is more important in physics. The circumference of a circle is arbitrarily divided into 360 degrees (°). A right angle, for example, corresponds to 90°. Each degree is divided into 60 minutes (′) and each minute into 60 seconds (″). The measure of an arbitrary angle is expressed in degrees, minutes, and seconds, such as 23°42′34″.

To express a plane angle in radians, one draws, with an arbitrary radius R (Fig. 2–4), the arc AB with center at the vertex O of the angle. Then the measure of θ in radians (abbreviated rad) is

$$\theta = \frac{l}{R}, \tag{2.4}$$

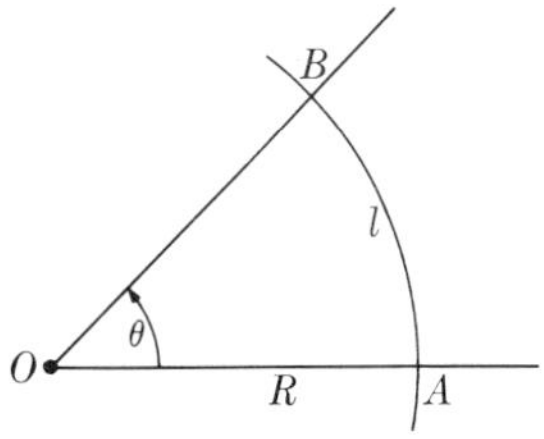

Figure 2–4

where l is the length of the arc AB. This method is based on the fact that, for a given angle, the ratio l/R is constant and independent of the radius, and is thus the measure of the angle expressed in radians. Note that l and R must be expressed in the same units of length. From Eq. (2.4), we have

$$l = R\theta. \tag{2.5}$$

Noting that the circumference of a circle is $2\pi R$, we see that a complete plane angle around a point, measured in radians, is $2\pi R/R = 2\pi$ rad. So 2π rad are equivalent to 360°, and

$$1° = \frac{\pi}{180}\text{ rad} = 0.017453\text{ rad}, \qquad 1\text{ rad} = \frac{180°}{\pi} = 57°17'44.9''.$$

2.6 Solid Angles

A *solid angle* is the space included inside a conical (or pyramidal) surface, as in Fig. 2–5. Its value, expressed in *steradians* (abbreviated sterad), is obtained by drawing, with arbitrary radius R and center at the vertex O, a spherical surface and applying the relation

$$\Omega = \frac{S}{R^2}, \tag{2.6}$$

where S is the area of the spherical cap intercepted by the solid angle. Since the surface area of a sphere is $4\pi R^2$, we conclude that the complete solid angle around a point is 4π steradians. The solid angle formed by the three mutually perpendicular coordinate axes OX, OY, and OZ (Fig. 2–6), is $\frac{1}{8}(4\pi)$ or $\pi/2$ steradians.

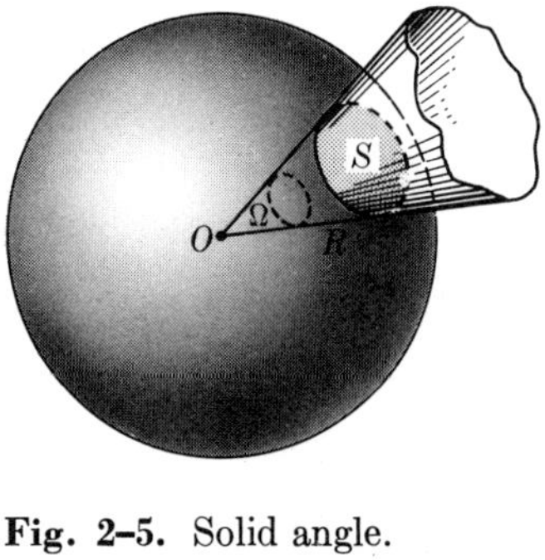

Fig. 2–5. Solid angle.

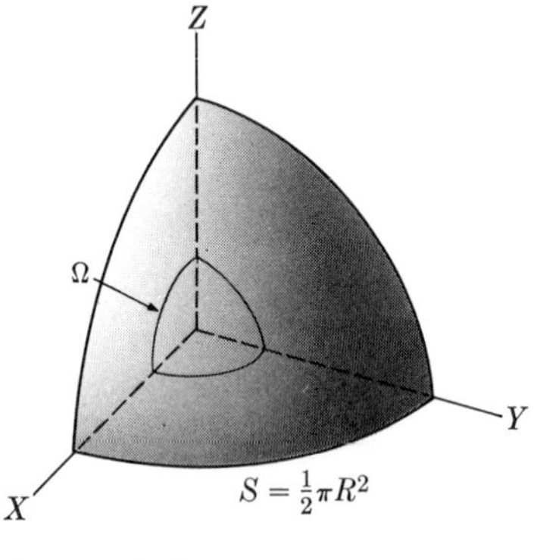

Figure 2–6

When the solid angle is small (Fig. 2–7), the surface area S becomes dS, and is not necessarily a spherical cap, but may be a small plane surface perpendicular to OP so that

$$d\Omega = \frac{dS}{R^2}. \tag{2.7}$$

In some instances the surface dS is not perpendicular to OP, but its normal N makes an angle θ with OP (Fig. 2–8). Then it is necessary to project dS on a plane perpendicular to OP, which gives us the area $dS' = dS \cos\theta$. Thus

$$d\Omega = \frac{dS\cos\theta}{R^2}, \tag{2.8}$$

an expression that will be very useful in future discussions.

2.7 Precision and Accuracy

The word precision usually has a connotation of accuracy. In the world of measurement, however, precision has the connotation of inaccuracy. What we mean is that when a physical property is described by some numerical quantity and some units, the numerical quantity is dependent on a number of different factors, including the particular piece of apparatus used to make the measurement, the type and number of measurements made, and the method employed by the experimenter to extract the number from the apparatus. Unless the numerical quantity is accompanied by another which describes the precision of the measurement, the number quoted is as good as useless. A number may be extremely accurate (that is, be exactly correct), but not be precise because the person quoting the number has failed to state at least something about his method of measurement.

Let us consider a few examples in order to clarify these ideas. If one sees a basket containing seven apples, the statement "I count seven apples in the basket" is a straightforward quote of a numerical quantity. It is precise and accurate, since the number of units to be counted is small and integral. If there are two people, one *slowly* putting apples into the basket and another *slowly* removing them, then one can make accurate and precise statements about the number of apples at any given time.

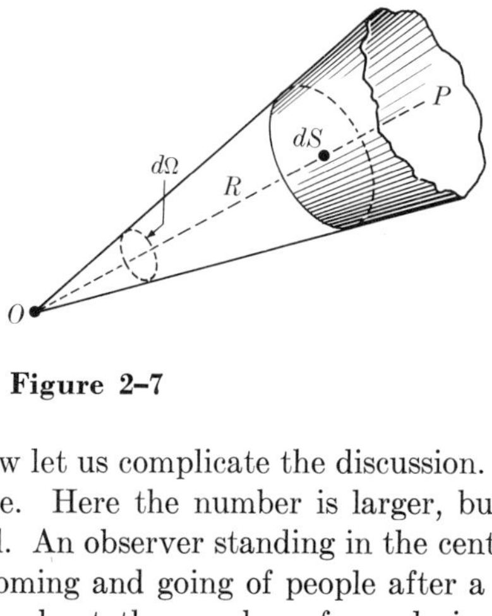

Figure 2–7

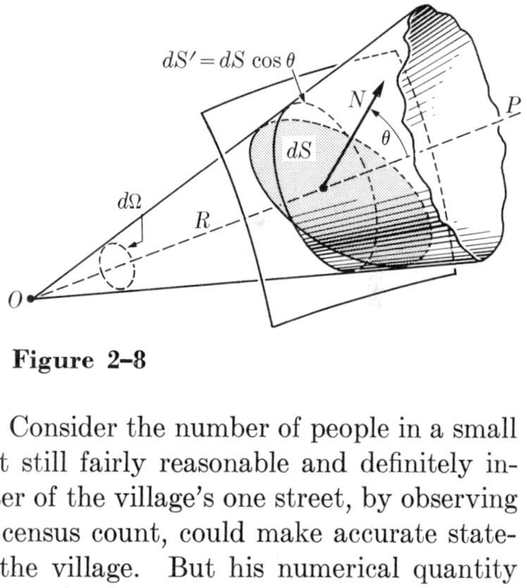

Figure 2–8

Now let us complicate the discussion. Consider the number of people in a small village. Here the number is larger, but still fairly reasonable and definitely integral. An observer standing in the center of the village's one street, by observing the coming and going of people after a census count, could make accurate statements about the number of people in the village. But his numerical quantity would not necessarily be precise, since it would be difficult for him to discover the exact time of the birth and death of the townspeople. Make the village a city or a county, and the job becomes even more difficult.

Let us now ask: Why do we need an accurate counting of the number of the inhabitants of a county? In order to provide different services for all the inhabitants, it is really not necessary to know, at each moment of time, the exact number of them. Rather do we need an accurate accounting whose precision depends on the particular service in question. For instance, to determine the number of new schools to be built in an area we must have a different kind of numerical precision for the population than would be necessary if we had to determine the number of fire departments needed. If we state the county's population with a precision of 1%, we mean that the number quoted may be 1% greater or 1% less than the actual population, *but we do not know which,* nor does it matter in many cases. In a village of 200 people, a precision of 1% means that we know the population within 2 people. In a county of 100,000 people, the precision is within 1000 people. If we know the population of the United States with a precision of 1%, our population figure may be off by as much as one and a half million, *but we do not know exactly.* Obviously, under some conditions, a precision of greater than 1% is necessary; under others, less precision may suffice.

Up to this point we have been concerned with the operation of counting itself. The assumption is that, given enough information and an ability to process the information rapidly, we could find out the exact population. Whether it is necessary to know this precisely or not has already been discussed. Now we must realize that there are operations which do *not* give us a number of units. For instance, it is true that at a particular point in a room there is an exact value of the temperature. Its value, however, depends on a definition, since temperature is a human conception. Nevertheless, we do not measure temperature itself by a counting method; rather, we measure the length of a column of mercury, a column whose length *represents* the temperature. For various reasons the measured length of the column will not be recorded identically every time it is read, even if the temperature remains constant. One of the major reasons for the variations in the readings is the finite space between divisions on the scale. A meter stick ordinarily has a distance of 1 mm between its divisions. Therefore, if a meter stick is read to the nearest division, the reading *at each end* may be in error by as much as $\frac{1}{2}$ mm. There are other types of reading errors that are taken up in specialized books on the topic. (See the references at the end of the chapter for a few selected texts and articles on measurement.)

The precision, or uncertainty, of a number allows us to define the number of *significant figures* associated with the quantity. For example, if a measurement is quoted as $642.54389 \pm 1\%$, this means that the uncertainty is around 6.4. Therefore we are justified in retaining only those figures in the number that are truly significant. In this case the number should be quoted as $642 \pm 1\%$ or 642 ± 6. When the student sees a physical property (such as the velocity of light or Avogadro's number) quoted in this text, the number will be quoted to the first five significant figures, even though the number may be known more precisely; the precision will not be specified. If the student wishes to use these numbers in the calculation of an uncertainty, he may consider the least significant number quoted to be precise to ± 1.

When one performs a series of mathematical operations using numbers that have a stated precision, the simplest procedure is to perform the operations, one at a time, disregarding the significant-figure problem until the conclusion of the multiplication, or whatever. Then the resultant number should be reduced to a number having the same number of significant figures (i.e., the same precision) as the least accurate of the numbers.

2.8 Measurement in the Laboratory

With a relatively simple example, the period of a pendulum, we shall describe the methods used in obtaining the numerical quantity associated with a physical property. The *period* of a pendulum is the time between two consecutive passes of the bob through the same point, moving in the same direction. A particular pendulum was set to swing, and its period for a single oscillation was measured fifty separate times. Table 2–3 contains the fifty measurements, in seconds.

From the table you may see that there is no one particular period for the pendulum. What we must do is to take these fifty measurements of the period, determine some *average value*, and then determine the precision of this average value. By adding all the periods and then dividing by the total number of measurements, we find that the *mean* (or average) *value* for the period of the pendulum is 3.248 seconds. (Note that for the moment we have kept the entire number; we shall modify it at the proper time.) By taking the difference between this mean value and each measurement, we obtain the *deviation* of each measurement from the mean. The sum of the absolute values of the deviations divided by the number of measurements is called the *mean deviation*, which gives an indication of the precision of the measurement. For our example, the mean deviation of the period is 0.12 second. Therefore, we should write the period of the pendulum, as measured in the laboratory, as 3.25 ± 0.12 seconds, or $3.25 \pm 4\%$ seconds (approximately).

Another way of expressing the precision of the measurement is by use of the *rms deviation*, defined as the square root of the quantity obtained by adding the *squares* of the deviations divided by the number of measurements. For our measurements, the rms (root-mean-square) deviation is 0.15 second. The extra effort in obtaining the rms deviation is well worth the task, since a relatively simple meaning may be attached to it. Assuming that the randomness that appears in the set of measurements is not due to any bias, but that these are just *normal fluctuations*, the rms deviation tells us that roughly two-thirds of all the measurements fall within this deviation from the mean value. Or, to put it another way, we now have confidence that, the very next time we take the measurement of the period of our pendulum with the same apparatus, there is a 67% chance that we shall measure a period of no more than 3.40 seconds or less than 3.10 seconds.

TABLE 2–3

3.12	3.18	3.25	3.32	3.32
3.62	3.33	3.30	3.42	3.27
3.33	3.28	3.15	3.12	3.20
3.17	3.18	3.20	3.18	2.98
3.17	3.52	3.35	3.33	3.38
3.58	3.02	3.00	3.32	3.08
3.27	3.35	3.63	3.15	3.38
3.00	3.15	3.27	2.90	3.27
2.97	3.18	3.28	3.28	3.37
3.18	3.45	3.18	3.27	3.20

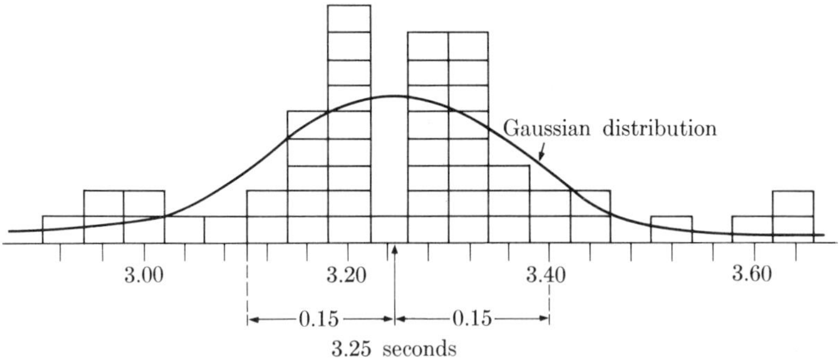

Fig. 2–9. Histogram showing the number of measurements of the period of a pendulum, as shown in Table 2–3, in each time interval of 0.04 s. The corresponding Gaussian distribution is indicated by the solid line.

To show this situation in a slightly different manner, Fig. 2–9 is a *histogram*, on which the frequency distribution of the given readings is plotted. There is an apparent randomness to the manner in which the number of the various readings occur. As more and more readings are taken, however, a definite pattern begins to take shape, showing that the frequency of appearance of a given measurement is proportionately less the larger its deviation from the mean value. The familiar bell-shaped curve is what results. Analysis shows that the curve under which the peak of the histogram fits more and more closely as the number of measurements increases has an analytic form called the *Gaussian* or *normal distribution.*

References

1. "Symbols, Units, and Nomenclature in Physics," *Physics Today*, June 1962, page 20
2. "Mathematics in the Modern World," R. Courant, *Scientific American*, September 1964, page 40
3. "Mathematics in the Physical Sciences," F. Dyson, *Scientific American*, September 1964, page 128
4. "Probability," M. Kac, *Scientific American*, September 1964, page 92
5. "The Limits of Measurement," R. Furth, *Scientific American*, July 1950, page 48
6. *A Brief History of Weights and Measures Standards of the United States.* Washington, D.C.: Government Printing Office, 1963
7. *Experimentation: An Introduction to Measurement Theory and Experiment Design*, by D. Baird. Englewood Cliffs, N.J.: Prentice-Hall, 1962
8. *Experimentation and Measurement*, by W. Youden. New York: Scholastic Book Services, Scholastic Magazines, Inc., 1962
9. *The Feynman Lectures on Physics*, Volume I, by R. Feynman, R. Leighton, and M. Sands. Reading, Mass.: Addison-Wesley, 1963, Chapters 5 and 6

Problems

2.1 Atomic masses as given in Table A–1 are expressed in *atomic mass units*, abbreviated amu. One amu is equal to 1.6604×10^{-27} kg. Express, in kilograms and grams, the masses of one atom of (a) hydrogen and (b) oxygen.

2.2 How many water molecules, each composed of one atom of oxygen and two atoms of hydrogen, are there in one gram? In 18 grams? In one cubic centimeter?

2.3 It was said in Section 2.3 that the kilogram could be defined as the mass of 5.0188×10^{25} atoms of the ^{12}C isotope, whose mass is defined as exactly 12.0000 amu. Verify that this definition is compatible with the value of the amu given in Problem 2.1.

2.4 Consider molecules of hydrogen, of oxygen, and of nitrogen, each composed of two identical atoms. Calculate the number of molecules of each of these gases (at STP) in one m^3. Use the values of relative densities given in Table 2–2. Extend your calculation to other gases. What general conclusion can you draw from this result?

2.5 Assuming that air is composed of 20% oxygen and 80% nitrogen and that these gases have molecules each comprised of two atoms, obtain the "effective" molecular mass of air. Estimate the number of molecules in one cubic centimeter of air at STP. How many molecules are oxygen, and how many are nitrogen?

2.6 The density of interstellar gas in our galaxy is estimated to be about 10^{-21} kg m^{-3}. Assuming that the gas is mainly hydrogen, estimate the number of hydrogen atoms per cubic centimeter. Compare the result with air at STP (Problem 2.5).

2.7 A glass containing water has a radius of 2 cm. In 2 hours the water level drops 1 mm. Estimate, in grams per hour, the rate at which water is evaporating. How many water molecules are evaporating per second from each square centimeter of water surface? (We suggest that the student perform this experiment and obtain his own data. Why do you get different results on different days?)

2.8 One *mole* of a substance is defined as an amount, in *grams*, numerically equal to its molecular mass expressed in amu. (When we refer to a chemical element and not a compound, we use the atomic mass.) Verify that the number of molecules (or atoms) in one mole of *any* substance is the same, and is equal to 6.0225×10^{23}. This number, called *Avogadro's constant*, is a very important physical constant.

2.9 Using the data in Tables 2–2 and A–1, estimate the average separation between molecules in hydrogen at STP (gas), in water (liquid), and in iron (solid).

2.10 The mass of an atom is practically all in its nucleus. The radius of the nucleus of uranium is 8.68×10^{-15} m. Using the atomic mass of uranium given in Table A–1, obtain the density of "nuclear matter." This nucleus contains 238 particles or "nucleons." Estimate the average separation between nucleons. From your result, would you conclude that it is reasonable to treat nuclear matter in the same manner as matter in bulk, i.e., aggregates of atoms and molecules?

2.11 Using the data from Table 13–1, obtain the average density of the earth and of the sun. When you compare these values with the data in Table 2–2, what do you conclude about the structure of these two bodies?

2.12 Estimate the average density of the universe, using the information given in Section 1.3. Assuming that all atoms are distributed uniformly over all the universe, how many atoms would there be in each cubic centimeter? Assume that all atoms are hydrogen.

2.13 The speed of light in vacuum is 2.9979×10^8 m s^{-1}. Express it in miles per hour. How many times could a light ray travel around the earth in one second?

(Use Table 13–1 for data about the earth.) What distance would it travel in one year? This distance is called a *light year*.

2.14 The radius of the earth's orbit is 1.49×10^{11} m. This length is called an *astronomical unit*. Express a light year in astronomical units (see Problem 2.13).

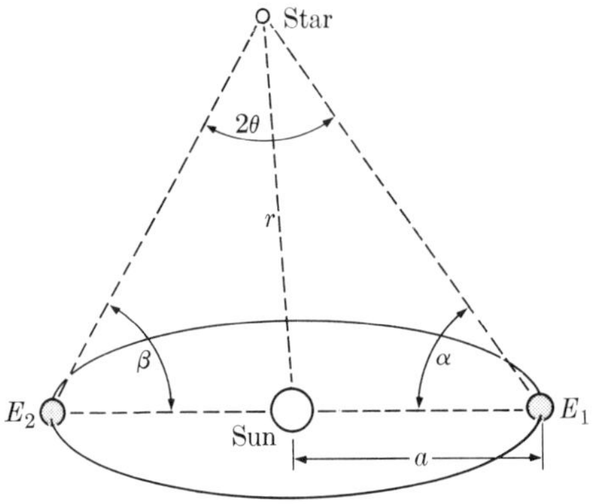

Figure 2–10

2.15 *Parallax* is the difference in the apparent direction of an object, due to a change in the position of the observer. (Hold a pencil in front of you and close first the right and then the left eye. Note that in each case the pencil appears against a different background.) *Stellar parallax* is the change in the apparent position of a star as a result of the earth's orbital motion around the sun. It is expressed quantitatively by one-half the angle subtended by the earth's diameter E_1E_2 perpendicular to the line joining the star and the sun (see Fig. 2–10). It is given by $\theta = \frac{1}{2}(180° - \alpha - \beta)$, where the angles α and β are measured at the two positions E_1 and E_2 separated by 6 months. The distance r from the star to the sun can be obtained from $a = r\theta$, where a is the radius of the earth's orbit and θ is expressed in radians. The star with the largest parallax of 0.76″ (i.e., the closest star) is α-Centauri. Find its distance from the sun expressed in meters, in light years, and in astronomical units.

2.16 A *parsec* is equal to the distance from the sun corresponding to a star whose parallax is 1″. Express the parsec in meters, light years, and astronomical units. Express the distance in parsecs in terms of the parallax in seconds of arc.

2.17 The distance between San Francisco and New York, measured along the great circle passing through these two cities, is 2571 mi. Compute the angle between the verticals at the two cities.

2.18 Using the data in the caption of Fig. 1–6, determine the angle subtended by the diameter of the Great Nebula M-31 when observed from the earth. Express it in radians and in degrees of arc. Also find the solid angle subtended by the nebula.

2.19 By looking at the table of trigonometric functions in the Appendix, find the angle at which $\sin\theta$ and $\tan\theta$ differ by (a) 10% (b) 1% (c) 0.1%. Do the same for $\sin\theta$ and θ, and for $\tan\theta$ and θ, where θ is expressed in radians. What conclusion can you draw from your result?

2.20 Given the three numbers: 49238.42; 6.382×10^4; 86.545. (a) Add the numbers. (b) Multiply all three together. (c) Add the first two and multiply by the third. (d) Multiply the last two and divide by the first. Give all answers to the proper number of significant figures.

2.21 Use the data listed in Table 2–3 to check the listed value for mean value, mean deviation, and rms deviation. How many significant figures should be quoted in the result?

2.22 The table below contains a set of ten readings of some physical property (e.g., the thickness of a piece of paper, or the weight of a stone, etc.).

116	125	108	111	113
113	124	111	136	111

(a) Determine the mean value of these numbers. Determine the mean deviation and the rms (or standard) deviation. (b) Make some judgment about keeping or discarding the single reading of 136. (If it is discarded, the mean value of the nine remaining data points is 114.7 and the standard deviation becomes 5.6.)

2.23 Take a small ball or a pencil and let it roll down the slope of a long book. Measure the time it takes for the ball or pencil to go from rest, at the top, to the bottom when it hits the table. Repeat the experiment ten (or more) times. Determine the mean value for the roll and its precision, expressed by the rms deviation. If you do not have a sweep-second hand, use your pulse as a timing source.

2.24 Take a census of members of your class. Determine the height and weight of each member. Discriminate so that you cover only one sex and have an age span of no more than three years. Calculate the mean height, mean weight, and the rms deviation. Note that you cannot talk about the precision of your measurement in the same sense as above. Why?

3
VECTORS

3.1 Introduction

This chapter will serve as an introduction to, or review of, the essential ideas associated with a branch of mathematics most important to the physical scientist. Vector algebra is important because it enables the scientist to write in a convenient, terse, shorthand notation some very complicated expressions. For example, in ordinary algebra the equation

$$3x + 2y = 6$$

is a shorthand notation for all possible pairs of x- and y-values that satisfy this equation. It is also possible to describe this same relation in yet another way; namely, by the shorthand notation of a graphical plot of this equation, as shown in Fig. 3–1. Both these examples are readily understandable to any student who has studied algebra and analytic geometry, because he understands the shorthand notation. In the same manner, vector algebra is readily understandable, once the shorthand notation is understood.

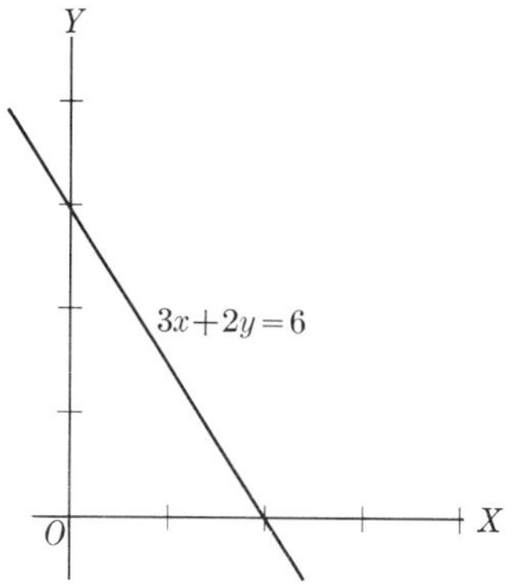

Figure 3–1

By the end of this chapter it will be discovered that vector notation is not unlike the notation of algebra and analytic geometry. The major difference is in the interpretation of this notation. A thoughtful reading of this chapter accompanied by careful working of all exercises will save the student many difficult moments in succeeding chapters.

3.2 Concept of Direction

When we are given a straight line, we can move along it in two opposite senses; these are distinguished by assigning to each a sign, plus or minus. Once the positive sense has been determined, we say that the line is oriented and call it an *axis*. The coordinate axes X and Y are oriented lines in which the positive senses are as indicated in Fig. 3–2. The positive sense is usually indicated by an arrow. An oriented line or axis defines a *direction*. Parallel lines oriented in the same sense

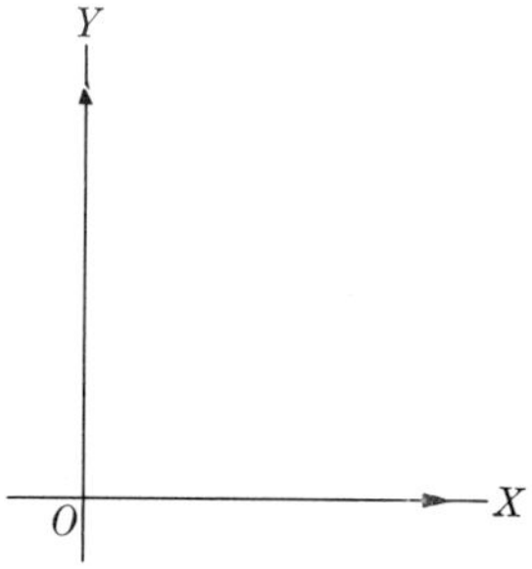

Fig. 3–2. Oriented coordinate axes.

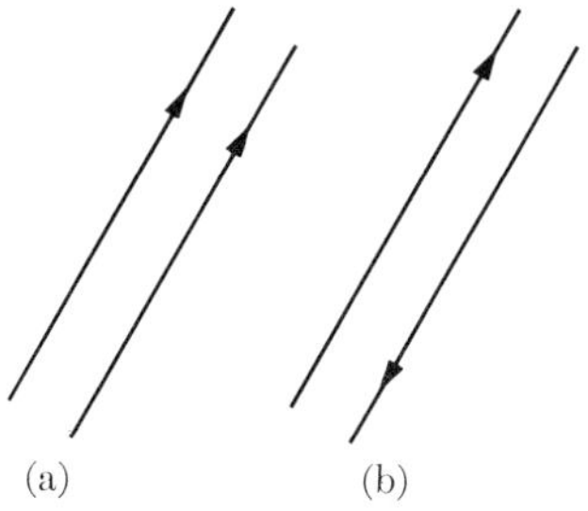

Fig. 3–3. Parallel and antiparallel directions.

define the same direction (Fig. 3–3a), but if they have opposite orientations they define opposite directions (Fig. 3–3b).

Directions in a plane are determined by an angle, which is the angle between a *reference* direction or axis and the direction we want to indicate, measured counterclockwise (Fig. 3–4). Opposite directions are determined by the angles θ and $\pi + \theta$ (or $180° + \theta$).

In three-dimensional space it is necessary to use two angles to fix a direction. The choice most frequently used is the one indicated in Fig. 3–5. The direction OA is determined by:

(i) the angle θ (less than 180°) it makes with axis OZ,

(ii) the angle ϕ between the plane AOZ and the plane XOZ, measured counterclockwise.

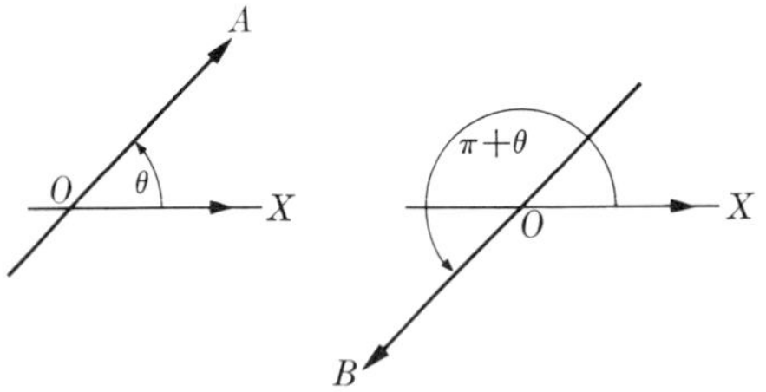

Fig. 3–4. In a plane, opposite directions are defined by angles θ and $\pi + \theta$.

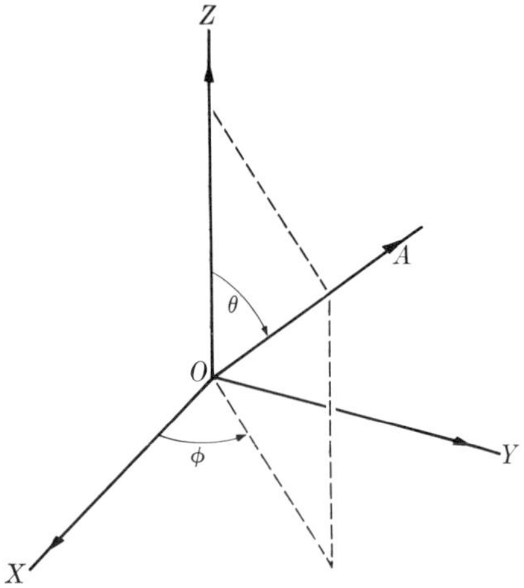

Fig. 3–5. Two angles are required to define a direction in space.

We leave it to the student to verify that the opposite direction is determined by the angles $\pi - \theta$ and $\pi + \phi$.

3.3 Scalars and Vectors

Many physical quantities are completely determined by their magnitude, expressed in some convenient unit. These quantities are called *scalars*. For example, to specify the volume of a body it is necessary only to indicate how many cubic meters or cubic feet it occupies. To know a temperature it is enough to read a conveniently located thermometer. Time, mass, charge, and energy are also scalar quantities.

Other physical quantities require, for their complete determination, a direction in addition to their magnitude. Such quantities we call *vectors*. The most obvious case is *displacement*. The displacement of a body is determined by the effective *distance* it has moved and the *direction* in which it moved. For example, if a particle is displaced from O to A (Fig. 3–6), the displacement is determined by the distance $d = 5$ and the angle $\theta \cong 37°$. Velocity is also a vector quantity, since the motion is determined by the rate of displacement *and* the direction of the displacement. Similarly, force and acceleration are vector quantities. Other physical quantities that are vectors will appear in succeeding chapters.

Vectors are represented graphically by line segments having the same direction as the vector (indicated by an arrow) and a length proportional to the magnitude. When written down, a symbol in boldface type such as $\boldsymbol{V}$ or with an arrow, as $\vec{V}$, indicates a vector (i.e., magnitude plus direction), while V refers to the magnitude only (sometimes, however, the magnitude will be indicated by $|\boldsymbol{V}|$). A *unit vector* is a vector whose magnitude is one. A vector $\boldsymbol{V}$ parallel to the unit vector $\boldsymbol{u}$ can be expressed in the form

$$\boldsymbol{V} = \boldsymbol{u}V. \tag{3.1}$$

The negative of a vector is another vector that has the same magnitude but opposite direction.

If two vectors $\boldsymbol{V}$ and $\boldsymbol{V}'$ are parallel to each other, they may be written as $\boldsymbol{V} = \boldsymbol{u}V$ and $\boldsymbol{V}' = \boldsymbol{u}V'$, where the unit vector $\boldsymbol{u}$ is the same. Thus if $\lambda = V/V'$ we may write

$$\boldsymbol{V} = \lambda \boldsymbol{V}'.$$

Reciprocally, wherever an equation such as the preceding holds for two vectors $\boldsymbol{V}$ and $\boldsymbol{V}'$, they are parallel.

3.4 Addition of Vectors

To understand the rule for addition of vectors we shall consider first the case of displacements. If a particle is displaced first from A to B (Fig. 3–7), represented by vector $\boldsymbol{d}_1$, and then from B to C, or $\boldsymbol{d}_2$, the result is equivalent to a single displacement from A to C, or $\boldsymbol{d}$, which we write symbolically as $\boldsymbol{d} = \boldsymbol{d}_1 + \boldsymbol{d}_2$. This expression must not be confused with $d = d_1 + d_2$, which refers only to the magnitudes and does not hold in this case. The procedure can be generalized to fit any kind of vectors. Therefore we say that $\boldsymbol{V}$ is the sum of $\boldsymbol{V}_1$ and $\boldsymbol{V}_2$ if it is ob-

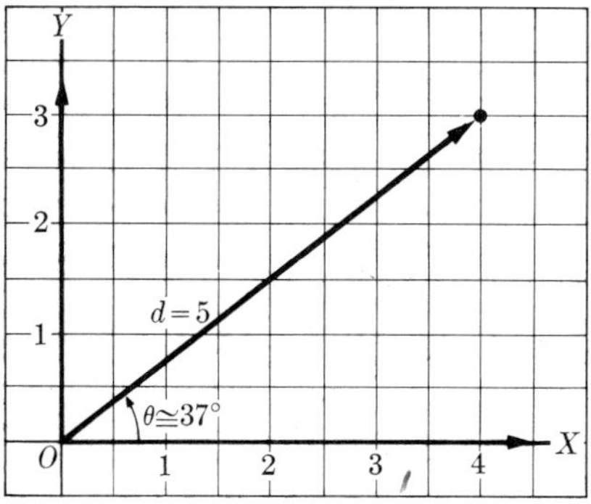

Fig. 3–6. Displacement is a vector quantity.

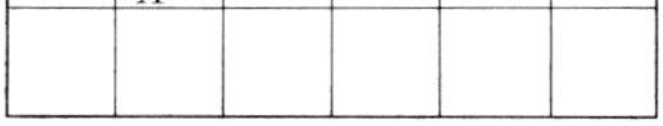

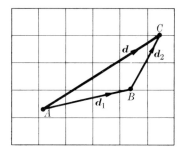

Fig. 3–7. Vector addition of two displacements.

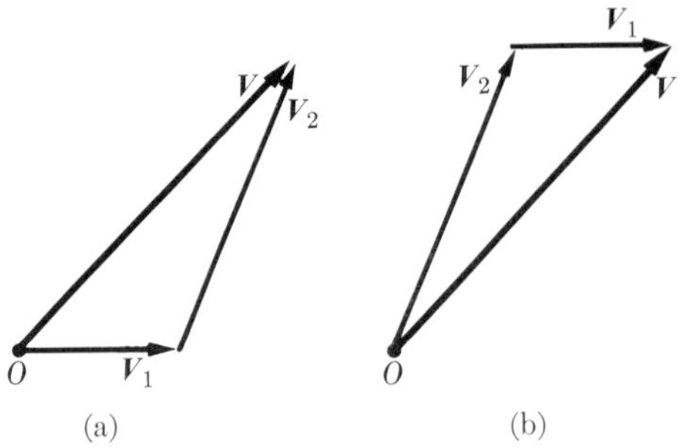

Fig. 3–8. Vector addition is commutative.

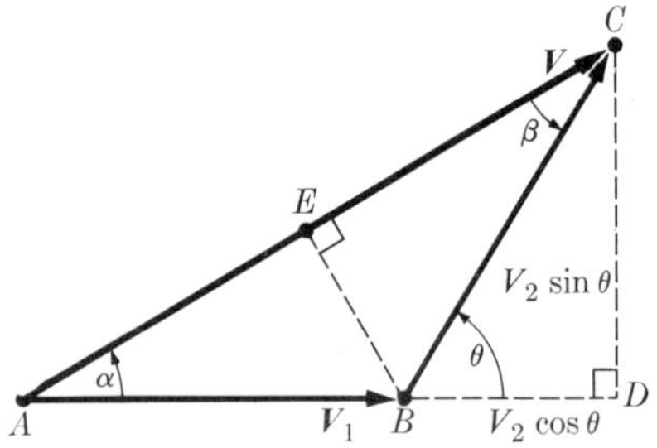

Figure 3–9

tained as indicated in Fig. 3–8. We can also see in the figure that the vector sum is commutative, the result being the same if the order in which the vectors are added is reversed; this is a direct consequence of the geometry of the method. The geometrical relation of Fig. 3–8 is expressed algebraically by

$$\boldsymbol{V} = \boldsymbol{V}_1 + \boldsymbol{V}_2. \tag{3.2}$$

To compute the magnitude of $\boldsymbol{V}$ we see from Fig. 3–9 that $(AC)^2 = (AD)^2 + (DC)^2$. But $AD = AB + BD = V_1 + V_2 \cos\theta$ and $DC = V_2 \sin\theta$. Therefore $V^2 = (V_1 + V_2\cos\theta)^2 + (V_2 \sin\theta)^2 = V_1^2 + V_2^2 + 2V_1V_2\cos\theta$, or

$$V = \sqrt{V_1^2 + V_2^2 + 2V_1V_2\cos\theta}. \tag{3.3}$$

To determine the direction of $\boldsymbol{V}$, we need only find the angle α. From the figure we see that in triangle ACD, $CD = AC \sin\alpha$, and in triangle BDC, $CD = BC\sin\theta$. Therefore $V\sin\alpha = V_2\sin\theta$ or

$$\frac{V}{\sin\theta} = \frac{V_2}{\sin\alpha}.$$

Similarly, $BE = V_1 \sin\alpha = V_2 \sin\beta$ or

$$\frac{V_2}{\sin\alpha} = \frac{V_1}{\sin\beta}.$$

Combining both results, one gets the symmetrical relation

$$\frac{V}{\sin\theta} = \frac{V_1}{\sin\beta} = \frac{V_2}{\sin\alpha}. \tag{3.4}$$

We have thus derived two fundamental trigonometric expressions, the Law of Cosines and the Law of Sines. In the special case when $\boldsymbol{V}_1$ and $\boldsymbol{V}_2$ are perpendicular (Fig. 3–10), $\theta = \frac{1}{2}\pi$ and the following relations hold:

$$V = \sqrt{V_1^2 + V_2^2}; \qquad \tan\alpha = \frac{V_2}{V_1}. \tag{3.5}$$

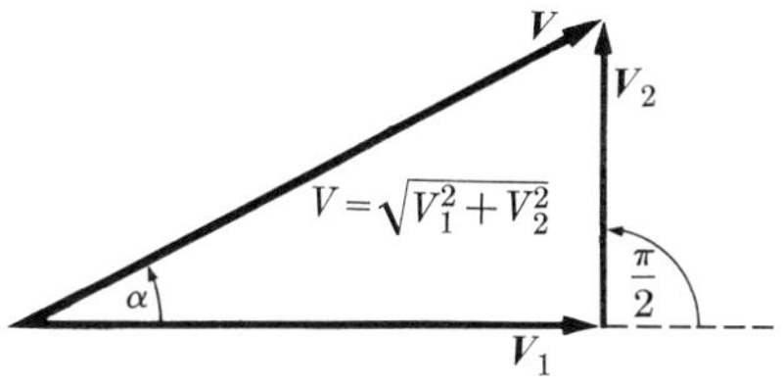

Figure 3–10

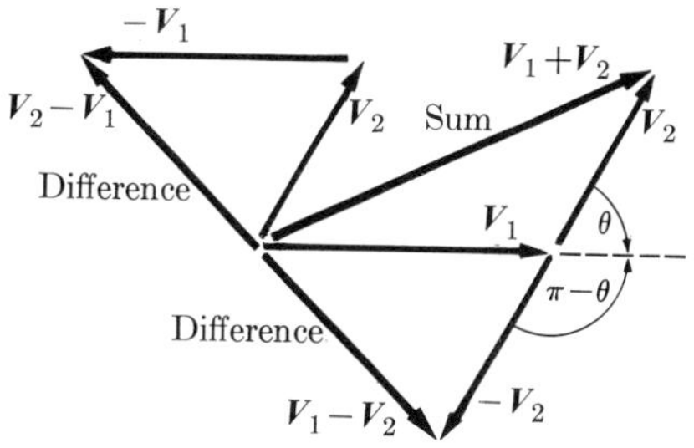

Fig. 3–11. Vector difference is anticommutative.

The *difference* between two vectors is obtained by adding to the first the negative (or opposite) of the second (Fig. 3–11); that is,

$$\boldsymbol{D} = \boldsymbol{V}_1 - \boldsymbol{V}_2 = \boldsymbol{V}_1 + (-\boldsymbol{V}_2).$$

Note that $\boldsymbol{V}_2 - \boldsymbol{V}_1 = -\boldsymbol{D}$; that is, if the vectors are subtracted in the reverse order, the opposite vector results; i.e., vector difference is anticommutative. The magnitude of the difference is

$$D = \sqrt{V_1^2 + V_2^2 + 2V_1V_2 \cos(\pi - \theta)}$$

or

$$D = \sqrt{V_1^2 + V_2^2 - 2V_1V_2 \cos \theta. \qquad (3.6)$$

EXAMPLE 3.1. Given two vectors: $\boldsymbol{A}$ is 6 units long and makes an angle of $+36°$ with the positive X-axis; $\boldsymbol{B}$ is 7 units long and is in the direction of the negative X-axis. Find: (a) the sum of the two vectors; (b) the difference between the two vectors.

Solution: Before starting to apply the previous equations, *draw* the vectors on a set of coordinate axes (Fig. 3–12). We see from Fig. 3–7, 3–8, or 3–9 that, in order to add the two vectors, one of the vectors must be set with its tail at the head of the other. This may be done by moving either vector or both, just so long as the direction of the vector is not changed (Fig. 3–13). In any case the vector $\boldsymbol{C} = \overrightarrow{OE}$ results.

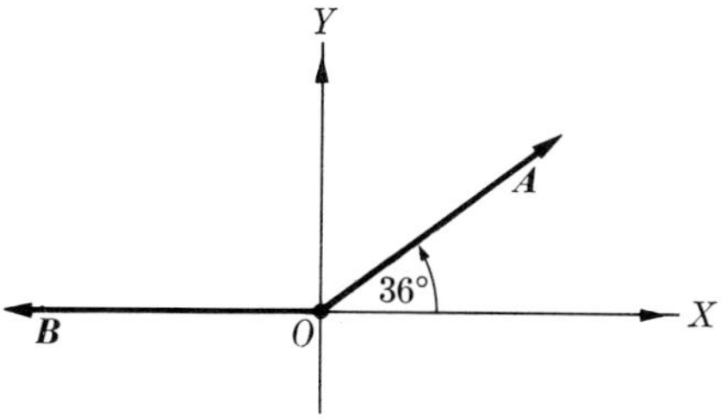

Figure 3–12

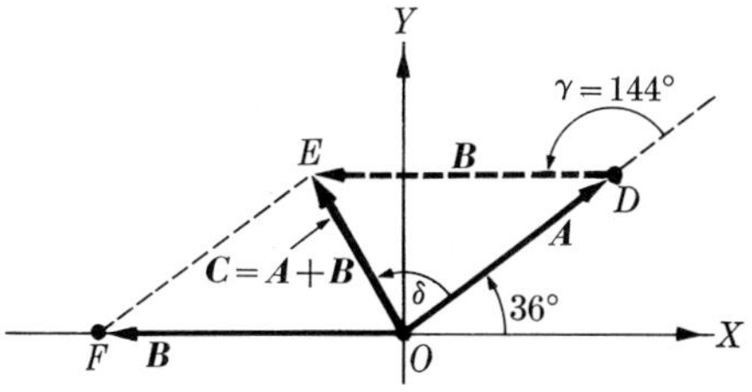

Figure 3–13

(a) From Fig. 3–13 we see that we may write either: $\boldsymbol{C} = \boldsymbol{A} + \boldsymbol{B}$ or $\boldsymbol{C} = \boldsymbol{B} + \boldsymbol{A}$.

Using the triangle ODE, $\boldsymbol{C}$ may be found as $\boldsymbol{A} + \boldsymbol{B}$. In order to find the magnitude of $\boldsymbol{C}$ by application of Eq. (3.3), we first recognize that we can equate $\boldsymbol{A}$ to $\boldsymbol{V}_1$, $\boldsymbol{B}$ to $\boldsymbol{V}_2$, $\boldsymbol{C}$ to $\boldsymbol{V}$, and the angle $\gamma = 180° - 36° = 144°$ to the angle θ. This results in:

$$C = \sqrt{36 + 49 + 2(6)(7)\cos 144°} = 4.128 \text{ units.}$$

To find the angle between $\boldsymbol{C}$ and $\boldsymbol{A}$, we apply Eq. (3.4), which reads in this case

$$\frac{C}{\sin \gamma} = \frac{B}{\sin \delta},$$

so that

$$\sin \delta = \frac{B \sin 144°}{C} = 0.996 \qquad \text{and} \qquad \delta \cong 85°.$$

Therefore $\boldsymbol{C}$ is 4.128 units long and in a direction that makes an angle of $36° + 85° = +121°$ with the positive X-axis.

(b) To find the difference between two vectors, we must know, just as in ordinary arithmetic, which quantity is being subtracted from which. That is to say, if the vector $\boldsymbol{D}$ is defined as $\boldsymbol{A} - \boldsymbol{B}$ (Fig. 3–14), then $\boldsymbol{B} - \boldsymbol{A}$ is equal to $-\boldsymbol{D}$.

Thus, using the statements of equivalence from part (a) above, and from Eq. (3.6), we find the magnitude of $\boldsymbol{D} = \boldsymbol{A} - \boldsymbol{B}$ as

$$D = \sqrt{36 + 49 - 2(6)(7)\cos 144°} = 12.31 \text{ units.}$$

To find the direction of $\boldsymbol{D}$, we use Eq. (3.4):

$$\frac{D}{\sin 36°} = \frac{|-\boldsymbol{B}|}{\sin \alpha};$$

or, since $|-\boldsymbol{B}| = B$,

$$\sin \alpha = \frac{B \sin 36°}{D} = 0.334$$

or

$$\alpha = 19.5°;$$

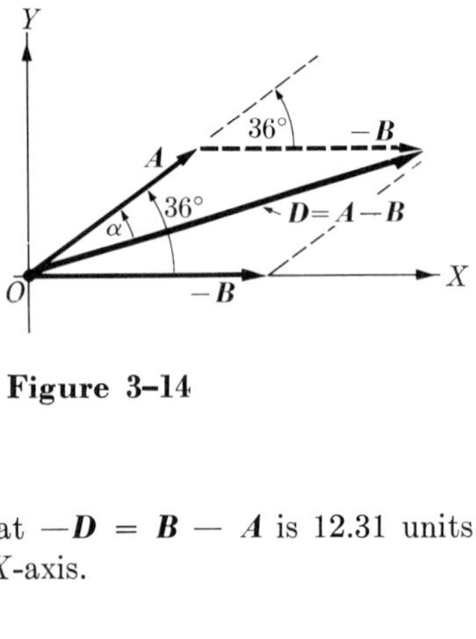

Figure 3–14

and thus $\boldsymbol{D}$ is 12.31 units long and makes an angle of $36° - 19.5° = 16.5°$ with the positive X-axis.

It is left as an exercise for the student to prove that $-\boldsymbol{D} = \boldsymbol{B} - \boldsymbol{A}$ is 12.31 units long and makes an angle of $+196.5°$ with the positive X-axis.

3.5 Components of a Vector

Any vector $\boldsymbol{V}$ can always be considered as the sum of two (or more) vectors, and the number of possibilities is infinite. Each set of vectors which, when added, give $\boldsymbol{V}$ are called the *components* of $\boldsymbol{V}$.

The ones most commonly used are the *rectangular components;* i.e., the vector is expressed as the sum of two mutually perpendicular vectors (Fig. 3–15). Then, as we see from the figure, $\boldsymbol{V} = \boldsymbol{V}_x + \boldsymbol{V}_y$, with

$$V_x = V \cos \alpha \qquad \text{and} \qquad V_y = V \sin \alpha. \tag{3.7}$$

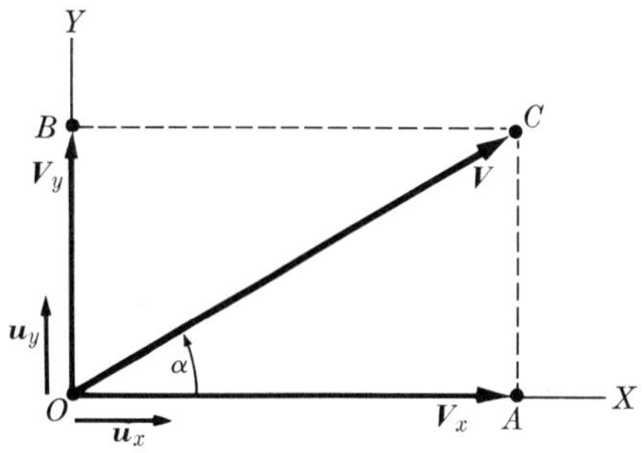

Fig. 3–15. Rectangular components of a vector in a plane.

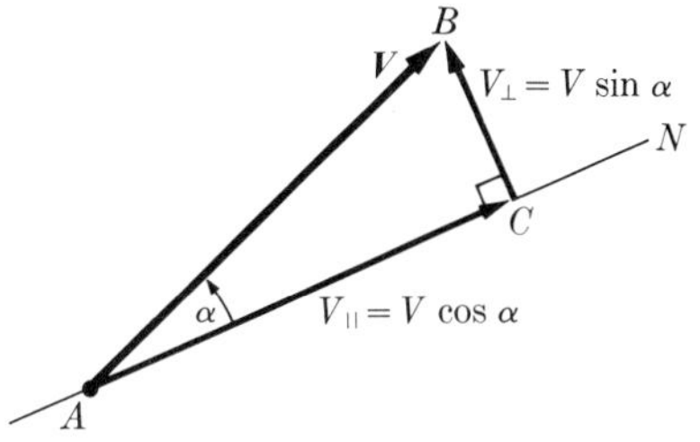

Fig. 3–16. Components of a vector in a certain direction.

Defining unit vectors $\boldsymbol{u}_x$ and $\boldsymbol{u}_y$ in the directions of the X- and Y-axes, we note that

$$\boldsymbol{V}_x = \overrightarrow{OA} = \boldsymbol{u}_x V_x, \qquad \boldsymbol{V}_y = \overrightarrow{OB} = \boldsymbol{u}_y V_y.$$

Therefore we have

$$\boldsymbol{V} = \boldsymbol{u}_x V_x + \boldsymbol{u}_y V_y. \tag{3.8}$$

This equation expresses a vector in terms of its rectangular components in two dimensions. Using Eq. (3.7), we may also write for Eq. (3.8) $\boldsymbol{V} = \boldsymbol{u}_x V \cos\alpha + \boldsymbol{u}_y V \sin\alpha = V(\boldsymbol{u}_x \cos\alpha + \boldsymbol{u}_y \sin\alpha)$. When we compare this result with Eq. (3.1), or just make $V = 1$, we conclude that a unit vector can be written as

$$\boldsymbol{u} = \boldsymbol{u}_x \cos\alpha + \boldsymbol{u}_y \sin\alpha. \tag{3.9}$$

Note that the component of a vector in a particular direction is equal to the projection of the vector in that direction (Fig. 3–16). From the figure, we see that $V_{\parallel} = V\cos\alpha$. Also from Fig. 3–16, we see that BC is that component of $\boldsymbol{V}$ perpendicular to the chosen direction AN, and we can see that $V_{\perp} = BC = V\sin\alpha$. Thus

$$\boldsymbol{V} = \boldsymbol{V}_{\parallel} + \boldsymbol{V}_{\perp}.$$

There are three rectangular components in space: V_x, V_y, V_z (Fig. 3–17). The student may verify from the figure that they are computed according to

$$\begin{aligned} V_x &= V\sin\theta\cos\phi, \\ V_y &= V\sin\theta\sin\phi, \\ V_z &= V\cos\theta, \end{aligned} \tag{3.10}$$

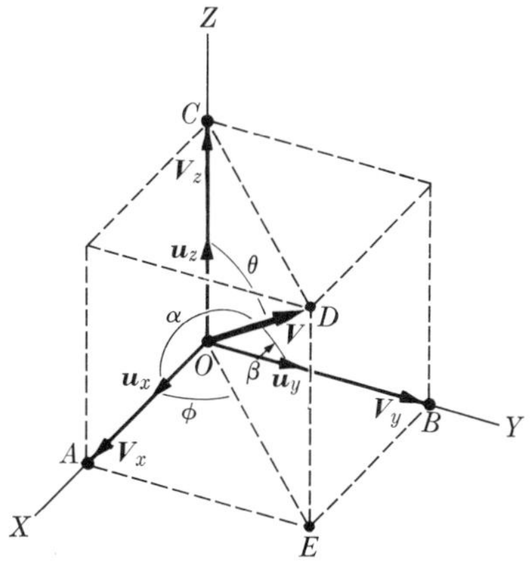

Fig. 3–17. Rectangular components of a vector in three dimensions.

from which it follows, by direct computation, that

$$V^2 = V_x^2 + V_y^2 + V_z^2. \tag{3.11}$$

Defining three unit vectors $\boldsymbol{u}_x$, $\boldsymbol{u}_y$, $\boldsymbol{u}_z$ parallel to the X-, Y-, and Z-axes, respectively, we have

$$\boldsymbol{V} = \boldsymbol{u}_x V_x + \boldsymbol{u}_y V_y + \boldsymbol{u}_z V_z. \tag{3.12}$$

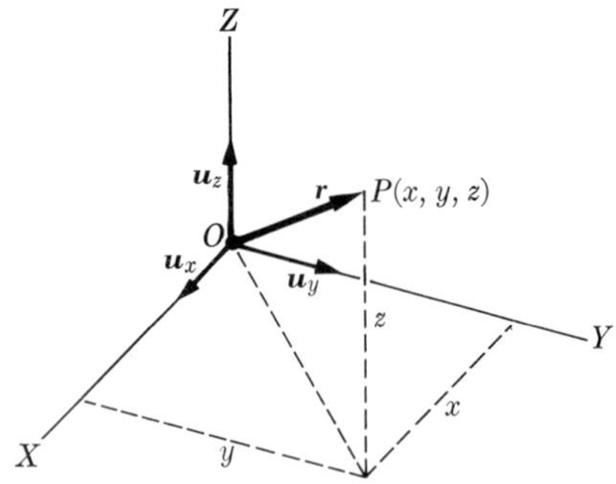

Fig. 3–18. The position vector.

Note that if we designate by α and β the angles the vector $\boldsymbol{V}$ makes with the X- and Y-axes, respectively, we also have, by similarity with the third of Eqs. (3.10),

$$V_x = V \cos \alpha, \qquad V_y = V \cos \beta.$$

Using these two and $V_z = V \cos \theta$ in Eq. (3.11), we obtain the relation

$$\cos^2 \alpha + \cos^2 \beta + \cos^2 \theta = 1.$$

The quantities $\cos \alpha$, $\cos \beta$, and $\cos \theta$ are called the *direction cosines* of a vector.

An important case of a three-dimensional vector is the *position vector* $\boldsymbol{r} = \overrightarrow{OP}$ of a point P having coordinates (x, y, z). From Fig. 3–18 we see that

$$\boldsymbol{r} = \overrightarrow{OP} = \boldsymbol{u}_x x + \boldsymbol{u}_y y + \boldsymbol{u}_z z. \tag{3.13}$$

The relative position vector of two points P_1 and P_2 is $\boldsymbol{r}_{21} = \overrightarrow{P_1P_2}$ (Fig. 3–19). From the figure we note that $\overrightarrow{OP_2} = \overrightarrow{OP_1} + \overrightarrow{P_1P_2}$, so that

$$\begin{aligned} \boldsymbol{r}_{21} &= \overrightarrow{P_1P_2} = \overrightarrow{OP_2} - \overrightarrow{OP_1} = \boldsymbol{r}_2 - \boldsymbol{r}_1 \\ &= \boldsymbol{u}_x(x_2 - x_1) + \boldsymbol{u}_y(y_2 - y_1) + \boldsymbol{u}_z(z_2 - z_1). \end{aligned} \tag{3.14}$$

Note that $\overrightarrow{P_2P_1} = -\overrightarrow{P_1P_2}$. It should be observed that, by applying Eq. (3.11) to Eq. (3.14), we obtain the expression of analytic geometry for the distance between two points:

$$r_{21} = \sqrt{(x_2 - x_1)^2 + (y_2 - y_1)^2 + (z_2 - z_1)^2}.$$

EXAMPLE 3.2. Find the distance between the two points (6, 8, 10) and (—4, 4, 10).

Solution: We draw a set of rectangular axes and identify the two points (Fig. 3–20). We see that both points are in a plane parallel to the XY-plane, since they are both a distance (height) of 10 units in the Z-direction. From Eq. (3.14), we find that the vector $\boldsymbol{r}_{21}$ is

$$\begin{aligned} \boldsymbol{r}_{21} &= \boldsymbol{u}_x(-4 - 6) + \boldsymbol{u}_y(4 - 8) + \boldsymbol{u}_z(10 - 10) \\ &= \boldsymbol{u}_x(-10) + \boldsymbol{u}_y(-4) + \boldsymbol{u}_z(0) = -\boldsymbol{u}_x(10) - \boldsymbol{u}_y(4). \end{aligned}$$

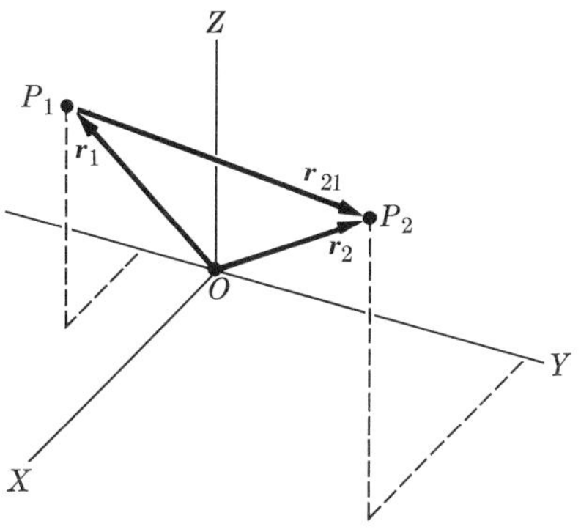

Figure 3–19

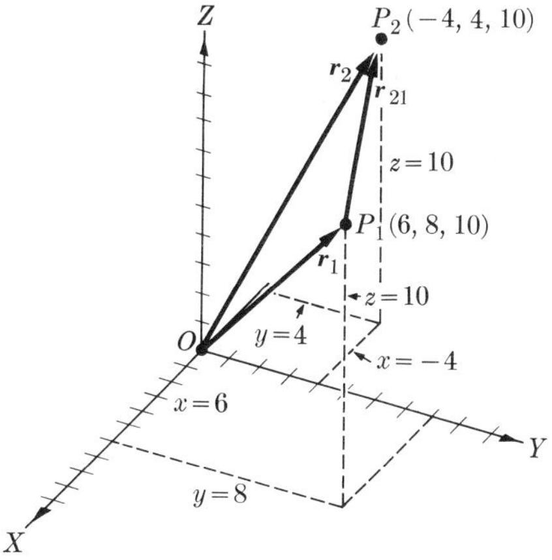

Figure 3–20

Using Eq. (3.11), we find that the magnitude is

$$r_{21}^2 = 100 + 16 = 116 \qquad \text{or} \qquad r_{21} = 10.77 \text{ units}.$$

EXAMPLE 3.3. Find the components of the vector that is 13 units long and makes an angle θ of 22.6° with the Z-axis, and whose projection in the XY-plane makes an angle ϕ of 37° with the $+X$-axis (*cf.* Fig. 3–17). Find also the angles with the X- and Y-axes.

Solution: Using Fig. 3–17 as our figure for the problem, we say that

$$V = 13 \text{ units}, \qquad \theta = 22.6°, \qquad \cos\theta = 0.923,$$
$$\sin\theta = 0.384, \qquad \phi = 37°, \qquad \cos\phi = 0.800, \qquad \sin\phi = 0.600.$$

Now a simple application of Eq. (3.10) yields

$$V_x = 13(0.384)\,(0.800) = 4.0 \text{ units},$$
$$V_y = 13(0.384)\,(0.600) = 3.0 \text{ units},$$
$$V_z = 13(0.923) = 12.0 \text{ units}.$$

In terms of Eq. (3.12) we may write:

$$\boldsymbol{V} = \boldsymbol{u}_x(4) + \boldsymbol{u}_y(3) + \boldsymbol{u}_z(12).$$

For the angles α and β that $\boldsymbol{V}$ makes with the X- and Y-axes, we have

$$\cos\alpha = \frac{V_x}{V} = 0.308 \qquad \text{or} \qquad \alpha = 72.1°,$$

$$\cos\beta = \frac{V_y}{V} = 0.231 \qquad \text{or} \qquad \beta = 77°.$$

EXAMPLE 3.4. Express the equation of a straight line parallel to a vector $\boldsymbol{V} = \boldsymbol{u}_x A + \boldsymbol{u}_y B + \boldsymbol{u}_z C$ and passing through a point P_0.

Solution: Designating by $\boldsymbol{r}_0$ the position vector of P_0 (Fig. 3–21) and by $\boldsymbol{r}$ the position vector on any point P on the straight line, we have from Eq. (3.14) that $\overrightarrow{P_0P} = \boldsymbol{r} - \boldsymbol{r}_0$. But the vector $\overrightarrow{P_0P}$ must be parallel to $\boldsymbol{V}$, and therefore we may write $\overrightarrow{P_0P} = \lambda\boldsymbol{V}$, where λ is a parameter still undetermined. Then

$$\boldsymbol{r} - \boldsymbol{r}_0 = \lambda\boldsymbol{V}$$

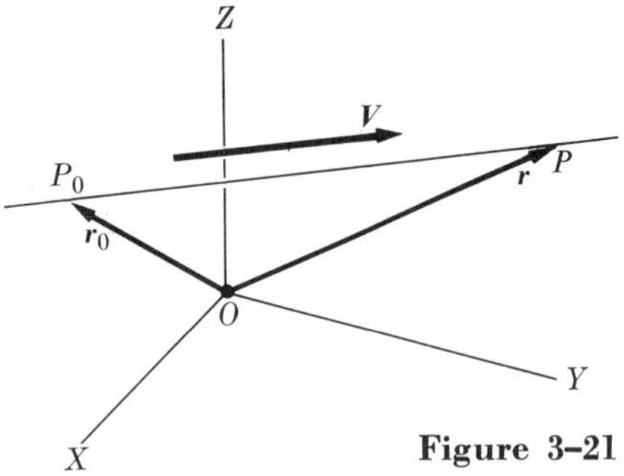

Figure 3–21

is the equation of the straight line, and by varying λ, we obtain the different position vectors $\boldsymbol{r}$. Separating the equation into rectangular components, we have

$$x - x_0 = \lambda A, \qquad y - y_0 = \lambda B, \qquad z - z_0 = \lambda C,$$

or

$$\frac{x - x_0}{A} = \frac{y - y_0}{B} = \frac{z - z_0}{C},$$

which is one of the forms used in analytic geometry to express a straight line.

3.6 Addition of Several Vectors

To add several vectors $\boldsymbol{V}_1, \boldsymbol{V}_2, \boldsymbol{V}_3, \ldots$, we extend the procedure indicated in Fig. 3–8 for the case of two vectors. The method for three vectors is shown in Fig. 3–22. That is, we draw one vector after another, the vector sum being indicated by the line going from the origin of the first to the end of the last. Then

$$\boldsymbol{V} = \boldsymbol{V}_1 + \boldsymbol{V}_2 + \boldsymbol{V}_3 + \cdots. \tag{3.15}$$

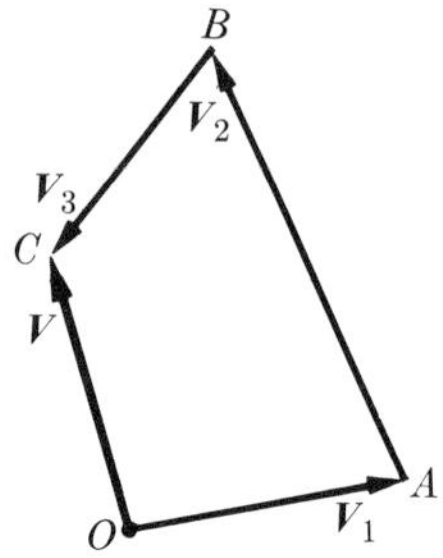

Fig. 3–22. Addition of several vectors.

There is no simple formula to express $\boldsymbol{V}$ in terms of $\boldsymbol{V}_1, \boldsymbol{V}_2, \boldsymbol{V}_3, \ldots$, and it is better to utilize the method of components. Let us consider, for simplicity, the case where all vectors are in one plane, so that we need to use only two components. Then

$$\begin{aligned}\boldsymbol{V} &= (\boldsymbol{u}_x V_{1x} + \boldsymbol{u}_y V_{1y}) + (\boldsymbol{u}_x V_{2x} + \boldsymbol{u}_y V_{2y}) \\ &\quad + (\boldsymbol{u}_x V_{3x} + \boldsymbol{u}_y V_{3y}) + \cdots \\ &= \boldsymbol{u}_x(V_{1x} + V_{2x} + V_{3x} + \cdots) \\ &\quad + \boldsymbol{u}_y(V_{1y} + V_{2y} + V_{3y} + \cdots).\end{aligned}$$

Therefore

$$\begin{aligned}V_x &= V_{1x} + V_{2x} + V_{3x} + \cdots = \textstyle\sum_i V_{ix} = \sum_i V_i \cos\alpha_i, \\ V_y &= V_{1y} + V_{2y} + V_{3y} + \cdots = \textstyle\sum_i V_{iy} = \sum_i V_i \sin\alpha_i,\end{aligned} \tag{3.16}$$

where α_i is the angle $\boldsymbol{V}_i$ makes with the positive X-axis and $V_i \cos\alpha_i$ and $V_i \sin\alpha_i$ are the components of $\boldsymbol{V}_i$ along the X- and Y-axes. Once we know V_x and V_y, we compute $\boldsymbol{V}$, using Eq. (3.5). We now illustrate the procedure with a numerical example.

EXAMPLE 3.5. Find the resultant of the sum of the following five vectors:

$$V_1 = u_x(4) + u_y(-3) \text{ units}, \qquad V_2 = u_x(-3) + u_y(2) \text{ units},$$
$$V_3 = u_x(2) + u_y(-6) \text{ units}, \qquad V_4 = u_x(7) + u_y(-8) \text{ units},$$

and

$$V_5 = u_x(9) + u_y(1) \text{ units}.$$

Solution: Applying Eq. (3.16), we have

$$V_x = 4 - 3 + 2 + 7 + 9 = 19 \text{ units},$$
$$V_y = -3 + 2 - 6 - 8 + 1 = -14 \text{ units},$$

or

$$V = u_x(19) - u_y(14) \text{ units}.$$

The magnitude of V is $V = \sqrt{(19)^2 + (-14)^2} = 23.55$ units. Its direction is found from $\tan \alpha = V_y/V_x = -0.738$ or $\alpha = -36.4°$, which is the angle V makes with the X-axis.

3.7 Application to Kinematic Problems

As an illustration of how to manipulate vectors in some simple physical situations, we shall now consider a few kinematic examples. The only physical assumption required is that we recognize that velocity is a vector quantity.

Suppose, for example, that we have a boat moving with a velocity V_B relative to the water. If the water is still, V_B is also the velocity of the boat as measured by an observer on the shore. But if the water is flowing at a certain rate, this introduces a drift factor which affects the boat's velocity. Thus the resultant velocity of the boat, as measured by an observer on the shore, is the vector sum of the velocity of the boat V_B relative to the water and the drift velocity V_C due to the water current. That is, $V = V_B + V_C$. A similar logic applies to objects moving through the air, such as airplanes.

EXAMPLE 3.6. A motorboat is heading due north at 15 mi hr^{-1} in a place where the current is 5 mi hr^{-1} in the direction S 70° E. Find the resultant velocity of the boat.

Solution: This problem is solved graphically in Fig. 3–23, where V_B is the boat velocity, V_C the current or drift velocity, and V the resultant velocity obtained from

$$V = V_B + V_C.$$

This is based on the physical fact that the resultant velocity is the vector sum of the velocity of the boat relative to the water plus the drift velocity V_C due to the current.

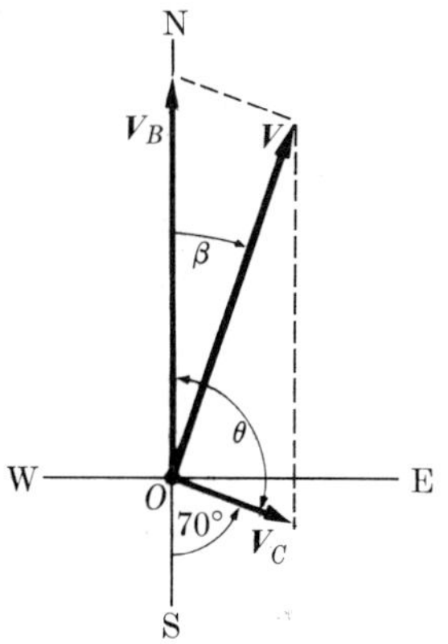

Figure 3–23

Analytically, since $\theta = 110°$, we have

$$V = \sqrt{15^2 + 5^2 + 2(15)(5)\cos 110°} = 14.1 \text{ mi hr}^{-1},$$

which gives the magnitude of the resultant velocity. To obtain the direction, we apply Eq. (3.4),

$$\frac{V}{\sin\theta} = \frac{V_C}{\sin\beta} \quad \text{or} \quad \sin\beta = \frac{V_C \sin\theta}{V} = 0.332,$$

giving $\beta = 19.4°$. Thus the resultant motion is in the direction N 19.4° E.

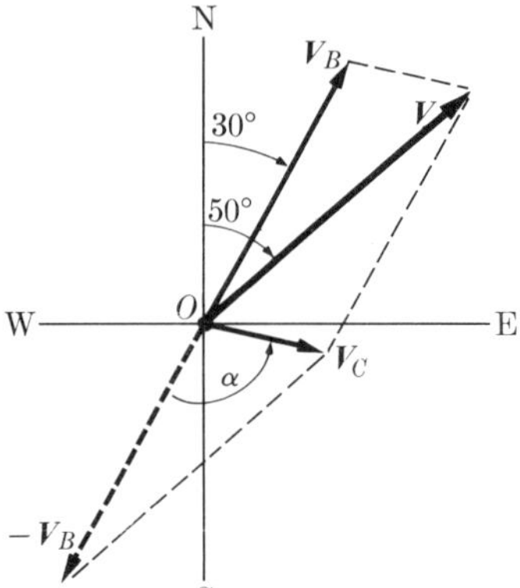

Figure 3–24

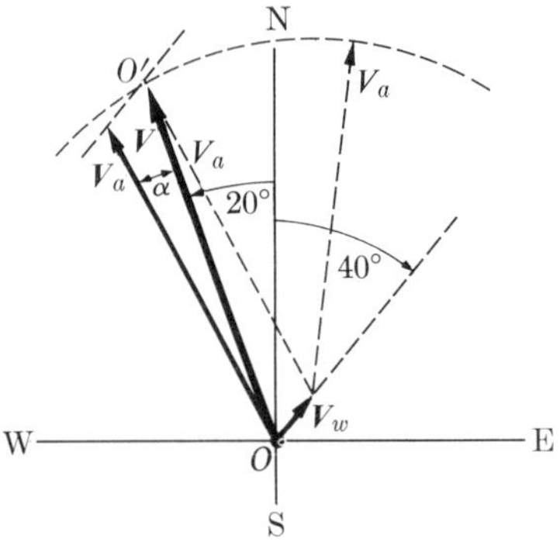

Figure 3–25

EXAMPLE 3.7. A racing boat is heading in the direction N 30° E at 25 mi hr^{-1} in a place where the current is such that the resultant motion is 30 mi hr^{-1} in the direction N 50° E. Find the velocity of the current.

Solution: Again designating the velocity of the boat by $\boldsymbol{V}_B$, the velocity of the current by $\boldsymbol{V}_C$, and the resultant velocity by $\boldsymbol{V}$, we have $\boldsymbol{V} = \boldsymbol{V}_B + \boldsymbol{V}_C$, so that $\boldsymbol{V}_C = \boldsymbol{V} - \boldsymbol{V}_B$. The vectors $\boldsymbol{V}$ and $\boldsymbol{V}_B$ have been drawn in Fig. 3–24, as well as the difference between them, which gives $\boldsymbol{V}_C$. To compute V_C, we note that the angle between $\boldsymbol{V}$ and $-\boldsymbol{V}_B$ is 160°. Thus

$$V_C = \sqrt{30^2 + 25^2 + 2(30)(25)\cos 160°} = 10.8 \text{ mi hr}^{-1}.$$

To obtain the direction of $\boldsymbol{V}_C$, we first obtain the angle α between $\boldsymbol{V}$ and $-\boldsymbol{V}_B$, using Eq. (3.4),

$$\frac{V}{\sin\alpha} = \frac{V_C}{\sin 160°} \quad \text{or} \quad \sin\alpha = \frac{V \sin 160°}{V_C} = 0.951,$$

giving $\alpha = 72°$. Therefore the angle with the SN-axis is $72° - 30° = 42°$, and the direction of $\boldsymbol{V}_C$ is S 42° E.

EXAMPLE 3.8. The speed of an airplane in still air is 200 mi hr^{-1}. It is desired to go from O to O', the direction of OO' being N 20° W. The wind is 30 mi hr^{-1} in the direction N 40° E. Find the direction in which the plane is headed and its resultant velocity.

Solution: Let us designate the velocity of the airplane by $\boldsymbol{V}_a$ and that of the wind by $\boldsymbol{V}_w$. The resultant velocity is, as before,

$$\boldsymbol{V} = \boldsymbol{V}_a + \boldsymbol{V}_w.$$

In this case we know that $\boldsymbol{V}$ must have the direction OO'. Thus the vector $\boldsymbol{V}_a$ must be drawn in such a way that, when added to $\boldsymbol{V}_w$, the resultant is along OO'. This has been done in Fig. 3–25 by drawing a circle of radius V_a, with center at the end of $\boldsymbol{V}_w$, and finding the circle's intersection with line OO'.

To proceed analytically, we note that the angle between $\boldsymbol{V}$ and $\boldsymbol{V}_w$ is $20° + 40° = 60°$. Thus, using Eq. (3.4), we obtain

$$\frac{V_a}{\sin 60°} = \frac{V_w}{\sin \alpha} \quad \text{or} \quad \sin \alpha = \frac{V_w \sin 60°}{V_a} = 0.130,$$

giving $\alpha = 7.8°$. Therefore the direction of $\boldsymbol{V}_a$ must be N 27.8° W. The angle between $\boldsymbol{V}_a$ and $\boldsymbol{V}_w$ is $\theta = 27.8° + 40° = 67.8°$, and the magnitude of the resultant velocity, using Eq. (3.3), is

$$V = \sqrt{200^2 + 30^2 + 2 \times 200 \times 30 \cos 67.8°} = 204 \text{ mi hr}^{-1}.$$

Is it possible that this problem has two solutions, or no solution at all? We leave the answer to the student.

EXAMPLE 3.9. Find the acceleration of a body that slides along a plane inclined at an angle of θ.

Solution: Let P (Fig. 3–26) be a body sliding down the plane AB without friction. The plane AB is inclined an angle θ. If the plane were not there, the body would fall freely along the vertical with the acceleration due to gravity $g = 9.8 \text{ m s}^{-2}$ (see Example 5.2). The components of g parallel and perpendicular to the plane (called, respectively, a and a') are given by $a = g \sin \theta$ and $a' = g \cos \theta$.

The component a gives the acceleration of the body along the plane.

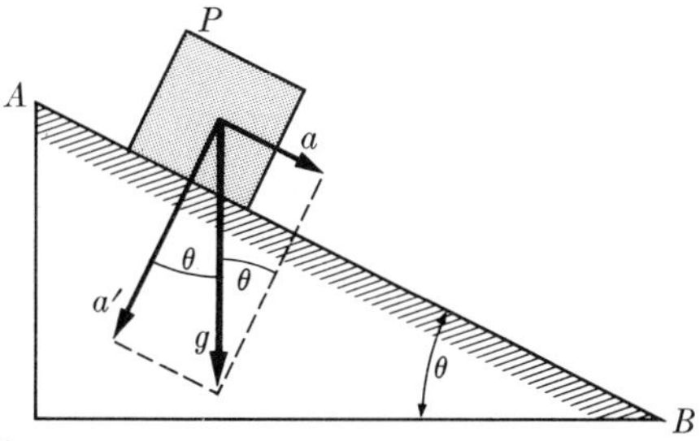

Fig. 3–26. Acceleration along an inclined plane.

3.8 Scalar Product

It is possible to define other operations with vectors besides their addition. One of these operations is the scalar product; another is the vector product.

The *scalar product* of two vectors $\boldsymbol{A}$ and $\boldsymbol{B}$, represented by the symbol $\boldsymbol{A} \cdot \boldsymbol{B}$ (read "A dot B"), is defined as the scalar quantity obtained by finding the product of the magnitudes of $\boldsymbol{A}$ and $\boldsymbol{B}$ and the cosine of the angle between the two vectors,

$$\boldsymbol{A} \cdot \boldsymbol{B} = AB \cos \theta. \tag{3.17}$$

Obviously $\boldsymbol{A} \cdot \boldsymbol{A} = A^2$, since the angle in this case is zero. If the two vectors are perpendicular ($\theta = \pi/2$), the scalar product is zero. Therefore the condition of perpendicularity is expressed by $\boldsymbol{A} \cdot \boldsymbol{B} = 0$. Because of its definition, the scalar product is commutative; that is, $\boldsymbol{A} \cdot \boldsymbol{B} = \boldsymbol{B} \cdot \boldsymbol{A}$, since $\cos\theta$ is the same in both cases. The scalar product is distributive with respect to the sum; that is,

$$\boldsymbol{C} \cdot (\boldsymbol{A} + \boldsymbol{B}) = \boldsymbol{C} \cdot \boldsymbol{A} + \boldsymbol{C} \cdot \boldsymbol{B}. \tag{3.18}$$

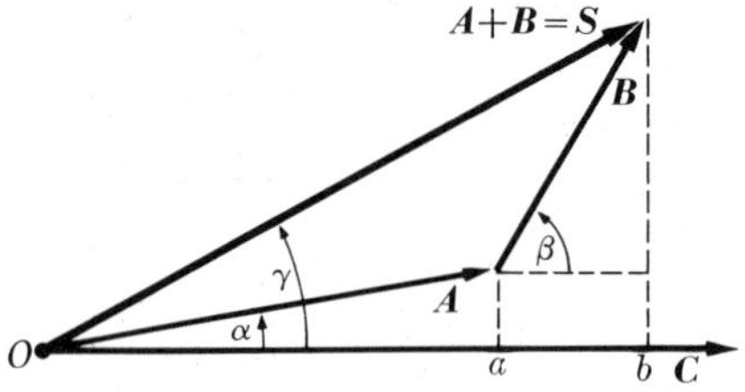

Fig. 3–27. The scalar product is distributive.

To prove the distributive property, we note from Fig. 3–27 that

$$\boldsymbol{C} \cdot (\boldsymbol{A} + \boldsymbol{B}) = |\boldsymbol{C}|\,|\boldsymbol{A} + \boldsymbol{B}| \cos\gamma = C(Ob),$$

because $|\boldsymbol{A} + \boldsymbol{B}| \cos\gamma = Ob$. Similarly, $\boldsymbol{C} \cdot \boldsymbol{A} = CA \cos\alpha = C(Oa)$ and $\boldsymbol{C} \cdot \boldsymbol{B} = CB \cos\beta = C(ab)$. Adding, we obtain

$$\boldsymbol{C} \cdot \boldsymbol{A} + \boldsymbol{C} \cdot \boldsymbol{B} = C(Oa + ab) = C(Ob).$$

Therefore Eq. (3.18) is proved. The scalar products among the unit vectors $\boldsymbol{u}_x$, $\boldsymbol{u}_y$, and $\boldsymbol{u}_z$ are

$$\boldsymbol{u}_x \cdot \boldsymbol{u}_x = \boldsymbol{u}_y \cdot \boldsymbol{u}_y = \boldsymbol{u}_z \cdot \boldsymbol{u}_z = 1, \qquad \boldsymbol{u}_x \cdot \boldsymbol{u}_y = \boldsymbol{u}_y \cdot \boldsymbol{u}_z = \boldsymbol{u}_z \cdot \boldsymbol{u}_x = 0. \tag{3.19}$$

Writing $\boldsymbol{A}$ and $\boldsymbol{B}$ in terms of their rectangular components, in accordance with Eq. (3.12), and applying the distributive law (3.18), we have

$$\begin{aligned} \boldsymbol{A} \cdot \boldsymbol{B} &= (\boldsymbol{u}_x A_x + \boldsymbol{u}_y A_y + \boldsymbol{u}_z A_z) \cdot (\boldsymbol{u}_x B_x + \boldsymbol{u}_y B_y + \boldsymbol{u}_z B_z) \\ &= (\boldsymbol{u}_x \cdot \boldsymbol{u}_x) A_x B_x + (\boldsymbol{u}_x \cdot \boldsymbol{u}_y) A_x B_y + (\boldsymbol{u}_x \cdot \boldsymbol{u}_z) A_x B_z \\ &\quad + (\boldsymbol{u}_y \cdot \boldsymbol{u}_x) A_y B_x + (\boldsymbol{u}_y \cdot \boldsymbol{u}_y) A_y B_y + (\boldsymbol{u}_y \cdot \boldsymbol{u}_z) A_y B_z \\ &\quad + (\boldsymbol{u}_z \cdot \boldsymbol{u}_x) A_z B_x + (\boldsymbol{u}_z \cdot \boldsymbol{u}_y) A_z B_y + (\boldsymbol{u}_z \cdot \boldsymbol{u}_z) A_z B_z. \end{aligned}$$

Applying relations (3.19), we finally obtain

$$\boldsymbol{A} \cdot \boldsymbol{B} = A_x B_x + A_y B_y + A_z B_z, \tag{3.20}$$

a result which has many applications. Note that

$$A^2 = \boldsymbol{A} \cdot \boldsymbol{A} = A_x^2 + A_y^2 + A_z^2,$$

in agreement with Eq. (3.11).

We can apply the properties of the scalar product to derive quite easily the formula (3.3) for the sum of two vectors. From $\boldsymbol{V} = \boldsymbol{V}_1 + \boldsymbol{V}_2$, we have

$$\begin{aligned} V^2 &= (\boldsymbol{V}_1 + \boldsymbol{V}_2) \cdot (\boldsymbol{V}_1 + \boldsymbol{V}_2) = V_1^2 + V_2^2 + 2\boldsymbol{V}_1 \cdot \boldsymbol{V}_2 \\ &= V_1^2 + V_2^2 + 2V_1V_2 \cos\theta. \end{aligned}$$

This result can be extended without difficulty to any number of vectors. Suppose that $\boldsymbol{V} = \boldsymbol{V}_1 + \boldsymbol{V}_2 + \boldsymbol{V}_3 + \cdots = \sum_i \boldsymbol{V}_i$. Then

$$\begin{aligned} V^2 &= (\boldsymbol{V}_1 + \boldsymbol{V}_2 + \boldsymbol{V}_3 + \cdots)^2 \\ &= V_1^2 + V_2^2 + V_3^2 + \cdots + 2\boldsymbol{V}_1 \cdot \boldsymbol{V}_2 + 2\boldsymbol{V}_1 \cdot \boldsymbol{V}_3 \\ &\quad + \cdots + 2\boldsymbol{V}_2 \cdot \boldsymbol{V}_3 + \cdots, \end{aligned}$$

or, in a compact notation,

$$V^2 = \sum_{\substack{\text{all} \\ \text{vectors}}} V_i^2 + 2\sum_{\substack{\text{all} \\ \text{pairs}}} \boldsymbol{V}_i \cdot \boldsymbol{V}_j.$$

EXAMPLE 3.10. Find the angle between the vectors $\boldsymbol{A} = 2\boldsymbol{u}_x + 3\boldsymbol{u}_y - \boldsymbol{u}_z$ and $\boldsymbol{B} = -\boldsymbol{u}_x + \boldsymbol{u}_y + 2\boldsymbol{u}_z$.

Solution: We first compute their scalar product, using Eq. (3.20):

$$\boldsymbol{A} \cdot \boldsymbol{B} = 2(-1) + 3(1) + (-1)2 = -1.$$

Also

$$A = \sqrt{4 + 9 + 1} = \sqrt{14} = 3.74 \text{ units}$$

and

$$B = \sqrt{1 + 1 + 4} = \sqrt{6} = 2.45 \text{ units}.$$

Thus from Eq. (3.17), we have

$$\cos\theta = \frac{\boldsymbol{A} \cdot \boldsymbol{B}}{AB} = -\frac{1}{9.17} = -0.109,$$

corresponding to $\theta = 96.3°$.

EXAMPLE 3.11. Express the equation of a plane perpendicular to a vector $\boldsymbol{V} = \boldsymbol{u}_x A + \boldsymbol{u}_y B + \boldsymbol{u}_z C$ and passing through a point P_0.

Solution: Designating the position vector of P_0 by $\boldsymbol{r}_0$ (Fig. 3–28), and the position vector of any point P of the plane by $\boldsymbol{r}$, we see that the vector

$$\overrightarrow{P_0P} = \boldsymbol{r} - \boldsymbol{r}_0$$

must be perpendicular to $\boldsymbol{V}$. Thus

$$\boldsymbol{V} \cdot (\boldsymbol{r} - \boldsymbol{r}_0) = 0$$

is the equation that must be satisfied by the position vectors $\boldsymbol{r}$ of all the points on the plane. Using Eq. (3.20), we may write

$$A(x - x_0) + B(y - y_0) + C(z - z_0) = 0,$$

which is the form in which the equation of a plane perpendicular to a given line is usually written in analytic geometry.

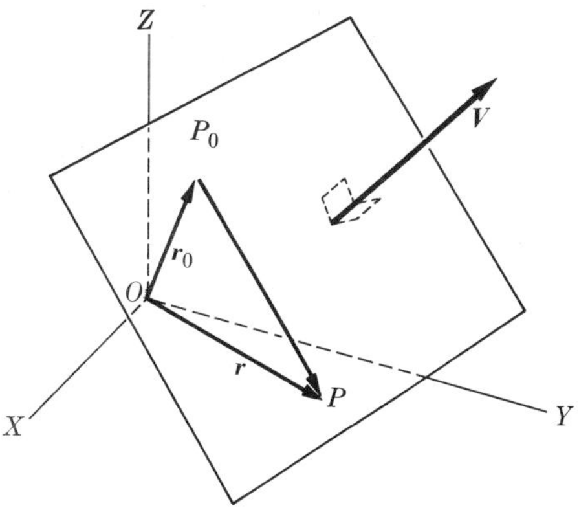

Fig. 3–28. Vector equation of a plane.

3.9 Vector Product

The vector product of two vectors $\boldsymbol{A}$ and $\boldsymbol{B}$, represented by the symbol $\boldsymbol{A} \times \boldsymbol{B}$ (read "A cross B"), is defined as the vector perpendicular to the plane determined by $\boldsymbol{A}$ and $\boldsymbol{B}$ and in the direction of advance of a right-handed screw rotated from $\boldsymbol{A}$ to $\boldsymbol{B}$ (Fig. 3–29). A right-handed screw is one that, if one's right hand is placed as shown in Fig. 3–29, with the fingers pointing in the direction of rotation, the screw advances in the direction of the thumb. Most ordinary screws are right-handed.

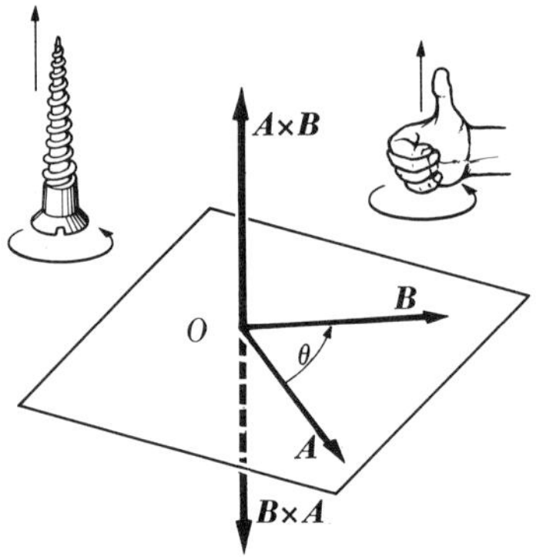

Fig. 3–29. Vector relations in the vector product.

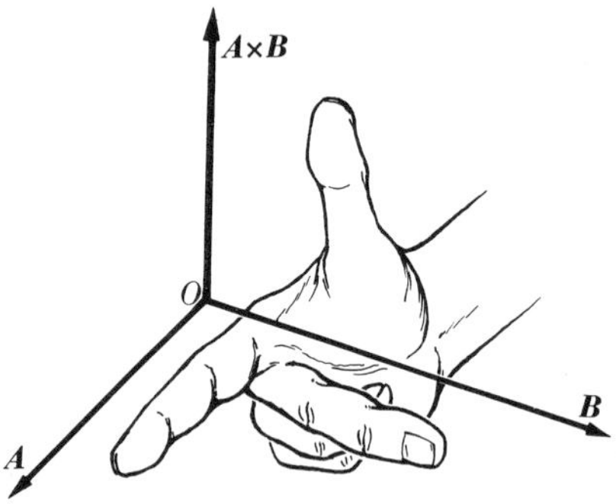

Fig. 3–30. Right-hand rule for the vector product.

The magnitude of the vector product $\boldsymbol{A} \times \boldsymbol{B}$ is given by

$$|\boldsymbol{A} \times \boldsymbol{B}| = AB \sin \theta. \tag{3.21}$$

Another simple rule useful in establishing the direction of $\boldsymbol{A} \times \boldsymbol{B}$ is as follows: Place the thumb, forefinger, and middle finger of the right hand in the position shown in Fig. 3–30. If the forefinger and the middle finger point in the directions of $\boldsymbol{A}$ and $\boldsymbol{B}$, respectively, the thumb points in the direction of $\boldsymbol{A} \times \boldsymbol{B}$. Actually, the rule is more general, and the vectors $\boldsymbol{A}$, $\boldsymbol{B}$, and $\boldsymbol{A} \times \boldsymbol{B}$ can be sequentially assigned to the fingers by starting at any finger, so long as the following *cyclic* order is maintained.

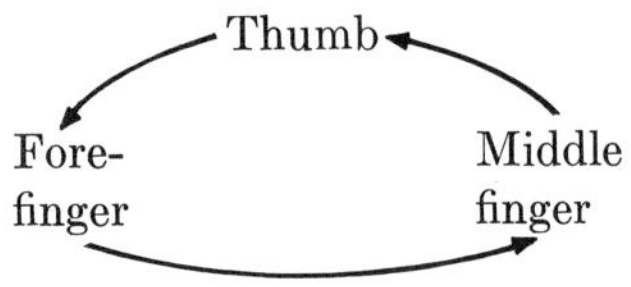

From the definition of the vector product, we conclude that

$$\boldsymbol{A} \times \boldsymbol{B} = -\boldsymbol{B} \times \boldsymbol{A}, \tag{3.22}$$

because the sense of rotation of the screw is reversed when the order of the vectors is changed, so that the vector product is anticommutative. If two vectors are parallel, $\theta = 0°$, $\sin\theta = 0$, and the vector product is zero. Therefore the condition of parallelism is expressed by $\boldsymbol{A} \times \boldsymbol{B} = 0$. Obviously $\boldsymbol{A} \times \boldsymbol{A} = 0$.

Note that the magnitude of the vector product is equal to the area of the parallelogram formed by the two vectors, or is equal to twice the area of the triangle made with their resultant. This can be seen as follows (Fig. 3–31). The magnitude of $\boldsymbol{A} \times \boldsymbol{B}$ is $AB \sin\theta$. But $B \sin\theta = h$, where h is the height of the parallelogram formed with $\boldsymbol{A}$ and $\boldsymbol{B}$ as sides. Thus

$$|\boldsymbol{A} \times \boldsymbol{B}| = Ah = \text{area of parallelogram.}$$

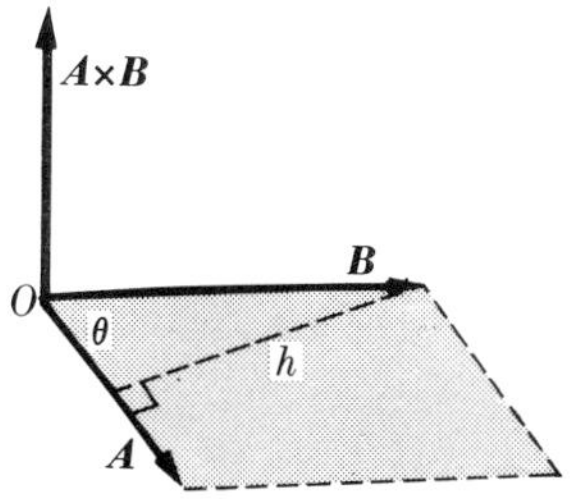

Fig. 3–31. The vector product is equivalent to the area of the parallelogram defined by the two vectors.

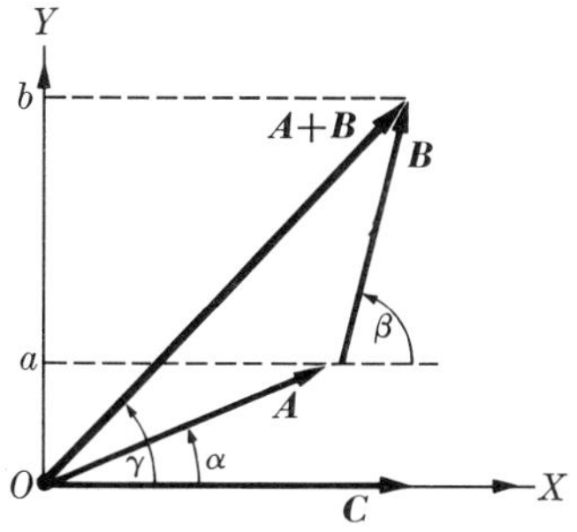

Fig. 3–32. The vector product is distributive.

The vector product is distributive relative to the sum; that is,

$$\boldsymbol{C} \times (\boldsymbol{A} + \boldsymbol{B}) = \boldsymbol{C} \times \boldsymbol{A} + \boldsymbol{C} \times \boldsymbol{B}. \tag{3.23}$$

The proof when the three vectors are in a plane is very simple. In this case (Fig. 3–32) the three vector products appearing in Eq. (3.23) are perpendicular to the page of the book, and it is only necessary to verify that relation (3.23) holds for the magnitudes. But

$$|\boldsymbol{C} \times (\boldsymbol{A} + \boldsymbol{B})| = |\boldsymbol{C}||\boldsymbol{A} + \boldsymbol{B}| \sin\gamma = C(Ob).$$

Similarly,

$$|\boldsymbol{C} \times \boldsymbol{A}| = CA \sin\alpha = C(Oa); \qquad |\boldsymbol{C} \times \boldsymbol{B}| = CB \sin\beta = C(ab).$$

When we add, we obtain

$$|\boldsymbol{C} \times \boldsymbol{A}| + |\boldsymbol{C} \times \boldsymbol{B}| = C(Oa + ab) = C(Ob).$$

Therefore Eq. (3.23) is proved both in magnitude and direction. The proof in the general case of three vectors in space is similar, but somewhat more complex.*

* For a general proof, see G. B. Thomas, *Calculus and Analytic Geometry*, third edition; Reading, Mass.: Addison-Wesley, 1962, Section 13–4.

The vector products among the unit vectors, $\boldsymbol{u}_x$, $\boldsymbol{u}_y$, $\boldsymbol{u}_z$ are

$$\begin{aligned}\boldsymbol{u}_x \times \boldsymbol{u}_y &= -\boldsymbol{u}_y \times \boldsymbol{u}_x = \boldsymbol{u}_z,\\ \boldsymbol{u}_y \times \boldsymbol{u}_z &= -\boldsymbol{u}_z \times \boldsymbol{u}_y = \boldsymbol{u}_x,\\ \boldsymbol{u}_z \times \boldsymbol{u}_x &= -\boldsymbol{u}_x \times \boldsymbol{u}_z = \boldsymbol{u}_y,\\ \boldsymbol{u}_x \times \boldsymbol{u}_x &= \boldsymbol{u}_y \times \boldsymbol{u}_y = \boldsymbol{u}_z \times \boldsymbol{u}_z = 0.\end{aligned} \tag{3.24}$$

Writing $\boldsymbol{A}$ and $\boldsymbol{B}$ in terms of their rectangular components, according to Eq. (3.12), and applying the distributive law (3.23), we have

$$\begin{aligned}\boldsymbol{A} \times \boldsymbol{B} &= (\boldsymbol{u}_xA_x + \boldsymbol{u}_yA_y + \boldsymbol{u}_zA_z) \times (\boldsymbol{u}_xB_x + \boldsymbol{u}_yB_y + \boldsymbol{u}_zB_z)\\ &= (\boldsymbol{u}_x \times \boldsymbol{u}_x)A_xB_x + (\boldsymbol{u}_x \times \boldsymbol{u}_y)A_xB_y + (\boldsymbol{u}_x \times \boldsymbol{u}_z)A_xB_z\\ &\quad + (\boldsymbol{u}_y \times \boldsymbol{u}_x)A_yB_x + (\boldsymbol{u}_y \times \boldsymbol{u}_y)A_yB_y + (\boldsymbol{u}_y \times \boldsymbol{u}_z)A_yB_z\\ &\quad + (\boldsymbol{u}_z \times \boldsymbol{u}_x)A_zB_x + (\boldsymbol{u}_z \times \boldsymbol{u}_y)A_zB_y + (\boldsymbol{u}_z \times \boldsymbol{u}_z)A_zB_z.\end{aligned}$$

Applying relations (3.24), we obtain finally

$$\begin{aligned}\boldsymbol{A} \times \boldsymbol{B} &= \boldsymbol{u}_x(A_yB_z - A_zB_y) + \boldsymbol{u}_y(A_zB_x - A_xB_z)\\ &\quad + \boldsymbol{u}_z(A_xB_y - A_yB_x).\end{aligned} \tag{3.25}$$

Equation (3.25) may also be written in the more compact determinantal form,

$$\boldsymbol{A} \times \boldsymbol{B} = \begin{vmatrix} \boldsymbol{u}_x & \boldsymbol{u}_y & \boldsymbol{u}_z \\ A_x & A_y & A_z \\ B_x & B_y & B_z \end{vmatrix}. \tag{3.26}$$

Note on determinants. A determinant is a convenient notation for arranging quantities that have to be combined in a certain symmetric way. A second-order determinant is a 2×2 array of numbers evaluated according to the rule:

$$\begin{vmatrix} a_1 & a_2 \\ b_1 & b_2 \end{vmatrix} = a_1b_2 - a_2b_1.$$

Note that what we do is to multiply along the diagonals and subtract. A third-order determinant is a 3×3 array of numbers evaluated according to the rule:

$$\begin{aligned}\begin{vmatrix} a_1 & a_2 & a_3 \\ b_1 & b_2 & b_3 \\ c_1 & c_2 & c_3 \end{vmatrix} &= a_1\begin{vmatrix} b_2 & b_3 \\ c_2 & c_3 \end{vmatrix} + a_2\begin{vmatrix} b_3 & b_1 \\ c_3 & c_1 \end{vmatrix} + a_3\begin{vmatrix} b_1 & b_2 \\ c_1 & c_2 \end{vmatrix}\\ &= a_1(b_2c_3 - b_3c_2) + a_2(b_3c_1 - b_1c_3) + a_3(b_1c_2 - b_2c_1).\end{aligned}$$

Note the order in which the columns appear in each term. The student may verify that by applying this rule to Eq. (3.26), he will obtain Eq. (3.25). For more information on determinants, the student should consult G. B. Thomas, *Calculus and Analytic Geometry*, third edition; Reading, Mass.: Addison-Wesley, Sections 8–1 and 8–2.

EXAMPLE 3.12. Find the area of the parallelogram determined by the vectors

$$\boldsymbol{A} = 2\boldsymbol{u}_x + 3\boldsymbol{u}_y - \boldsymbol{u}_z \quad \text{and} \quad \boldsymbol{B} = -\boldsymbol{u}_x + \boldsymbol{u}_y + 2\boldsymbol{u}_z.$$

Solution: First we compute the vector product of $\boldsymbol{A}$ and $\boldsymbol{B}$, using Eq. (3.26):

$$\boldsymbol{A} \times \boldsymbol{B} = \begin{vmatrix} \boldsymbol{u}_x & \boldsymbol{u}_y & \boldsymbol{u}_z \\ 2 & 3 & -1 \\ -1 & 1 & 2 \end{vmatrix} = 7\boldsymbol{u}_x - 3\boldsymbol{u}_y + 5\boldsymbol{u}_z.$$

Then the area of the parallelogram is just the magnitude of $\boldsymbol{A} \times \boldsymbol{B}$, or

$$\text{Area} = |\boldsymbol{A} \times \boldsymbol{B}| = \sqrt{49 + 9 + 25} = 9.110 \text{ units}.$$

EXAMPLE 3.13. Find the distance from point P (4, —1, 5) to the straight line passing through points P_1 (—1, 2, 0) and P_2 (1, 1, 4).

Solution: The geometry of the problem has been illustrated in Fig. 3–33. It is seen that $d = P_1P \sin\theta$. We introduce the vectors

$$\boldsymbol{A} = \overrightarrow{P_1P} \quad \text{and} \quad \boldsymbol{B} = \overrightarrow{P_1P_2},$$

so that, using Eq. (3.14), we obtain

$$\boldsymbol{A} = \overrightarrow{P_1P} = 5\boldsymbol{u}_x - 3\boldsymbol{u}_y + 5\boldsymbol{u}_z,$$
$$\boldsymbol{B} = \overrightarrow{P_1P_2} = 2\boldsymbol{u}_x - \boldsymbol{u}_y + 4\boldsymbol{u}_z.$$

We then see that

$$d = A \sin\theta = \frac{AB \sin\theta}{B} = \frac{|\boldsymbol{A} \times \boldsymbol{B}|}{B}.$$

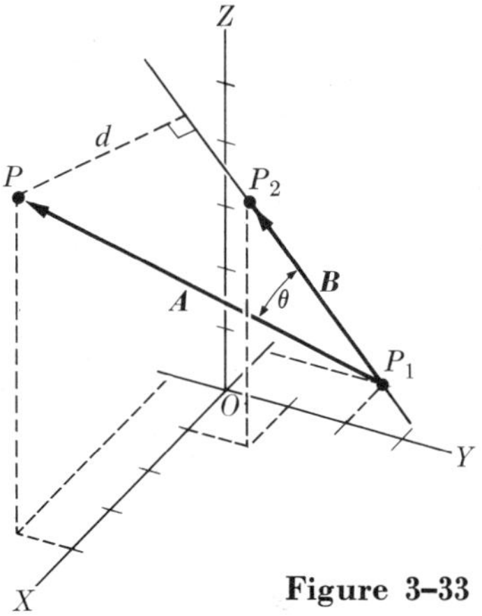

Figure 3–33

Thus, using Eq. (3.26) to compute the vector product of $\boldsymbol{A}$ and $\boldsymbol{B}$, we get

$$\boldsymbol{A} \times \boldsymbol{B} = \begin{vmatrix} \boldsymbol{u}_x & \boldsymbol{u}_y & \boldsymbol{u}_z \\ 5 & -3 & 5 \\ 2 & -1 & 4 \end{vmatrix} = -7\boldsymbol{u}_x - 10\boldsymbol{u}_y + 1\boldsymbol{u}_z.$$

Then $|\boldsymbol{A} \times \boldsymbol{B}| = \sqrt{49 + 100 + 1} = \sqrt{150} = 12.25$, and since $B = \sqrt{4 + 1 + 16} = \sqrt{21} = 4.582$, we obtain

$$d = \frac{|\boldsymbol{A} \times \boldsymbol{B}|}{B} = 2.674.$$

3.10 Vector Representation of an Area

In the discussion related to Fig. 3–31, we indicated that the vector product $\boldsymbol{A} \times \boldsymbol{B}$ is equal in magnitude to the area of the parallelogram whose sides are defined by vectors $\boldsymbol{A}$ and $\boldsymbol{B}$. This suggests the possibility of considering associating a vector with any surface.

Let us consider a *plane* surface S (Fig. 3–34) whose periphery L is oriented as indicated by the arrow. We shall adopt the convention of representing it by a vector $\boldsymbol{S}$, whose magnitude is equal to the area of the surface and whose direction is perpendicular to the surface. The sense of the vector is the direction in which a right-handed screw advances when its head is rotated in the same sense as the periphery is oriented.

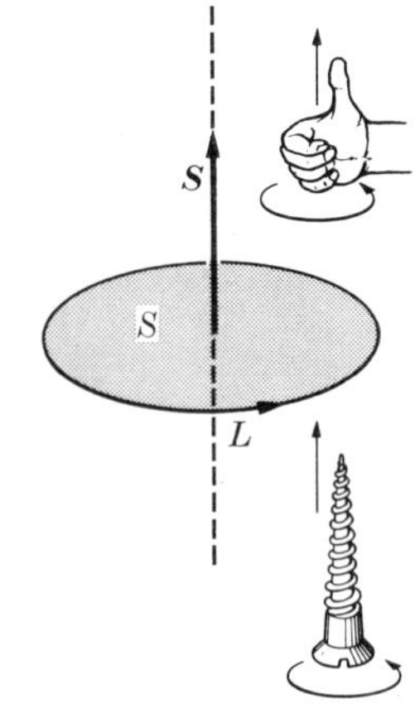

Fig. 3–34. Vector representation of a surface.

The components of $\boldsymbol{S}$ have a simple geometric meaning. Suppose that the plane of surface S makes an angle θ with the XY-plane (Fig. 3–35). The projection of S on the XY-plane is $S \cos \theta$, as is well known from solid geometry. But the normal to the plane of the surface also makes an angle θ with the Z-axis. Thus the Z-component of the vector $\boldsymbol{S}$ is $S_z = S \cos \theta$. Therefore we conclude that the components of $\boldsymbol{S}$ along the coordinate axes are equal to the projections of the surface on the three coordinate planes.

If the surface is *not* plane, it may always be divided into a large number of very small areas (Fig. 3–36) each one practically plane, and each represented by a vector $\boldsymbol{S}_i$. Thus the vector representing the curved surface is

$$\boldsymbol{S} = \boldsymbol{S}_1 + \boldsymbol{S}_2 + \boldsymbol{S}_3 + \cdots = \textstyle\sum_i \boldsymbol{S}_i.$$

In this case the magnitude of $\boldsymbol{S}$ is not equal to the area of the curved surface, which is $\sum_i S_i$; however, the magnitudes of its three components are equal to the areas of the projections of the surface on the three coordinate planes.

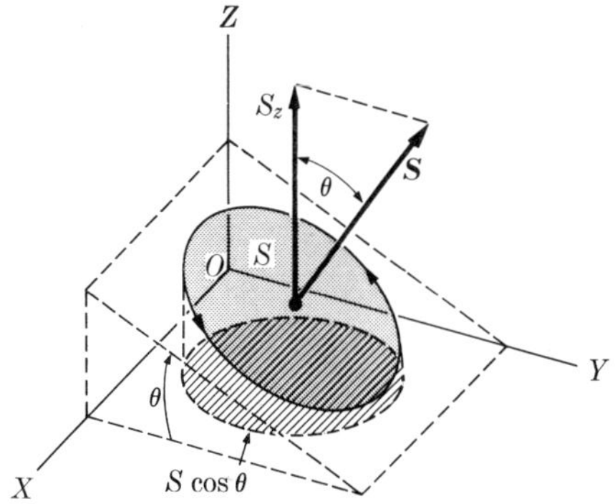

Fig. 3–35. Projection of a surface on a plane.

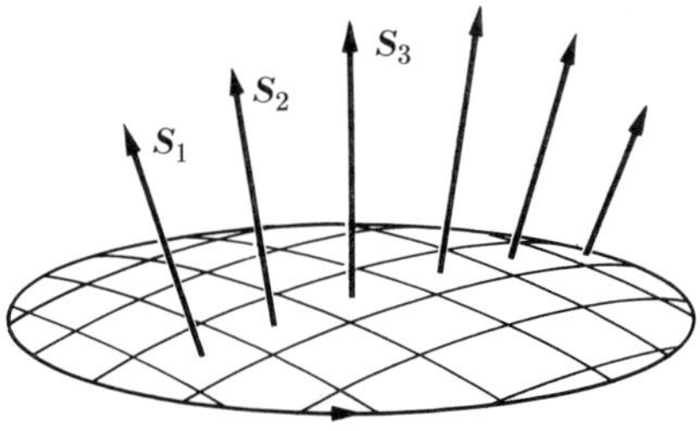

Fig. 3–36. Vector addition of surfaces.

For example, let us consider a plot of land, of which part is horizontal and part on the slope of a hill, as indicated in Fig. 3–37. If S_1 and S_2 are the areas of each portion, the total area of land usable for farming is $S_1 + S_2$. However, if the plot is going to be used for a building, the actual usable land is the projection of the plot on a horizontal plane, or $S_1 + S_2 \cos \theta$. The vector $\boldsymbol{S} = \boldsymbol{S}_1 + \boldsymbol{S}_2$, represent-

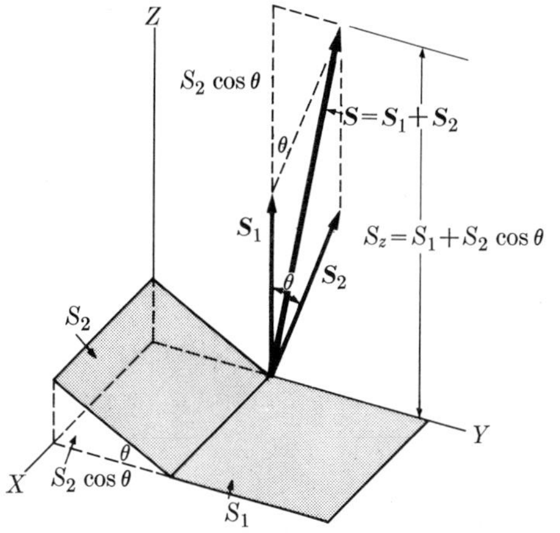

Figure 3–37

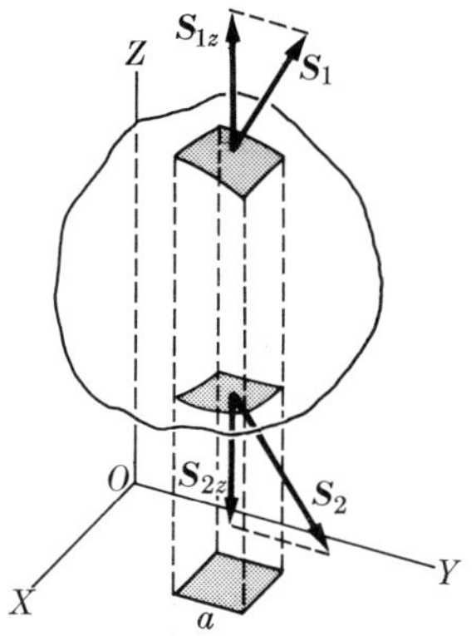

Fig. 3–38. A closed surface is represented by a null vector.

ing the whole plot, has a magnitude $S = \sqrt{S_1^2 + S_2^2 + 2S_1S_2\cos\theta}$, which is smaller than $S_1 + S_2$. But its component along the vertical Z-axis is $S_z = S_1 + S_2 \cos\theta$, in agreement with the projection of the plot on the horizontal XY-plane.

Finally, consider a *closed surface*, as shown in Fig. 3–38. Divide this surface into small plane surfaces, each one represented by a vector $\mathbf{S}_i$ in the *outward* direction. We can always associate the small areas in pairs such that their combined projection is zero. For example, in Fig. 3–38, the two areas S_1 and S_2 have the same projection in the XY-plane, but with opposite signs. Thus $S_{1z} = a$ and $S_{2z} = -a$. Adding all such pairs we get $S_z = \sum_i S_{iz} = 0$. By the same argument we see that the same result holds for the components of $\mathbf{S} = \sum_i \mathbf{S}_i$ along the other two axes. Therefore, $\mathbf{S} = 0$, or *the vector representing a closed surface is zero.*

References

1. *Vectors, A Programmed Text for Introductory Physics.* New York: Appleton-Century-Crofts, 1962
2. *Elementary Vectors,* by E. Wolstenholme. New York: Pergamon Press, 1964
3. *Mechanics* (second edition), by K. Symon. Reading, Mass.: Addison-Wesley, 1964, Sections 3–1 and 3–3
4. *Physical Mechanics* (third edition), by R. Lindsay. Princeton, N.J.: Van Nostrand, 1963, Section 1–3
5. *Vector Mechanics,* by D. Christie. New York: McGraw-Hill, 1964
6. *Introduction to Engineering Mechanics,* by J. Huddleston. Reading, Mass.: Addison-Wesley, 1961, Chapters 2 and 7
7. *The Feynman Lectures on Physics,* Volume I, by R. Feynman, R. Leighton, and M. Sands. Reading, Mass.: Addison-Wesley, 1963, Chapter 11

Problems

3.1 Two vectors, 6 and 9 units long, form an angle of (a) 0°, (b) 60°, (c) 90°, (d) 150°, and (e) 180°. Find the magnitude and direction of their resultant with respect to the shorter vector.

3.2 Find the angle between two vectors, 10 and 15 units long, when their resultant is (a) 20 units long and (b) 12 units long. Draw the appropriate figure.

3.3 Two vectors form an angle of 110°. One of the vectors is 20 units long and makes an angle of 40° with the vector sum of the two. Find the magnitude of the second vector and of the vector sum.

3.4 The resultant vector of two other vectors is 10 units long and forms an angle of 35° with one of the component vectors, which is 12 units long. Find the magnitude of the other vector and the angle between the two.

3.5 Find the angle between two vectors, 8 and 10 units long, when the resultant vector makes an angle of 50° with the larger vector. Also calculate the magnitude of the resultant vector.

3.6 The resultant of two vectors is 30 units long and forms angles of 25° and 50° with them. Find the magnitude of the two vectors.

3.7 Two vectors, 10 and 8 units long, form an angle of (a) 60°, (b) 90°, and (c) 120°. Find the magnitude of the *difference* and the angle with respect to the larger vector.

3.8 Find the rectangular components of a vector 15 units long when it forms an angle, with respect to the positive X-axis, of (a) 50°, (b) 130°, (c) 230°, and (d) 310°.

3.9 Three vectors in a plane are, respectively, 6, 5, and 4 units long. The first and second form an angle of 50°, while the second and third form an angle of 75°. Find the magnitude and direction of the resultant with respect to the larger vector.

3.10 Given four coplanar vectors 8, 12, 10, and 6 units long, respectively; the last three make angles with the first of 70°, 150°, and 200°, respectively. Find the magnitude and direction of the resultant vector.

3.11 An airplane is supposed to travel from A in a direction due north to B, and then return to A. The distance between A and B is L. The air speed of the plane is v and the wind velocity is v'. (a) Show that the time for the round trip in still air, $v' = 0$, is $t_a = 2L/v$. (b) Show that the time for the round trip when the wind is directed due east (or west) is

$$t_b = t_a/\sqrt{1 - (v'^2/v^2)}.$$

(c) Show that the time for the round trip when the wind is directed due north (or south) is $t_c = t_a/1 - (v'^2/v^2)$. (d) What is the feasibility of trips (b) or (c) when $v' = v$? For a given v', which time is greater, t_b or t_c?

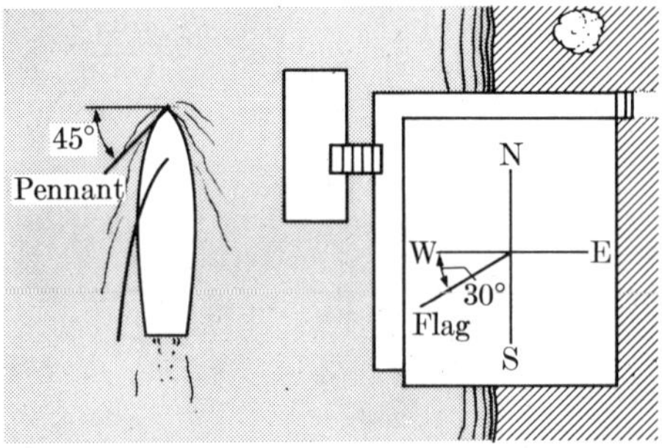

Figure 3–39

3.12 The pennant on the masthead of a sailboat streams back at an angle of 45°, as shown in Fig. 3–39, but the flag on the clubhouse extends out at 30° south of west. (a) If the speed of the boat is 10 km hr^{-1}, find the wind velocity. (b) Find the apparent wind velocity for an observer on the boat.

3.13 Prove that if the magnitudes of the sum and the difference of two vectors are equal, the vectors are perpendicular.

3.14 Prove that if the sum and the difference of two vectors are perpendicular, the vectors have equal magnitudes.

3.15 Verify that the magnitude of the sum and difference of two vectors $\boldsymbol{A}$ and $\boldsymbol{B}$, expressed in rectangular coordinates, are given by

$$S = [(A_x + B_x)^2 + (A_y + B_y)^2 + (A_z + B_z)^2]^{1/2}$$

and

$$D = [(A_x - B_x)^2 + (A_y - B_y)^2 + (A_z - B_z)^2]^{1/2},$$

respectively.

3.16 Given the vectors

$$\boldsymbol{A} = \boldsymbol{u}_x(3) + \boldsymbol{u}_y(4) + \boldsymbol{u}_z(-5)$$

and

$$\boldsymbol{B} = \boldsymbol{u}_x(-1) + \boldsymbol{u}_y(1) + \boldsymbol{u}_z(2).$$

Find: (a) the magnitude and direction of their resultant, (b) the same for their difference, $\boldsymbol{A} - \boldsymbol{B}$, and (c) the angle between $\boldsymbol{A}$ and $\boldsymbol{B}$.

3.17 Find the resultant of the sum of the following vectors:

(a) $\boldsymbol{V}_1 = \boldsymbol{u}_x(5) + \boldsymbol{u}_y(-2) + \boldsymbol{u}_z$,

(b) $\boldsymbol{V}_2 = \boldsymbol{u}_x(-3) + \boldsymbol{u}_y(1) + \boldsymbol{u}_z(-7)$,

(c) $\boldsymbol{V}_3 = \boldsymbol{u}_x(4) + \boldsymbol{u}_y(7) + \boldsymbol{u}_z(6)$.

Obtain the magnitude of the resultant and the angles it makes with the X-, Y-, and Z-axes.

3.18 Given three vectors:

(a) $\boldsymbol{V}_1 = \boldsymbol{u}_x(-1) + \boldsymbol{u}_y(3) + \boldsymbol{u}_z(4)$,

(b) $\boldsymbol{V}_2 = \boldsymbol{u}_x(3) + \boldsymbol{u}_y(-2) + \boldsymbol{u}_z(-8)$,

(c) $\boldsymbol{V}_3 = \boldsymbol{u}_x(4) + \boldsymbol{u}_y(4) + \boldsymbol{u}_z(4)$.

(a) By direct manipulation, determine whether there is any difference between the vector products $\boldsymbol{V}_1 \times (\boldsymbol{V}_2 \times \boldsymbol{V}_3)$ and $(\boldsymbol{V}_1 \times \boldsymbol{V}_2) \times \boldsymbol{V}_3$. (b) Find $\boldsymbol{V}_1 \cdot (\boldsymbol{V}_2 \times \boldsymbol{V}_3)$ and $(\boldsymbol{V}_1 \times \boldsymbol{V}_2) \cdot \boldsymbol{V}_3$ and determine whether there is any difference. Compute $(\boldsymbol{V}_3 \times \boldsymbol{V}_1) \cdot \boldsymbol{V}_2$ and compare this result with the previous two.

3.19 Express $\boldsymbol{V}_1 \cdot (\boldsymbol{V}_2 \times \boldsymbol{V}_3)$ in determinant form. Derive from it its symmetry properties; that is,

$$\boldsymbol{V}_1 \cdot \boldsymbol{V}_2 \times \boldsymbol{V}_3 = \boldsymbol{V}_3 \cdot \boldsymbol{V}_1 \times \boldsymbol{V}_2 = \boldsymbol{V}_2 \cdot \boldsymbol{V}_3 \times \boldsymbol{V}_1.$$

Prove that the value of the triple product is equal to the volume of the parallelepiped made from the three vectors.

3.20 Prove that

$$\boldsymbol{V}_1 \times (\boldsymbol{V}_2 \times \boldsymbol{V}_3) = (\boldsymbol{V}_1 \cdot \boldsymbol{V}_2)\boldsymbol{V}_2 - (\boldsymbol{V}_1 \cdot \boldsymbol{V}_2)\boldsymbol{V}_3.$$

[*Hint:* Place the X-axis along $\boldsymbol{V}_3$ and the Y-axis so that $\boldsymbol{V}_2$ is in the XY-plane, and check by direct expansion.]

3.21 Find the distance between two points, $P_1(4, 5, -7)$ and $P_2(-3, 6, 12)$. Also write the equation of the straight line passing through them.

3.22 Find the distance from point $P(4, 5, -7)$ to the straight line which passes through point $Q(-3, 6, 12)$ and is parallel to the vector $\boldsymbol{V} = \boldsymbol{u}_x(4) - \boldsymbol{u}_y(1) + \boldsymbol{u}_z(3)$. Also find the distance from point P to the plane through Q perpendicular to $\boldsymbol{V}$.

3.23 Prove that the distance between the line passing through P_1 parallel to $\boldsymbol{V}_1$ and the line through P_2 parallel to $\boldsymbol{V}_2$ is $\overrightarrow{P_1P_2} \cdot \boldsymbol{V}_1 \times \boldsymbol{V}_2/|\boldsymbol{V}_1 \times \boldsymbol{V}_2|$. [*Note:* The distance between two skew lines is defined as the length of the shortest line perpendicular to both lines.] Write the above result in expanded form, using the coordinates of P_1 and P_2 and the components of $\boldsymbol{V}_1$ and $\boldsymbol{V}_2$. Apply to the case when $P_1(4, 5, -7)$, $P_2(-3, 6, 12)$, $\boldsymbol{V}_1 = \boldsymbol{u}_x + \boldsymbol{u}_y + \boldsymbol{u}_z$, and $\boldsymbol{V}_2 = \boldsymbol{u}_x(-2) + \boldsymbol{u}_y(1) + \boldsymbol{u}_z(3)$.

3.24 Given a line passing through $P(4, 5, -7)$ parallel to $\boldsymbol{V}_1 = \boldsymbol{u}_x(-1) + \boldsymbol{u}_y(2) + \boldsymbol{u}_z(-4)$ and a plane through $Q(-3, 6, 12)$ perpendicular to $\boldsymbol{V}_2 = \boldsymbol{u}_x + \boldsymbol{u}_y(-1) + \boldsymbol{u}_z(2)$. (a) Write the respective equations in rectangular coordinates. (b) Find the point of intersection of the line and the plane. (c) Find the angle between the line and the plane.

3.25 Find the equation of the line which passes through $P(4, 5, -7)$ and is parallel to the line of intersection of the planes $3x - 2y + 5z = 10$ and $x + y - 2 = 4$. Find also the equation of the intersection.

3.26 Prove that if $\boldsymbol{V}_1$, $\boldsymbol{V}_2$, and $\boldsymbol{V}_3$ add to zero, then $\boldsymbol{V}_1 \times \boldsymbol{V}_3 = \boldsymbol{V}_3 \times \boldsymbol{V}_2 = \boldsymbol{V}_2 \times \boldsymbol{V}_1$. From these relations, conclude that $V_1/\sin \angle V_2V_3 = V_2/\sin \angle V_3V_1 = V_3/\sin \angle V_1V_2$ where $\angle V_iV_j$ means the angle between vectors $\boldsymbol{V}_i$ and $\boldsymbol{V}_j$.

3.27 Prove that if two vectors have the same magnitude V and make an angle θ, their sum has a magnitude $S = 2V \cos \frac{1}{2}\theta$ and their difference is $D = 2V \sin \frac{1}{2}\theta$.

3.28 Using the components of V_1 and V_2 expressed in spherical form (Eq. 3.10), prove that the angle between the vectors may be found from

$$\cos \theta_{12} = \sin \theta_1 \sin \theta_2 \cos (\phi_1 - \phi_2) + \cos \theta_1 \cos \theta_2,$$

where θ_{12} is the angle between the vectors. This result is of great use in astronomical computations. Adapt this result to obtain the angle between the verticals at San Francisco (latitude: 37° 45′ N; longitude: 122° 27′ W) and New York (latitude: 40° 40′ N; longitude: 73° 50′ W). Check your answer against that of Problem 2.17.

3.29 Given the set of 3 noncoplanar vectors $\boldsymbol{a}_1$, $\boldsymbol{a}_2$, $\boldsymbol{a}_3$, the vectors

$$\boldsymbol{a}^1 = \frac{\boldsymbol{a}_2 \times \boldsymbol{a}_3}{\boldsymbol{a}_1 \cdot \boldsymbol{a}_2 \times \boldsymbol{a}_3},$$

$$\boldsymbol{a}^2 = \frac{\boldsymbol{a}_3 \times \boldsymbol{a}_1}{\boldsymbol{a}_1 \cdot \boldsymbol{a}_2 \times \boldsymbol{a}_3},$$

$$\boldsymbol{a}^3 = \frac{\boldsymbol{a}_1 \times \boldsymbol{a}_2}{\boldsymbol{a}_1 \cdot \boldsymbol{a}_2 \times \boldsymbol{a}_3}$$

are called the *reciprocal* vectors. Prove that $\boldsymbol{a}^i \cdot \boldsymbol{a}_i = 1$ and $\boldsymbol{a}^i \cdot \boldsymbol{a}_j = 0$, where i and j take the values 1, 2, 3. Discuss the geometrical arrangement of the reciprocal vectors $\boldsymbol{a}^1$, $\boldsymbol{a}^2$, $\boldsymbol{a}^3$ relative to $\boldsymbol{a}_1$, $\boldsymbol{a}_2$, $\boldsymbol{a}_3$.

3.30 Prove that any vector $\boldsymbol{V}$ can be written in either of the two alternative forms

$$\boldsymbol{V} = (\boldsymbol{V} \cdot \boldsymbol{a}^1)\boldsymbol{a}_1 + (\boldsymbol{V} \cdot \boldsymbol{a}^2)\boldsymbol{a}_2 + (\boldsymbol{V} \cdot \boldsymbol{a}^3)\boldsymbol{a}_3 = \textstyle\sum_i (\boldsymbol{V} \cdot \boldsymbol{a}^i)\boldsymbol{a}_i$$

or

$$\boldsymbol{V} = (\boldsymbol{V} \cdot \boldsymbol{a}_1)\boldsymbol{a}^1 + (\boldsymbol{V} \cdot \boldsymbol{a}_2)\boldsymbol{a}^2 + (\boldsymbol{V} \cdot \boldsymbol{a}_3)\boldsymbol{a}^3 = \textstyle\sum_i (\boldsymbol{V} \cdot \boldsymbol{a}_i)\boldsymbol{a}^i.$$

3.31 Calling $\boldsymbol{V} \cdot \boldsymbol{a}_i = V_i$ and $V^i = \boldsymbol{V} \cdot \boldsymbol{a}^i$ the *covariant* and *contravariant* components of $\boldsymbol{V}$, and

$$g_{ij} = \boldsymbol{a}_i \cdot \boldsymbol{a}_j, \qquad g^{ij} = \boldsymbol{a}^i \cdot \boldsymbol{a}^j,$$

prove that

$$V^j = \textstyle\sum_i V_i g^{ij}, \qquad V_j = \textstyle\sum_i V^i g_{ij},$$

and

$$V^2 = \textstyle\sum_i V_iV^i = \sum_{ij} V_iV_jg^{ij} = \sum_{ij} V^iV^jg_{ij}.$$

These relations are very important in vector calculations using nonrectangular coordinates, and are especially useful in solid-state physics when one is dealing with the crystalline structure of solids.

3.32 Prove that

$$\boldsymbol{a}^1 \cdot \boldsymbol{a}^2 \times \boldsymbol{a}^3 = 1/\boldsymbol{a}_1 \cdot \boldsymbol{a}_2 \times \boldsymbol{a}_3.$$

3.33 Prove that $\boldsymbol{r} = \boldsymbol{a}s^2 + \boldsymbol{b}s + \boldsymbol{c}$ (where $\boldsymbol{a}$, $\boldsymbol{b}$, and $\boldsymbol{c}$ are constant vectors and s a scalar variable) represents a parabola lying in the plane determined by vectors $\boldsymbol{a}$ and $\boldsymbol{b}$ and passing through a point whose position vector is $\boldsymbol{c}$.

3.34 Show that a unit vector in three dimensions can be expressed as

$$\boldsymbol{u} = \boldsymbol{u}_x \cos \alpha + \boldsymbol{u}_y \cos \beta + \boldsymbol{u}_z \cos \theta,$$

where the angles α, β, and θ are as defined in Fig. 3–17.

3.35 Using the fact that the vector representing a closed surface is zero, prove that two surfaces having the same closed line as a boundary are represented by the same vector.

3.36 An open surface is limited by a triangle with vertices at $(0, 0, 0)$, $(2, 0, 0)$, and $(0, 2, 0)$. It is composed of three triangular surfaces each having one side coincident with the sides of the triangle and one common vertex at point (a, b, c). Show that the vector representing the complete surface is independent of (a, b, c). Was this result to be expected in view of Problem 3.35?

3.37 A tetrahedron is a solid body limited by four triangular surfaces. Consider the tetrahedron with vertices at points $(0, 0, 0)$, $(2, 0, 0)$, $(0, 2, 0)$, and $(1, 1, 2)$. Find: (a) the vector representing each face; (b) the vector representing the whole tetrahedron; (c) the magnitude of the surface of the tetrahedron. Were you expecting the result obtained in (b)?

3.38 Using vector methods, find: (a) the length of the diagonals of a cube; (b) their angles with the adjacent sides; (c) their angles with the adjacent faces; (d) the angles between the diagonals.

3.39 The faces of a regular tetrahedron are equilateral triangles of side a. Find, using vector methods, the angle of each side with the opposite face and the distance from one vertex to the opposite face.

4
FORCES

4.1 Introduction

An important usage of vector algebra is its application to the composition of forces. The precise definition of force will be analyzed in Chapter 7, where we shall discuss the dynamics of motion. However, to gain more skill in the manipulation of vectors, we shall now discuss the composition of forces, and in particular the equilibrium of forces, a problem of wide application in engineering.

We shall assume at present an intuitive notion of force, derived from our everyday experience, such as the force needed to push or pull a given weight, the force exerted by certain tools, etc. This intuitive notion suggests that force is a vector quantity having magnitude (or intensity) and direction. Experience confirms that forces are combined according to the rules of vector algebra. In this chapter we shall consider forces applied only to mass points or particles and rigid bodies.

In the MKSC system, the unit of force is the *newton* (abbreviated N), which will be defined in Section 7.8. In this chapter, however, we shall also express force in other units, such as *kilogram-force* (kgf), *pound-force* (lbf), *poundal* (pdl), and *ton* (T). These units, which are frequently used in engineering, have equivalences with the newton as follows:

$$1 \text{ kgf} = 9.8 \text{ N}, \qquad 1 \text{ lbf} = 0.46 \text{ kgf} \approx 4.45 \text{ N},$$
$$1 \text{ pdl} = 0.031 \text{ lbf} \approx 0.138 \text{ N}, \qquad 1 \text{ T} = 2000 \text{ lbf} \approx 8900 \text{ N}.$$

It is customary in engineering practice, when referring to pounds-force and to kilograms-force, to say simply "pounds" and "kilograms," although these actually refer to units of mass.

4.2 Composition of Concurrent Forces

If the forces are concurrent (i.e., if they are all applied at the same point), their resultant is their vector sum, obtained according to the method explained in Section 3.6. Therefore, the resultant $\boldsymbol{R}$ of several concurrent forces $\boldsymbol{F}_1, \boldsymbol{F}_2, \boldsymbol{F}_3, \ldots$ is

$$\boldsymbol{R} = \boldsymbol{F}_1 + \boldsymbol{F}_2 + \boldsymbol{F}_3 + \cdots = \textstyle\sum \boldsymbol{F}_i. \tag{4.1}$$

If the forces are coplanar, say in the XY-plane, we have, in view of Eq. (3.16), that $\boldsymbol{R} = \boldsymbol{u}_x R_x + \boldsymbol{u}_y R_y$, where

$$R_x = \textstyle\sum F_{ix} = \sum F_i \cos \alpha_i, \qquad R_y = \sum F_{iy} = \sum F_i \sin \alpha_i. \tag{4.2}$$

The magnitude of $\boldsymbol{R}$ is $R = \sqrt{R_x^2 + R_y^2}$, and its direction is given by the angle α such that $\tan \alpha = R_y/R_x$. We must assume that the resultant $\boldsymbol{R}$ is physically equivalent to the components $\boldsymbol{F}_1, \boldsymbol{F}_2, \boldsymbol{F}_3, \ldots$.

EXAMPLE 4.1. Find the resultant of the following forces acting on a body at O (Fig. 4–1). Force $\boldsymbol{F}_1$ is equal to 1200 lbf, force $\boldsymbol{F}_2$ is equal to 900 lbf, force $\boldsymbol{F}_3$ is 300 lbf, and force $\boldsymbol{F}_4$ is 800 lbf. The directions are as indicated in the figure.

Solution: First we express each force in terms of its components along the X- and Y-axes, using in each case the angle between the positive X-axis and the force. Thus

$$\begin{aligned}
\boldsymbol{F}_1 &= \boldsymbol{u}_x(1200)\ \text{lbf},\\
\boldsymbol{F}_2 &= \boldsymbol{u}_x(F_2\cos 40°) + \boldsymbol{u}_y(F_2\sin 40°) = \boldsymbol{u}_x(689.4) + \boldsymbol{u}_y(578.5)\ \text{lbf},\\
\boldsymbol{F}_3 &= \boldsymbol{u}_x(F_3\cos 120°) + \boldsymbol{u}_y(F_3\sin 120°) = \boldsymbol{u}_x(-150) + \boldsymbol{u}_y(259.8)\ \text{lbf},\\
\boldsymbol{F}_4 &= \boldsymbol{u}_x(F_4\cos 230°) + \boldsymbol{u}_y(F_4\sin 230°) = \boldsymbol{u}_x(-514.2) + \boldsymbol{u}_y(-612.8)\ \text{lbf}.
\end{aligned}$$

Then since $\boldsymbol{R} = \boldsymbol{F}_1 + \boldsymbol{F}_2 + \boldsymbol{F}_3 + \boldsymbol{F}_4$, we have

$$\begin{aligned}
R_x &= 1200 + 689.4 - 150 - 514.2 = 1225.2\ \text{lbf},\\
R_y &= 0 + 578.5 + 259.8 - 612.8 = 225.5\ \text{lbf},
\end{aligned}$$

or $\boldsymbol{R} = \boldsymbol{u}_x(1225.2) + \boldsymbol{u}_y(225.5)$ lbf, from which the magnitude and direction of the resultant force can be found to be $R = 1245.4$ lbf and $\alpha = 10.4°$.

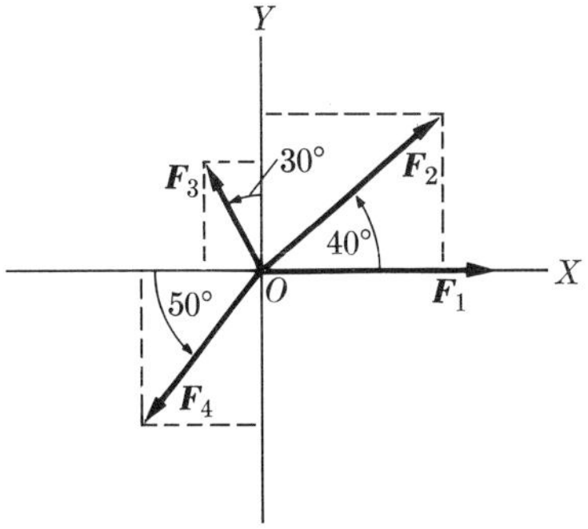

Figure 4–1

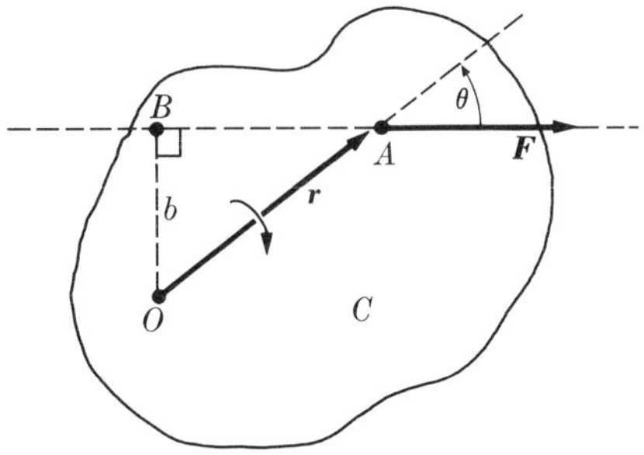

Fig. 4–2. Torque of a force.

4.3 Torque

Consider a force $\boldsymbol{F}$ acting on a body C that can rotate about point O (Fig. 4–2). If the force does not pass through O, the net effect will be to rotate the body around O. Our daily experience suggests that the rotating effectiveness of $\boldsymbol{F}$ increases with the perpendicular distance (called *lever arm*) $b = OB$ from O to the line of action of the force. For example, when we open a door, we always push or pull as far as possible from the hinges and attempt to keep the direction of our push or pull perpendicular to the door. This experience therefore suggests the convenience of defining a physical quantity τ that will be called *torque*, according to

$$\tau = Fb, \tag{4.3}$$

or torque = force × lever arm. Accordingly, torque must be expressed as the product of a unit of force and a unit of distance. Thus in the MKSC system, torque is expressed in newtons meter or N m. But other units, such as kgf m or lbf ft, are also used.

Noting from the figure that $b = r \sin \theta$, we also may write

$$\tau = Fr \sin \theta. \tag{4.4}$$

Comparing this equation with Eq. (3.21), we conclude that the torque may be considered as a vector quantity given by the vector product

$$\boldsymbol{\tau} = \boldsymbol{r} \times \boldsymbol{F}, \tag{4.5}$$

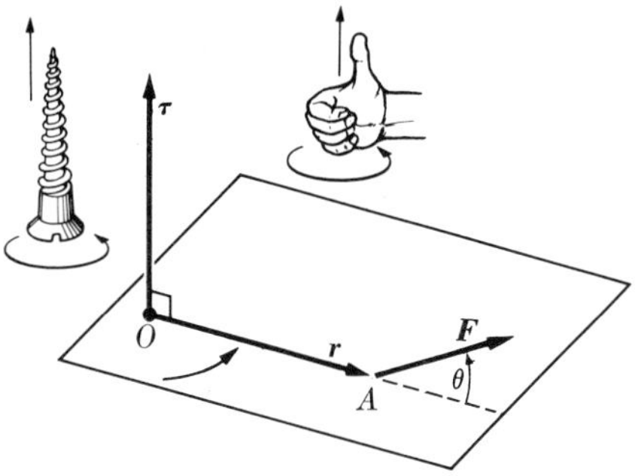

Fig. 4–3. Vector relation between torque, force, and position vector.

where $\boldsymbol{r}$ is the position vector, relative to O, of the point A on which the force is acting. According to the properties of the vector product, the torque is represented by a vector perpendicular to both $\boldsymbol{r}$ and $\boldsymbol{F}$; that is, perpendicular to the plane that may be drawn through both $\boldsymbol{r}$ and $\boldsymbol{F}$, and directed according to the sense of advance of a right-handed screw rotated in the same sense as the rotation produced by $\boldsymbol{F}$ around O. This is indicated in Fig. 4–3.

Remembering that $\boldsymbol{r} = \boldsymbol{u}_x x + \boldsymbol{u}_y y + \boldsymbol{u}_z z$ and $\boldsymbol{F} = \boldsymbol{u}_x F_x + \boldsymbol{u}_y F_y + \boldsymbol{u}_z F_z$, we have, by application of Eq. (3.26),

$$\boldsymbol{\tau} = \begin{vmatrix} \boldsymbol{u}_x & \boldsymbol{u}_y & \boldsymbol{u}_z \\ x & y & z \\ F_x & F_y & F_z \end{vmatrix} = \boldsymbol{u}_x(yF_z - zF_y) + \boldsymbol{u}_y(zF_x - xF_z) + \boldsymbol{u}_z(xF_y - yF_x); \tag{4.6}$$

or $\tau_x = yF_z - zF_y$, $\tau_y = zF_x - xF_z$, and $\tau_z = xF_y - yF_x$. In particular, if both $\boldsymbol{r}$ and $\boldsymbol{F}$ are in the XY-plane, $z = 0$ and $F_z = 0$, so that

$$\boldsymbol{\tau} = \boldsymbol{u}_z(xF_y - yF_x), \tag{4.7}$$

and is parallel to the Z-axis, as illustrated in Fig. 4–4. In magnitude, we have

$$\tau = xF_y - yF_x. \tag{4.8}$$

Note that a force may be displaced along its line of action without changing its torque because the distance b remains the same. Thus when x and y are left arbitrary, Eq. (4.8) expresses the equation of the line of action of the force having a torque τ.

EXAMPLE 4.2. Determine the torque applied to the body in Fig. 4–5, where $\boldsymbol{F}$ is 6 N and makes an angle of 30° with the X-axis and $\boldsymbol{r}$ is 45 cm long and makes an angle of 50° with the $+X$-axis. Find also the equation of the line of action of the force.

Solution: We may proceed in two different ways. First, from the figure we see that the lever arm of F (since $r = 45$ cm $= 0.45$ m) is $b = r \sin 20° = (0.45 \text{ m})(0.342) = 0.154$ m.

Thus the torque around O is

$$\tau = Fb = (6 \text{ N})(0.154 \text{ m}) = 0.924 \text{ N m}.$$

Strictly speaking, we must write -0.924 N m, because the rotation around O is clockwise, corresponding to a screw advancing in the $-Z$ direction, or into the paper.

As a second method, we may use Eq. (4.8), since the problem is in two dimensions. Now

$$x = r\cos 50^\circ = 0.289 \text{ m}, \qquad y = r\sin 50^\circ = 0.345 \text{ m},$$
$$F_x = F\cos 30^\circ = 5.196 \text{ N}, \qquad F_y = F\sin 30^\circ = 3.0 \text{ N}.$$

Thus

$$\tau = xF_y - yF_x = 0.867 - 1.792 = -0.925 \text{ N m},$$

in agreement with our previous result. This method has the additional advantage of also giving the sign.

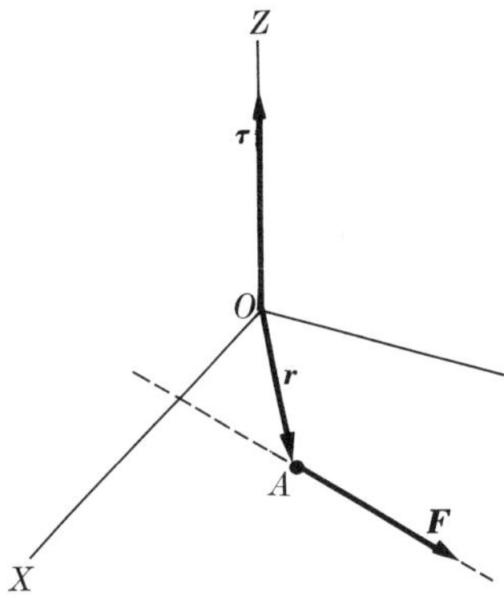

Figure 4–4

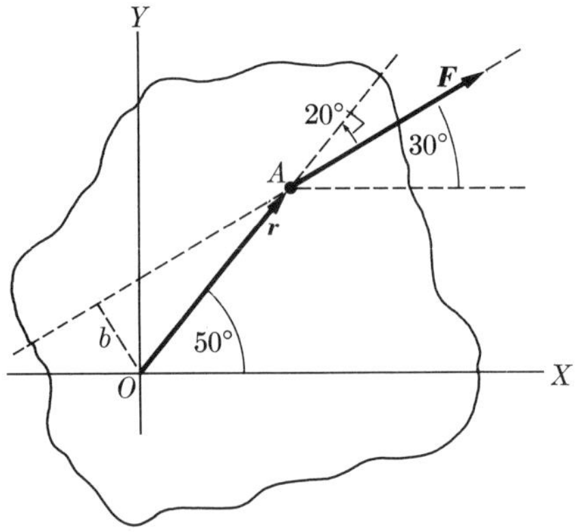

Figure 4–5

To obtain the equation of the line of action of $\boldsymbol{F}$, we simply leave x and y arbitrary in Eq. (4.8), resulting in

$$-0.925 = 3x - 5.196y.$$

4.4 Torque of Several Concurrent Forces

Consider now the case of several concurrent forces $\boldsymbol{F}_1$, $\boldsymbol{F}_2$, $\boldsymbol{F}_3$, ... acting on a point A (Fig. 4–6). The torque of each $\boldsymbol{F}_i$ relative to O is $\boldsymbol{\tau}_i = \boldsymbol{r} \times \boldsymbol{F}_i$; note that we write $\boldsymbol{r}$ and not $\boldsymbol{r}_i$ because all forces are applied at the same point. The torque of the resultant $\boldsymbol{R}$ is $\boldsymbol{\tau} = \boldsymbol{r} \times \boldsymbol{R}$, where $\boldsymbol{R} = \boldsymbol{F}_1 + \boldsymbol{F}_2 + \boldsymbol{F}_3 + \cdots$ and $\boldsymbol{r}$ is again the common position vector. Applying the distributive property of the vector product, we have

$$\begin{aligned}\boldsymbol{r} \times \boldsymbol{R} &= \boldsymbol{r} \times (\boldsymbol{F}_1 + \boldsymbol{F}_2 + \boldsymbol{F}_3 + \cdots) \\ &= \boldsymbol{r} \times \boldsymbol{F}_1 + \boldsymbol{r} \times \boldsymbol{F}_2 + \boldsymbol{r} \times \boldsymbol{F}_3 + \cdots\end{aligned}$$

Therefore

$$\tau = \tau_1 + \tau_2 + \tau_3 + \cdots = \sum \tau_i. \qquad (4.9)$$

In words, the torque of the resultant is equal to the vector sum of the torques of the component forces if they are concurrent.

If all the forces are coplanar, and O is also in the same plane, all torques appearing in Eq. (4.9) have the same direction perpendicular to the plane, and the relation (4.9) can be written as

$$\tau = \sum \tau_i. \qquad (4.10)$$

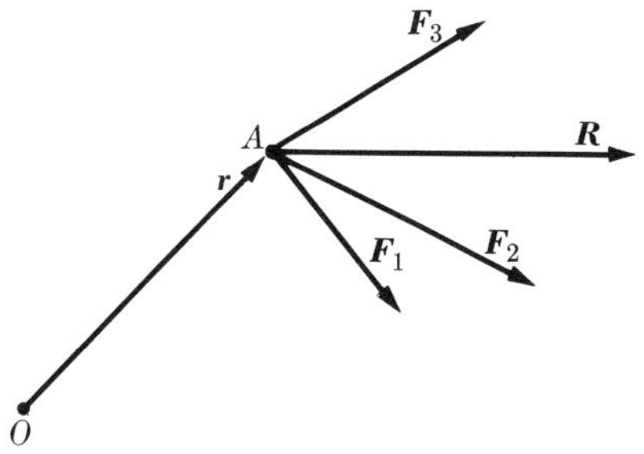

Fig. 4–6. When the forces are concurrent, the torque of the resultant is equal to the vector sum of the torque of the components.

Equation (4.9) proves that *a system of concurrent forces can be replaced by a single force,* its resultant, that is completely equivalent to the system in so far as translational and rotational effects are concerned.

EXAMPLE 4.3. Consider three forces applied at point A of Fig. 4–7, with $r = 1.5$ ft and

$$\begin{aligned} \boldsymbol{F}_1 &= \boldsymbol{u}_x(6) + \boldsymbol{u}_y(0) + \boldsymbol{u}_z(0) \text{ lbf}, \\ \boldsymbol{F}_2 &= \boldsymbol{u}_x(6) - \boldsymbol{u}_y(7) + \boldsymbol{u}_z(14) \text{ lbf}, \\ \boldsymbol{F}_3 &= \boldsymbol{u}_x(5) + \boldsymbol{u}_y(0) - \boldsymbol{u}_z(3) \text{ lbf}. \end{aligned}$$

Using O as the reference point, find the resultant torque due to these forces.

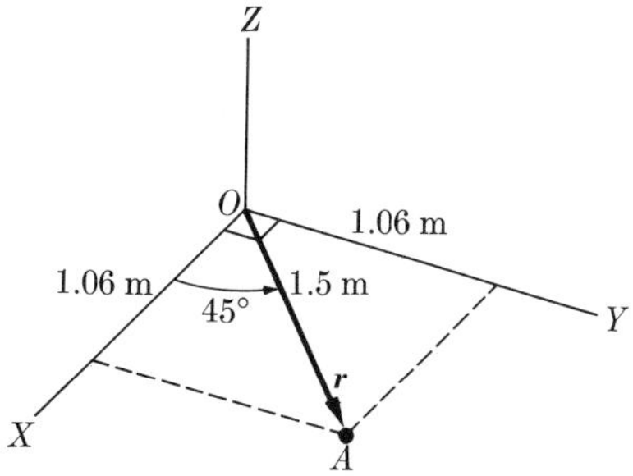

Figure 4–7

Solution: First, using the concept $\boldsymbol{\tau} = \boldsymbol{r} \times \boldsymbol{R}$, where $\boldsymbol{R} = \sum \boldsymbol{F}_i$, we have

$$\begin{aligned} \boldsymbol{R} &= \boldsymbol{u}_x(6 + 6 + 5) + \boldsymbol{u}_y(0 - 7 + 0) + \boldsymbol{u}_z(0 + 14 - 3) \text{ lbf} \\ &= \boldsymbol{u}_x(17) - \boldsymbol{u}_y(7) + \boldsymbol{u}_z(11) \text{ lbf}. \end{aligned}$$

Using this value along with $\boldsymbol{r} = \boldsymbol{u}_x(1.06) + \boldsymbol{u}_y(1.06)$ ft, we can write the resultant torque, using Eq. (4.6), as

$$\boldsymbol{\tau} = \boldsymbol{r} \times \boldsymbol{R} = \boldsymbol{u}_x(11.66) - \boldsymbol{u}_y(11.66) - \boldsymbol{u}_z(25.44) \text{ ft-lbf}.$$

The resultant torque can also be found by applying Eq. (4.9) as $\boldsymbol{\tau} = \boldsymbol{\tau}_1 + \boldsymbol{\tau}_2 + \boldsymbol{\tau}_3$. Now, again applying Eq. (4.6) to each component force, we have

$$\begin{aligned} \boldsymbol{\tau}_1 &= \boldsymbol{r} \times \boldsymbol{F}_1 = \boldsymbol{u}_x(0) + \boldsymbol{u}_y(0) - \boldsymbol{u}_z(6.36) \text{ ft-lbf}, \\ \boldsymbol{\tau}_2 &= \boldsymbol{r} \times \boldsymbol{F}_2 = \boldsymbol{u}_x(14.84) - \boldsymbol{u}_y(14.84) - \boldsymbol{u}_z(13.78) \text{ ft-lbf}, \\ \boldsymbol{\tau}_3 &= \boldsymbol{r} \times \boldsymbol{F}_3 = -\boldsymbol{u}_x(3.18) + \boldsymbol{u}_y(3.18) - \boldsymbol{u}_z(5.30) \text{ ft-lbf}. \end{aligned}$$

Adding the three torques, we obtain our previous result for $\boldsymbol{\tau}$. In this way we have verified Eq. (4.9). The student should verify that $\boldsymbol{\tau} \cdot \boldsymbol{R} = 0$, indicating that $\boldsymbol{\tau}$ and $\boldsymbol{R}$ are perpendicular for concurrent forces.

4.5 Composition of Forces Applied to a Rigid Body

When the forces are not applied to the same point, but act on a rigid body, it is necessary to distinguish two effects: translation and rotation. The translation of the body is determined by the vector sum of the forces; that is,

$$\boldsymbol{R} = \boldsymbol{F}_1 + \boldsymbol{F}_2 + \boldsymbol{F}_3 + \boldsymbol{F}_4 + \cdots = \sum \boldsymbol{F}_i. \tag{4.11}$$

In this case the point of application of $\boldsymbol{R}$ is still undetermined. The rotational effect on the body is determined by the vector sum of the torques of the forces, all evaluated with respect to the same point:

$$\boldsymbol{\tau} = \boldsymbol{\tau}_1 + \boldsymbol{\tau}_2 + \boldsymbol{\tau}_3 + \cdots = \sum \boldsymbol{\tau}_i. \tag{4.12}$$

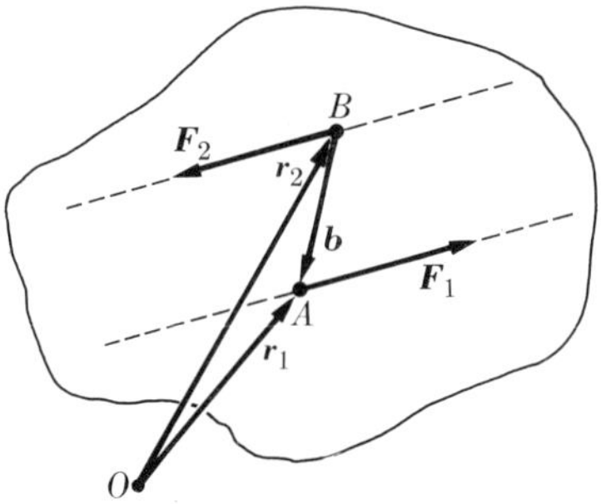

Fig. 4–8. Couple.

At first sight it seems logical to suggest, then, that force $\boldsymbol{R}$ should be applied at a point chosen in such a way that the torque due to $\boldsymbol{R}$ is equal to $\boldsymbol{\tau}$, a situation that, as we know, always holds in the case of concurrent forces. If that is possible, the force $\boldsymbol{R}$ so applied is equivalent to the system, both in translation and rotation.

Generally, however, this is not possible because the torque of $\boldsymbol{R}$ is a vector perpendicular to $\boldsymbol{R}$ and in many cases $\boldsymbol{R}$ and $\boldsymbol{\tau}$, given by Eqs. (4.11) and (4.12), are not perpendicular. Therefore, in general, a system of forces acting on a rigid body cannot be reduced to a single force or resultant equal to the vector sum of the forces.

As a simple example let us consider a *couple*, which is defined as a system of two forces of equal magnitude but opposite directions acting along parallel lines (Fig. 4–8). The resultant or vector sum of the two forces is obviously zero, $\boldsymbol{R} = \boldsymbol{F}_1 + \boldsymbol{F}_2 = 0$, indicating that the couple produces no translational effect. On the other hand, the vector sum of the torques, taking into account the fact that $\boldsymbol{F}_2 = -\boldsymbol{F}_1$, is

$$\begin{aligned} \boldsymbol{\tau} = \boldsymbol{\tau}_1 + \boldsymbol{\tau}_2 &= \boldsymbol{r}_1 \times \boldsymbol{F}_1 + \boldsymbol{r}_2 \times \boldsymbol{F}_2 = \boldsymbol{r}_1 \times \boldsymbol{F}_1 - \boldsymbol{r}_2 \times \boldsymbol{F}_1 \\ &= (\boldsymbol{r}_1 - \boldsymbol{r}_2) \times \boldsymbol{F}_1 = \boldsymbol{b} \times \boldsymbol{F}_1, \end{aligned} \tag{4.13}$$

where $\boldsymbol{b} = \boldsymbol{r}_1 - \boldsymbol{r}_2$ is called the lever arm of the couple. Therefore $\boldsymbol{\tau} \neq 0$, and the couple produces a rotational effect. Note that $\boldsymbol{b}$ is independent of the position of O, and therefore the torque of the system is independent of the origin about which the torque is computed. Obviously it is impossible to find a single force satisfying all these conditions.

Returning to the general case, we observe that a system of forces can always be reduced to a force *and* a couple. The force is chosen equal to $\boldsymbol{R}$ for translational equivalence and is applied at the point about which the torques were evaluated, so that its torque is zero. The couple with a torque equal to $\boldsymbol{\tau}$ is then chosen for rotational equivalence.

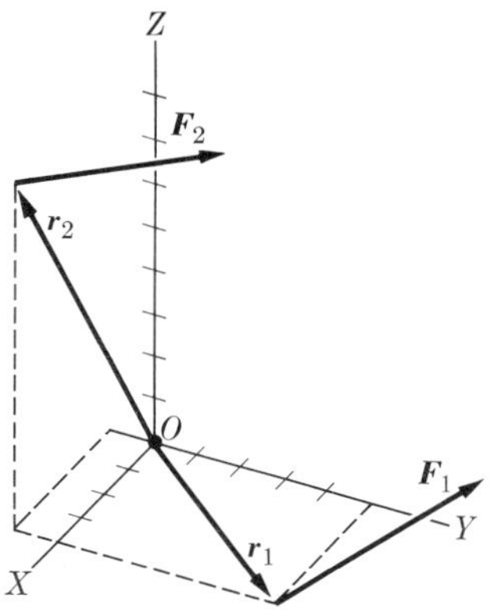

Figure 4–9

EXAMPLE 4.4. Find the resultant force and the resultant torque of the system illustrated in Fig. 4–9, where

$$\boldsymbol{F}_1 = \boldsymbol{u}_x(3) + \boldsymbol{u}_y(4) + \boldsymbol{u}_z(4) \text{ N}$$

and

$$\boldsymbol{F}_2 = \boldsymbol{u}_x(-2) + \boldsymbol{u}_y(5) + \boldsymbol{u}_z(1) \text{ N},$$

and the points of application are A (0.4 m, 0.5 m, 0) and B (0.4 m, —0.1 m, 0.8 m).

Solution: We first find the resultant,

$$\boldsymbol{R} = \boldsymbol{F}_1 + \boldsymbol{F}_2 = \boldsymbol{u}_x(1) + \boldsymbol{u}_y(9) + \boldsymbol{u}_z(5) \text{ N}.$$

Next we find the torque of each force about O:

$$\boldsymbol{\tau}_1 = \boldsymbol{r}_1 \times \boldsymbol{F}_1 = \boldsymbol{u}_x(2) + \boldsymbol{u}_y(-1.6) + \boldsymbol{u}_z(0.1) \text{ N m}.$$

$$\boldsymbol{\tau}_2 = \boldsymbol{r}_2 \times \boldsymbol{F}_2 = \boldsymbol{u}_x(-4.1) + \boldsymbol{u}_y(-2.0) + \boldsymbol{u}_z(1.8) \text{ N m}.$$

Therefore

$$\boldsymbol{\tau} = \boldsymbol{\tau}_1 + \boldsymbol{\tau}_2 = \boldsymbol{u}_x(-2.1) + \boldsymbol{u}_y(-3.6) + \boldsymbol{u}_z(1.9) \text{ N m}.$$

To see now if $\boldsymbol{R}$ can be located so that its torque is equal to $\boldsymbol{\tau}$, we must discover first if $\boldsymbol{\tau}$ and $\boldsymbol{R}$ are perpendicular. Applying Eq. (3.20), we find

$$\boldsymbol{\tau} \cdot \boldsymbol{R} = (-2.1)(1) + (-3.6)(9) + (1.8)(5) = -25.5 \text{ N m}.$$

So $\boldsymbol{\tau} \cdot \boldsymbol{R}$ is different from zero. Therefore the system of Fig. 4–9 cannot be reduced to a single force.

4.6 Composition of Coplanar Forces

When the forces are all in a plane, it is always possible to reduce the system to one resultant force $\boldsymbol{R}$, given by Eq. (4.1) (unless it reduces to a couple if $\boldsymbol{R} = 0$ but $\boldsymbol{\tau} \neq 0$), because in this case $\boldsymbol{\tau}$ is always perpendicular to $\boldsymbol{R}$. Placing the origin of coordinates O at the center of torques in the plane of the forces, we note that $\boldsymbol{\tau}_1, \boldsymbol{\tau}_2, \ldots$ and also $\boldsymbol{\tau} = \sum_i \boldsymbol{\tau}_i$ are all perpendicular to the plane, as we see by application of Eqs. (4.6) or (4.7), and from Fig. 4–4. Therefore, $\boldsymbol{R}$ and $\boldsymbol{\tau}$ are perpendicular, and it is possible to place $\boldsymbol{R}$ at such a distance $\boldsymbol{r}$ from O that its torque is equal to $\boldsymbol{\tau}$, that is, $\boldsymbol{r} \times \boldsymbol{R} = \boldsymbol{\tau}$. In this case the vector relation $\boldsymbol{\tau} = \sum_i \boldsymbol{\tau}_i$ can be replaced by the scalar equation $\tau = \sum_i \tau_i$, where each τ_i is computed according to Eq. (4.8), because all vectors have the same direction. Therefore, if R_x and R_y are the rectangular components of $\boldsymbol{R}$, then $\boldsymbol{R}$ must be placed at a point

(x, y) such that

$$xR_y - yR_x = \tau. \tag{4.14}$$

This is the equation of a straight line that corresponds to the line of action of the resultant force; i.e., there is not a single point of application, but rather a line of application.

More elaborate reasoning shows that this result holds even when the center of torques is outside the plane of the forces.

EXAMPLE 4.5. Determine the resultant of the system of forces illustrated in Fig. 4–10, all acting in one plane. The magnitudes of the forces are $F_1 = 10$ kgf, $F_2 = 8$ kgf, $F_3 = 7$ kgf. The side of each square is 0.1 m.

Solution: We first write each force in vector form:

$$\begin{aligned} \boldsymbol{F}_1 &= \boldsymbol{u}_x(10)\text{ kgf}, \\ \boldsymbol{F}_2 &= \boldsymbol{u}_x(F_2 \cos 135°) + \boldsymbol{u}_y(F_2 \sin 135°) = \boldsymbol{u}_x(-5.66) + \boldsymbol{u}_y(5.66)\text{ kgf}, \\ \boldsymbol{F}_3 &= -\boldsymbol{u}_y(7)\text{ kgf}. \end{aligned}$$

The resultant force $\boldsymbol{R} = \boldsymbol{F}_1 + \boldsymbol{F}_2 + \boldsymbol{F}_3$ is thus

$$\boldsymbol{R} = \boldsymbol{u}_x(4.34) + \boldsymbol{u}_y(-1.34)\text{ kgf}$$

or $R = 4.54$ kgf, and it makes an angle $\alpha = -17.1°$ with the X-axis.

The coordinates of the points of application of the forces are A (0.2 m, 0), B (0.5 m, 0.3 m), and C (0, 0.5 m). Using Eq. (4.8), we compute

$$\begin{aligned} \tau_1 &= -(0.3\text{ m})(10\text{ kgf}) = -3.00\text{ kgf m}, \\ \tau_2 &= -(0.5\text{ m})(-5.66\text{ kgf}) = +2.83\text{ kgf m}, \\ \tau_3 &= (0.2\text{ m})(-7\text{ kgf}) = -1.40\text{ kgf m}. \end{aligned}$$

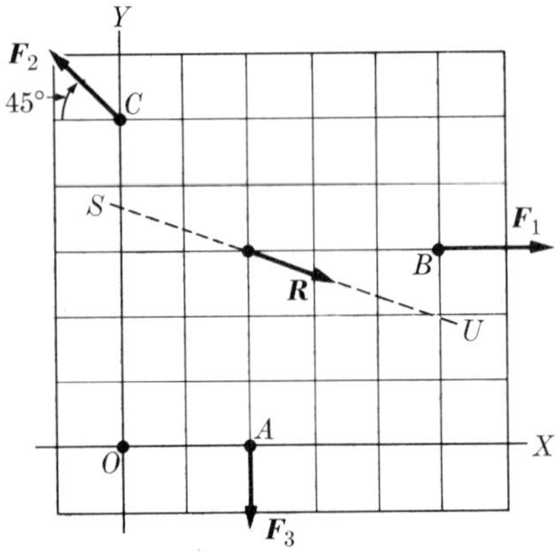

Figure 4–10

Thus $\tau = \tau_1 + \tau_2 + \tau_3 = -1.57$ kgf m, and is a vector along the Z-axis. To find the line of action of the resultant we apply Eq. (4.14), leaving x and y arbitrary. Then

$$x(-1.34) - y(4.34) = -1.57$$

or

$$1.34x + 4.44y = 1.57,$$

corresponding to the straight line SU.

4.7 Composition of Parallel Forces

Let us consider a system of forces parallel to a unit vector $\boldsymbol{u}$. Then $\boldsymbol{F}_i = \boldsymbol{u}F_i$, where F_i is positive or negative depending on whether the direction of $\boldsymbol{F}_i$ is the same as $\boldsymbol{u}$ or opposite. The vector sum is

$$\boldsymbol{R} = \textstyle\sum_i \boldsymbol{F}_i = \sum_i \boldsymbol{u}F_i = \boldsymbol{u}(\sum_i F_i), \tag{4.15}$$

and therefore is also parallel to $\boldsymbol{u}$. The magnitude of the resultant is then

$$R = \textstyle\sum_i F_i. \tag{4.16}$$

The vector sum of the torques is

$$\boldsymbol{\tau} = \textstyle\sum_i \boldsymbol{r}_i \times \boldsymbol{F}_i = \sum_i \boldsymbol{r}_i \times \boldsymbol{u}F_i = (\sum_i \boldsymbol{r}_i F_i) \times \boldsymbol{u},$$

which is perpendicular to $\boldsymbol{u}$ and therefore also perpendicular to $\boldsymbol{R}$. Accordingly, by placing $\boldsymbol{R}$ at a proper position $\boldsymbol{r}_c$, it is possible to equate its torque to $\boldsymbol{\tau}$; that is, $\boldsymbol{r}_c \times \boldsymbol{R} = \boldsymbol{\tau}$. Introducing the expressions for $\boldsymbol{R}$ and $\boldsymbol{\tau}$ given above, we may write

$$\boldsymbol{r}_c \times \boldsymbol{u}(\textstyle\sum_i F_i) = (\sum_i \boldsymbol{r}_i F_i) \times \boldsymbol{u}$$

or

$$[\boldsymbol{r}_c(\textstyle\sum_i F_i)] \times \boldsymbol{u} = (\sum_i \boldsymbol{r}_i F_i) \times \boldsymbol{u}.$$

This equation is satisfied if $\boldsymbol{r}_c(\sum_i F_i) = \sum_i \boldsymbol{r}_i F_i$ or

$$\boldsymbol{r}_c = \frac{\sum_i \boldsymbol{r}_i F_i}{\sum_i F_i} = \frac{\boldsymbol{r}_1 F_1 + \boldsymbol{r}_2 F_2 + \cdots}{F_1 + F_2 + \cdots}. \tag{4.17}$$

The point defined by $\boldsymbol{r}_c$ above is called the *center of parallel forces.* We conclude that a system of parallel forces can be reduced to a single force, parallel to each of the forces, given by Eq. (4.15), and acting on the point given by Eq. (4.17).

The vector equation (4.17) can be separated into its three component equations:

$$x_c = \frac{\sum_i x_i F_i}{\sum_i F_i}, \qquad y_c = \frac{\sum_i y_i F_i}{\sum_i F_i}, \qquad z_c = \frac{\sum_i z_i F_i}{\sum_i F_i}, \tag{4.18}$$

where we have designated by x_c, y_c, and z_c the coordinates of the point defined by $\boldsymbol{r}_c$.

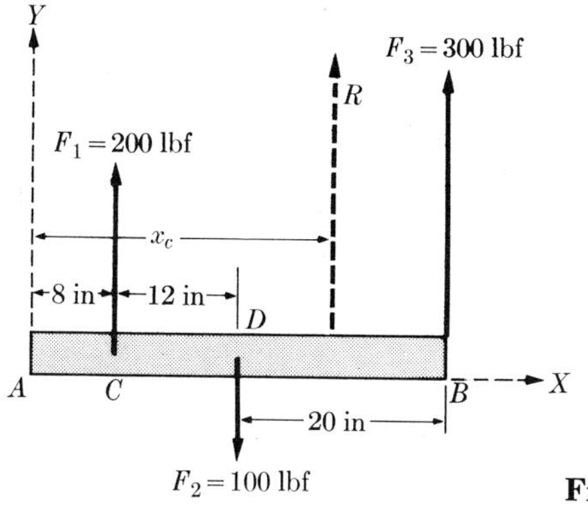

Figure 4–11

EXAMPLE 4.6. Find the resultant of the forces acting on the bar of Fig. 4–11.

Solution: Taking the upward direction as positive and using Eq. (4.16), we find the resultant to be

$$R = \textstyle\sum_i F_i = F_1 - F_2 + F_3 = 400 \text{ lbf}.$$

To determine its point of application we use Eq. (4.18). Only the first equation is required, since all the forces are on a line. Taking point A as the origin, we obtain

$$x_c = \frac{\sum_i F_i x_i}{\sum_i F_i}$$

$$= \frac{(200 \text{ lbf})(8 \text{ in}) + (-100 \text{ lbf})(20 \text{ in}) + (300 \text{ lbf})(40 \text{ in})}{400 \text{ lbf}} = 29 \text{ in.}$$

The point taken as the origin is immaterial. To show that this is so, let us take point D as the origin. Then

$$x_c = \frac{(200 \text{ lbf})(-12 \text{ in}) + (-100 \text{ lbf})(0 \text{ in}) + (300 \text{ lbf})(20 \text{ in})}{400 \text{ lbf}} = 9 \text{ in.}$$

This point is exactly the same as before, since $AD = 20$ in.

4.8 Center of Mass

Every particle subject to the earth's gravitational field is acted on by a force $\boldsymbol{W}$, called its weight. The direction of this force, if extended, passes through the center of the earth. In Section 7.6, it will be seen that when m is the mass of the particle and $\boldsymbol{g}$ the acceleration due to gravity, the following relation exists:

$$\boldsymbol{W} = m\boldsymbol{g}. \tag{4.19}$$

Although the weights intersect at the center of the earth, they may be considered parallel when they act on particles comprising a body of relatively small dimensions. Therefore the resultant weight of a body is given by $W = \sum_i m_i g$, where the sum extends over all particles comprising the body, and is applied at a point given by

$$\boldsymbol{r}_c = \frac{\sum_i \boldsymbol{r}_i m_i g}{\sum_i m_i g} = \frac{\sum_i m_i \boldsymbol{r}_i}{\sum_i m_i}, \tag{4.20}$$

in accordance with Eq. (4.17). Using Eq. (4.18), we may write the components of Eq. (4.20) as

$$x_c = \frac{\sum_i m_i x_i}{\sum_i m_i}, \qquad y_c = \frac{\sum_i m_i y_i}{\sum_i m_i}, \qquad z_c = \frac{\sum_i m_i z_i}{\sum_i m_i}, \tag{4.21}$$

A point defined by Eqs. (4.20) or (4.21) is called the *center of mass* of the system of particles, abbreviated CM.* The concept of center of mass is important not only in relation to the composition of parallel forces. It also plays an essential role in the analysis of the motion of a system of particles and, in particular, of a rigid body, as will be seen in Chapters 9 and 10.

* Actually the weight is applied at a slightly different point called the *center of gravity*. For practical purposes there is no difference between the points unless the body is very large.

TABLE 4–1 Centers of Mass

Figure	Position of CM
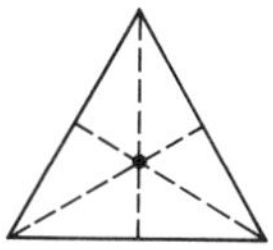	*Triangular plate* Point of intersection of the three medians
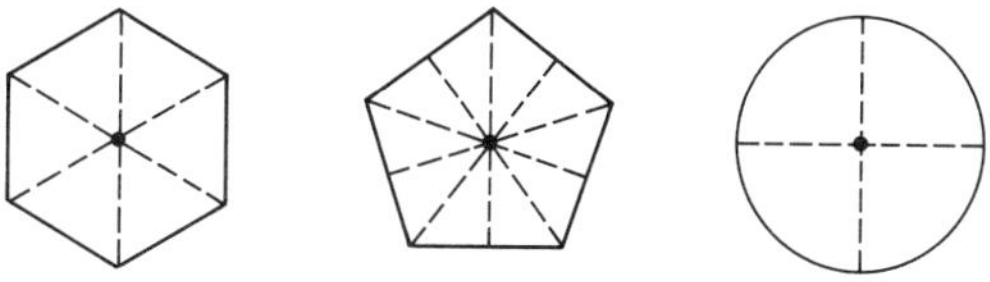	*Regular polygon and circular plate* At the geometrical center of the figure
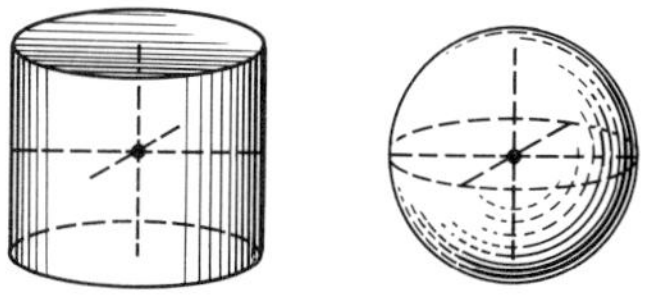	*Cylinder and sphere* At the geometrical center of the figure
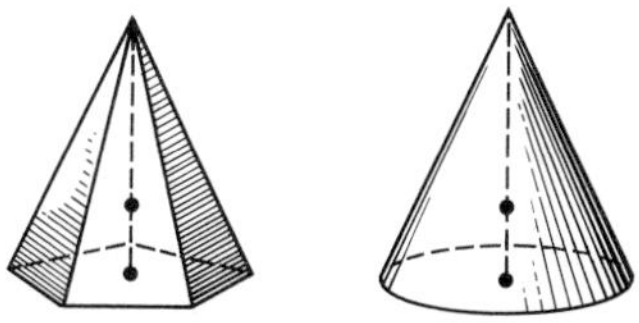	*Pyramid and cone* On line joining vertex with center of base and at $\frac{1}{4}$ of the length measured from the base
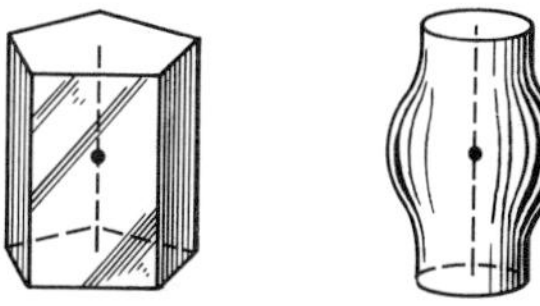	*Figure with axial symmetry* Some point on the axis of symmetry
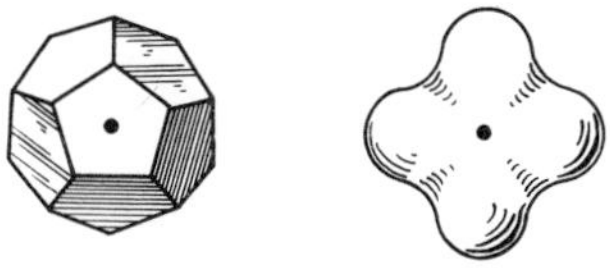	*Figure with center of symmetry* At the center of symmetry

Considering a body composed of a large number of particles, all very compact, we may assume that it has a continuous structure. If ρ is its density at each point, we may divide the volume into volume elements dV, and the mass in each will be $dm = \rho\, dV$. Therefore, when we replace the sums in Eq. (4.21) by integrals, the center of mass is given by

$$x_c = \frac{\int \rho x\, dV}{\int \rho\, dV}, \qquad y_c = \frac{\int \rho y\, dV}{\int \rho\, dV}, \qquad z_c = \frac{\int \rho z\, dV}{\int \rho\, dV}. \tag{4.22}$$

If the body is homogeneous, ρ is constant and cancels out from Eqs. (4.22), resulting in

$$x_c = \frac{\int x\, dV}{\int dV} = \frac{\int x\, dV}{V}, \tag{4.23}$$

with similar equations for y_c and z_c. In this case the center of mass is determined exclusively by the geometry of the body.*

When the homogeneous body has some symmetry, the calculation is simplified because the center of mass must coincide with the symmetry element. If a body has a *center* of symmetry, such as a sphere, a parallelepiped, etc., the center of mass coincides with it. If the body has an *axis* of symmetry, such as a cone, the center of mass is on the axis. (See Table 4–1.)

EXAMPLE 4.7. Find the center of mass of the particles located as shown in Fig. 4–12. The values of the masses are $m_1 = 5$ kg, $m_2 = 30$ kg, $m_3 = 20$ kg, $m_4 = 15$ kg. The side of each square is 5 cm.

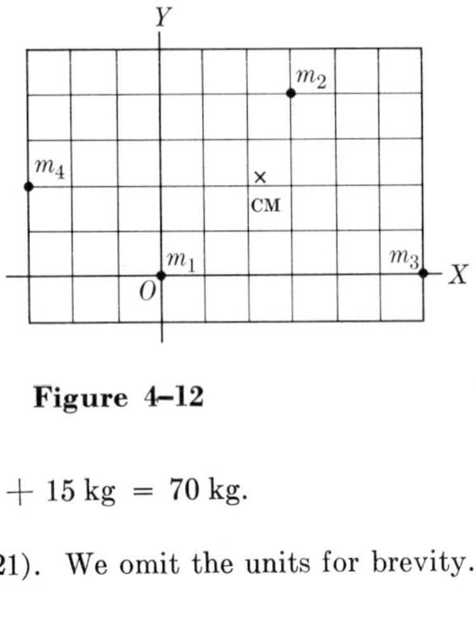

Figure 4–12

Solution: We must find first the total mass m:

$$m = \sum_i m_i = 5 \text{ kg} + 30 \text{ kg} + 20 \text{ kg} + 15 \text{ kg} = 70 \text{ kg}.$$

Next we apply the first and second equations of (4.21). We omit the units for brevity. The result is

$$x_c = \frac{(5)(0) + (30)(15) + (20)(30) + (15)(-15)}{70} = 11.8 \text{ cm},$$

$$y_c = \frac{(5)(0) + (30)(20) + (20)(0) + (15)(10)}{70} = 10.7 \text{ cm}.$$

The center of mass is thus located at the point indicated by CM in Fig. 4–12.

---

* For the technique of computing the center of mass, see any calculus text; for example, *Calculus and Analytic Geometry*, third edition, by G. B. Thomas. Reading, Mass.: Addison-Wesley, 1962, Sections 5–9, 15–3, and 15–6.

4.9 Statics. Equilibrium of a Particle

Statics is the branch of mechanics that deals with the equilibrium of bodies. A particle is in equilibrium if the sum of all the forces acting on it is zero; that is,

$$\sum_i \boldsymbol{F}_i = 0. \tag{4.24}$$

The above equation is equivalent to

$$\sum_i F_{ix} = 0; \qquad \sum_i F_{iy} = 0; \qquad \sum_i F_{iz} = 0. \tag{4.25}$$

We shall now illustrate how to solve some simple problems involving equilibrium of a particle.

EXAMPLE 4.9. Discuss the equilibrium of three forces acting on a particle.

Solution: We shall consider the three forces illustrated in Fig. 4–13. If the forces are in equilibrium, it means that

$$\boldsymbol{F}_1 + \boldsymbol{F}_2 + \boldsymbol{F}_3 = 0,$$

so that if we draw a polygon with the three forces we must obtain a triangle, as shown in Fig. 4–14. This indicates that the three concurrent forces in equilibrium must be in one plane. Also, applying the Law of Sines (M.15) to this triangle, we get

$$\frac{F_1}{\sin \alpha} = \frac{F_2}{\sin \beta} = \frac{F_3}{\sin \gamma}, \tag{4.26}$$

which is a very useful formula relating the magnitudes of the forces and the angles between them.

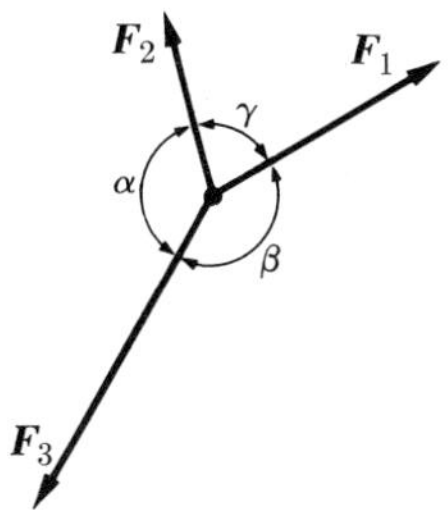

Figure 4–13

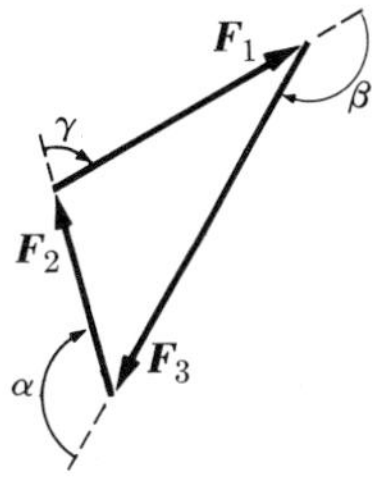

Figure 4–14

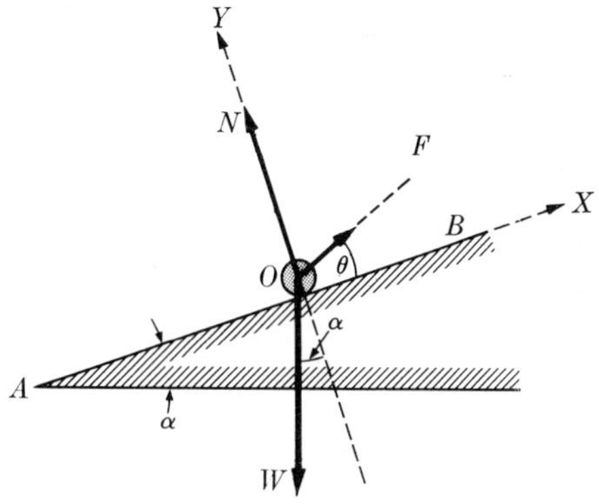

Fig. 4–15. Equilibrium on an inclined plane.

EXAMPLE 4.10. Discuss the equilibrium of a particle on a smooth inclined plane.

Solution: The particle O resting on inclined plane AB (Fig. 4–15) is subject to the following forces: its weight $\boldsymbol{W}$, the pull $\boldsymbol{F}$, and the normal reaction of the plane $\boldsymbol{N}$. We wish to express F and N in terms of W, α, and θ. We may proceed in two different ways.

Using the Law of Sines, Eq. (4.26), and considering the geometry of Fig. 4–15, we have

$$\frac{F}{\sin(180° - \alpha)} = \frac{N}{\sin(90° + \alpha + \theta)} = \frac{W}{\sin(90° - \theta)}$$

or

$$\frac{F}{\sin\alpha} = \frac{N}{\cos(\alpha + \theta)} = \frac{W}{\cos\theta},$$

giving for F and N

$$F = \frac{W\sin\alpha}{\cos\theta}, \qquad N = \frac{W\cos(\alpha+\theta)}{\cos\theta}.$$

As an alternative procedure, we may introduce axes X and Y as shown in the figure and apply the first two equations of (4.25). The result is

$$\sum_i F_{ix} = F\cos\theta - W\sin\alpha = 0,$$
$$\sum_i F_{iy} = F\sin\theta - W\cos\alpha + N = 0.$$

From the first we obtain

$$F\cos\theta = W\sin\alpha \qquad \text{or} \qquad F = \frac{W\sin\alpha}{\cos\theta},$$

in agreement with our previous result. From the second, using the expression already found for F, we have

$$N = W\cos\alpha - F\sin\theta = W\cos\alpha - \frac{W\sin\alpha\sin\theta}{\cos\theta}$$
$$= W\frac{\cos\alpha\cos\theta - \sin\alpha\sin\theta}{\cos\theta} = W\frac{\cos(\alpha+\theta)}{\cos\theta},$$

which again is the previously obtained result. The student must decide, in each particular problem, which method is more direct or convenient.

4.10 Statics. Equilibrium of a Rigid Body

When forces are acting on a rigid body, it is necessary to consider equilibrium relative to both translation and rotation. Therefore the two following conditions are required:

I. The sum of all the forces must be zero (translational equilibrium):

$$\sum_i \boldsymbol{F}_i = 0. \qquad (4.27)$$

II. The sum of all the torques relative to any point must be zero (rotational equilibrium):

$$\sum_i \boldsymbol{\tau}_i = 0. \qquad (4.28)$$

If the forces are all in one plane, the above conditions reduce to the following three algebraic equations:

$$\textstyle\sum_i F_{ix} = 0, \qquad \sum_i F_{iy} = 0, \qquad \sum_i \tau_i = 0. \tag{4.29}$$

Since these are three simultaneous equations, problems in plane statics are determined only if there are three unknown quantities. We now illustrate the technique of solving some typical problems of plane statics.

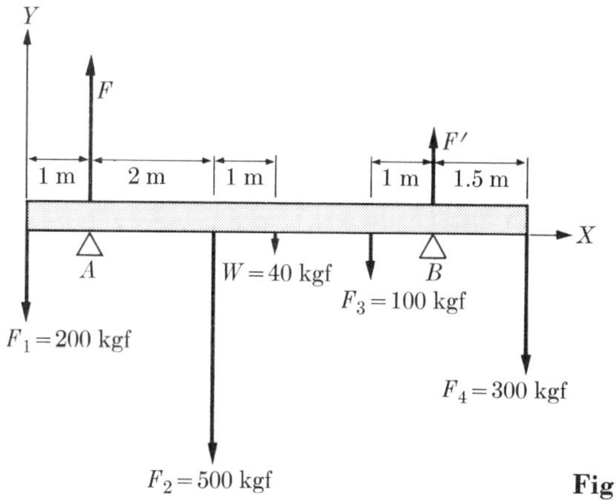

Figure 4–16

EXAMPLE 4.11. The bar of Fig. 4–16 is resting in equilibrium on points A and B, under the action of the forces indicated. Find the forces exerted on the bar at points A and B. The bar weighs 40 kgf and its length is 8 m.

Solution: Applying first the condition (4.27) for translational equilibrium, we have

$$\textstyle\sum F_i = F + F' - 200 - 500 - 40 - 100 - 300 = 0$$

or

$$F + F' = 1140 \text{ kgf}. \tag{4.30}$$

Second, we apply condition (4.28) for rotational equilibrium. It is more convenient to compute the torques relative to A, because in this way the torque of force F is zero. Thus

$$\begin{aligned}\textstyle\sum_i \tau_i = {} & (-200)(-1) + F(0) + (-500)(2) + (-40)(3) \\ & + (-100)(4.5) + F'(5.5) + (300)(7) = 0\end{aligned}$$

or $F' = 132.7$ kgf. Combining this result with Eq. (4.30), we obtain $F = 1007.3$ kgf, which solves the problem.

EXAMPLE 4.12. A ladder AB weighing 40 lbf rests against a vertical wall, making an angle of 60° with the floor. Find the forces on the ladder at A and B. The ladder is provided with rollers at A so that the friction with the vertical wall is negligible.

Solution: The forces acting on the ladder are illustrated in Fig. 4–17. The weight $\boldsymbol{W}$ is at the center C of the ladder. Force $\boldsymbol{F}_1$ is required to prevent the ladder from sliding and results from friction with the floor. Forces $\boldsymbol{F}_2$ and $\boldsymbol{F}_3$ are the normal reactions at the floor and the vertical wall. Using the three conditions of equilibrium, as stated in Eq. (4.29), we have

$$\begin{aligned} \sum F_{ix} &= -F_1 + F_3 = 0, \\ \sum F_{iy} &= -W + F_2 = 0. \end{aligned} \tag{4.31}$$

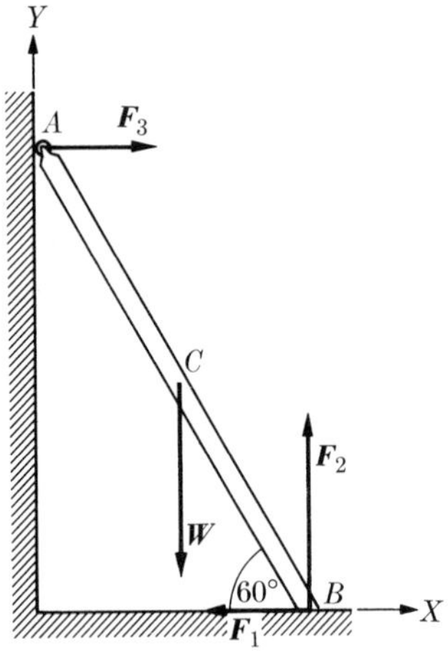

Figure 4–17

Calling L the length of the ladder and taking torques around B so that the torques of the unknown forces $\boldsymbol{F}_1$ and $\boldsymbol{F}_2$ are zero, we have for the third equation of equilibrium,

$$\sum \tau_i = W(\tfrac{1}{2}L \cos 60°) - F_3(L \sin 60°) = 0$$

or

$$F_3 = \frac{W \cos 60°}{2 \sin 60°} = 11.52 \text{ lbf}.$$

Then Eqs. (4.31) give

$$F_1 = F_3 = 11.52 \text{ lbf}$$

and

$$F_2 = W = 40 \text{ lbf}.$$

Note that if the ladder has no roller at A, a frictional force parallel to the vertical wall is also present at A. Thus we have four unknown forces, and some additional assumption is required to solve the problem.

References

1. *Mechanics* (second edition), by K. Symon. Reading, Mass.: Addison-Wesley, 1964, Section 3–2
2. *Physical Mechanics* (third edition), by R. Lindsay. Princeton, N.J.: Van Nostrand, 1963, Section 1–7
3. *Vector Mechanics*, by D. Christie. New York: McGraw-Hill, 1964, Chapters 3, 4, 10, and 11
4. *Introduction to Engineering Mechanics*, by J. Huddleston. Reading, Mass.: Addison-Wesley, 1961, Chapters 3, 5, 6, and 8
5. *The Feynman Lectures on Physics*, Volume I, by R. Feynman, R. Leighton, and M. Sands. Reading, Mass.: Addison-Wesley, 1963, Chapter 12
6. *Foundations of Modern Physical Science*, by G. Holton and D. H. D. Roller. Reading, Mass.: Addison-Wesley, 1958, Chapter 4

Problems

4.1 A telephone pole is held in a vertical position by means of a cable that is fixed on the pole at a height of 10 m and also fixed to the ground 7 m from the base of the pole. If the tension in the cable is 500 lbf, what are the horizontal and vertical forces exerted on the pole by the cable?

4.2 A block weighing 6 kgf is on a smooth horizontal surface. It is pushed with a stick (which forms a 30° angle with the horizontal) by a force of 6 kgf. (a) What is the total perpendicular force exerted on the surface? (b) What is the force parallel to the surface?

4.3 An inclined plane is 2 m high and 5 m long. There is a stone block (weight 10 kgf) on the plane, held in place by a fixed obstacle. Find the force exerted by the block (a) on the plane and (b) on the obstacle.

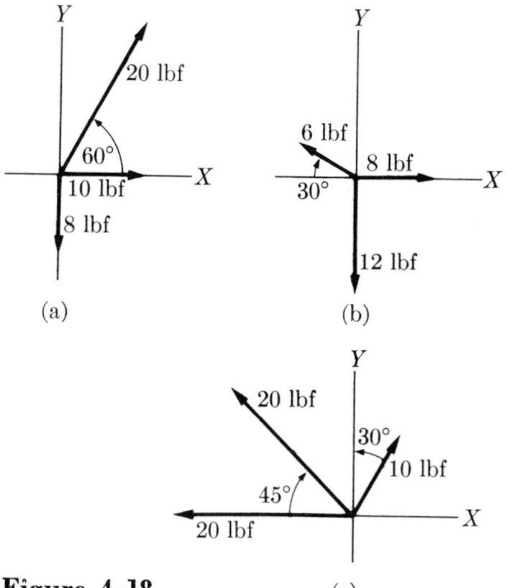

Figure 4–18

4.4 Find the magnitude and direction of the resultant of the system of forces repre-ted in Fig. 4–18.

4.5 Four coplanar forces (30 N, 40 N, 20 N, and 50 N) are all acting concurrently on a body. The angles between the forces are, consecutively, 50°, 30°, and 60°. Calculate the magnitude of the resultant force and the angle it makes with the 30-N force.

4.6 Given the following three forces: $\boldsymbol{F}_1 = \boldsymbol{u}_x(500)$ lbf; $\boldsymbol{F}_2 = \boldsymbol{u}_x(0) + \boldsymbol{u}_y(-200) + \boldsymbol{u}_z(100)$ lbf; $\boldsymbol{F}_3 = \boldsymbol{u}_x(-100) + \boldsymbol{u}_y(50) + \boldsymbol{u}_z(-400)$ lbf. (a) Determine the magnitude and direction of the resultant force. (b) Determine the resultant torque of the above forces, if they are all applied at the point (4, −3, 15), with respect to the origin O. Use the resultant force to determine the resultant torque.

4.7 Find the torque, with respect to the origin O, of each force given in Problem 4.6, when each is applied at the point (4, −3, 15). Prove that the resultant torque is perpendicular to the resultant force.

4.8 (a) Find the resultant torque about point O of the forces listed in Problem 4.6 when they are applied at different points: $\boldsymbol{F}_1$ at (3, 8, 10); $\boldsymbol{F}_2$ at (−2, 0, 4); $\boldsymbol{F}_3$ at (4, −25, 10). (b) Find $\boldsymbol{R} \cdot \boldsymbol{\tau}$ and indicate the minimum reduction of the system.

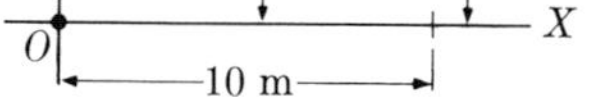

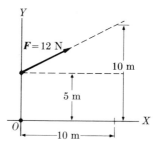

Figure 4–19

4.9 Calculate the torque of the force in Fig. 4–19 with respect to the origin. Determine the equation of the line of action of the force.

4.10 Determine (Fig. 4–20) the resultant force and resultant torque about O of three forces, 50 N, 80 N, and 100 N, all

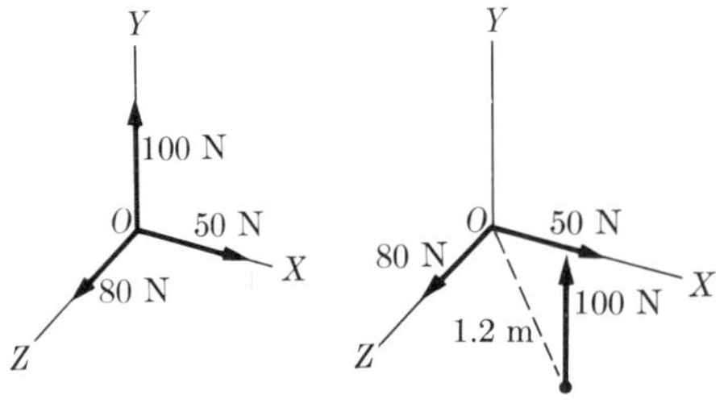

Figure 4–20

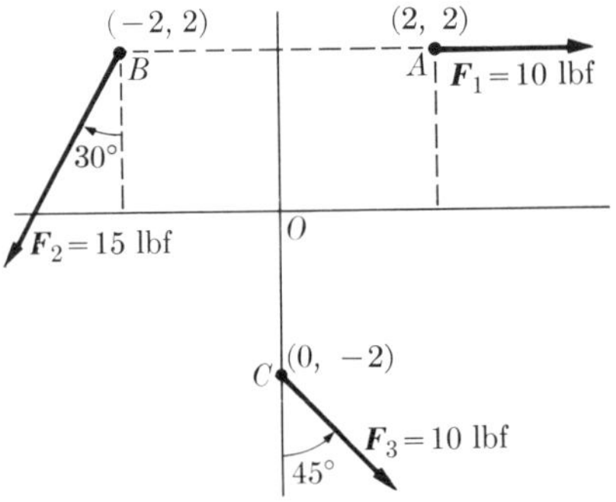

Figure 4–22

mutually perpendicular to one another (a) if they are concurrent; (b) if the line of action of the 100-N force is 1.2 m from the point of concurrency of the other two.

4.11 A rigid rectangle $ABCD$, with $AB = CD = 0.4$ m and $BC = DA = 0.6$ m, has five forces acting on it: at A, a 6-N force acting in the direction AB, a 4-N force acting along AC, and a 3-N force acting along AD; at C, a 5-N force acting in direction CD and a 4-N force acting in the direction CB. Determine the resultant force, also the torque with respect to points A, B, and the geometric center.

4.12 Two parallel forces, with the same sense, are 0.2 m apart. If one of the forces is 13 N and the resultant has a line of action 0.08 m from the other force, find (a) the magnitude of the resultant and (b) the magnitude of the other force.

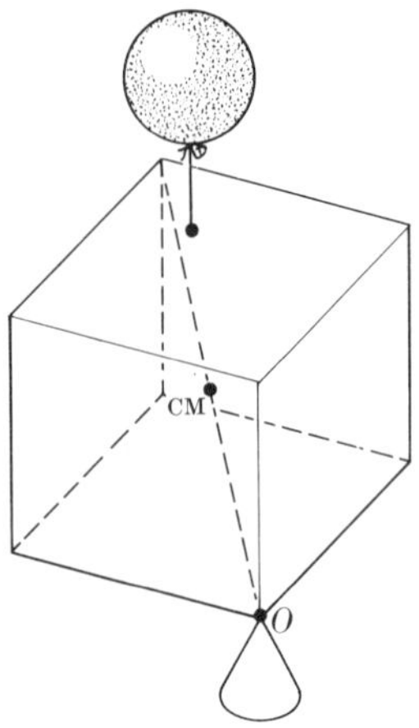

Figure 4–21

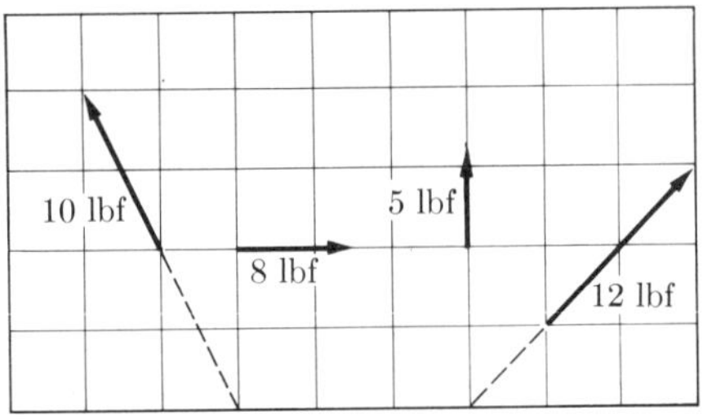

Figure 4–23

4.13 Two parallel forces, with the same sense, have magnitudes of 20 N and 30 N. The distance from the line of action of the resultant to the larger force is 0.8 m. Find the distance between the forces.

4.14 Solve the previous two problems, assuming that the forces have opposite senses.

4.15 A cube of uniform density, which weighs 10 lbf and is 2 ft on each side, rests on a point at one of its vertices (Fig. 4–21). Where must a gas-filled balloon (that has an upward lifting capability of 8 lbf) be attached so that the cube "floats" in the horizontal position shown in the figure? What is the force at O?

4.16 Find the magnitude and position of the resultant of the system of forces represented in Fig. 4–22. The coordinates of the points A, B, and C are given in feet.

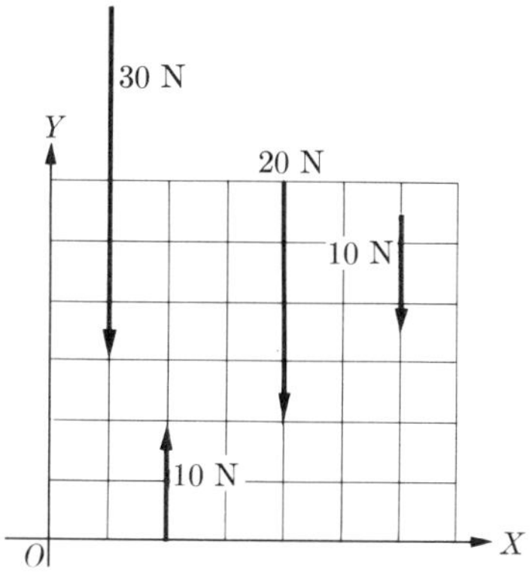

Figure 4–24

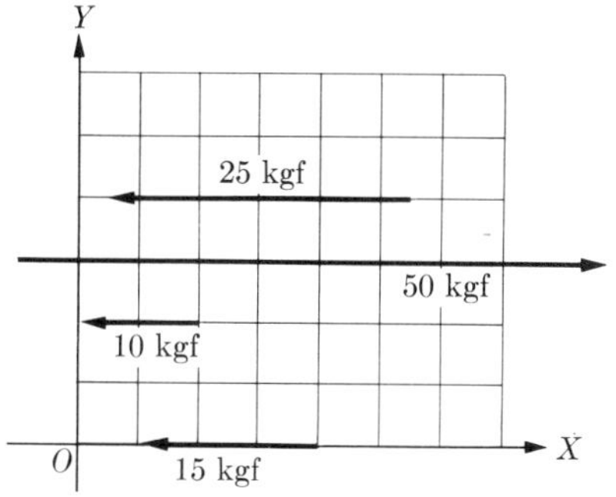

Figure 4–25

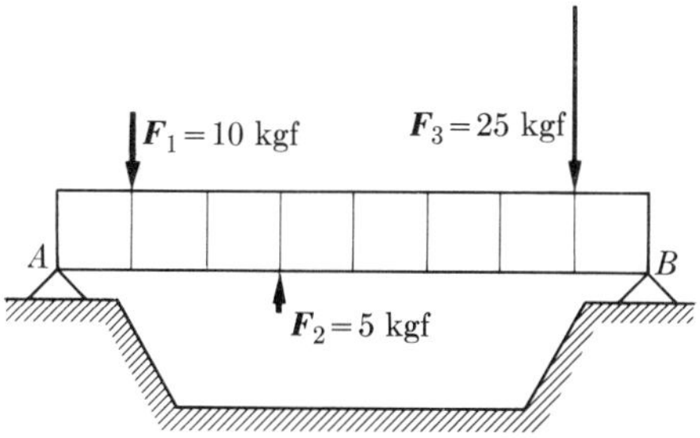

Figure 4–26

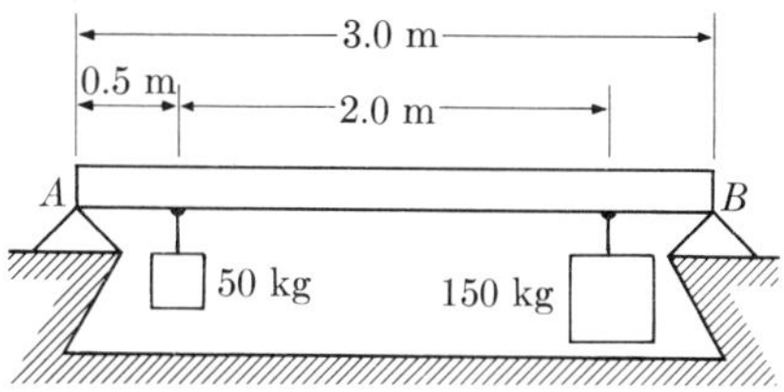

Figure 4–27

4.17 Find the magnitude and position of the resultant of the forces represented in Fig. 4–23. Each square is 1 ft on a side.

4.18 Reduce the system of forces in Fig. 4–24.

4.19 Reduce the system of forces represented in Fig. 4–25. Squares are 1 cm^2.

4.20 Prove that if $\boldsymbol{R} = \sum_i \boldsymbol{F}_i$ is the resultant of a system of concurrent forces and $\boldsymbol{\tau}_O$ is their torque relative to the point 0, the torque relative to A is

$$\boldsymbol{\tau}_A = \boldsymbol{\tau}_O + \boldsymbol{r}_{AO} \times \boldsymbol{R}.$$

4.21 A stick is 2 m long and its weight is 5 gmf (4900 dynes). There are forces of 3000, 2000, and 1500 dynes acting downward at 0, 50, and 200 cm from one end, and forces of 5000 and 13,000 dynes acting upward at 20 and 100 cm from the same end. Determine the magnitude and line of action of the resultant.

4.22 Find the magnitude and position of the resultant of the system of forces represented in Fig. 4–26. Each segment of the beam AB is 1 decimeter. Also find the force needed at A and B to balance the other forces.

4.23 The beam AB is uniform and has a mass of 100 kg. It is resting on its ends A and B and is supporting the masses, as shown in Fig. 4–27. Calculate the reactions at the supports.

4.24 Determine the tensions on the ropes AC and BC (Fig. 4–28) if M weighs 40 lbf.

4.25 The body represented in Fig. 4–29 weighs 40 kgf. It is held in equilibrium by means of the rope AB and under the action

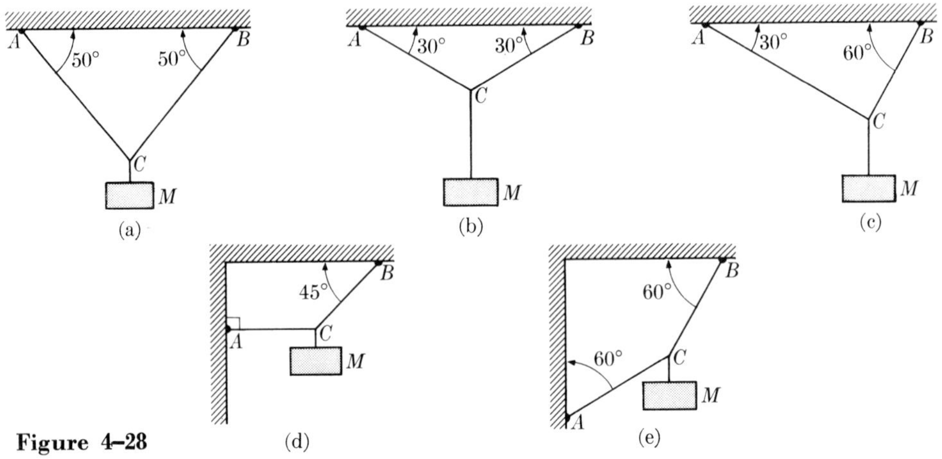

Figure 4–28

of the horizontal force ***F***. Given that $AB = 150$ cm and the distance between the wall and the body is 90 cm, calculate the value of the force ***F*** and the tension in the rope.

4.26 For Fig. 4–30, calculate the angle θ and the tension in the rope AB if $M_1 =$ 300 lbf and $M_2 = 400$ lbf.

4.27 A boy weighing 120 lbf is holding onto a chinning bar. What force does each of his arms exert on the bar when (a) his arms are parallel to each other and (b) each arm makes an angle of 30° with the vertical? Plot the force as a function of the angle. What do you conclude from the graph?

4.28 A rope $ABCD$ is hanging from the fixed points A and D. At B there is a weight of 12 kgf and at C an unknown weight. If the angle of AB with the horizontal is 60°, BC is horizontal, and CD forms an angle of 30° with the horizontal, calculate the value W would have to have in order for the system to be in equilibrium.

4.29 Three ropes, located in a vertical plane, are fixed to different points on a horizontal ceiling. The other extremes are held at a point A, from which a weight W is hanging. The angles formed by the ropes with the horizontal are, respectively, 35°, 100°, and 160°. The tensions in the first two ropes are, respectively, 100 kgf and 75 kgf. Calculate the tension in the third rope, and also the weight W.

4.30 Prove that if three forces are in equilibrium, they must be concurrent; that is, their lines of action, extended, must meet at the same point.

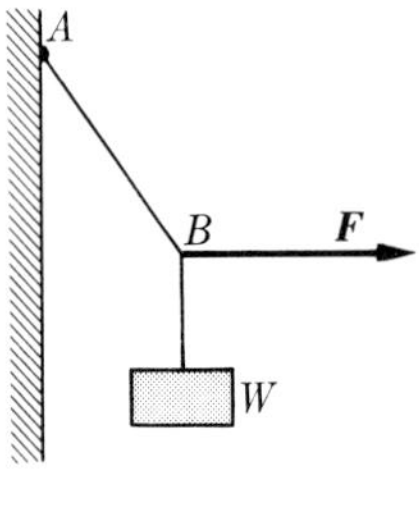

Figure 4–29

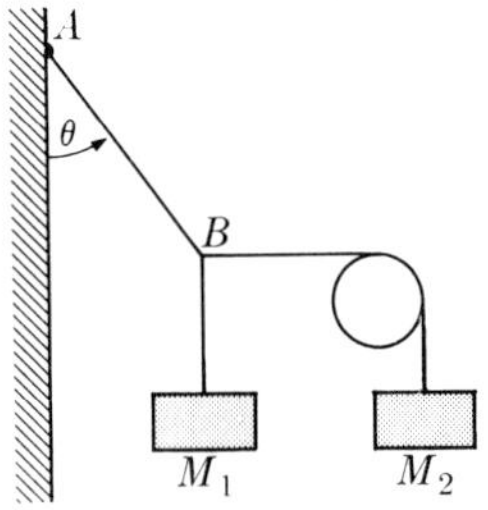

Figure 4–30

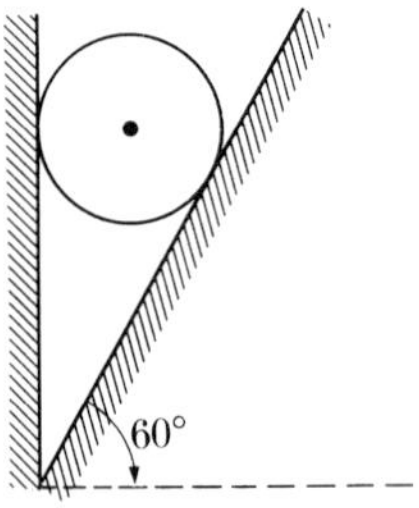

Figure 4–31

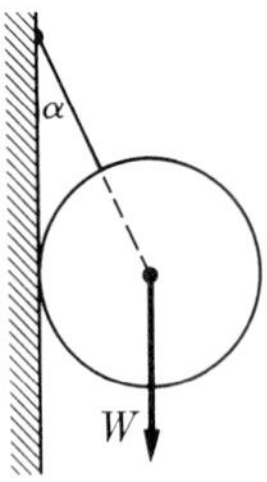

Figure 4–32

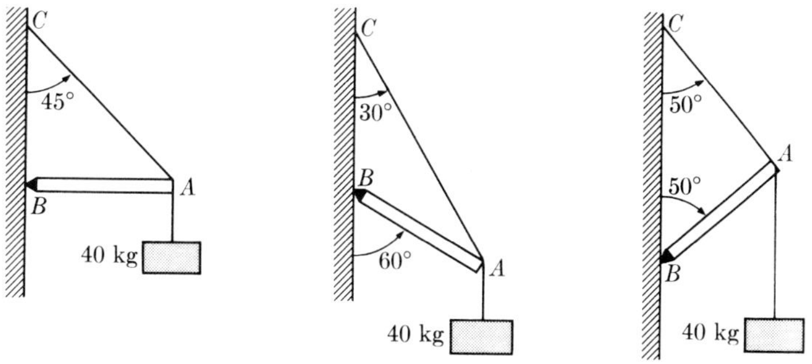

Figure 4–33 (a) (b) (c)

4.31 A sphere whose weight is 50 kgf is leaning on two smooth planes, respectively inclined 30° and 45° with respect to the horizontal. Calculate the reactions of the two planes on the sphere.

4.32 A sphere (Fig. 4–31) weighing 50 lbf is leaning against a smooth wall, held there by a smooth inclined plane that forms a 60° angle with the horizontal. Calculate the reaction of the wall and the plane on the sphere.

4.33 A sphere of weight W is held by the rope AB (Fig. 4–32) and leans on the smooth vertical wall AC. If α is the angle between the rope and the wall, determine the tension in the rope and the reaction of the wall on the sphere.

4.34 Determine the forces (Fig. 4–33) that the beam BA and the cable AC exert on A, assuming that M weighs 40 kgf and the weight of the cable and the beam may be neglected.

4.35 Determine the horizontal and vertical reactions (Fig. 4–33) at the point B and the tension in the cable AC, assuming that the beam has a 20-kg mass.

4.36 Find the forces $\boldsymbol{F}$, $\boldsymbol{F}'$, $\boldsymbol{N}$, and $\boldsymbol{H}$ in Fig. 4–34. CE and DC are cables. Neglect the weight of the boom.

4.37 Discuss the result of the previous problem as the distance $b = AG$ tends toward zero.

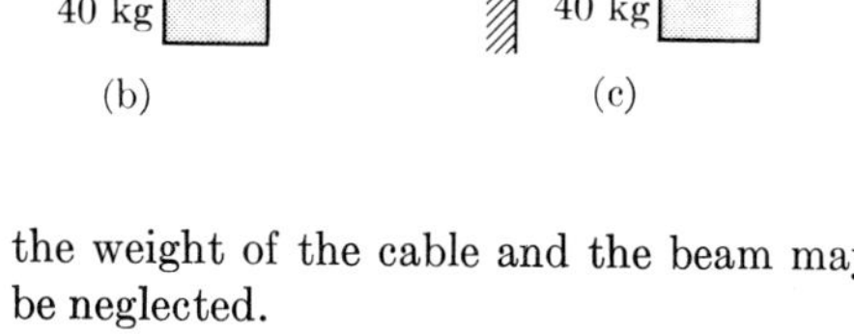

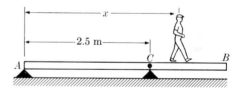

Figure 4–35

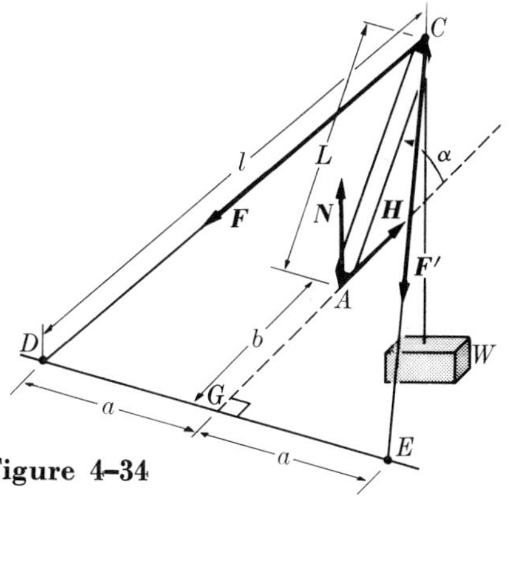

Figure 4–34

4.38 The uniform beam AB in Fig. 4–35 is 4.0 m long and weighs 100 kgf. There is a fixed point C around which the beam can rotate. The beam is resting on point A. A man weighing 75 kgf is walking along the beam, starting at A. Calculate the maximum distance the man can go from A and still maintain equilibrium. Plot the reaction at A as a function of the distance x.

4.39 There are forces acting on the beam AB as shown in Fig. 4–36. Determine the magnitude and position of the resultant.

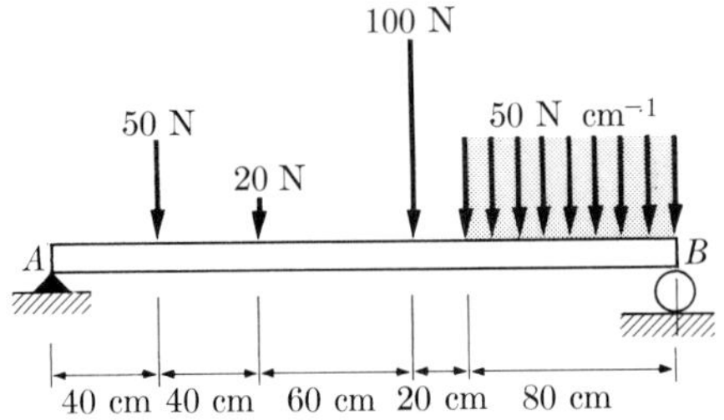

Figure 4–36

4.40 The beam AB in Fig. 4–37 is 1.2 m long and is of negligible weight. The spheres C and D (respectively 40 kg and 20 kg), linked by the beam CD, are resting on it. The distance between the centers of the spheres is 0.3 m. Calculate the distance x so that the reaction at B is $\frac{1}{2}$ of the reaction at A.

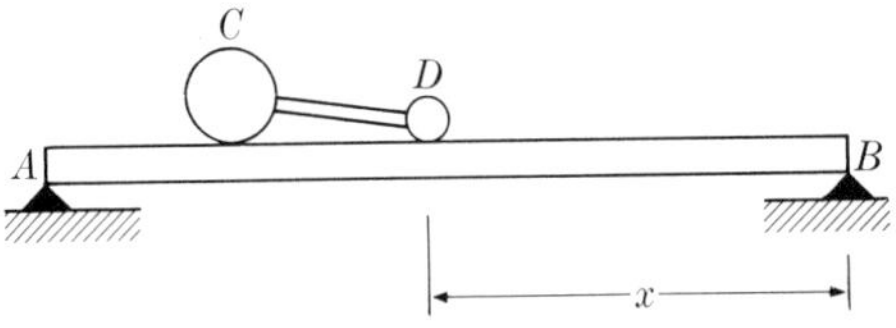

Figure 4–37

4.41 A bridge 100 m long and weighing 10,000 kgf is held up by two columns at its ends. What are the reactions on the columns when there are three cars on the bridge at 30 m, 60 m, and 80 m from one end, whose weights are, respectively, 1500 kgf, 1000 kgf, and 1200 kgf?

4.42 Consider the three cars of Problem 4.41, all moving at the same speed, 10 m s^{-1}, and in the same direction. Plot the reactions of the columns as a function of time, with $t = 0$ at the position given in Problem 4.41. Extend your plot until all cars are off the bridge.

4.43 A 20-kg plank, 8.0 m long, rests on the banks of a narrow creek. A 100-kg man walks across the plank. Plot the reaction at *each* end of the plank as a function of the distance of the man from the end.

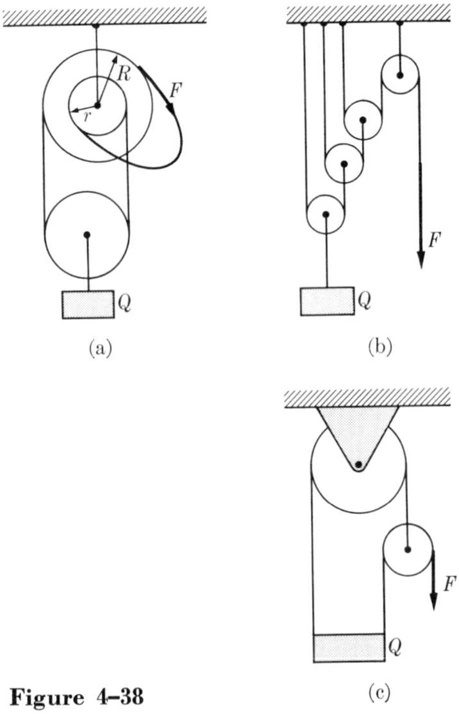

Figure 4–38

4.44 Find the force F needed to maintain equilibrium, in terms of Q, for each case shown in Fig. 4–38. The pulleys marked C are movable.

4.45 Calculate the weight P needed to maintain equilibrium in the system shown in Fig. 4–39, in which A is 100 kgf and Q is 10 kgf. The plane and the pulleys are all smooth. Rope AC is horizontal and rope AB is parallel to the plane. Also calculate the reaction of the plane on the weight A.

4.46 A stick of mass m and length l (Fig. 4–40) is placed into a perfectly smooth

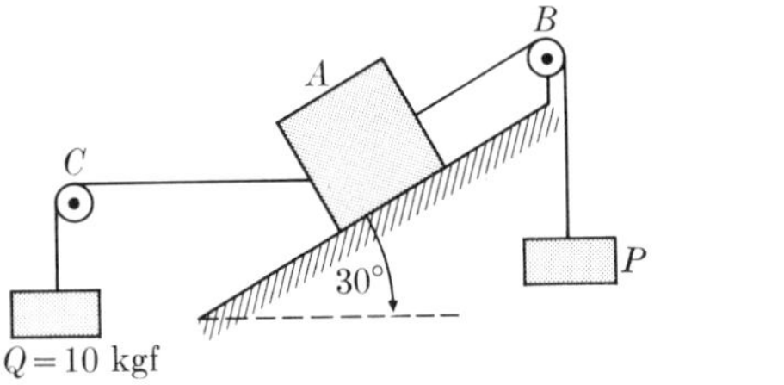

Figure 4–39

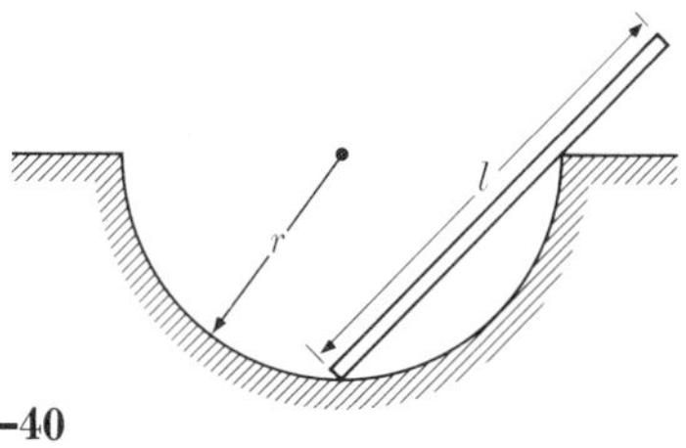

Figure 4–40

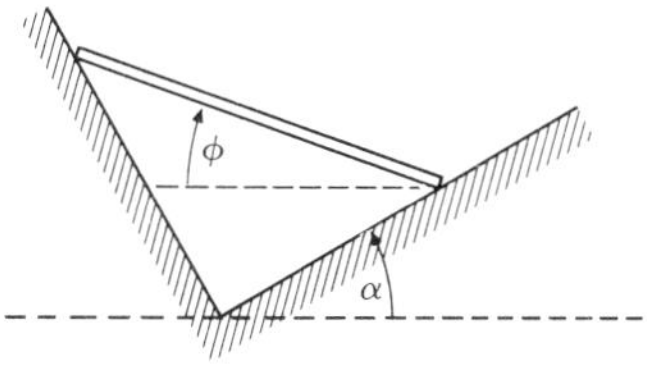

Figure 4–41

hemisphere of radius r. Find the position of equilibrium of the stick. Calculate the reactions of the hemisphere on the stick. Discuss the solution for $l > 2r$ and $l < 2r$.

4.47 A stick of mass 6 kg and length 0.8 m is placed on the smooth right angle shown in Fig. 4–41. Determine the position of equilibrium and the reaction forces as a function of the angle α.

4.48 Two identical spheres are placed in the system shown in Fig. 4–42. Calculate the reactions of the surfaces on the spheres. Show that each sphere is independently in equilibrium.

4.49 Repeat Example 4.12 of the text with a (vertical) frictional force that is always exactly 0.3 F_3. Everything else in the example remains the same.

4.50 Prove that the resultant of the forces F_1 and F_2 in Fig. 4–17 passes through the point of intersection of F_3 and W, and is equal and opposite to their resultant. Was this result to be expected?

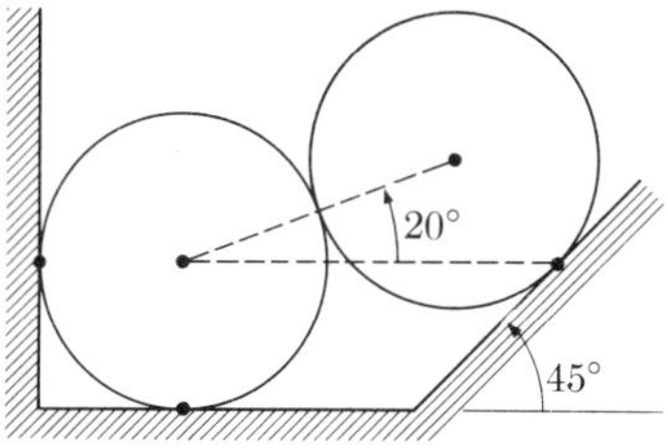

Figure 4–42

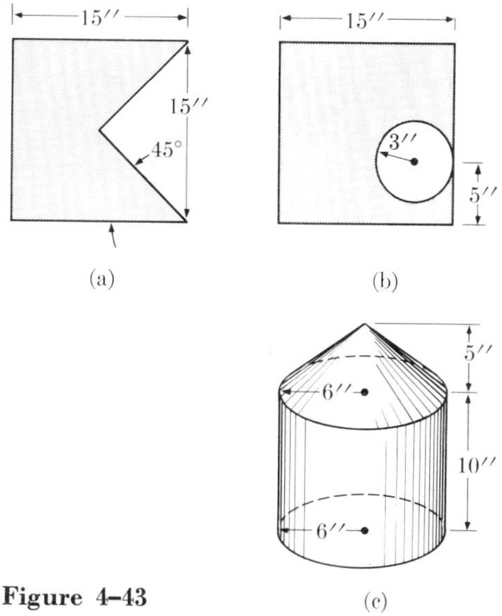

Figure 4–43

4.51 Find the center of mass of the three homogeneous bodies shown in Fig. 4–43.

4.52 Find the center of mass of (a) the earth–moon system and (b) the sun–earth system. Use the data listed in Table 13–1.

4.53 Find the coordinates of the center of mass of the homogeneous body represented in Fig. 4–44; $AB = 3$ cm, $BC = 2$ cm, $CD = 1.5$ cm, $DE = 6$ cm, $EF = 4$ cm, $FG = 2$ cm.

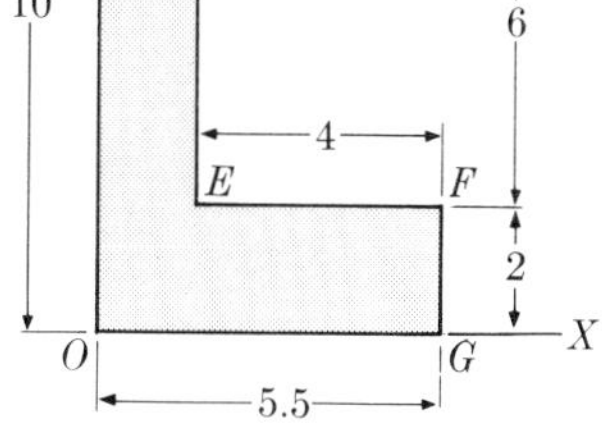

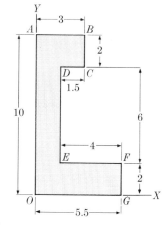

Figure 4–44

4.54 Determine the position of the CM of the following molecules: (a) CO, the distance between the C and O atoms being 1.13×10^{-10} m. (b) CO_2; this is a linear molecule with the C atom in the middle, equidistant from the two O atoms. (c) H_2O; this molecule is bent with the O atom at the vertex, the O–H distance is 0.91×10^{-10} m, and the angle between the two O-H bonds is 105°. (d) NH_3; this is a pyramidal molecule with the N atom at the vertex, the N–H distance is 1.01×10^{-10} m, and the angle between two N-H bonds is 108°.

4.55 Four equal masses are at the vertices of a regular tetrahedron of side a. Find the position of their CM.

PART 1
MECHANICS

The most fundamental and obvious phenomenon we observe around us is *motion*. Blowing air, waves in the ocean, flying birds, running animals, falling leaves—all these are motion phenomena. Practically all imaginable processes can be traced back to the motion of certain objects. The earth and the planets move around the sun; electrons move inside the atom, giving rise to absorption and emission of light, or they move inside a metal, producing an electric current; gas molecules move, giving rise to pressure. Our everyday experience tells us that the motion of a body is influenced by the bodies that surround it; that is, by its *interactions* with them. What the physicist and the engineer do, essentially, is to arrange things in such a way that, under the mutual interactions of the particles, a certain kind of motion is produced. In a TV tube, the electron beam must move in a certain fashion to produce a pattern on the screen. In a thermal engine, the molecules of the burnt fuel must move in such a way that a piston or a turbine moves in a desired direction. A chemical reaction is the consequence of certain atomic motions resulting in a new arrangement, forming new classes of molecules. The role of the physicist is to discover the reasons for all these motions; and the role of the engineer is to arrange things so that useful motions are produced, motions which will make our life easier. There are several general rules or principles that apply to all kinds of motion, no matter what the nature of the interactions. This set of principles, and the theory that underlies it, is called *mechanics*.

To analyze and predict the nature of motions resulting from the different kinds of interactions, some important concepts have been invented, such as *momentum*, *force*, and *energy*. If the momentum, force, and/or energy are initially known, they can be expressed in a quantitative way and rules can be established by which the resulting motions can be predicted. Momentum, force, and energy are so important that we can rarely analyze a process without expressing it in terms of them.

Mechanics, which is the science of motion, is also the science of momentum, force, and energy. It is one of the fundamental areas of physics, and must be understood thoroughly before beginning a consideration of particular interactions. In Galileo's time this basic role of mechanics was already recognized, the idea being condensed in the statement, "*Ignorato motu, ignoratur natura.*" Mechanics will be studied in Chapters 5 through 12.

The science of mechanics as we understand it today is mainly the result of the genius of Sir Isaac Newton, who produced the great synthesis called Newton's principles. However, many more people have contributed to its advance. Some of the more illustrious names are Archimedes, Galileo, Kepler, Descartes, Huygens, Lagrange, Hamilton, Mach, and Einstein.

5 KINEMATICS

5.1 Introduction

We say that an object is in motion relative to another when its position, measured relative to the second body, is changing with time. On the other hand, if this relative position does not change with time, the object is at relative rest. Both rest and motion are relative concepts; that is, they depend on the condition of the object relative to the body that serves as reference. A tree and a house are at rest relative to the earth, but in motion relative to the sun. When a train passes a station we say that the train is in motion relative to the station. But a passenger in the train might as well say that the station is in motion relative to the train, moving in the opposite direction.

To describe motion, therefore, the observer must define a *frame of reference* relative to which the motion is analyzed. In Fig. 5–1 we have indicated two observers O and O' and a particle P. These observers use frames of reference XYZ and $X'Y'Z'$, respectively. If O and O' are at rest relative to each other, they will observe the same motion of P. But if O and O' are in relative motion, their observations of the motion of P will be different.

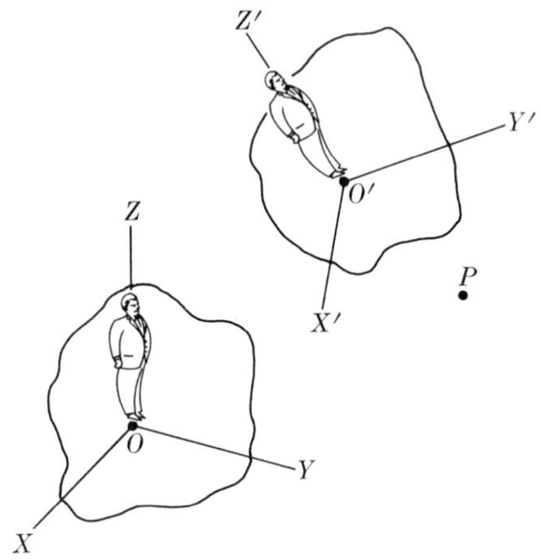

Fig. 5–1. Two different observers study the motion of P.

For example, let us consider two observers, one on the sun and the other on the earth (Fig. 5–2), both studying the motion of the moon. To the terrestrial observer using frame $X'Y'Z'$, the moon appears to describe an almost circular path around

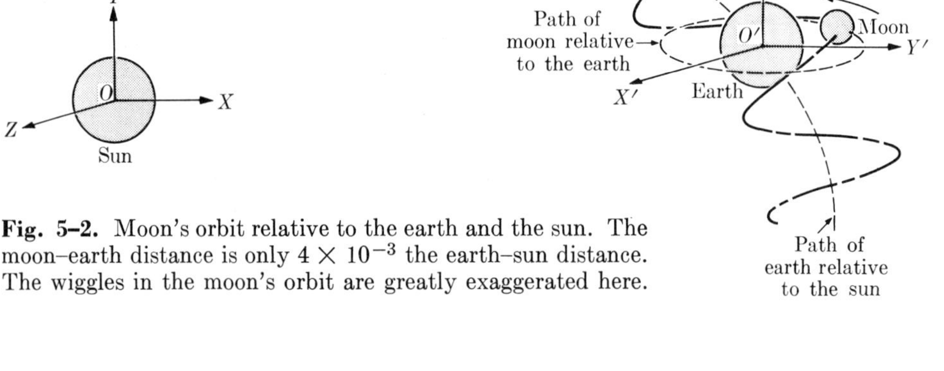

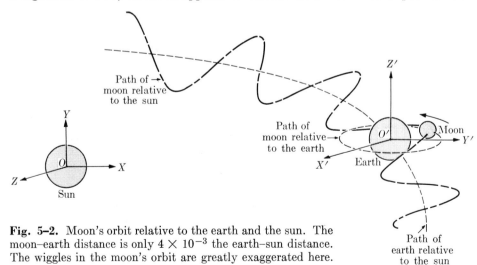

Fig. 5–2. Moon's orbit relative to the earth and the sun. The moon–earth distance is only 4×10^{-3} the earth–sun distance. The wiggles in the moon's orbit are greatly exaggerated here.

the earth. However, to the solar observer, using frame XYZ, the moon's orbit appears as a wavy line. However, if the observers know their relative motion, they can easily reconcile their respective observations. In Chapter 6 we shall discuss in more detail this important matter of comparing data gathered by observers who are in relative motion. For the time being we shall assume that we have a well-defined frame of reference.

5.2 Rectilinear Motion: Velocity

The motion of a body is rectilinear when its trajectory is a straight line. Let us take the OX-axis of Fig. 5–3, coincident with the trajectory. The position of the object is defined by its displacement x from an arbitrary point O, or origin. In principle, the displacement can be correlated with the time by means of a functional relation $x = f(t)$. Obviously, x may be positive or negative. Suppose that at time t the object is at position A, with $OA = x$. At a later time t', it is at B, with $OB = x'$. The *average velocity* between A and B is defined by

$$v_{\text{ave}} = \frac{x' - x}{t' - t} = \frac{\Delta x}{\Delta t}, \tag{5.1}$$

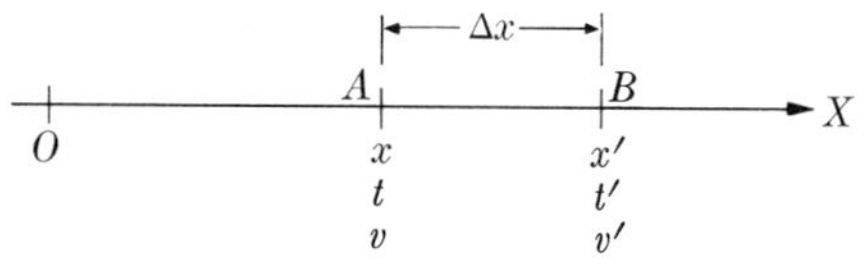

Figure 5–3

where $\Delta x = x' - x$ is the displacement of the particle and $\Delta t = t' - t$ is the elapsed time. Thus *the average velocity during a certain time interval is equal to the average displacement per unit time during the time interval.* To determine the *instantaneous velocity* at a point, such as A, we must make the time interval Δt as small as possible, so that essentially no changes in the state of motion occur during that small interval. In mathematical language this is equivalent to computing the limiting value of the fraction appearing in Eq. (5.1) when the denominator Δt approaches zero. This is written in the form

$$v = \lim_{\Delta t \to 0} v_{\text{ave}} = \lim_{\Delta t \to 0} \frac{\Delta x}{\Delta t}.$$

But this is the definition of the time derivative of x; that is,

$$v = \frac{dx}{dt}, \tag{5.2}$$

so that *we obtain the instantaneous velocity by computing the time derivative of the displacement.* Operationally, the instantaneous velocity is found by observing the moving body at two very close positions separated by the small distance dx and measuring the small time interval dt required to go from one position to the other. In the future the term "velocity" will always refer to instantaneous velocity.

If we know $v = f(t)$, we may solve Eq. (5.2) for x by the process of integration. That is, from Eq. (5.2) we have $dx = v\,dt$; then, integrating, we have

$$\int_{x_0}^{x} dx = \int_{t_0}^{t} v\,dt,$$

where x_0 is the value of x at time t_0. And, since $\int_{x_0}^{x} dx = x - x_0$,

$$x = x_0 + \int_{t_0}^{t} v\,dt. \tag{5.3}$$

To understand the physical meaning of Eq. (5.3), the student should realize that $v\,dt$ represents the displacement of the body in the short time interval dt. Thus, dividing the time interval $t - t_0$ into successive small intervals dt_1, dt_2, $dt_3, \ldots$, we find that the corresponding displacements are $v_1\,dt_1$, $v_2\,dt_2$, $v_3\,dt_3, \ldots$, and the total displacement between t_0 and t is the sum of all these. It should be noted that $v_1, v_2, v_3, \ldots$ are the values of the velocity in each time interval. Then, according to the meaning of a definite integral,

$$\text{Displacement} = v_1\,dt_1 + v_2\,dt_2 + v_3\,dt_3 + \cdots = \sum_i v_i\,dt_i = \int_{t_0}^{t} v\,dt.$$

This displacement is of course $x - x_0$, in agreement with Eq. (5.3). We must observe that the displacement Δx (or dx) may be positive or negative depending on whether the motion of the particle is to the right or to the left, resulting in a positive or negative sign for the velocity. Thus the sign of the velocity in rectilinear motion indicates the direction of motion. The direction is along $+OX$ if the velocity is positive and along $-OX$ if it is negative.

Sometimes the concept of *speed* is used, defined as distance/time. It is always positive, and is numerically equal to the magnitude of the velocity; i.e., speed $= |v|$. However, in general, the average speed does not have the same value as the average velocity. Also, it is important not to confuse the "displacement" $x - x_0$ in the time $t - t_0$ with the "distance" moved in the same time. The displacement is computed by Eq. (5.3), but the distance is obtained by $\int_{t_0}^{t} |v|\,dt$. For example, in going from city A to city B, which is 100 mi east of A, a driver may first go to city C, which is 50 mi west of A, and then turn back and go to B. The distance covered has been 200 mi, but the displacement is still 100 mi. If the motion takes place in 4 hr the average speed is 200 mi/4 hr $=$ 50 mi hr^{-1}, but the average velocity is 100 mi/4 hr $=$ 25 mi hr^{-1}.

In the MKSC system of units, velocity is expressed in meters per second, or m s^{-1}, this being the velocity of a body moving through one meter in one second with constant velocity. Of course, the velocity can also be expressed in any combination of space and time units, such as miles per hour, feet per minute, etc.

EXAMPLE 5.1. A particle moves along the X-axis in such a way that its position at any instant is given by $x = 5t^2 + 1$, where x is in meters and t is in seconds. Compute its average velocity in the time interval between (a) 2 s and 3 s, (b) 2 s and 2.1 s, (c) 2 s and 2.001 s, (d) 2 s and 2.00001 s. Also compute (e) the instantaneous velocity at 2 s.

Solution: We call $t_0 = 2$ s, which is common for the entire problem. Using $x = 5t^2 + 1$, we have $x_0 = 5(2)^2 + 1 = 21$ m. Therefore, for each question, $\Delta x = x - x_0 = x - 21$ and $\Delta t = t - t_0 = t - 2$.

(a) For $t = 3$ s, we have $\Delta t = 1$ s, $x = 5(3)^2 + 1 = 46$ m, and $\Delta x = 46$ m $-$ 21 m $= 25$ m. Thus

$$v_{\text{ave}} = \frac{\Delta x}{\Delta t} = \frac{25 \text{ m}}{1 \text{ s}} = 25 \text{ m s}^{-1}.$$

(b) For $t = 2.1$ s, we have $\Delta t = 0.1$ s, $x = 5(2.1)^2 + 1 = 23.05$ m, and $\Delta x = 2.05$ m. Thus

$$v_{\text{ave}} = \frac{\Delta x}{\Delta t} = \frac{2.05 \text{ m}}{0.1 \text{ s}} = 20.5 \text{ m s}^{-1}.$$

(c) For $t = 2.001$ s, we have $\Delta t = 0.001$ s, $x = 5(2.001)^2 + 1 = 21.020005$ m, and $\Delta x = 0.020005$ m. Thus

$$v_{\text{ave}} = \frac{\Delta x}{\Delta t} = \frac{0.020005 \text{ m}}{0.001 \text{ s}} = 20.005 \text{ m s}^{-1}.$$

(d) The student may verify for himself that for $t = 2.00001$ s, $v_{\text{ave}} = 20.00005$ m s^{-1}.

(e) We note then that as Δt becomes smaller, the velocity approaches the value 20 m s^{-1}. We may thus expect that this is the instantaneous velocity at $t = 2$ s. In fact,

$$v = \frac{dx}{dt} = \frac{d}{dt}(5t^2 + 1) = 10t.$$

When we set $t = 2$ s, then we obtain $v = 20$ m s^{-1}, which is the answer to (e).

5.3 Rectilinear Motion: Acceleration

In general, the velocity of a body is a function of time. If the velocity remains constant, the motion is said to be *uniform*. Again referring to Fig. 5–3, suppose that at time t the object is at A with velocity v, and at time t' it is at B with velocity v'. The *average acceleration* between A and B is defined by

$$a_{\text{ave}} = \frac{v' - v}{t' - t} = \frac{\Delta v}{\Delta t}, \tag{5.4}$$

where $\Delta v = v' - v$ is the change in velocity and, as before, $\Delta t = t' - t$ is the elapsed time. Thus *the average acceleration during a certain time interval is the change in velocity per unit time during the time interval.*

The *instantaneous acceleration* is the limiting value of the average acceleration when the time interval Δt becomes very small. That is,

$$a = \lim_{\Delta t \to 0} a_{\text{ave}} = \lim_{\Delta t \to 0} \frac{\Delta v}{\Delta t},$$

resulting in

$$a = \frac{dv}{dt}, \tag{5.5}$$

so that we obtain the instantaneous acceleration by computing the time derivative of the velocity. Operationally, the instantaneous acceleration is found by observing the small change of velocity dv that takes place in a very small time interval dt. In the future, whenever we say "acceleration," we shall mean the instantaneous acceleration.

In general, the acceleration varies during the motion. If the rectilinear motion has constant acceleration, the motion is said to be *uniformly accelerated.*

If the velocity increases in absolute value with time, the motion is said to be "accelerated"; but if the velocity decreases in absolute value with time, the motion is termed retarded or "decelerated."

If we know the acceleration, we may compute the velocity by integrating Eq. (5.5). From Eq. (5.5) we have $dv = a\,dt$, and, integrating, we obtain

$$\int_{v_0}^{v} dv = \int_{t_0}^{t} a\,dt,$$

where v_0 is the velocity at the time t_0. Then, since $\int_{v_0}^{v} dv = v - v_0$,

$$v = v_0 + \int_{t_0}^{t} a\,dt. \tag{5.6}$$

As in the case of displacement, the physical meaning of Eq. (5.6) is readily understood. We know that $a\,dt$ gives the change in velocity during a short time interval dt. Thus, again dividing the time interval $t - t_0$ into successive small time intervals dt_1, dt_2, dt_3, ..., we find that the corresponding changes in velocity are $a_1\,dt_1$, $a_2\,dt_2$, $a_3\,dt_3$, ..., where $a_1, a_2, a_3, \ldots$ are the values of the acceleration in each time interval, and the total change $v - v_0$ of the velocity between t_0 and t is the sum of these. That is,

$$\begin{aligned}\text{Change in velocity} = v - v_0 &= a_1\,dt_1 + a_2\,dt_2 + a_3\,dt_3 + \cdots \\ &= \sum_i a_i\,dt_i = \int_{t_0}^{t} a\,dt.\end{aligned}$$

The acceleration is also related to the position by combining Eqs. (5.2) and (5.5). That is,

$$a = \frac{dv}{dt} = \frac{d}{dt}\left(\frac{dx}{dt}\right)$$

or

$$a = \frac{d^2x}{dt^2}\cdot \tag{5.7}$$

Another important relation between position and velocity can be obtained in the following way. From Eq. (5.5) we write $dv = a\,dt$. When we multiply the left-hand side of this equation by the left-hand side of Eq. (5.2) and repeat for the right-hand sides, we have

$$v\,dv = a\,dt\left(\frac{dx}{dt}\right) = a\,dx.$$

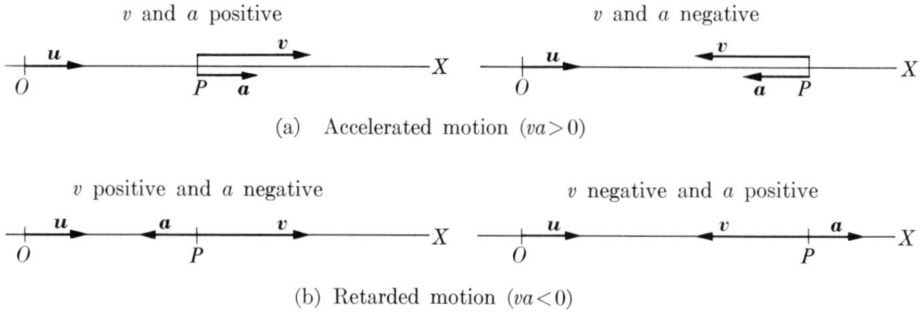

Fig. 5–4. Vector relation between velocity and acceleration in rectilinear motion.

Integrating, we obtain

$$\int_{v_0}^{v} v\,dv = \int_{x_0}^{x} a\,dx$$

or

$$\tfrac{1}{2}v^2 - \tfrac{1}{2}v_0^2 = \int_{x_0}^{x} a\,dx. \tag{5.8}$$

This equation is particularly useful in computing the velocity when the relation between x and a is known, so that the integral on the right-hand side may be computed.

In the MKSC system, the acceleration is expressed in meters per second per second, or (m/s)/s = m s^{-2}, this being the acceleration of a body whose velocity increases one meter per second in one second, with constant acceleration. But the acceleration may also be expressed in other units, such as (mi/hr)/s.

5.4 Vector Representation of Velocity and Acceleration in Rectilinear Motion

The velocity in rectilinear motion is represented by a vector whose length is given by Eq. (5.2) and whose direction coincides with that of the motion (Fig. 5–4). The acceleration is also represented by a vector of magnitude given by Eq. (5.5) and in the direction OX or the opposite, depending on whether it is positive or negative. If $\boldsymbol{u}$ is a unit vector in the positive direction of the X-axis, we may write in vector form

$$\boldsymbol{v} = \boldsymbol{u}v = \boldsymbol{u}\frac{dx}{dt} \quad \text{and} \quad \boldsymbol{a} = \boldsymbol{u}\frac{dv}{dt}\cdot$$

Vectors $\boldsymbol{v}$ and $\boldsymbol{a}$ point along $\boldsymbol{u}$ or in the opposite direction, depending on the signs of dx/dt and dv/dt, respectively. The motion is accelerated or retarded, depending on whether $\boldsymbol{v}$ and $\boldsymbol{a}$ point in the same direction or in opposite directions (Fig. 5–4). A simple rule is: If v and a have the same sign, the motion is accelerated; if the signs are opposite, the motion is retarded.

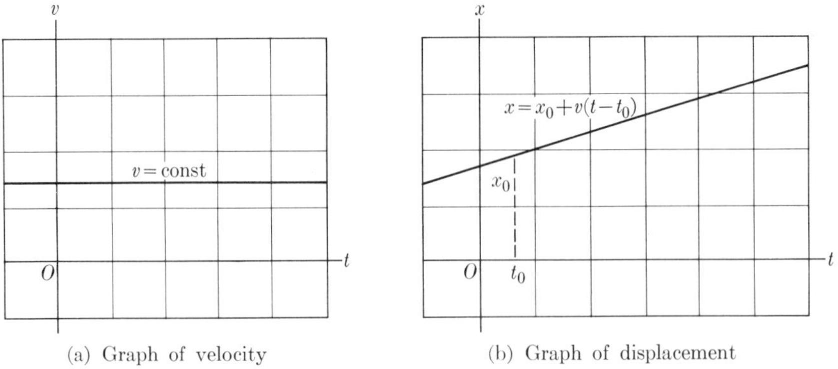

Fig. 5–5. Graph of velocity and displacement in uniform motion.

EXAMPLE 5.2. Uniform rectilinear motion.

Solution: In this case v is constant. Therefore $a = dv/dt = 0$; i.e., there is no acceleration. Also from Eq. (5.3), when v is constant, we have

$$x = x_0 + \int_{t_0}^{t} v\,dt = x_0 + v\int_{t_0}^{t} dt = x_0 + v(t - t_0).$$

In Fig. 5–5(a), we plot v as a function of t. We also, in Fig. 5–5(b), plot x as a function of t.

EXAMPLE 5.3. Uniformly accelerated rectilinear motion.

Solution: In this case a is constant. Therefore, from Eq. (5.6), we have

$$v = v_0 + \int_{t_0}^{t} a\,dt = v_0 + a\int_{t_0}^{t} dt = v_0 + a(t - t_0), \tag{5.10}$$

and from Eq. (5.3), we have

$$x = x_0 + \int_{t_0}^{t} [v_0 + a(t - t_0)]\,dt = x_0 + v_0\int_{t_0}^{t} dt + a\int_{t_0}^{t} (t - t_0)\,dt,$$

or

$$x = x_0 + v_0(t - t_0) + \tfrac{1}{2}a(t - t_0)^2. \tag{5.11}$$

It is also useful to obtain the relation derived from Eq. (5.8),

$$\tfrac{1}{2}v^2 - \tfrac{1}{2}v_0^2 = a\int_{x_0}^{x} dx = a(x - x_0).$$

Then

$$v^2 = v_0^2 + 2a(x - x_0). \tag{5.12}$$

The most important case of uniformly accelerated motion is that of free vertical motion under the action of gravity. In this case, taking the upward direction as positive, we define $a = -g$, the minus sign being due to the fact that the gravitational acceleration is downward. The value of g varies from one place on the earth's surface to another, but

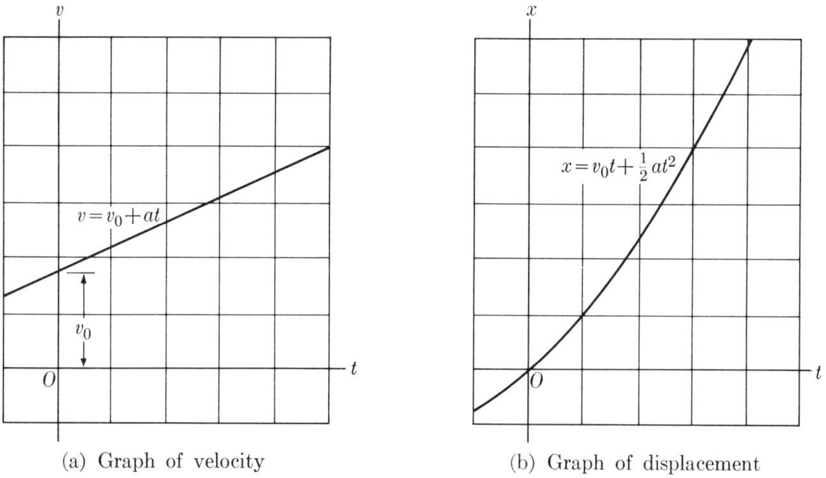

Fig. 5–6. Graph of velocity and displacement in uniformly accelerated motion.

is always very close to $g = 9.8 \text{ m s}^{-2} = 32.2 \text{ ft s}^{-2}$. This value is the same for all bodies, and may be considered independent of height, so long as we do not go far from the earth's surface, since the acceleration of gravity decreases when the distance above or below the earth's surface increases (Chapter 13).

We may plot both v and x against time. When, for simplicity, we set $t_0 = 0$ and $x_0 = 0$, Eq. (5.10) becomes $v = v_0 + at$ and Eq. (5.11) becomes $x = v_0t + \frac{1}{2}at^2$. Both equations have been plotted in Fig. 5–6. Graphs of this kind are very useful in analyzing all types of motion.

EXAMPLE 5.4. A body moves along the X-axis according to the law

$$x = 2t^3 + 5t^2 + 5,$$

where x is in feet and t is in seconds. Find (a) the velocity and the acceleration at any time, (b) the position, velocity, and acceleration at $t = 2$ s and 3 s, and (c) the average velocity and acceleration between $t = 2$ s and $t = 3$ s.

Solution: (a) Using Eqs. (5.2) and (5.5), we may write

$$v = \frac{dx}{dt} = \frac{d}{dt}(2t^3 + 5t^2 + 5) = 6t^2 + 10t \text{ ft s}^{-1},$$

$$a = \frac{dv}{dt} = \frac{d}{dt}(6t^2 + 10t) = 12t + 10 \text{ ft s}^{-2}.$$

(b) At $t = 2$ s, using the respective expressions, we have

$$x = 41 \text{ ft}, \qquad v = 44 \text{ ft s}^{-1}, \qquad a = 34 \text{ ft s}^{-2}.$$

Similarly, for $t = 3$ s, the student may verify that

$$x = 104 \text{ ft}, \qquad v = 84 \text{ ft s}^{-1}, \qquad a = 46 \text{ ft s}^{-2}.$$

(c) To find the average velocity and acceleration between $t = 2$ s and $t = 3$ s, we have $\Delta t = 1$ s, and from (b) we have $\Delta x = 63$ ft, $\Delta v = 40$ ft s^{-1}. Thus

$$v_{\text{ave}} = \frac{\Delta x}{\Delta t} = \frac{63 \text{ ft}}{1 \text{ s}} = 63 \text{ ft s}^{-1}, \qquad a_{\text{ave}} = \frac{\Delta v}{\Delta t} = \frac{40 \text{ ft s}^{-1}}{1 \text{ s}} = 40 \text{ ft s}^{-2}.$$

EXAMPLE 5.5. The acceleration of a body moving along the X-axis is $a = (4x - 2)$ m s^{-2}, where x is in meters. Given that $v_0 = 10$ m s^{-1} at $x_0 = 0$ m, find the velocity at any other position.

Solution: Since the acceleration is expressed here as a function of position rather than as a function of time, we cannot use the definition $a = dv/dt$ for obtaining the velocity by integration. Instead we must use Eq. (5.8), with $v_0 = 10$ m s^{-1} and $x_0 = 0$. Thus

$$\tfrac{1}{2}v^2 - \tfrac{1}{2}(10)^2 = \int_0^x (4x - 2)\, dx$$

or

$$v^2 = 100 + 2(2x^2 - 2x)_0^x = 4x^2 - 4x + 100$$

and thus

$$v = \sqrt{4x^2 - 4x + 100}.$$

Should we write a $\pm$ sign in front of the radical? If so, what would its meaning be? We suggest that the student make a plot of the velocity v as a function of the position x.

We leave the student to find x as a function of time t by using the definition $v = dx/dt$, and from that result to obtain v and a as functions of time. [For obtaining $x(t)$, it may be necessary to look at a table of integrals.]

EXAMPLE 5.6. A bullet is fired straight upward with a velocity of 98 m s^{-1} from the top of a building 100 m high. Find (a) its maximum height above the ground, (b) the time required to reach it, (c) the velocity it has when it reaches the ground, and (d) the total time which elapses before the bullet reaches the ground.

Solution: Referring to Fig. 5–7 and using Eqs. (5.10) and (5.11), with $t_0 = 0$, $v_0 = 98$ m s^{-1}, $x_0 = x_A = 100$ m (the origin of coordinates C has been placed at the street) and $a = -g = -9.8$ m s^{-2}, we have at any time t,

$$v = 98 - 9.8t,$$
$$x = 100 + 98t - 4.9t^2.$$

At the point of maximum height $v = 0$. Thus $98 - 9.8t = 0$ or $t = 10$ s. Replacing this value in the expression for x, we have

$$x_B = 100 + 98(10) - 4.9(10)^2$$
$$= 590 \text{ m}.$$

To obtain the time required to reach the ground

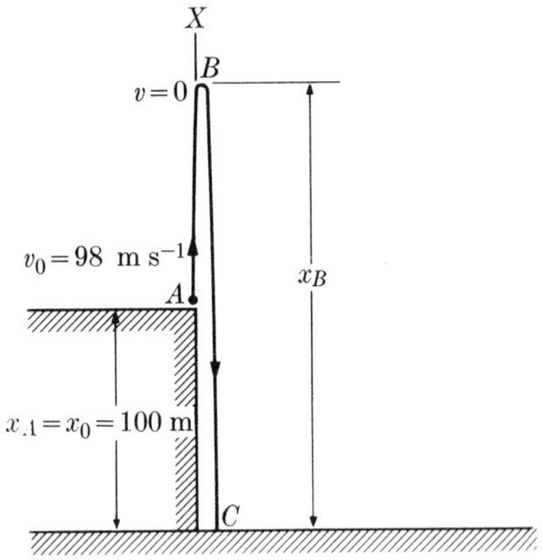

Figure 5–7

(that is, point C), we set $x_C = 0$, since C is our origin of coordinates. Then

$$0 = 100 + 98t - 4.9t^2.$$

This is a second-degree equation in t, whose roots are

$$t = -0.96 \text{ s} \qquad \text{and} \qquad t = 20.96 \text{ s}.$$

The negative answer corresponds to a time previous to the shooting ($t = 0$) and must be discarded, since it has no physical meaning in this problem (it may have in others). To obtain the velocity at C, we introduce the value $t = 20.96$ s in the expression for v_C, obtaining

$$v_C = 98 - 9.8(20.96) = -107.41 \text{ m s}^{-1}.$$

The negative sign means that the bullet is moving downward. It is suggested that the student verify the results for x_B and v_C by using Eq. (5.12), which for this problem reads

$$v^2 = 9604 - 19.6(x - 100).$$

Also the student should solve the problem by placing the origin of coordinates at A. Then

$$x_0 = x_A = 0 \text{ and } x_C = -100 \text{ m}.$$

EXAMPLE 5.7. A particle moves along the X-axis according to the law $x = t^3 - 3t^2 - 9t + 5$. During which intervals of time is the particle moving in the positive X-direction and during which is it moving in the negative X-direction? During which time intervals is the motion accelerated and during which is it retarded? Make a plot of x, v, and a as functions of time.

Solution: By applying Eq. (5.2), we can find the velocity of the particle at any time to be $v = dx/dt = 3t^2 - 6t - 9$. This may be rewritten in the form $v = 3(t + 1)(t - 3)$. Using Eq. (5.5), we can find the acceleration to be $a = 6t - 6 = 6(t - 1)$. The graphs of x, v, and a as functions of time are shown in Fig. 5-8. We note that, for $t < -1$, the velocity is positive and the motion is in the positive X-direction. At $t = -1$, $x = 10$, and the velocity is zero. For $-1 < t < 3$, the velocity is negative and the motion is reversed, the particle moving in the negative X-direction. At $t = 3$, when $x = -22$, the velocity is again zero. For $t > 3$, the velocity is once more positive and the motion is again

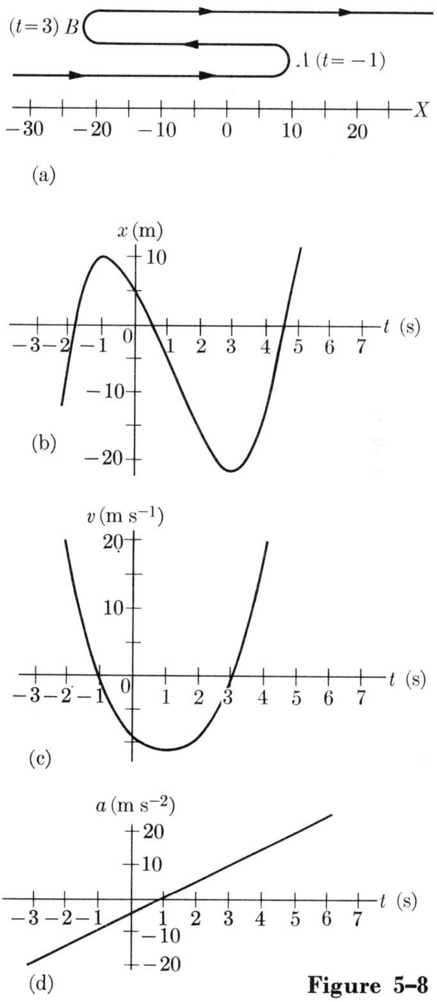

Figure 5–8

reversed, the particle now moving in the positive X-direction. The whereabouts of the particle are shown in Fig. 5–8(a); the turning points, where the velocity is zero, are marked A and B.

Looking at the graph of the velocity as well as the acceleration, we see that for $t < -1$ the motion is retarded (the magnitude of v decreases, or v and a have opposite signs). For $-1 < t < 1$, the motion is accelerated; for $1 < t < 3$, the motion is again retarded; finally, for $t > 3$, it is accelerated.

This example illustrates how useful the graphs of x, v, and a as functions of time are in disclosing the characteristics of the motion.

5.5 Curvilinear Motion: Velocity

Let us now consider a particle describing a curvilinear path P, as illustrated in Fig. 5–9. At time t the particle is at point A, given by position vector $\boldsymbol{r} = \overrightarrow{OA} = \boldsymbol{u}_x x + \boldsymbol{u}_y y + \boldsymbol{u}_z z$. At a later time t', the particle will be at B with $\boldsymbol{r}' = \overrightarrow{OB} = \boldsymbol{u}_x x' + \boldsymbol{u}_y y' + \boldsymbol{u}_z z'$. Although the particle has moved along the arc $AB = \Delta s$, the *displacement*, which is a vector, is $\overrightarrow{AB} = \Delta \boldsymbol{r}$. Note from the figure that $\boldsymbol{r}' = \boldsymbol{r} + \Delta \boldsymbol{r}$, and therefore

$$\begin{aligned} \overrightarrow{AB} &= \Delta \boldsymbol{r} = \boldsymbol{r}' - \boldsymbol{r} = \boldsymbol{u}_x(x' - x) + \boldsymbol{u}_y(y' - y) + \boldsymbol{u}_z(z' - z) \\ &= \boldsymbol{u}_x(\Delta x) + \boldsymbol{u}_y(\Delta y) + \boldsymbol{u}_z(\Delta z), \end{aligned} \tag{5.13}$$

where $\Delta x = x' - x$, $\Delta y = y' - y$, and $\Delta z = z' - z$. The average velocity, also a vector, is defined by

$$\boldsymbol{v}_{\text{ave}} = \frac{\Delta \boldsymbol{r}}{\Delta t}, \tag{5.14}$$

or, using Eq. (5.13),

$$\boldsymbol{v}_{\text{ave}} = \boldsymbol{u}_x \frac{\Delta x}{\Delta t} + \boldsymbol{u}_y \frac{\Delta y}{\Delta t} + \boldsymbol{u}_z \frac{\Delta z}{\Delta t}. \tag{5.15}$$

The average velocity is represented by a vector parallel to the displacement $\overrightarrow{AB} = \Delta \boldsymbol{r}$. To compute the instantaneous velocity we must, as in previous cases, make Δt very small. That is,

$$\boldsymbol{v} = \lim_{\Delta t \to 0} \boldsymbol{v}_{\text{ave}} = \lim_{\Delta t \to 0} \frac{\Delta \boldsymbol{r}}{\Delta t}. \tag{5.16}$$

Now when Δt approaches zero, point B approaches point A, as indicated by the points B', B'', . . . in Fig. 5–10. During this process the vector $\overrightarrow{AB} = \Delta \boldsymbol{r}$ changes continuously in magnitude *and* direction, and so does the average velocity. In the limit when B is very close to A, the vector $\overrightarrow{AB} = \Delta \boldsymbol{r}$ coincides in direction with the tangent AT. In curvilinear motion, therefore, the instantaneous velocity is a vector *tangent* to the path, and is given by

$$\boldsymbol{v} = \frac{d\boldsymbol{r}}{dt}. \tag{5.17}$$

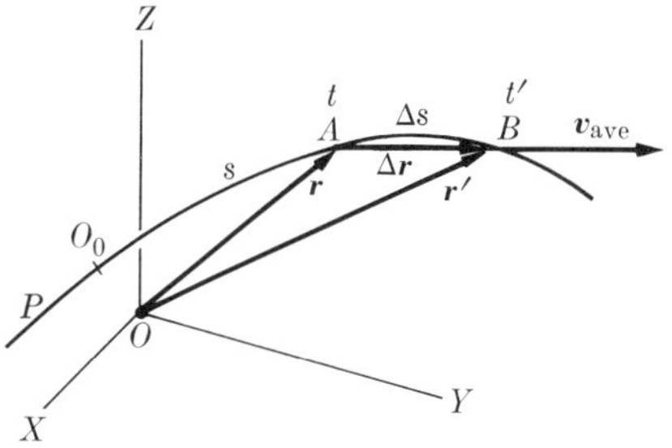

Fig. 5–9. Displacement and average velocity in curvilinear motion.

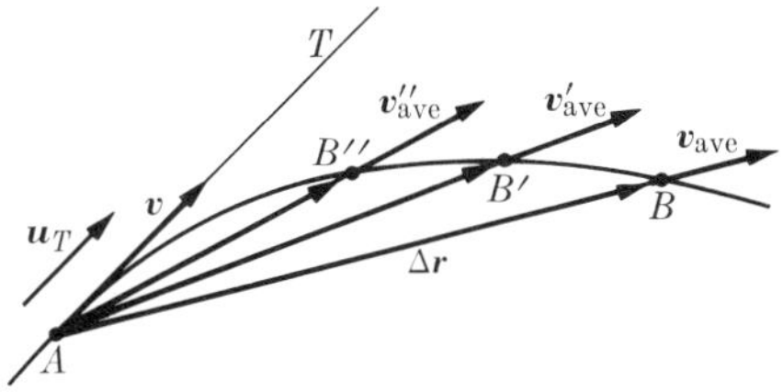

Fig. 5–10. The velocity is tangent to the path in curvilinear motion.

Or, if we take into account Eq. (5.15), the velocity is

$$\boldsymbol{v} = \boldsymbol{u}_x \frac{dx}{dt} + \boldsymbol{u}_y \frac{dy}{dt} + \boldsymbol{u}_z \frac{dz}{dt}, \tag{5.18}$$

indicating that the components of the velocity along the X-, Y-, and Z-axes are

$$v_x = \frac{dx}{dt}, \qquad v_y = \frac{dy}{dt}, \qquad v_z = \frac{dz}{dt}, \tag{5.19}$$

and the magnitude of the velocity, often called the speed, is

$$v = \sqrt{v_x^2 + v_y^2 + v_z^2}. \tag{5.20}$$

In passing from Eq. (5.16) to Eq. (5.17), we may proceed in a slightly different way. Let O_0 (Fig. 5–9) be an arbitrary reference point on the path. Then $s = O_0A$ gives the position of the particle as measured by the displacement *along* the curve. As in the rectilinear case, s may be positive or negative, depending on which side of O_0 the particle is. When the particle moves from A to B, the displacement Δs along the curve is given by the length of the arc AB. Multiplying and dividing Eq. (5.16) by $\Delta s =$ arc AB, we obtain

$$\boldsymbol{v} = \lim_{\Delta t \to 0} \frac{\Delta \boldsymbol{r}}{\Delta s}\frac{\Delta s}{\Delta t} = \left(\lim_{\Delta s \to 0} \frac{\Delta \boldsymbol{r}}{\Delta s}\right)\left(\lim_{\Delta t \to 0} \frac{\Delta s}{\Delta t}\right),$$

in which we indicate in the first factor that $\Delta s \to 0$ when $\Delta t \to 0$ (see Fig. 5–10). Now from Fig. 5–9 we can see that the magnitude of $\Delta \boldsymbol{r}$ is about equal to Δs, and the closer B is to A, the closer the magnitude of $\Delta \boldsymbol{r}$ is to Δs. Therefore $\lim_{\Delta s \to 0} \Delta \boldsymbol{r}/\Delta s$ represents a vector having unit magnitude and a direction tangent to the path. That is,

$$\frac{d\boldsymbol{r}}{ds} = \lim_{\Delta s \to 0} \frac{\Delta \boldsymbol{r}}{\Delta s} = \boldsymbol{u}_T. \tag{5.21}$$

On the other hand,

$$\lim_{\Delta t \to 0} \frac{\Delta s}{\Delta t} = \frac{ds}{dt}. \tag{5.22}$$

Therefore we can write $\boldsymbol{v}$ in the form

$$\boldsymbol{v} = \boldsymbol{u}_T \frac{ds}{dt} = \boldsymbol{u}_T v, \tag{5.23}$$

where $ds/dt = v$ gives the value of the velocity, and the unit vector $\boldsymbol{u}_T$ gives the direction of the velocity. The fact that $v = ds/dt$ is the value of the velocity is in agreement with our previous definition of velocity in Eq. (5.2), since now ds is the displacement along the curvilinear path in the time dt. So ds plays the same role in curvilinear motion as dx does in rectilinear motion. The only difference between Eqs. (5.23) and (5.2) is the inclusion of the direction element, as given by the tangent unit vector $\boldsymbol{u}_T$, which was previously introduced in Section 5.4.

5.6 Curvilinear Motion: Acceleration

In curvilinear motion the velocity, in general, changes both in magnitude and in direction. The magnitude of the velocity changes because the particle may speed up or slow down. The direction of the velocity changes because the velocity is tangent to the path and the path bends continuously. Figure 5–11 indicates the velocity at times t and t', when the particle is at A and B, respectively. The vector change in velocity in going from A to B is indicated by $\Delta\boldsymbol{v}$ in the vector triangle; that is, since, from the triangle, $\boldsymbol{v} + \Delta\boldsymbol{v} = \boldsymbol{v}'$, then $\Delta\boldsymbol{v} = \boldsymbol{v}' - \boldsymbol{v}$. Hence the average acceleration, in the time interval Δt, which is a vector, is defined by

$$\boldsymbol{a}_{\text{ave}} = \frac{\Delta\boldsymbol{v}}{\Delta t}, \tag{5.24}$$

and is parallel to $\Delta\boldsymbol{v}$. Since $\boldsymbol{v} = \boldsymbol{u}_x v_x + \boldsymbol{u}_y v_y + \boldsymbol{u}_z v_z$, we have that $\Delta\boldsymbol{v} = \boldsymbol{u}_x\,\Delta v_x + \boldsymbol{u}_y\,\Delta v_y + \boldsymbol{u}_z\,\Delta v_z$ and

$$\boldsymbol{a}_{\text{ave}} = \boldsymbol{u}_x \frac{\Delta v_x}{\Delta t} + \boldsymbol{u}_y \frac{\Delta v_y}{\Delta t} + \boldsymbol{u}_z \frac{\Delta v_z}{\Delta t}. \tag{5.25}$$

The instantaneous acceleration, which in the future will be referred to simply as acceleration, is defined by

$$\boldsymbol{a} = \lim_{\Delta t \to 0} \boldsymbol{a}_{\text{ave}} = \lim_{\Delta t \to 0} \frac{\Delta\boldsymbol{v}}{\Delta t}$$

or

$$\boldsymbol{a} = \frac{d\boldsymbol{v}}{dt}. \tag{5.26}$$

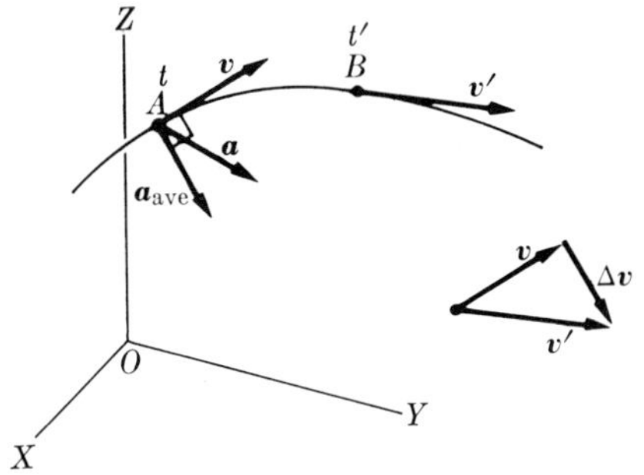

Fig. 5–11. Acceleration in curvilinear motion.

Acceleration is a vector that has the same direction as the instantaneous change in velocity. Since velocity changes in the direction in which the curve bends, acceleration is always pointing toward the concavity of the curve, and in general

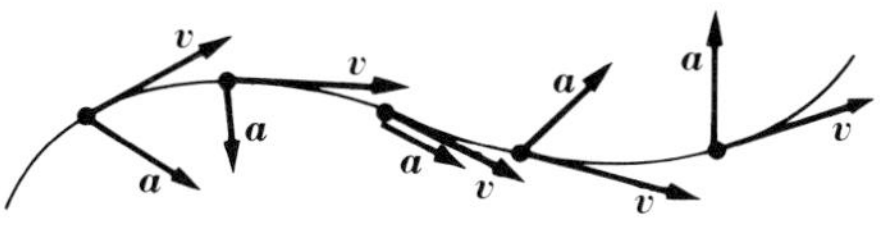

Fig. 5–12. Vector relation between velocity and acceleration in curvilinear motion.

is neither tangent nor perpendicular to the path, as indicated in Fig. 5–12. Remembering Eq. (5.17), we can also write Eq. (5.26) in the form

$$\boldsymbol{a} = \frac{d^2\boldsymbol{r}}{dt^2}. \tag{5.27}$$

From Eq. (5.25) we observe that

$$\boldsymbol{a} = \boldsymbol{u}_x \frac{dv_x}{dt} + \boldsymbol{u}_y \frac{dv_y}{dt} + \boldsymbol{u}_z \frac{dv_z}{dt}, \tag{5.28}$$

so that the components of the acceleration along the X-, Y-, and Z-axes are

$$a_x = \frac{dv_x}{dt}, \qquad a_y = \frac{dv_y}{dt}, \qquad a_z = \frac{dv_z}{dt}, \tag{5.29}$$

or, by virtue of Eq. (5.19) or Eq. (5.27),

$$a_x = \frac{d^2x}{dt^2}, \qquad a_y = \frac{d^2y}{dt^2}, \qquad a_z = \frac{d^2z}{dt^2}. \tag{5.30}$$

The magnitude of the acceleration is

$$a = \sqrt{a_x^2 + a_y^2 + a_z^2}. \tag{5.31}$$

In curvilinear motion we usually know the equation of the path; that is, we know the coordinates of the moving particle as functions of time. These coordinates are given by the equations

$$x = x(t), \qquad y = y(t), \qquad z = z(t).$$

By applying Eqs. (5.19) and (5.29), we can compute the velocity and the acceleration. In other cases the problem is the opposite: we know the components of the acceleration as a function of time; that is,

$$a_x = a_x(t), \qquad a_y = a_y(t), \qquad a_z = a_z(t).$$

Then, by using Eq. (5.29) and integrating, we obtain the components of the velocity, and by integrating Eq. (5.19) we obtain the coordinates as functions of time.

5.7 Motion Under Constant Acceleration

The case in which acceleration is constant, both in magnitude and direction, is of special importance. If $\boldsymbol{a} =$ const we have, by integrating Eq. (5.26),

$$\int_{\boldsymbol{v}_0}^{\boldsymbol{v}} d\boldsymbol{v} = \int_{t_0}^{t} \boldsymbol{a}\, dt = \boldsymbol{a}\int_{t_0}^{t} dt = \boldsymbol{a}(t - t_0), \tag{5.32}$$

where $\boldsymbol{v}_0$ is the velocity at time t_0. Then, since $\int_{\boldsymbol{v}_0}^{\boldsymbol{v}} d\boldsymbol{v} = \boldsymbol{v} - \boldsymbol{v}_0$,

$$\boldsymbol{v} = \boldsymbol{v}_0 + \boldsymbol{a}(t - t_0) \tag{5.33}$$

gives the velocity at any other time. Substituting this result in Eq. (5.17), and integrating, we obtain

$$\int_{\boldsymbol{r}_0}^{\boldsymbol{r}} d\boldsymbol{r} = \int_{t_0}^{t} [\boldsymbol{v}_0 + \boldsymbol{a}(t - t_0)]\, dt = \boldsymbol{v}_0\int_{t_0}^{t} dt + \boldsymbol{a}\int_{t_0}^{t} (t - t_0)\, dt,$$

where $\boldsymbol{r}_0$ gives the position at time t_0. Then

$$\boldsymbol{r} = \boldsymbol{r}_0 + \boldsymbol{v}_0(t - t_0) + \tfrac{1}{2}\boldsymbol{a}(t - t_0)^2, \tag{5.34}$$

which gives the position of the particle at any time. These results must be compared with Eqs. (5.10) and (5.11) obtained for rectilinear motion under constant acceleration. In rectilinear motion, both the velocity and the acceleration have the same (or opposite) direction. However, in the more general case we are discussing now, $\boldsymbol{v}_0$ and $\boldsymbol{a}$ may have different directions. Therefore $\boldsymbol{v}$ as given by Eq. (5.33) is not parallel to $\boldsymbol{a}$, but is always in the plane defined by $\boldsymbol{v}_0$ and $\boldsymbol{a}$. Also, from Eq. (5.34), we see that the endpoint of the vector $\boldsymbol{r}$ is always in the plane parallel to $\boldsymbol{v}_0$ and $\boldsymbol{a}$, and which passes through the point defined by $\boldsymbol{r}_0$. We conclude then that motion under constant acceleration is always in a plane. Also Eq. (5.34) indicates that the path of the motion is a parabola (see Problem 3.33).

One of the most interesting uses of these equations is their application to the motion of a projectile. In this case $\boldsymbol{a} = \boldsymbol{g} =$ acceleration of gravity. We shall choose the XY-plane coincident with the plane defined by $\boldsymbol{v}_0$ and $\boldsymbol{a} = \boldsymbol{g}$, the Y-axis directed upward so that $\boldsymbol{g} = -\boldsymbol{u}_y g$, and the origin O coincident with $\boldsymbol{r}_0$ (Fig. 5–13). Then

$$\boldsymbol{v}_0 = \boldsymbol{u}_x v_{0x} + \boldsymbol{u}_y v_{0y},$$

where

$$v_{0x} = v_0 \cos\alpha, \qquad v_{0y} = v_0 \sin\alpha. \tag{5.35}$$

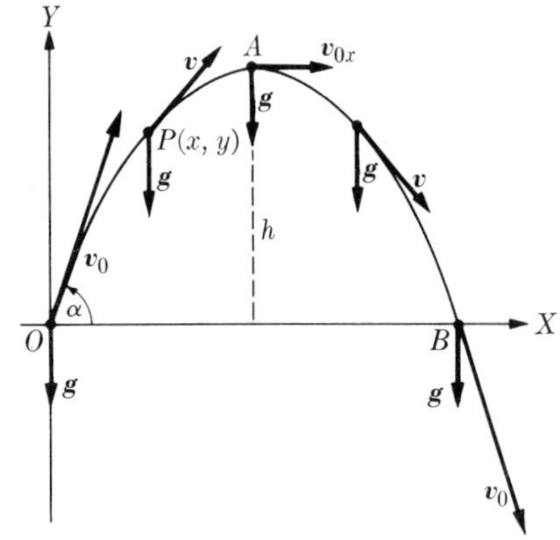

Fig. 5–13. When the acceleration is constant the path is a parabola.

Equation (5.33) can be separated into its components (setting $t_0 = 0$) by writing

$$\boldsymbol{v} = \boldsymbol{u}_x v_x + \boldsymbol{u}_y v_y = (\boldsymbol{u}_x v_{0x} + \boldsymbol{u}_y v_{0y}) - \boldsymbol{u}_y g t$$

or

$$v_x = v_{0x}, \qquad v_y = v_{0y} - gt, \tag{5.36}$$

indicating that the X-component of $\boldsymbol{v}$ remains constant, as it should, since there is no acceleration in that direction. Similarly, Eq. (5.34) with $\boldsymbol{r}_0 = 0$ and $t_0 = 0$, when separated into its components, becomes

$$\boldsymbol{r} = \boldsymbol{u}_x x + \boldsymbol{u}_y y = (\boldsymbol{u}_x v_{0x} + \boldsymbol{u}_y v_{0y})t - \boldsymbol{u}_y \tfrac{1}{2} g t^2$$

or

$$x = v_{0x} t, \qquad y = v_{0y} t - \tfrac{1}{2} g t^2, \tag{5.37}$$

which gives the coordinates of the particle as functions of time. The time required for the projectile to reach the highest point A is obtained by setting $v_y = 0$ in Eq. (5.36) since, at that point, the velocity of the projectile is horizontal. Then

$$t = \frac{v_{0y}}{g} \qquad \text{or} \qquad t = \frac{v_0 \sin \alpha}{g} \cdot \tag{5.38}$$

The maximum height h is obtained by substituting this value of t in the second equation of (5.37), resulting in

$$h = \frac{v_0^2 \sin^2 \alpha}{2g} \cdot \tag{5.39}$$

The time required for the projectile to return to ground level at B, called the *time of flight*, can be obtained by making $y = 0$ in Eq. (5.37). The time is obviously twice the value given by Eq. (5.38), or $2v_0 \sin \alpha / g$. The *range* $R = OB$ is the total horizontal distance covered, and is obtained by substituting the value for the time of flight in the first equation of (5.37), resulting in

$$R = v_{0x} \frac{2v_0 \sin \alpha}{g} = \frac{2v_0^2 \sin \alpha \cos \alpha}{g}$$

or

$$R = \frac{v_0^2 \sin 2\alpha}{g} \cdot \tag{5.40}$$

Note that the range is a maximum for $\alpha = 45°$. The equation of the path is obtained by eliminating the time t between the two equations in (5.37), giving

$$y = -\frac{g}{2v_0^2 \cos^2 \alpha} x^2 + x \tan \alpha, \tag{5.41}$$

which is the equation of a parabola, since both $\tan \alpha$ and the quantity multiplying x^2 are constants.

The results we have obtained are valid when: (1) The range is small enough so that the curvature of the earth may be neglected. (2) The altitude is small

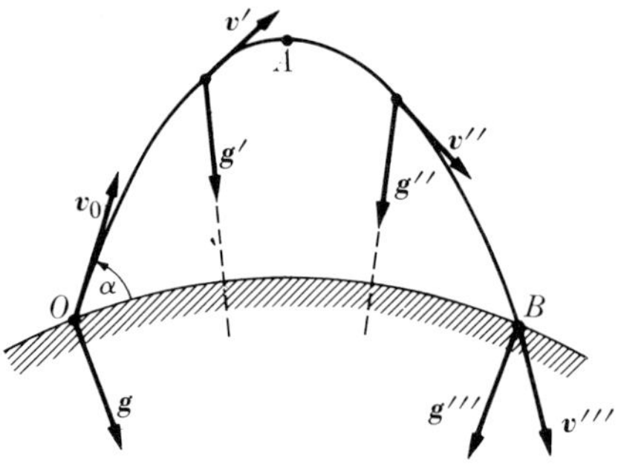

Fig. 5–14. The path of the long-range projectile is not a parabola, but an arc of an ellipse.

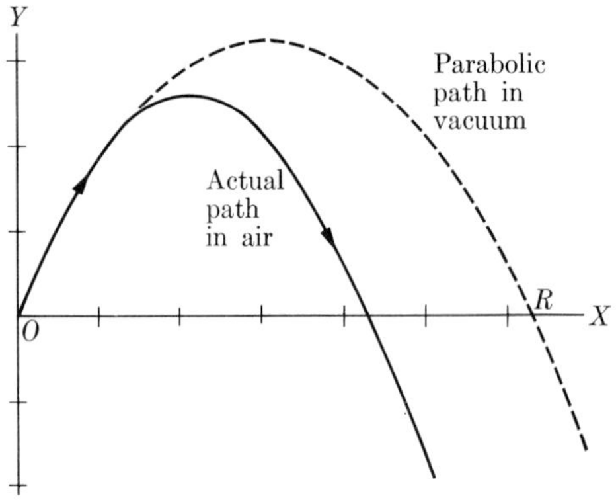

Fig. 5–15. Effect of air resistance on the motion of a projectile.

enough so that the variation of gravity with height may be neglected. (3) The initial velocity is small enough so that air resistance may be neglected. For a long-range projectile, such as an ICBM, the situation is as depicted in Fig. 5–14, where all g-vectors point toward the center of the earth and vary with height. The path is, in this case, an arc of an ellipse, as will be discussed in Chapter 13. If we take into account the resistance of the air, the path departs from a parabola, as shown in Fig. 5–15, and the range is diminished.

EXAMPLE 5.8. A gun fires a bullet with a velocity of 200 m s^{-1} at an angle of 40° with the ground. Find the velocity and position of the bullet after 20 s. Also find the range and the time required for the bullet to return to ground.

Solution: From Fig. 5–16, noting that $v_0 = 200$ m s^{-1} and $\alpha = 40°$, we have that $v_{0x} = v_0 \cos \alpha = 153.2$ m s^{-1} and $v_{0y} = v_0 \sin \alpha = 128.6$ m s^{-1}. Thus the components of the velocity at any time are given by $v_x = 153.2$ m s^{-1} and $v_y = 128.6 - 9.8t$ m s^{-1}, and the coordinates of the bullet are

$$x = 153.2t \text{ m}, \qquad y = 128.6t - 4.9t^2 \text{ m}.$$

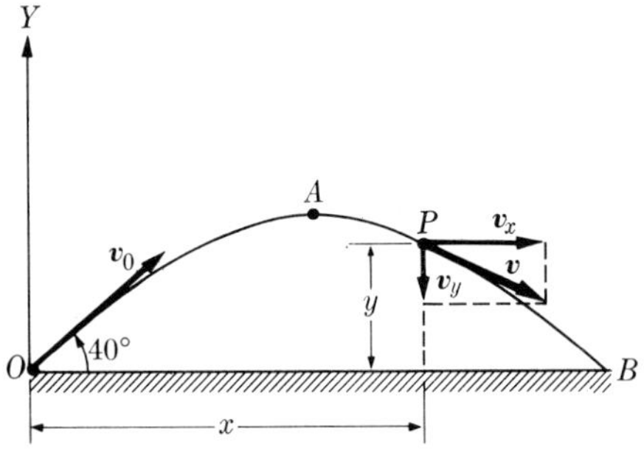

Fig. 5–16. Velocity in projectile motion.

For $t = 20$ s, we have simply $v_x = 153.2$ m s^{-1} and $v_y = -67.4$ m s^{-1}. The fact that v_y is negative means that the bullet is descending. The velocity is $v = \sqrt{v_x^2 + v_y^2} = 167.4$ m s^{-1}. Similarly the position of P is given by $x = 3064$ m and $y = 612$ m. The student must verify that the height of A is 843.7 m, that the range $R = OB$ is 4021 m, and that the time required to go from O to B is 26.24 s.

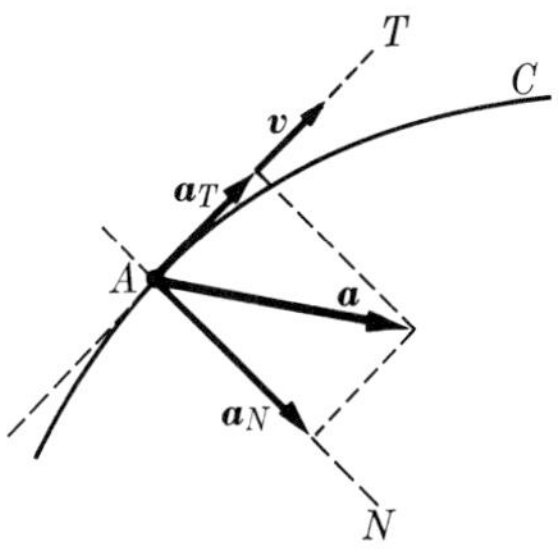

Fig. 5–17. Tangential and normal acceleration in curvilinear motion.

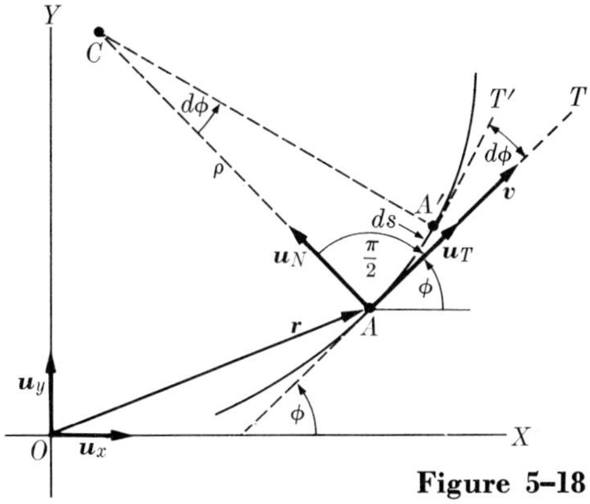

Figure 5–18

5.8 Tangential and Normal Components of Acceleration

Consider a particle describing a curved path (Fig. 5–17). For simplicity we shall assume that the curve is plane but the results we shall derive will be valid for motion along any curve. At time t the particle is at A with velocity $\boldsymbol{v}$ and acceleration $\boldsymbol{a}$. Since $\boldsymbol{a}$ is pointing toward the concave side of the path, we may decompose it into a tangential component $\boldsymbol{a}_T$—parallel to the tangent AT and called *tangential acceleration*—and a normal component $\boldsymbol{a}_N$—parallel to the normal AN and called *normal acceleration.* Each of these components has a well-defined physical meaning. When the particle moves, the magnitude of the velocity may change, and this change is related to the tangential acceleration. Also the direction of the velocity changes, and this change is related to the normal acceleration. That is:

Change in magnitude of velocity: tangential acceleration.

Change in direction of velocity: normal acceleration.

Let us draw at A (Fig. 5–18) the unit vector $\boldsymbol{u}_T$ tangent to the curve. The velocity, according to Eq. (5.23), is expressed as $\boldsymbol{v} = \boldsymbol{u}_T v$. Thus the acceleration will be

$$\boldsymbol{a} = \frac{d\boldsymbol{v}}{dt} = \frac{d}{dt}(\boldsymbol{u}_T v) = \boldsymbol{u}_T \frac{dv}{dt} + \frac{d\boldsymbol{u}_T}{dt} v.$$

If the path were a straight line, the vector $\boldsymbol{u}_T$ would be constant in magnitude and direction and $d\boldsymbol{u}_T/dt = 0$. But when the path is curved, the *direction* of $\boldsymbol{u}_T$ varies along the curve, giving a nonvanishing value for $d\boldsymbol{u}_T/dt$. To proceed we must compute $d\boldsymbol{u}_T/dt$. Let us introduce the unit vector $\boldsymbol{u}_N$, normal to the curve and directed toward the concave side. Letting ϕ be the angle that the tangent to the curve at A makes with the X-axis, we may write, using Eq. (3.9),

$$\begin{aligned} \boldsymbol{u}_T &= \boldsymbol{u}_x \cos\phi + \boldsymbol{u}_y \sin\phi, \\ \boldsymbol{u}_N &= \boldsymbol{u}_x \cos\left(\phi + \frac{\pi}{2}\right) + \boldsymbol{u}_y \sin\left(\phi + \frac{\pi}{2}\right) \\ &= -\boldsymbol{u}_x \sin\phi + \boldsymbol{u}_y \cos\phi. \end{aligned}$$

Thus

$$\frac{d\boldsymbol{u}_T}{dt} = -\boldsymbol{u}_x \sin\phi \frac{d\phi}{dt} + \boldsymbol{u}_y \cos\phi \frac{d\phi}{dt} = \boldsymbol{u}_N \frac{d\phi}{dt}.$$

This indicates that $d\boldsymbol{u}_T/dt$ is normal to the curve. Now

$$\frac{d\phi}{dt} = \frac{d\phi}{ds}\frac{ds}{dt} = v\frac{d\phi}{ds},$$

where $ds = AA'$ is the small arc through which the particle moved in the time dt. The normals to the curve at A and A' intersect at a point C called the *center of curvature*. Calling $\rho = CA$ the *radius of curvature* and using Eq. (2.4), we may write $ds = \rho\, d\phi$ or $d\phi/ds = 1/\rho$. Thus $d\phi/dt = v/\rho$ and

$$\frac{d\boldsymbol{u}_T}{dt} = \boldsymbol{u}_N \frac{v}{\rho}. \tag{5.42}$$

Introducing this result in the expression for $d\boldsymbol{v}/dt$, we finally obtain

$$\boldsymbol{a} = \boldsymbol{u}_T \frac{dv}{dt} + \boldsymbol{u}_N \frac{v^2}{\rho}. \tag{5.43}$$

The first term $[\boldsymbol{u}_T(dv/dt)]$ is a vector tangent to the curve, and is proportional to the time rate of change of the magnitude of the velocity; it corresponds to the tangential acceleration $\boldsymbol{a}_T$. The second term $[\boldsymbol{u}_N(v^2/\rho)]$ is a vector normal to the curve, and corresponds to the normal acceleration $\boldsymbol{a}_N$. It is associated with the change in direction because it corresponds to $d\boldsymbol{u}_T/dt$. For the magnitudes, we may write

$$a_T = \frac{dv}{dt}, \qquad a_N = \frac{v^2}{\rho}. \tag{5.44}$$

The magnitude of the acceleration at point A is then

$$a = \sqrt{a_T^2 + a_N^2} = \sqrt{(dv/dt)^2 + (v^4/\rho^2)}.$$

If the curvilinear motion is uniform (i.e., if the magnitude of the velocity remains constant), $v =$ constant, so that $a_T = 0$ and there is no tangential acceleration. On the other hand, if the motion is rectilinear (i.e., if the direction of the velocity does not change), the radius of curvature is infinite ($\rho = \infty$), so that $a_N = 0$ and there is no normal acceleration. It must be pointed out that the results we have obtained are valid for plane motion as well as for motion in space.

EXAMPLE 5.9. A disk D (Fig. 5–19) is rotating freely about its horizontal axis. A cord is wrapped around the outer circumference of the disk, and a body A, attached to the cord, falls under the action of gravity. The motion of A is uniformly accelerated but, as will be seen in Chapter 10, its acceleration is less than that due to gravity. At $t = 0$ the velocity of body A is 0.04 m s^{-1}, and 2 s later A has fallen 0.2 m. Find the tangential and normal accelerations, at any instant, of any point on the rim of the disk.

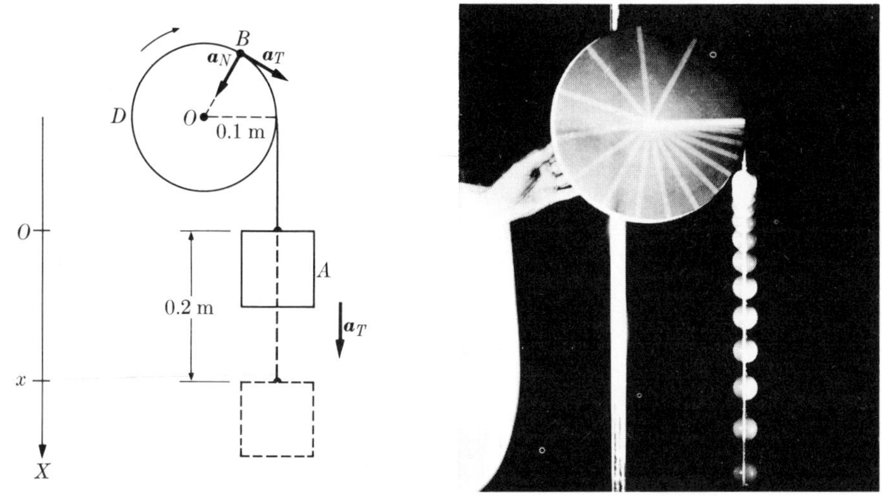

(a) (b)

Fig. 5–19. The multiflash photograph in (b) shows that the mass falls with uniformly accelerated motion. (Verify this by taking actual measurements on the photograph.)

Solution: Given that the origin of coordinates is at the position $t = 0$, the equation of the uniformly accelerated motion of A is $x = v_0 t + \frac{1}{2}at^2$. But we know that $v_0 = 0.04 \text{ m s}^{-1}$. Thus

$$x = 0.04t + \tfrac{1}{2}at^2 \text{ m}.$$

Setting $t = 2$ s, we must have $x = 0.2$ m. Thus $a = 0.06 \text{ m s}^{-2}$. That is,

$$x = 0.04t + 0.03t^2 \text{ m}.$$

Therefore the velocity of A is

$$v = \frac{dx}{dt} = 0.04 + 0.06t \text{ m s}^{-1}.$$

This equation also gives the velocity of any point B on the rim of the disk. The tangential acceleration of B is thus the same as the acceleration of A,

$$a_T = \frac{dv}{dt} = 0.06 \text{ m s}^{-2},$$

while, since $\rho = 0.1$ m, the normal acceleration of B is

$$a_N = \frac{v^2}{\rho} = \frac{(0.04 + 0.06t)^2}{0.1} = 0.016 + 0.048t + 0.036t^2 \text{ m s}^{-2}.$$

The total acceleration of point B is thus $a = \sqrt{a_T^2 + a_N^2}$.

5.9 Circular Motion: Angular Velocity

Let us now consider the special case in which the path is a circle; i.e., *circular motion*. The velocity $\boldsymbol{v}$, being tangent to the circle, is perpendicular to the radius $R = CA$. When we measure distances along the circumference of the circle from point O, we have, from Fig. 5–20, that $s = R\theta$, according to Eq. (2.5). Therefore, applying Eq. (5.23) and considering the fact that R remains constant, we obtain

$$v = \frac{ds}{dt} = R\frac{d\theta}{dt}. \tag{5.45}$$

The quantity

$$\omega = \frac{d\theta}{dt} \tag{5.46}$$

is called *angular velocity*, and is equal to the time rate of change of the angle. It is expressed in radians per second, rad s^{-1}, or simply s^{-1}. Then

$$v = \omega R. \tag{5.47}$$

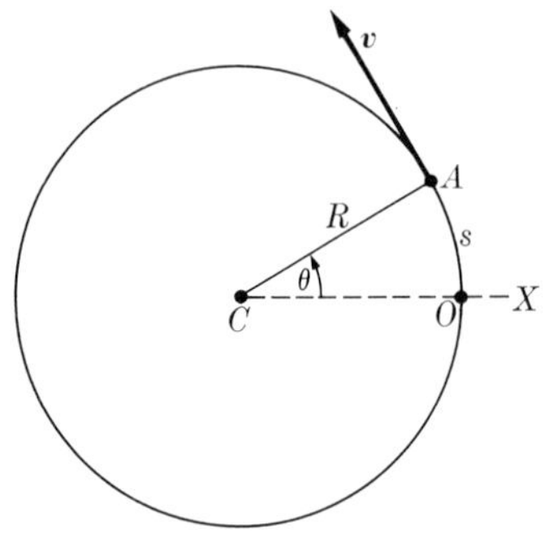

Fig. 5–20. Circular motion.

The angular velocity may be expressed as a vector quantity whose direction is perpendicular to the plane of motion in the sense of advance of a right-handed screw rotated in the same sense as the particle moves (Fig. 5–21). From the figure we see that $R = r \sin \gamma$ and that $\boldsymbol{\omega} = \boldsymbol{u}_z\, d\theta/dt$; therefore we may write, instead of Eq. (5.47),

$$v = \omega r \sin \gamma,$$

indicating that the following vector relation holds, both in magnitude and direction:

$$\boldsymbol{v} = \boldsymbol{\omega} \times \boldsymbol{r}. \tag{5.48}$$

Note that this is valid only for circular or rotational motion (motion with constant r and γ).

Of special interest is the case of *uniform circular motion*; i.e., motion with $\omega =$ constant. In this case, the motion is periodic and the particle passes through each point of the circle at regular intervals of time. The *period* P is the time required for a complete turn or revolution, and the *frequency* ν is the number of revolutions per unit time. So if in time t the particle makes n revolutions, the period is $P = t/n$ and the frequency is $\nu = n/t$. Both quantities are then

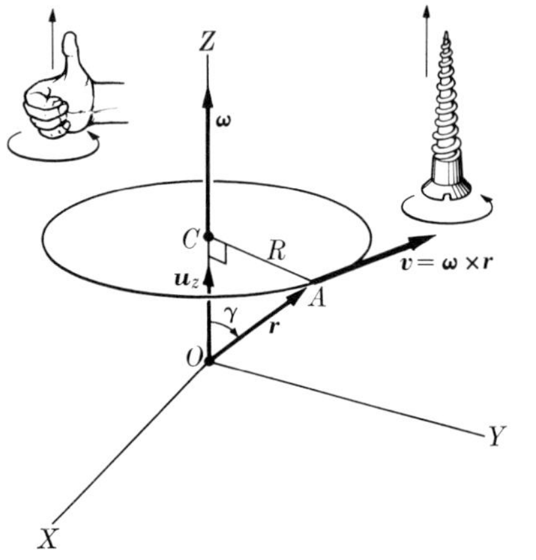

Fig. 5–21. Vector relation between angular velocity, linear velocity, and position vector in circular motion.

related by the following expression, which we shall often use,

$$\nu = \frac{1}{P}. \tag{5.49}$$

When the period is expressed in seconds, the frequency must be expressed in (seconds)$^{-1}$ or s^{-1}, which is a unit called a *hertz*, abbreviated Hz. The colloquial term is revolutions per second (rps) instead of s^{-1} or Hz. The unit was named hertz after the German physicist H. R. Hertz (1857–1894), who was the first to prove experimentally the existence of electromagnetic waves. Sometimes the frequency of a motion is expressed in revolutions per minute (rpm), which is the same as saying (minute)$^{-1}$. Obviously 1 min^{-1} = $\frac{1}{60}$ Hz.

The concepts of period and frequency are applicable to all periodic processes that occur in cyclic form; that is, those processes that repeat themselves after completing each cycle. For example, the motion of the earth around the sun is neither circular nor uniform, but periodic. It is a motion that repeats itself every time the earth completes one orbit. The *period* is the time required to complete one cycle, and the *frequency* is the number of cycles per second, one hertz corresponding to one cycle per second.

If ω is constant, we have, integrating Eq. (5.46),

$$\int_{\theta_0}^{\theta} d\theta = \int_{t_0}^{t} \omega\, dt = \omega \int_{t_0}^{t} dt \qquad \text{or} \qquad \theta = \theta_0 + \omega(t - t_0).$$

The student should compare this relation, which is valid for uniform circular motion, with the comparable expression for uniform rectilinear motion obtained in Example 5.2. Usually one sets $\theta_0 = 0$ and $t_0 = 0$, giving

$$\theta = \omega t \qquad \text{or} \qquad \omega = \frac{\theta}{t}. \tag{5.50}$$

For a complete revolution, $t = P$ and $\theta = 2\pi$, resulting in

$$\omega = \frac{2\pi}{P} = 2\pi\nu. \tag{5.51}$$

EXAMPLE 5.10. Find the angular velocity of the earth about its axis.

Solution: The first impulse of the student would naturally be to use Eq. (5.51), with $\omega = 2\pi/P$, and write for the period P the value of 8.640×10^4 s, corresponding to one mean solar day. However, if one worked it out this way, the result would be incorrect. Let us refer to Fig. 5–22 (not drawn to scale) and consider a point P. When the earth has completed one revolution about its polar axis, which is called a *sidereal* day, it will then be at E', due to its translational motion, and the point will be at P'. But to complete one day, the earth still has to rotate through the angle γ until the point is at P'', again facing the sun. The period of revolution of the earth (sidereal day) is then slightly less than 8.640×10^4 s. Its measured value is

$$P = 8.616 \times 10^4 \text{ s},$$

or about 240 s shorter than the mean solar day. The angular velocity of the earth is then

$$\omega = \frac{2\pi}{P} = 7.292 \times 10^{-5} \text{ rad s}^{-1}.$$

It is relatively simple to estimate this difference of 240 s. The earth covers its complete orbit around the sun in 365 days, which means that the angle γ corresponding to one day is slightly less than 1° or 0.01745 radian. The time required to move through this angle with the angular velocity given above is, by Eq. (5.50),

$$t = \frac{\theta}{\omega} = \frac{1.745 \times 10^{-2} \text{ rad}}{7.292 \times 10^{-5} \text{ rad s}^{-1}} = 239 \text{ s},$$

which is in excellent agreement with our previous result.

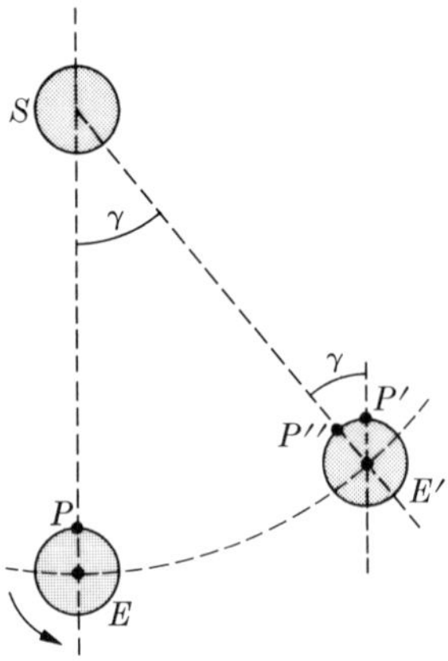

Fig. 5–22. Sidereal day.

5.10 Circular Motion: Angular Acceleration

When the angular velocity of a particle changes with time, the angular acceleration is defined by the vector

$$\boldsymbol{\alpha} = \frac{d\boldsymbol{\omega}}{dt}. \tag{5.52}$$

Since the circular motion is plane, the direction of $\boldsymbol{\omega}$ remains the same, and the relation Eq. (5.52) also holds for the magnitudes of the quantities involved. That is,

$$\alpha = \frac{d\omega}{dt} = \frac{d^2\theta}{dt^2}. \tag{5.53}$$

When the angular acceleration is constant (i.e., when the circular motion is uniformly accelerated), we have, by integration of Eq. (5.53),

$$\int_{\omega_0}^{\omega} d\omega = \int_{t_0}^{t} \alpha \, dt = \alpha \int_{t_0}^{t} dt$$

or

$$\omega = \omega_0 + \alpha(t - t_0), \tag{5.54}$$

where ω_0 is the value of ω at time t_0. Substituting Eq. (5.54) in (5.46), we obtain $d\theta/dt = \omega_0 + \alpha(t - t_0)$, and integrating again,

$$\int_{\theta_0}^{\theta} d\theta = \int_{t_0}^{t} \omega_0 \, dt + \alpha \int_{t_0}^{t} (t - t_0) \, dt,$$

so that

$$\theta = \theta_0 + \omega_0(t - t_0) + \tfrac{1}{2}\alpha(t - t_0)^2. \tag{5.55}$$

This gives the angular position at any time.

In the particular case of circular motion, we find, combining Eqs. (5.43) and (5.47) with Eq. (5.53), that the tangential (or transverse) acceleration is

$$a_T = \frac{dv}{dt} = R\frac{d\omega}{dt} = R\frac{d^2\theta}{dt^2} = R\alpha, \tag{5.56}$$

and the normal (or centripetal) acceleration is

$$a_N = \frac{v^2}{R} = \omega^2 R. \tag{5.57}$$

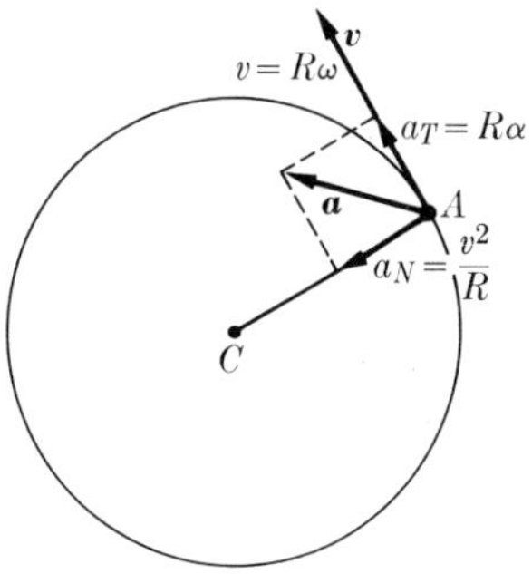

Fig. 5–23. Tangential and normal acceleration in circular motion.

The tangential and normal components of the acceleration in circular motion are illustrated in Fig. 5–23.

Note that in uniform circular motion (no angular acceleration, $\alpha = 0$), there is no tangential acceleration, but there is still a normal or centripetal acceleration due to the change in the direction of the velocity.

In this case of uniform circular motion we may compute the acceleration directly by using Eq. (5.48). Then, since $\boldsymbol{\omega}$ is constant,

$$\boldsymbol{a} = \frac{d\boldsymbol{v}}{dt} = \boldsymbol{\omega} \times \frac{d\boldsymbol{r}}{dt} = \boldsymbol{\omega} \times \boldsymbol{v}, \tag{5.58}$$

since $d\boldsymbol{r}/dt = \boldsymbol{v}$. Using Eq. (5.48) again, we may write the acceleration in the alternative form

$$\boldsymbol{a} = \boldsymbol{\omega} \times (\boldsymbol{\omega} \times \boldsymbol{r}). \tag{5.59}$$

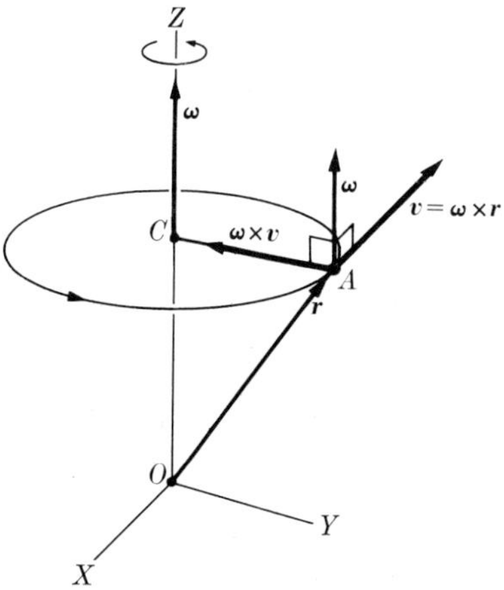

Figure 5–24

Since the circular motion is uniform, the acceleration given by Eqs. (5.58) or (5.59) must be the centripetal acceleration. This can be verified very easily. Referring to Fig. 5–24, we see that the vector $\boldsymbol{\omega} \times \boldsymbol{v}$ points toward the center of the circle, and its magnitude is $|\boldsymbol{\omega} \times \boldsymbol{v}| = \omega v = \omega^2 R$, since $\boldsymbol{\omega}$ and $\boldsymbol{v}$ are perpendicular and $v = \omega R$. This value coincides with our previous result (5.57).

EXAMPLE 5.11. The earth rotates uniformly about its axis with an angular velocity $\omega = 7.292 \times 10^{-5}\ \mathrm{s}^{-1}$. Find, in terms of the latitude, the velocity and the acceleration of a point on the earth's surface.

Solution: Due to the rotational motion of the earth, all points on its surface move with uniform circular motion. The latitude of point A (Fig. 5–25) is defined as the angle λ

made by the radius $r = CA$ with the radius CD lying on the equator. When the earth rotates around NS, a point such as A describes a circle of center B and radius $R = AB$ such that

$$R = r \cos \lambda.$$

The velocity of a point on the earth's surface is tangent to the circle, and thus parallel to the equator. Its magnitude, by Eq. (5.47), is

$$v = \omega R = \omega r \cos \lambda.$$

The acceleration $\boldsymbol{a}$ is centripetal because the motion is uniform, and is thus directed toward B. Its magnitude, by Eq. (5.57), is

$$a = \omega^2 R = \omega^2 r \cos \lambda. \tag{5.60}$$

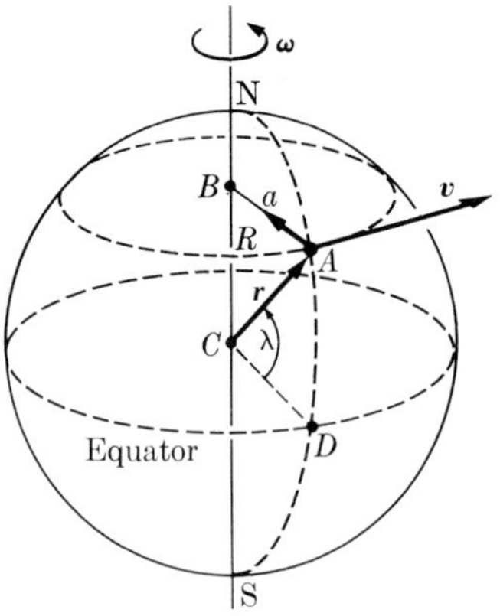

Fig. 5–25. Velocity and acceleration of a point on the earth.

Introducing the values of the angular velocity ($\omega = 7.292 \times 10^{-5}$ s^{-1}) and of the radius of the earth ($r = 6.35 \times 10^6$ m), we have

$$v = 459 \cos \lambda \text{ m s}^{-1},$$

and the acceleration is

$$a = 3.34 \times 10^{-2} \cos \lambda \text{ m s}^{-2}. \tag{5.61}$$

The maximum value of v occurs at the equator, at which $v = 459$ m s^{-1} or 1652 km hr^{-1} or about 1030 mi hr^{-1}! We do not feel the effects of such great velocity, because we have always been moving at that speed and our bodies and senses are accustomed to it. But we would immediately notice a change in it. Similarly, the maximum value of the acceleration is 3.34×10^{-2} m s^{-2}, which is about 0.3% of the acceleration due to gravity.

5.11 General Curvilinear Motion in a Plane

Consider Fig. 5–26, in which a particle describes a plane curved path. When it is at A, its velocity is given by $\boldsymbol{v} = d\boldsymbol{r}/dt$. Using the unit vectors $\boldsymbol{u}_r$ (parallel to $\boldsymbol{r}$) and $\boldsymbol{u}_\theta$ (perpendicular to $\boldsymbol{r}$), we may write $\boldsymbol{r} = \boldsymbol{u}_r r$. Therefore

$$\boldsymbol{v} = \frac{d\boldsymbol{r}}{dt} = \frac{d}{dt}(\boldsymbol{u}_r r) = \boldsymbol{u}_r \frac{dr}{dt} + \frac{d\boldsymbol{u}_r}{dt} r. \tag{5.62}$$

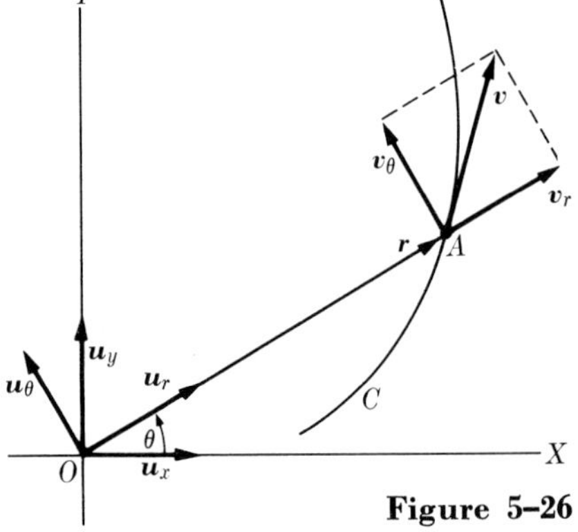

Figure 5–26

Now, using the rectangular components of

the two unit vectors,

$$\boldsymbol{u}_r = \boldsymbol{u}_x \cos\theta + \boldsymbol{u}_y \sin\theta \qquad \text{and} \qquad \boldsymbol{u}_\theta = -\boldsymbol{u}_x \sin\theta + \boldsymbol{u}_y \cos\theta,$$

we see that

$$\frac{d\boldsymbol{u}_r}{dt} = -\boldsymbol{u}_x \sin\theta \frac{d\theta}{dt} + \boldsymbol{u}_y \cos\theta \frac{d\theta}{dt} = \boldsymbol{u}_\theta \frac{d\theta}{dt},$$

and therefore we may write the velocity of the particle as

$$\boldsymbol{v} = \boldsymbol{u}_r \frac{dr}{dt} + \boldsymbol{u}_\theta r \frac{d\theta}{dt}. \tag{5.63}$$

The first part of this equation $[\boldsymbol{u}_r(dr/dt)]$ is a vector parallel to $\boldsymbol{r}$ and is called the *radial velocity*; it is due to the change in the distance r of the particle from O. The second part $[\boldsymbol{u}_\theta r(d\theta/dt)]$ is a vector perpendicular to $\boldsymbol{r}$ and is due to the change in the direction of $\boldsymbol{r}$, or the rotation of the particle around O; it is called the *transverse velocity*. That is,

$$v_r = \frac{dr}{dt}, \qquad v_\theta = r\frac{d\theta}{dt} = \omega r, \tag{5.64}$$

since $\omega = d\theta/dt$ is the angular velocity in this case. In circular motion there is no radial velocity because the radius is constant; that is, $dr/dt = 0$. The velocity is entirely transverse, as we can see by comparing Eq. (5.45) with the second relation in Eq. (5.64).

References

1. "The Perception of Motion," H. Wallach. *Sci. Am.*, July 1959, page 56
2. "Aristotle's Notion of Speed," R. Seeger. *Am. J. Phys.* **31,** 138 (1963)
3. *Mechanics*, Keith R. Symon. Reading, Mass.: Addison-Wesley, 1960, Sections 1–2, 3–4, 3–5, and 3–11
4. *Physical Mechanics*, Robert B. Lindsay. New York: Van Nostrand, 1961, Sections 1–4 and 1–5, Chapters 2 and 3
5. *Introduction to Engineering Mechanics*, John V. Huddleston. Reading, Mass.: Addison-Wesley, 1961, Chapter 5, Sections 6–5 and 6–6
6. *Vector Mechanics*, D. E. Christie. New York: McGraw-Hill, 1964, Chapter 5
7. *The Feynman Lectures on Physics*, Volume I. R. P. Feynman, R. B. Leighton, and M. L. Sands. Reading, Mass.: Addison-Wesley, 1963, Chapters 5 and 8
8. *Source Book in Physics*, W. F. Magie. Cambridge, Mass.: Harvard University Press, 1963, page 1 (Galileo); page 50 (Descartes); page 51 (Leibniz); page 55 (d'Alembert)
9. *Foundations of Modern Physical Science*, Gerald Holton and D. H. D. Roller. Reading, Mass.: Addison-Wesley, 1958, Chapters 1, 2, and 3

Problems

5.1 An electron falling on a TV screen has a velocity of 3×10^6 m s^{-1}. Assuming that if it has been accelerated from rest through a distance of 0.04 m, find its average acceleration.

5.2 A body is moving with an initial velocity of 3 m s^{-1}, and has a constant acceleration of 4 m s^{-2} in the same direction as the velocity. What is the velocity of the body and the distance covered at the end of 7 s? Solve the same problem for a body whose acceleration is in the direction opposite to that of the velocity. Write the expression for its displacement as a function of time.

5.3 An airplane, in taking off, covers a 600-m path in 15 s. Assuming a constant acceleration, calculate the takeoff velocity. Also calculate the acceleration in m s^{-2}.

5.4 An automobile, starting from rest, reaches 60 km hr^{-1} in 15 s. (a) Calculate the average acceleration in m min^{-2} and the distance moved. (b) Assuming that the acceleration is constant, how many more seconds will it take for the car to reach 80 km hr^{-1}? What has been the total distance covered?

5.5 A car starts from rest and moves with an acceleration of 1 m s^{-2} for 1 s. The motor is then turned off and the car is allowed to decelerate, due to friction, for 10 s at a rate of 5 cm s^{-2}. Then the brakes are applied and the car is brought to rest in 5 more seconds. Calculate the total distance traveled by the car. Make a plot of x, v, and a versus t.

5.6 A body moving with uniformly accelerated rectilinear motion travels 55 ft in 2 s. During the next 2 s, it covers 77 ft. Calculate the initial velocity of the body and its acceleration. How far will it travel in the next 4 s?

5.7 A car travels along the line OX with uniformly accelerated motion. At times t_1 and t_2, its position is x_1 and x_2, respectively. Show that its acceleration is $a = 2(x_2t_1 - x_1t_2)/t_1t_2(t_2 - t_1)$.

5.8 A car starts from rest with an acceleration of 4 m s^{-2} for 4 s. During the next 10 s it moves with uniform motion. The brakes are then applied and the car decelerates at a rate of 8 m s^{-2} until it stops. Make a plot of the velocity versus the time and prove that the area bounded by the curve and the time axis measures the total distance traveled.

5.9 A car is waiting for a red light to change. When the light turns green, the car accelerates uniformly for 6 s at a rate of 2 m s^{-2}, after which it moves with uniform velocity. At the instant that the car began to move at the light, a truck moving in the same direction, with a uniform motion of 10 m s^{-1}, passed by. In what length of time, and how far from the light, will the car and truck meet again?

5.10 An automobile is moving at the rate of 45 km hr^{-1} when a red light flashes on at an intersection. If the reaction time of the driver is 0.7 s, and the car decelerates at the rate of 7 m s^{-2} as soon as the driver applies the brakes, calculate how far the car travels from the time the driver notices the red light until the car is brought to a stop. "Reaction time" is the interval between the time the driver notices the light and the time he applies the brakes.

5.11 Two cars, A and B, are traveling in the same direction with velocities v_A and v_B, respectively. When car A is a distance d behind car B, the brakes on A are applied, causing a deceleration at the rate a. Demonstrate that in order that there be a collision between A and B, it is necessary that $v_A - v_B > \sqrt{2ad}$.

5.12 Two cars, A and B, are moving in the same direction. When $t = 0$, their respective velocities are 1 ft s^{-1} and 3 ft s^{-1}, and their respective accelerations are 2 ft s^{-2} and 1 ft s^{-2}. If car A is 1.5 ft ahead of car B at $t = 0$, calculate when they will be side by side.

5.13 A body is moving along a straight line according to the law $x = 16t - 6t^2$, where x is measured in meters and t in seconds. (a) Find the position of the body at $t = 1$ s. (b) At what times does the body pass the origin? (c) Calculate the average velocity for the time interval $0 < t < 2$ s. (d) Find the general expression for the average velocity for the interval $t_0 < t < (t_0 + \Delta t)$. (e) Calculate the instantaneous velocity at any given time. (f) Calculate the instantaneous velocity at $t = 0$. (g) At what times and positions will the body be stationary? (h) Find the general expression for the average acceleration for the time interval $t_0 < t < (t_0 + \Delta t)$. (i) Find the general expression for the instantaneous acceleration at any time. (j) At what times is the instantaneous acceleration zero? (k) Plot on a single set of axes x versus t, v versus t, and a versus t. (l) At what times(s) is the motion accelerated and at what time(s) is it retarded?

5.14 A body is moving along a straight line according to the law $v = t^3 + 4t^2 + 2$. If $x = 4$ ft when $t = 2$ s, find the value of x when $t = 3$ s. Also find its acceleration.

5.15 The acceleration of a body moving along a straight line is given by $a = 4 - t^2$, where a is in m s^{-2} and t is in seconds. Find the expressions for the velocity and displacement as functions of time, given that when $t = 3$ s, $v = 2$ m s^{-1} and $x = 9$ m.

5.16 A body is moving along a straight line. Its acceleration is given by $a = -2x$, where x is in feet and a is in ft s^{-2}. Find the relationship between the velocity and the distance, given that when $x = 0$, $v = 4$ ft s^{-1}.

5.17 The acceleration of a body moving along a straight line is given by $a = -Kv^2$, where K is a constant and where it is given that at $t = 0$, $v = v_0$. Find the velocity and the displacement as functions of time. Also find x as a function of t and v as a function of x.

5.18 For a body in rectilinear motion whose acceleration is given by $a = 32 - 4v$ (the initial conditions are $x = 0$ and $v = 4$ at $t = 0$), find v as a function of t, x as a function of t, and x as a function of v.

5.19 The position of a moving body in terms of time is given in Fig. 5–27. Indicate (a) where the motion is in the positive or negative X-direction, (b) when the motion is accelerated or retarded, (c) when the body passes through the origin, and (d) when the velocity is zero. Also make a sketch of the velocity and the acceleration as functions of time. Estimate from the graph the average velocity between (a) $t = 1$ s and $t = 3$ s, (b) $t = 1$ s and $t = 2.2$ s, (c) $t = 1$ s and $t = 1.8$ s.

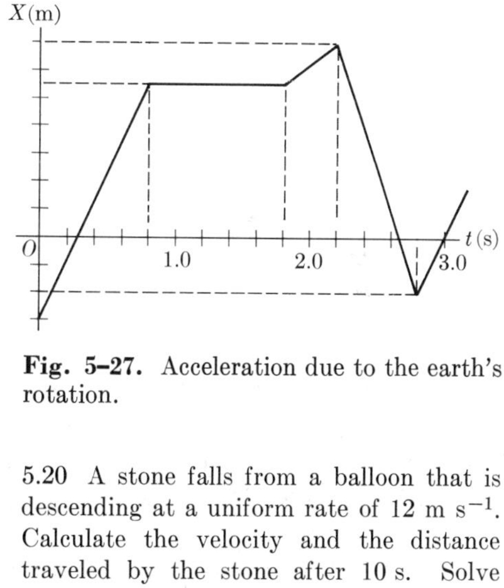

Fig. 5–27. Acceleration due to the earth's rotation.

5.20 A stone falls from a balloon that is descending at a uniform rate of 12 m s^{-1}. Calculate the velocity and the distance traveled by the stone after 10 s. Solve the same problem for the case of a balloon rising at the given velocity.

5.21 A stone is thrown vertically upward with a velocity of 20 m s^{-1}. When will its velocity be 6 m s^{-1} and what will its altitude be?

5.22 A stone is thrown upward from the bottom of a well 88 ft deep with an initial velocity of 240 ft s^{-1}. Calculate the amount of time it will take the stone to reach the edge of the well, and its velocity. Discuss the possible answers.

5.23 A man standing at the top of a building throws a ball vertically upward with a velocity of 40 ft s^{-1}. The ball reaches the ground 4.25 s later. What is the maximum height reached by the ball? How high is the building? With what velocity will it reach the ground?

5.24 A falling body travels 224 ft in the last second of its motion. Assuming that the body started from rest, determine the altitude from which the body fell and how long it took to reach the ground.

5.25 A stone is thrown vertically upward from the roof of a building with a velocity of 29.4 m s^{-1}. Another stone is dropped 4 s after the first is thrown. Prove that the first stone will pass the second exactly 4 s after the second was dropped.

5.26 One body is dropped while a second body, at the same instant, is thrown downward with an initial velocity of 100 cm s^{-1}. When will the distance between them be 18 m?

5.27 Two bodies are thrown vertically upward, with the same initial velocity of 100 cm s^{-1}, but 4 s apart. How long after the first one is thrown will they meet?

5.28 A body is allowed to drop freely. Show that the distance it travels during the nth second is $(n - \frac{1}{2})g$.

5.29 A stone is dropped from the top of a building. The sound of the stone hitting the ground is heard 6.5 s later. If the velocity of sound is 1120 ft s^{-1}, calculate the height of the building.

5.30 Calculate the angular velocity of a disk rotating with uniform motion of 13.2 rad every 6 s. Also calculate the period and frequency of rotation.

5.31 How long will it take the disk in the previous problem (a) to rotate through an angle of 780°, and (b) to make 12 revolutions?

5.32 Calculate the angular velocity of the three hands of a clock.

5.33 Calculate the angular velocity, the linear velocity, and the centripetal acceleration of the moon, deriving your answer from the fact that the moon makes a complete revolution in 28 days and that the average distance from the earth to the moon is 38.4×10^4 km.

5.34 Find (a) the magnitude of the velocity and (b) the centripetal acceleration of the earth in its motion around the sun. The radius of the earth's orbit is 1.49×10^{11} m and its period of revolution is 3.16×10^7 s.

5.35 Find the magnitude of the velocity and the centripetal acceleration of the sun in its motion through the Milky Way. The radius of the sun's orbit is 2.4×10^{20} m and its period of revolution is 6.3×10^{15} s.

5.36 A flywheel whose diameter is 3 m is rotating at 120 rpm. Calculate: (a) its frequency, (b) the period, (c) the angular velocity, and (d) the linear velocity of a point on the rim.

5.37 The angular velocity of a flywheel increases uniformly from 20 rad s^{-1} to 30 rad s^{-1} in 5 min. Calculate the angular acceleration and the total angle through which it has rotated.

5.38 A flywheel whose diameter is 8 ft has an angular velocity which decreases uniformly from 100 rpm at $t = 0$ to a standstill at $t = 4$ s. Calculate the tangential and the normal acceleration of a point on the rim of the wheel at $t = 2$ s.

5.39 An electron whose velocity is 4.0×10^5 m s^{-1} is acted on by a magnetic field that forces it to describe a circular path of radius 3.0 m. Find its centripetal acceleration.

5.40 A body, initially at rest ($\theta = 0$ and $\omega = 0$ at $t = 0$) is accelerated in a circular path of radius 1.3 m according to the equation $\alpha = 120t^2 - 48t + 16$. Find the angular position and angular velocity of the body as functions of time, and the tangential and centripetal components of its acceleration.

5.41 A point is moving on a circle according to the law $s = t^3 + 2t^2$, where s is measured in feet along the circle and t is in seconds. If the total acceleration of the point is $16\sqrt{2}$ ft s^{-2} when $t = 2$ s, calculate the radius of the circle.

5.42 A particle is moving in a circle according to the law $\theta = 3t^2 + 2t$, where θ is measured in radians and t in seconds. Calculate the angular velocity and angular acceleration after 4 s.

5.43 A wheel starts from rest and accelerates in such a manner that its angular velocity increases uniformly to 200 rpm in 6 s. After it has been rotating for some time at this speed, the brakes are applied, and it takes 5 min to stop the wheel. If the total number of revolutions of the wheel is 3100, calculate the total time of rotation.

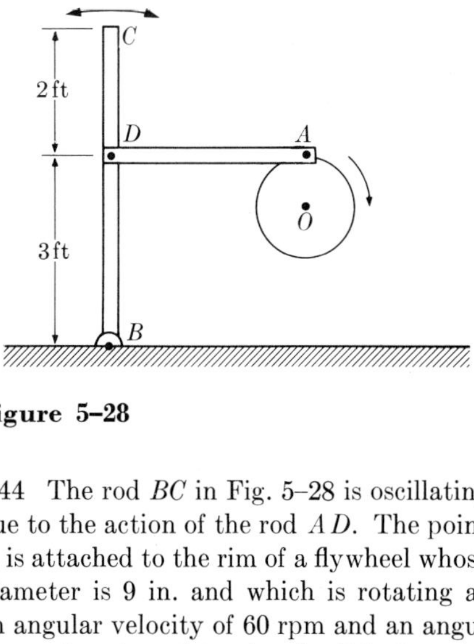

Figure 5–28

5.44 The rod BC in Fig. 5–28 is oscillating due to the action of the rod AD. The point A is attached to the rim of a flywheel whose diameter is 9 in. and which is rotating at an angular velocity of 60 rpm and an angular acceleration of 6 rad s^{-2}. Calculate (a) the linear velocity at the point D, (b) the angular velocity of BC, (c) the tangential and normal accelerations of point C, (d) the angular acceleration of BC, (e) the tangential acceleration at D.

5.45 A flywheel 4 ft in radius is rotating about a horizontal axis by means of a rope wound about its rim and having a weight at its end. If the vertical distance traveled by the weight is given by the equation $x = 40t^2$, where x is measured in feet and t in seconds, calculate the angular velocity and acceleration of the flywheel at any time.

5.46 The angular position of a particle moving along the circumference of a circle 5 ft in radius is given by the expression $\theta = 3t^2$, where θ is given in radians and t in seconds. Calculate the tangential, normal, and total acceleration of the particle when $t = 0.5$ s.

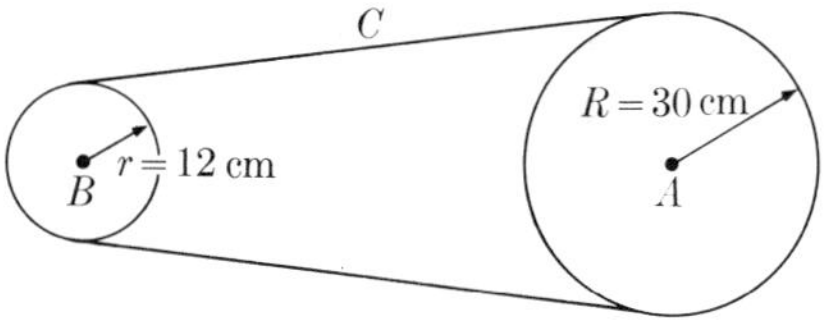

Figure 5–29

5.47 The wheel A (Fig. 5–29) whose radius is 30 cm starts moving from rest and increases its angular velocity uniformly at the rate of 0.4π rad s^{-1}. It transmits its motion to the wheel B by means of the belt C. Obtain a relation between the angular velocities and the radii of the two wheels. Find the time necessary for wheel B to reach an angular velocity of 300 rpm.

5.48 A ball is moving due north at 300 cm s^{-1} when a force is applied for 40 s, causing an acceleration of 10 cm s^{-2} due east, after which the force is removed. Determine (a) the magnitude and direction of the ball's final velocity, (b) the equation of its path, (c) its distance from the starting point, (d) its displacement from the starting point.

5.49 A train is moving at 72 km hr^{-1} when a lantern which is hanging on the end of the train, 4.9 m above the ground, shakes loose. Calculate the distance covered by the train in the time it takes for the lamp to fall to the ground. Where does the lamp fall relative to the train and to the tracks? What is its path relative to the train and to the track?

5.50 A car is traveling in a plane curve such that its rectangular coordinates, as a function of time, are given by $x = 2t^3 - 3t^2$, $y = t^2 - 2t + 1$. Assuming that t is given in seconds and the coordinates in meters, calculate (a) the position of the car when $t = 1$ s, (b) the rectangular components of the velocity at any time, (c) the rectangular components of the velocity when $t = 1$ s, (d) the velocity at any time, (e) the velocity when $t = 0$ s, (f) the time(s) when the velocity is zero, (g) the rectangular components of the acceleration at any time, (h) the rectangular components of the acceleration when $t = 1$ s, (i) the acceleration at any time, (j) the acceleration when $t = 0$ s, (k) the time(s) at which the acceleration will be parallel to the Y-axis.

5.51 A baseball player hits the ball so that it has a velocity of 48 ft s^{-1} and an angle of 30° above the horizontal. A second player, standing 100 ft from the batter and in the same plane as the ball's trajectory, begins to run the instant the ball is struck. Calculate his minimum velocity if he can reach up to 8 ft above the ground and the ball was 3 ft high when it was struck. How far did the second player have to run?

5.52 The coordinates of a moving particle are given by $x = t^2$, $y = (t - 1)^2$. Find its average velocity and acceleration in the time interval between t and $t + \Delta t$. Apply the results to the case when $t = 2$ s and $\Delta t = 1$ s, and compare with the values of the velocity and acceleration at $t = 2$ s. Graphically represent all vectors involved.

5.53 The position of a particle at time t is given by $x = A \sin \omega t$. Find its velocity and acceleration as a function of t and of x.

5.54 A point is moving with constant speed of 3 ft s^{-1}. The velocity has a direction such that it makes an angle of $(\pi/2)t$ rad with the positive OX-axis. If $x = y = 0$ when $t = 0$, find the equation of the trajectory of the particle.

5.55 The coordinates of a moving body are $x = t^2$, $y = (t - 1)^2$. (a) Find the Cartesian equation of the trajectory. [*Hint:* Eliminate t from the above equations.] (b) Draw a graph of the trajectory. (c) When is the velocity a minimum? (d) Find the coordinates when the velocity is 10 ft s^{-1}. (e) Calculate the tangential and normal accelerations at any time. (f) Calculate the tangential and normal accelerations when $t = 1$ s.

5.56 A particle is moving along a parabola $y = x^2$ in such a manner that at any time $v_x = 3$ ft s^{-1}. Calculate the magnitude and direction of the velocity and the acceleration of the particle at the point $x = \frac{2}{3}$ ft.

5.57 The coordinates of a moving body are $x = 2 \sin \omega t$, $y = 2 \cos \omega t$. (a) Find the Cartesian equation of the trajectory. (b) Calculate the value of the velocity at any time. (c) Calculate the tangential and normal components of the acceleration at any time. Identify the type of motion described by the above equations.

5.58 If the coordinates of a moving body are $x = at$, $y = b \sin at$, demonstrate that the value of the acceleration is proportional to the distance from the object undergoing this motion and the X-axis. Make a plot of the path.

5.59 A point is moving in the XY-plane in such a manner that $v_x = 4t^3 + 4t$, $v_y = 4t$. If the position of the point is (1, 2) when $t = 0$, find the Cartesian equation of the trajectory.

5.60 A particle is moving in the XY-plane according to the law $a_x = -4 \sin t$, $a_y = 3 \cos t$. If we are given that at $t = 0$, $x = 0$, $y = 3$, $v_x = 4$, $v_y = 0$: Find (a) the equation of the trajectory and (b) calculate the value of the velocity when $t = \pi/4$ s.

5.61 A projectile is shot with a velocity of 600 m s^{-1} at an angle of 60° with the horizontal. Calculate (a) the horizontal range, (b) the maximum height, (c) the velocity and height after 30 s, (d) the velocity and the time when the projectile is 10 km high.

5.62 A bomber plane is flying horizontally at an altitude of 1.2 km with a velocity of 180 km hr^{-1}. (a) How long before the plane is over its target should it drop a bomb? (b) What is the velocity of the bomb when it reaches the ground? (c) What is the bomb's velocity 10 s after it is dropped? (d) What is the bomb's velocity when it is 200 m high and when it strikes the ground? (e) What is the angle of the bomb's velocity as it strikes the ground? (f) What is the horizontal distance covered by the bomb?

5.63 A projectile is shot out at an angle of 35°. It strikes the ground at a horizontal distance of 4 km from the gun. Calculate (a) the initial velocity, (b) the time of the flight, (c) the maximum altitude, (d) the velocity at the point of maximum altitude.

5.64 A machine gun is situated at the top of a cliff at an altitude of 400 ft. It shoots a projectile with a velocity of 786 ft s^{-1} at an angle of 30° above the horizontal. Calculate the range (horizontal distance from the base of the cliff) of the gun. If a car is heading directly for the cliff at a velocity of 60 mi hr^{-1} along a horizontal road, how far away from the cliff should the car be for the gun to begin firing and hit it? Repeat the problem for a firing angle below the horizontal. Repeat the problem for a car moving away from the cliff.

5.65 A gun is placed at the base of a hill whose slope makes an angle ϕ with the horizontal. If the gun is set at an angle α with the horizontal and has a muzzle velocity v_0, find the distance, measured *along the hill,* at which the bullet will fall.

5.66 An airplane is flying horizontally at an altitude h with a velocity v. At the instant the plane is directly over an antiaircraft gun, the gun fires at the plane. Calculate the minimum velocity v_0 and the aiming angle α which the projectile would need in order to hit the plane.

5.67 A machine gun shoots a bullet with a velocity of 650 ft s^{-1}. Determine the angles at which the bullet will hit a target 450 ft away and 18 ft high.

5.68 Find the radius of curvature at the highest point of the path of a projectile fired at an initial angle α with the horizontal.

5.69 A hunter points at a squirrel on a branch of a tree. At the moment he fires his gun, the squirrel drops off the branch. Show that the squirrel should not have dropped if it had wanted to stay alive.

5.70 An airplane is flying horizontally at an altitude of 1 km and a velocity of 200 km hr^{-1}. It drops a bomb which is meant to hit a ship moving in the same direction at a velocity of 20 km hr^{-1}. Prove that the bomb should be dropped when the horizontal distance between the plane and the ship is 730 m. Solve the same problem for the case in which the ship is moving in the opposite direction.

5.71 Prove that for plane motion under a constant acceleration $\boldsymbol{a}$, the following relations hold:

$$v^2 = v_0 + 2\boldsymbol{a}\cdot(\boldsymbol{r} - \boldsymbol{r}_0)$$

and

$$\boldsymbol{r} = \tfrac{1}{2}(\boldsymbol{v} + \boldsymbol{v}_0)t.$$

5.72 A wheel of radius R rolls with constant velocity v_0 along a horizontal plane. Prove that the position of any point on its edge is given by the equations $x = R(\omega t - \sin \omega t)$ and $y = R(1 - \cos \omega t)$, where $\omega = v_0/R$ is the angular velocity of the wheel and t is measured from the instant when the point is initially in contact with the plane. Also find the components of the velocity and the acceleration of the point.

5.73 A wheel of radius R rolls along a horizontal plane. Prove that at each instant the velocity of each point is perpendicular to the line joining the point with the point of contact of the wheel with the plane. If ρ is the distance between these points, prove that the magnitude of the velocity of the moving point is $\omega\rho$. What do you conclude from these results?

5.74 Using the method explained in Section 5.11, prove that

$$d\boldsymbol{u}_\theta/dt = -\boldsymbol{u}_r\, d\theta/dt.$$

5.75 Show that the components of the acceleration along the unit vectors $\boldsymbol{u}_r$ and $\boldsymbol{u}_\theta$ (Fig. 5–26) are

$$a_r = \frac{d^2r}{dt^2} - r\left(\frac{d\theta}{dt}\right)^2, \quad a_\theta = 2\frac{dr}{dt}\frac{d\theta}{dt} + r\frac{d^2\theta}{dt^2}.$$

[*Hint:* Use the expression (5.63) for the velocity and take into account the values of $d\boldsymbol{u}_r/dt$ and $d\boldsymbol{u}_\theta/dt$.]

6
RELATIVE MOTION

6.1 Introduction

In the previous chapter we indicated that motion is a relative concept in that it must always be referred to a particular frame of reference, chosen by the observer. Since different observers may use different frames of reference, it is important to know how observations made by different observers are related. For example, most of the observations made on earth are related to a frame of reference attached to it, and therefore moving with the earth. Astronomers still prefer to refer the motion of a celestial body to the so-called *fixed stars*. In atomic physics the motion of the electrons is determined relative to the nucleus. An experimenter usually chooses a frame of reference in which his data-taking and analysis are most easily accomplished.

The possibility of defining an *absolute system* of reference at rest relative to *empty* space is a matter that has been discussed for centuries by physicists and philosophers. When it was assumed that empty space was "filled" with an imaginary substance called *ether*, having rather contradictory and impossible properties, the absolute system of reference was defined as one at rest relative to the ether. However, once people discarded the artificial and unnecessary idea of an ether, it became impossible to define such an absolute system, because in empty space there are no elements that can serve as reference points. As we shall show in this chapter, the matter has no relevance any more.

6.2 Relative Velocity

Let us consider two objects A and B and an observer O, using as frame of reference the axes XYZ (Fig. 6–1). The velocities of A and B relative to O are

$$\boldsymbol{V}_A = \frac{d\boldsymbol{r}_A}{dt}, \qquad \boldsymbol{V}_B = \frac{d\boldsymbol{r}_B}{dt}. \tag{6.1}$$

The velocities of B relative to A and of A relative to B are defined by

$$\begin{aligned} \boldsymbol{V}_{BA} &= \frac{d\boldsymbol{r}_{BA}}{dt}, \\ \boldsymbol{V}_{AB} &= \frac{d\boldsymbol{r}_{AB}}{dt}, \end{aligned} \tag{6.2}$$

where

$$\begin{aligned} \boldsymbol{r}_{BA} &= \overrightarrow{AB} = \boldsymbol{r}_B - \boldsymbol{r}_A, \\ \boldsymbol{r}_{AB} &= \overrightarrow{BA} = \boldsymbol{r}_A - \boldsymbol{r}_B. \end{aligned} \tag{6.3}$$

Note that, since $\boldsymbol{r}_{AB} = -\boldsymbol{r}_{BA}$, we also have

$$\boldsymbol{V}_{BA} = -\boldsymbol{V}_{AB}. \tag{6.4}$$

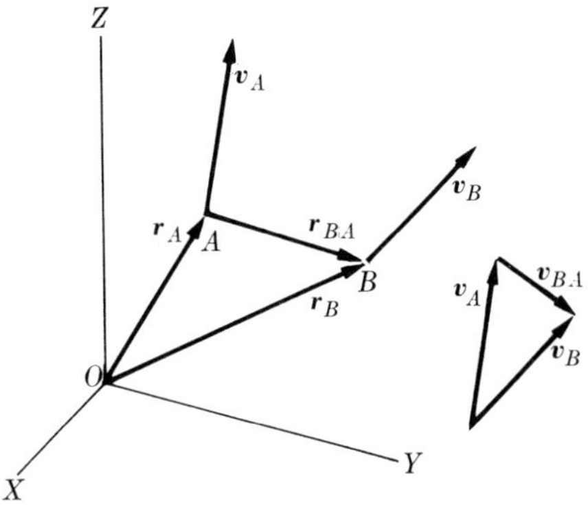

Fig. 6–1. Definition of relative velocity.

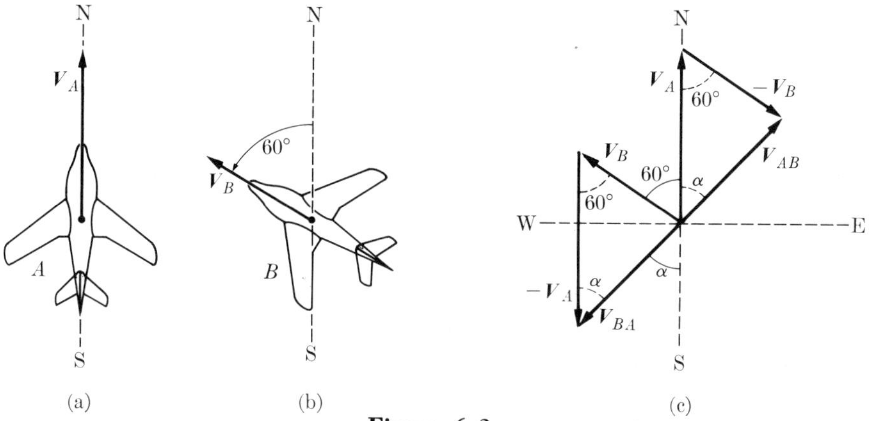

Figure 6–2

In other words, the velocity of B relative to A is equal and opposite to the velocity of A relative to B. Taking the derivative of Eq. (6.3) with respect to time, we obtain

$$\frac{d\boldsymbol{r}_{BA}}{dt} = \frac{d\boldsymbol{r}_B}{dt} - \frac{d\boldsymbol{r}_A}{dt}$$

or, using Eqs. (6.1) and (6.2), we have

$$\boldsymbol{V}_{BA} = \boldsymbol{V}_B - \boldsymbol{V}_A, \qquad \boldsymbol{V}_{AB} = \boldsymbol{V}_A - \boldsymbol{V}_B. \tag{6.5}$$

Therefore, to obtain the relative velocity of two bodies, one subtracts their velocities relative to the observer. Again taking the derivative of Eq. (6.5), we find that

$$\frac{d\boldsymbol{V}_{BA}}{dt} = \frac{d\boldsymbol{V}_B}{dt} - \frac{d\boldsymbol{V}_A}{dt},$$

with a similar expression for $d\boldsymbol{V}_{AB}/dt$. The first term is called the acceleration of B relative to A, and is designated by $\boldsymbol{a}_{BA}$. The other two terms are, respectively, the accelerations of B and A relative to O. Therefore

$$\boldsymbol{a}_{BA} = \boldsymbol{a}_B - \boldsymbol{a}_A \quad \text{and} \quad \boldsymbol{a}_{AB} = \boldsymbol{a}_A - \boldsymbol{a}_B. \tag{6.6}$$

EXAMPLE 6.1. An airplane A (Fig. 6–2) flies toward N at 300 mi hr^{-1} relative to the ground. At the same time another plane B flies in the direction N 60° W at 200 mi hr^{-1} relative to the ground. Find the velocity of A relative to B and of B relative to A.

Solution: In Fig. 6–2, the velocities of planes A and B relative to the ground have been represented at the left. On the right we have the velocity of A relative to B, that is, $\boldsymbol{V}_{AB} = \boldsymbol{V}_A - \boldsymbol{V}_B$, and of B relative to A, that is, $\boldsymbol{V}_{BA} = \boldsymbol{V}_B - \boldsymbol{V}_A$. We may note that $\boldsymbol{V}_{AB} = -\boldsymbol{V}_{BA}$, as it should be according to Eq. (6.4).

To compute $\boldsymbol{V}_{AB}$, we use Eq. (3.6), noting that the angle θ between $\boldsymbol{V}_A$ and $\boldsymbol{V}_B$ is 60°. Thus

$$V_{AB} = \sqrt{300^2 + 200^2 - 2 \times 300 \times 200 \times \cos 60^\circ} = 264.6 \text{ mi hr}^{-1}.$$

To obtain the direction of V_{AB}, we use the law of sines, Eq. (3.4),

$$\frac{V_B}{\sin\alpha} = \frac{V_{AB}}{\sin 60^\circ} \quad \text{or} \quad \sin\alpha = \frac{V_B \sin 60^\circ}{V_{AB}} = 0.654,$$

giving $\alpha = 40.7^\circ$. Therefore, to a passenger in plane B it seems as if plane A moves at 264.6 mi hr^{-1} in the direction N 40.7° E. The relative velocity V_{BA} has the same magnitude, 264.6 mi hr^{-1}, but the opposite direction, S 40.7° W.

6.3 Uniform Relative Translational Motion

Let us consider two observers O and O' who move, relative to each other, with translational uniform motion. That is, the observers do not rotate relative to each other. Therefore, observer O sees observer O' moving with velocity $\boldsymbol{v}$, while O' sees O moving with velocity $-\boldsymbol{v}$. We are interested in comparing their descriptions of the motion of an object, as, for example, when one observer is on the platform of a railroad station and another is in a passing train moving in a straight line, and both observers are watching the flight of a plane overhead.

We choose, for simplicity, the X- and X'-axes along the line of the relative motion (Fig. 6–3) and the YZ- and $Y'Z'$-axes parallel to each other; the coordinate axes will always remain parallel because of the absence of relative rotation. We shall also assume that at $t = 0$, O and O' are coincident, so that, with $\boldsymbol{v}$ as their constant relative velocity, we may write,

$$\overrightarrow{OO'} = \boldsymbol{v}t$$

and

$$\boldsymbol{v} = \boldsymbol{u}_x v.$$

Consider now a particle at A. From Fig. 6–3, we see that $\overrightarrow{OA} = \overrightarrow{OO'} + \overrightarrow{O'A}$ and since $\overrightarrow{OA} = \boldsymbol{r}$, $\overrightarrow{O'A} = \boldsymbol{r}'$, and $\overrightarrow{OO'} = \boldsymbol{v}t$, the position vectors of A as measured by O and O' are related by

$$\boldsymbol{r}' = \boldsymbol{r} - \boldsymbol{v}t. \tag{6.7}$$

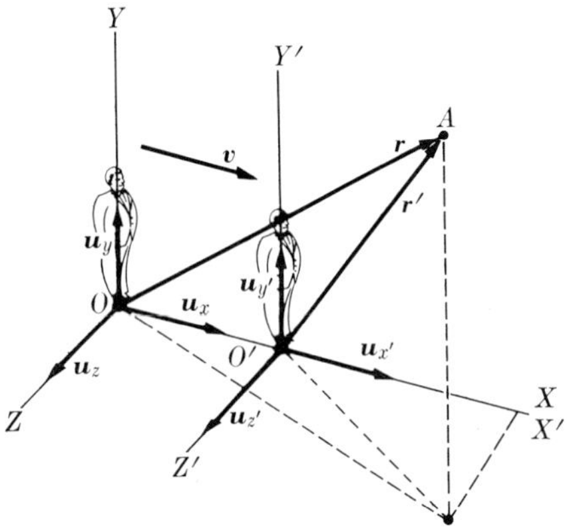

Fig. 6–3. Frames of reference in uniform relative translational motion.

The above vector equation can be separated into its three components, taking into account the fact that $\boldsymbol{v}$ is parallel to OX. Therefore

$$x' = x - vt, \quad y' = y, \quad z' = z, \quad t' = t. \tag{6.8}$$

We have added $t' = t$ to the three space equations to emphasize that we are assuming that the two observers are using the same time; that is, we assume that time measurements are independent of the motion of the observer. This seems very reasonable, but it is only an assumption, which may be disproved by experiment.

The set of equations (6.8) or the single vector equation (6.7), combined with $t' = t$, are called a *Galilean transformation.*

The velocity $\boldsymbol{V}$ of A relative to O is defined by

$$\boldsymbol{V} = \frac{d\boldsymbol{r}}{dt} = \boldsymbol{u}_x \frac{dx}{dt} + \boldsymbol{u}_y \frac{dy}{dt} + \boldsymbol{u}_z \frac{dz}{dt}$$

and the velocity $\boldsymbol{V}'$ of A relative to O' is,

$$\boldsymbol{V}' = \frac{d\boldsymbol{r}'}{dt} = \boldsymbol{u}_{x'} \frac{dx'}{dt} + \boldsymbol{u}_{y'} \frac{dy'}{dt} + \boldsymbol{u}_{z'} \frac{dz'}{dt}.$$

Note that we do not write $d\boldsymbol{r}'/dt'$ because we have assumed that $t = t'$, and hence $d\boldsymbol{r}'/dt'$ is the same as $d\boldsymbol{r}'/dt$. Taking the derivative of Eq. (6.7) relative to time and noting that $\boldsymbol{v}$ is constant, we have

$$\boldsymbol{V}' = \boldsymbol{V} - \boldsymbol{v}, \tag{6.9}$$

or noting that $V_x = dx/dt$, $V'_{x'} = dx'/dt$, etc., we may separate Eq. (6.9) into the three velocity components:

$$V'_{x'} = V_x - v, \qquad V'_{y'} = V_y, \qquad V'_{z'} = V_z. \tag{6.10}$$

These can also be obtained directly by taking the time derivative of Eqs. (6.8). Equations (6.9) or (6.10) give the Galilean rule for comparing the velocity of a body as measured by two observers in relative translational motion. For example, if A moves parallel to the OX-axis, we simply have

$$V' = V - v, \tag{6.11}$$

the other components being zero. But if A moves parallel to the OY-axis, $V_x = V_z = 0$, $V_y = V$, then $V'_{x'} = -v$ and $V'_{y'} = V$, $V'_{z'} = 0$, so that

$$V' = \sqrt{V^2 + v^2}. \tag{6.12}$$

The acceleration of A relative to O and O' is $\boldsymbol{a} = d\boldsymbol{V}/dt$ and $\boldsymbol{a}' = d\boldsymbol{V}'/dt$, respectively. Note again that we use the same t in both cases. From Eq. (6.9), noting that $d\boldsymbol{v}/dt = 0$ because $\boldsymbol{v}$ is constant, we obtain

$$\frac{d\boldsymbol{V}}{dt} = \frac{d\boldsymbol{V}'}{dt} \qquad \text{or} \qquad \boldsymbol{a}' = \boldsymbol{a}, \tag{6.13}$$

which, expressed in rectangular coordinates, is

$$a'_{x'} = a_x, \qquad a'_{y'} = a_y, \qquad \text{and} \qquad a'_{z'} = a_z. \tag{6.14}$$

In other words, both observers measure the same acceleration. That is, *the acceleration of a particle is the same for all observers in uniform relative translational motion.* This result offers us an example of a physical quantity—the acceleration of a particle—that appears to be independent of the motion of an observer; in other words, we have found that *acceleration remains invariant when passing from one frame of reference to any other which is in uniform relative translational motion.* This is the first time we see a physical quantity remain invariant under transformation. Later on we shall find other physical quantities that behave in the same manner. This result, as we shall see, has a profound influence on the formulation of laws in physics.

EXAMPLE 6.2. The velocity of sound in still air at 25°C (or 77°F) is 358 m s^{-1}. Find the velocity measured by an observer moving with a velocity of 90 km hr^{-1} (a) away from the source, (b) toward the source, (c) perpendicular to the direction of propagation in air, (d) in a direction such that the sound appears to propagate crosswise relative to the moving observer. Assume that the source is at rest relative to the ground.

Solution: Let us use a frame of reference XYZ (Fig. 6–4) fixed on the ground, and thus at rest relative to the air, and a frame $X'Y'Z'$ moving with the observer, with the X- and X'-axes parallel to the velocity of the observer, as in Fig. 6–3. Relative to XYZ, the sound source is at O, the velocity of the observer O' is $v = 90$ km $hr^{-1} = 25$ m s^{-1}, and the velocity of sound is $V = 358$ m s^{-1}. The velocity of sound, relative to $X'Y'Z'$, as recorded by the moving observer O', is V'. Applying Eq. (6.9) or (6.10), we have for case (a) $V' = V - v = 333$ m s^{-1}. In case (b), we note that O' moves along the negative direction of the X-axis. Thus we now have that $\boldsymbol{v} = -\boldsymbol{u}_x v$, changing Eq. (6.11)

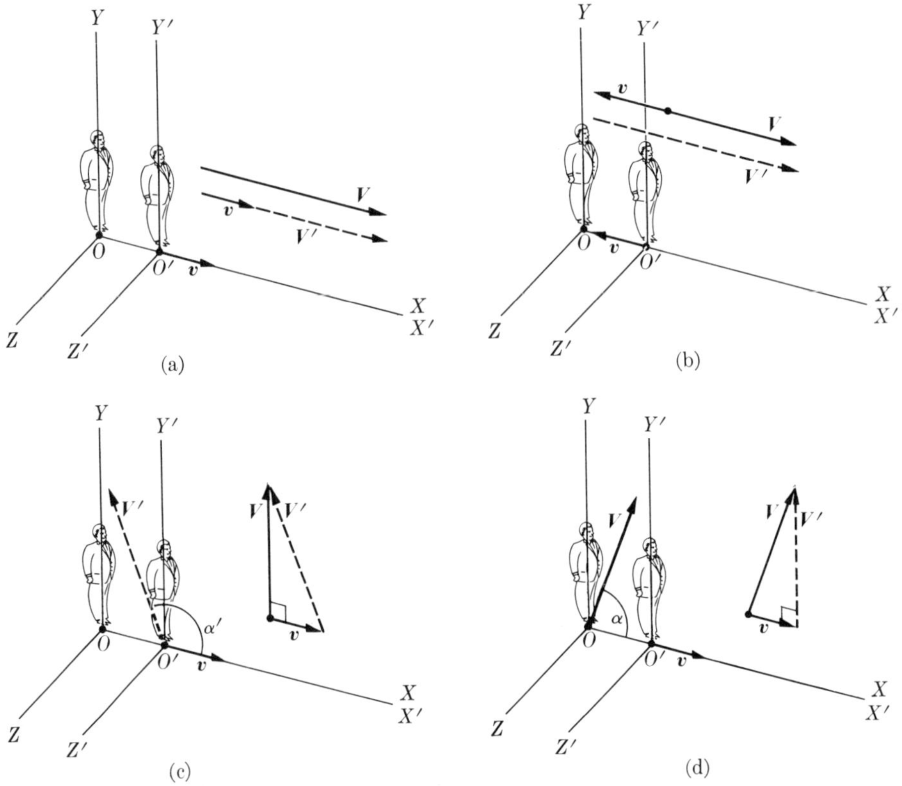

Figure 6–4

into $V' = V + v = 383$ m s^{-1}. For situation (c) we use Eq. (6.12), so that $V' = \sqrt{V^2 + v^2} = 358.9$ m s^{-1}. To the moving observer, the sound appears to propagate in a direction which makes an angle α' with the X'-axis such that

$$\tan \alpha' = \frac{V'_{y'}}{V'_{x'}} = \frac{V}{-v} = -15.32 \qquad \text{or} \qquad \alpha' = 93.7^\circ.$$

Finally, in case (d), the direction of propagation of the sound in air is such that it appears to O' to be moving in the Y'-direction. Thus $V'_{x'} = 0$, $V'_{y'} = V'$, and $V'_{z'} = 0$. Therefore, using Eq. (6.10), we have $0 = V_x - v$ or $V_x = v$ and $V' = V_y$. Thus $V^2 = V_x^2 + V_y^2 = v^2 + V'^2$ or $V' = \sqrt{V^2 - v^2} = 357.1$ m s^{-1}. In this case sound propagates through the still air in a direction making an angle α with the X-axis such that

$$\tan \alpha = \frac{V_y}{V_x} = \frac{V'}{v} = 14.385 \qquad \text{or} \qquad \alpha = 86.0^\circ.$$

6.4 Uniform Relative Rotational Motion

Let us now consider two observers O and O' rotating relative to each other but with no relative translational motion. For simplicity we shall assume that both O and O' are in the same region of space and that each uses a frame of reference attached to itself but with a common origin. For example, observer O, who uses the frame XYZ (Fig. 6–5), notes that the frame $X'Y'Z'$ attached to O' is rotating with angular velocity $\boldsymbol{\omega}$. To O', the situation is just the reverse; O' observes frame XYZ rotating with angular velocity $-\boldsymbol{\omega}$. The position vector $\boldsymbol{r}$ of particle A referred to XYZ is

$$\boldsymbol{r} = \boldsymbol{u}_x x + \boldsymbol{u}_y y + \boldsymbol{u}_z z, \tag{6.15}$$

and therefore the velocity of particle A as measured by O relative to its frame of reference XYZ is

$$\boldsymbol{V} = \frac{d\boldsymbol{r}}{dt} = \boldsymbol{u}_x \frac{dx}{dt} + \boldsymbol{u}_y \frac{dy}{dt} + \boldsymbol{u}_z \frac{dz}{dt}. \tag{6.16}$$

Similarly, the position vector of A referred to $X'Y'Z'$ is

$$\boldsymbol{r} = \boldsymbol{u}_{x'} x' + \boldsymbol{u}_{y'} y' + \boldsymbol{u}_{z'} z', \tag{6.17}$$

where, because the origins are coincident, the vector $\boldsymbol{r}$ is the same as in Eq. (6.15);

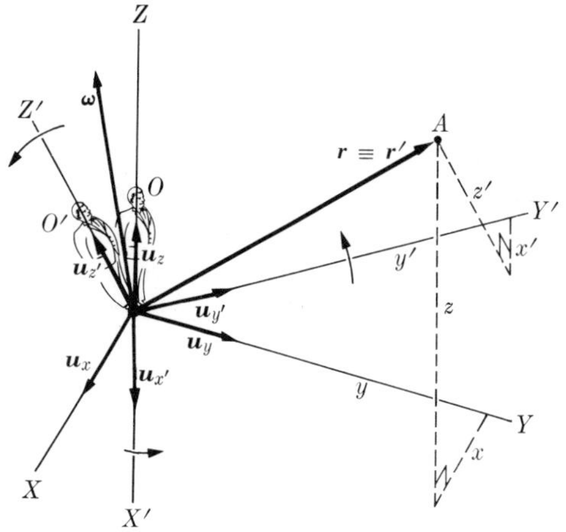

Fig. 6–5. Frames of reference in uniform relative rotational motion.

that is the reason why we have not written $\boldsymbol{r}'$. The velocity of A, as measured by O' relative to its own frame of reference $X'Y'Z'$, is

$$\boldsymbol{V}' = \boldsymbol{u}_{x'} \frac{dx'}{dt} + \boldsymbol{u}_{y'} \frac{dy'}{dt} + \boldsymbol{u}_{z'} \frac{dz'}{dt}. \tag{6.18}$$

In taking the derivative of Eq. (6.17), observer O' has assumed that his frame $X'Y'Z'$ is not rotating, and has therefore considered the unit vectors as constant in direction. However, observer O has the right to say that, to him, the frame $X'Y'Z'$ is rotating and therefore the unit vectors $\boldsymbol{u}_{x'}$, $\boldsymbol{u}_{y'}$, and $\boldsymbol{u}_{z'}$ are not constant in direction, and that in computing the time derivative of Eq. (6.17) one must write

$$\frac{d\boldsymbol{r}}{dt} = \boldsymbol{u}_{x'} \frac{dx'}{dt} + \boldsymbol{u}_{y'} \frac{dy'}{dt} + \boldsymbol{u}_{z'} \frac{dz'}{dt} + \frac{d\boldsymbol{u}_{x'}}{dt} x' + \frac{d\boldsymbol{u}_{y'}}{dt} y' + \frac{d\boldsymbol{u}_{z'}}{dt} z'. \tag{6.19}$$

Now the endpoints of vectors $\boldsymbol{u}_{x'}$, $\boldsymbol{u}_{y'}$, and $\boldsymbol{u}_{z'}$ are (by assumption) in uniform circular motion relative to O, with angular velocity $\boldsymbol{\omega}$. In other words, $d\boldsymbol{u}_{x'}/dt$ is the velocity of a point at unit distance from O and moving with uniform circular motion with angular velocity $\boldsymbol{\omega}$. Therefore, using Eq. (5.48), we have,

$$\frac{d\boldsymbol{u}_{x'}}{dt} = \boldsymbol{\omega} \times \boldsymbol{u}_{x'}, \qquad \frac{d\boldsymbol{u}_{y'}}{dt} = \boldsymbol{\omega} \times \boldsymbol{u}_{y'}, \qquad \frac{d\boldsymbol{u}_{z'}}{dt} = \boldsymbol{\omega} \times \boldsymbol{u}_{z'}.$$

Accordingly, from Eq. (6.19) we may write

$$\begin{aligned}\frac{d\boldsymbol{u}_{x'}}{dt} x' + \frac{d\boldsymbol{u}_{y'}}{dt} y' + \frac{d\boldsymbol{u}_{z'}}{dt} z' &= \boldsymbol{\omega} \times \boldsymbol{u}_{x'}x' + \boldsymbol{\omega} \times \boldsymbol{u}_{y'}y' + \boldsymbol{\omega} \times \boldsymbol{u}_{z'}z' \\ &= \boldsymbol{\omega} \times (\boldsymbol{u}_{x'}x' + \boldsymbol{u}_{y'}y' + \boldsymbol{u}_{z'}z') \\ &= \boldsymbol{\omega} \times \boldsymbol{r}.\end{aligned} \tag{6.20}$$

Introducing this result in Eq. (6.19), and using Eqs. (6.16) and (6.18), we finally get

$$\boldsymbol{V} = \boldsymbol{V}' + \boldsymbol{\omega} \times \boldsymbol{r}. \tag{6.21}$$

This expression gives the relation between the velocities $\boldsymbol{V}$ and $\boldsymbol{V}'$ of A, as recorded by observers O and O' in relative rotational motion.

To obtain the relation between the accelerations, we proceed in a similar way. The acceleration of A, as measured by O relative to XYZ, is

$$\boldsymbol{a} = \frac{d\boldsymbol{V}}{dt} = \boldsymbol{u}_x \frac{dV_x}{dt} + \boldsymbol{u}_y \frac{dV_y}{dt} + \boldsymbol{u}_z \frac{dV_z}{dt}. \tag{6.22}$$

The acceleration of A, as measured by O' relative to $X'Y'Z'$, when he again ignores the rotation, is

$$\boldsymbol{a}' = \boldsymbol{u}_{x'} \frac{dV'_{x'}}{dt} + \boldsymbol{u}_{y'} \frac{dV'_{y'}}{dt} + \boldsymbol{u}_{z'} \frac{dV'_{z'}}{dt}. \tag{6.23}$$

When we differentiate Eq. (6.21) with respect to t, remembering that we are assuming that $\boldsymbol{\omega}$ is constant, we obtain

$$\boldsymbol{a} = \frac{d\boldsymbol{V}}{dt} = \frac{d\boldsymbol{V}'}{dt} + \boldsymbol{\omega} \times \frac{d\boldsymbol{r}}{dt}. \tag{6.24}$$

Now, since $\boldsymbol{V}' = \boldsymbol{u}_{x'}V'_{x'} + \boldsymbol{u}_{y'}V'_{y'} + \boldsymbol{u}_{z'}V'_{z'}$, we obtain by differentiation

$$\frac{d\boldsymbol{V}'}{dt} = \boldsymbol{u}_{x'}\frac{dV'_{x'}}{dt} + \boldsymbol{u}_{y'}\frac{dV'_{y'}}{dt} + \boldsymbol{u}_{z'}\frac{dV'_{z'}}{dt} + \frac{d\boldsymbol{u}_{x'}}{dt}V'_{x'} + \frac{d\boldsymbol{u}_{y'}}{dt}V'_{y'} + \frac{d\boldsymbol{u}_{z'}}{dt}V'_{z'}.$$

The first three terms are just $\boldsymbol{a}'$, as given by Eq. (6.23), and the last three, by a procedure identical to that used to derive Eq. (6.20), are $\boldsymbol{\omega} \times \boldsymbol{V}'$. That is, by substituting the appropriate quantities into Eq. (6.20), we have

$$\boldsymbol{\omega} \times \boldsymbol{u}_{x'}V'_{x'} + \boldsymbol{\omega} \times \boldsymbol{u}_{y'}V'_{y'} + \boldsymbol{\omega} \times \boldsymbol{u}_{z'}V'_{z'} = \boldsymbol{\omega} \times (\boldsymbol{u}_{x'}V'_{x'} + \boldsymbol{u}_{y'}V'_{y'} + \boldsymbol{u}_{z'}V'_{z'}) = \boldsymbol{\omega} \times \boldsymbol{V}'.$$

Therefore $d\boldsymbol{V}'/dt = \boldsymbol{a}' + \boldsymbol{\omega} \times \boldsymbol{V}'$. Also from Eqs. (6.16) and (6.21), $d\boldsymbol{r}/dt = \boldsymbol{V} = \boldsymbol{V}' + \boldsymbol{\omega} \times \boldsymbol{r}$, so that

$$\boldsymbol{\omega} \times \frac{d\boldsymbol{r}}{dt} = \boldsymbol{\omega} \times (\boldsymbol{V}' + \boldsymbol{\omega} \times \boldsymbol{r}) = \boldsymbol{\omega} \times \boldsymbol{V}' + \boldsymbol{\omega} \times (\boldsymbol{\omega} \times \boldsymbol{r}).$$

Substituting both results in Eq. (6.24), we finally obtain

$$\boldsymbol{a} = \boldsymbol{a}' + 2\boldsymbol{\omega} \times \boldsymbol{V}' + \boldsymbol{\omega} \times (\boldsymbol{\omega} \times \boldsymbol{r}). \tag{6.25}$$

This equation gives the relation between the accelerations $\boldsymbol{a}$ and $\boldsymbol{a}'$ of A as recorded by observers O and O' in uniform relative rotational motion. The second term, $2\boldsymbol{\omega} \times \boldsymbol{V}'$, is called the *Coriolis acceleration*. The third term is similar to Eq. (5.59) and corresponds to a *centripetal acceleration*. Both the Coriolis and centripetal accelerations are the result of the relative rotational motion of the observers. In the next section we shall illustrate the use of these relations.

6.5 Motion Relative to the Earth

One of the most interesting applications of Eq. (6.25) is the study of a body's motion relative to the earth. As indicated in Example 5.10, the angular velocity of the earth is $\omega = 7.292 \times 10^{-5}$ rad s^{-1}. Its direction is that of the axis of rotation of the earth. Consider a point A on the earth's surface (Fig. 6–6). Let us call $\boldsymbol{g}_0$ the acceleration of gravity as measured by a nonrotating observer at A. Then $\boldsymbol{g}_0$ corresponds to $\boldsymbol{a}$ in Eq. (6.25). Solving Eq. (6.25) for $\boldsymbol{a}'$, we obtain the acceleration measured by an observer rotating with the earth:

$$\boldsymbol{a}' = \boldsymbol{g}_0 - 2\boldsymbol{\omega} \times \boldsymbol{V}' - \boldsymbol{\omega} \times (\boldsymbol{\omega} \times \boldsymbol{r}). \tag{6.26}$$

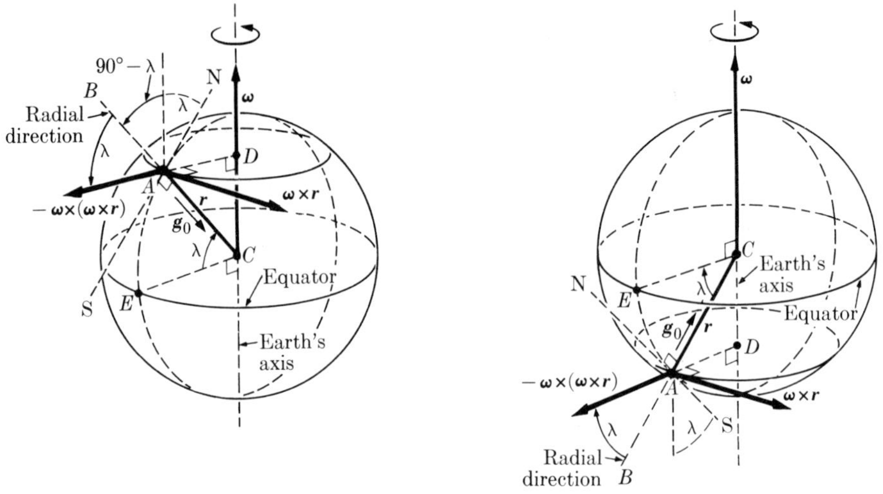

(a) Northern hemisphere (b) Southern hemisphere

Fig. 6–6. Centrifugal acceleration due to earth's rotation.

We shall first consider the case of a body initially at rest, or moving very slowly, so that the Coriolis term $-2\boldsymbol{\omega} \times \boldsymbol{V}'$ is zero or negligible when compared with the last term $-\boldsymbol{\omega} \times (\boldsymbol{\omega} \times \boldsymbol{r})$. The acceleration $\boldsymbol{a}'$ measured in this case is called the *effective acceleration* of gravity, and is designated by $\boldsymbol{g}$. Thus

$$\boldsymbol{g} = \boldsymbol{g}_0 - \boldsymbol{\omega} \times (\boldsymbol{\omega} \times \boldsymbol{r}). \tag{6.27}$$

This is the acceleration measured with a pendulum, as will be discussed in Chapter 12. Assuming that the earth is spherical (actually it departs slightly from this shape) and that there are no local anomalies, we may consider that $\boldsymbol{g}_0$ is pointing toward the center of the earth along the radial direction. Because the second term in Eq. (6.27), the direction of $\boldsymbol{g}$, called the *vertical*, deviates slightly from the radial direction; it is determined by a plumb line. Liquids always rest in equilibrium with their surface perpendicular to $\boldsymbol{g}$. However, for practical purposes, and in the absence of local disturbances, the vertical may be assumed to coincide with the radial direction.

Let us now analyze in more detail the last term in Eq. (6.27); that is, $-\boldsymbol{\omega} \times (\boldsymbol{\omega} \times \boldsymbol{r})$. This is called the *centrifugal acceleration* because, due to its reversed or negative sign, it points in the outward direction DA, as can be seen in Fig. 6–6. The angle λ that $r = CA$ makes with the equator is the latitude. Therefore the vector $\boldsymbol{\omega}$ makes an angle $90° - \lambda$ with CA in the northern hemisphere and $90° + \lambda$ in the southern hemisphere. The magnitude of $\boldsymbol{\omega} \times \boldsymbol{r}$ is then

$$\omega r \sin (90° \pm \lambda) = \omega r \cos \lambda,$$

and the direction of $\boldsymbol{\omega} \times \boldsymbol{r}$, being perpendicular to $\boldsymbol{\omega}$, is parallel to the equator.

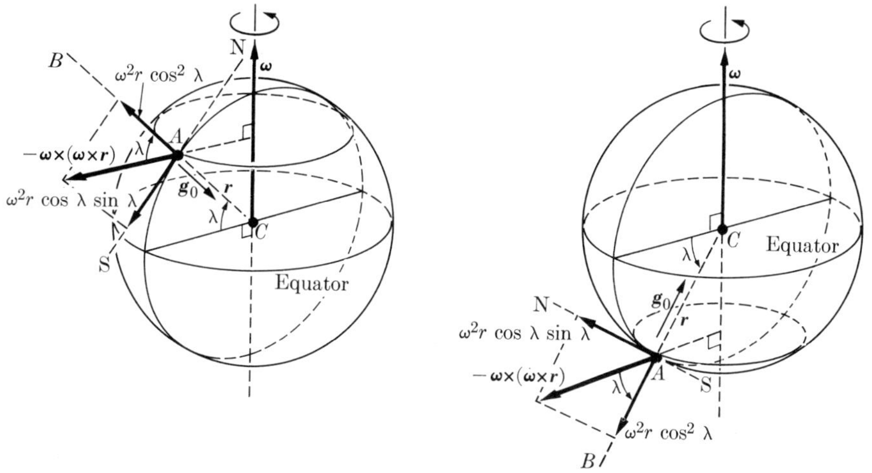

Fig. 6–7. Radial and horizontal components of the centrifugal acceleration.

Remembering Example 5.11, we find that the magnitude of the centrifugal acceleration $-\boldsymbol{\omega} \times (\boldsymbol{\omega} \times \boldsymbol{r})$ is

$$|-\boldsymbol{\omega} \times (\boldsymbol{\omega} \times \boldsymbol{r})| = \omega^2 r \cos\lambda = 3.34 \times 10^{-2} \cos\lambda \text{ m s}^{-2}, \qquad (6.28)$$

where $r = 6.35 \times 10^6$ m, which is the radius of the earth. This acceleration decreases from the equator to the poles, but is always very small when compared with the acceleration of gravity $g_0 = 9.80$ m s^{-2}. Its maximum value, at the equator, is about 0.3% of g_0 (see Example 5.11).

We shall now find the components of $-\boldsymbol{\omega} \times (\boldsymbol{\omega} \times \boldsymbol{r})$ along the radial direction AB and along the north-south (NS) line at A. In Fig. 6–7, as in Fig. 6–6, the line AB, which is the extension of CA, is the radial direction. The vector $\boldsymbol{\omega}$ obviously makes an angle λ with NS. As indicated before, the acceleration of gravity $\boldsymbol{g}_0$ points downward along AB. The centrifugal acceleration $-\boldsymbol{\omega} \times (\boldsymbol{\omega} \times \boldsymbol{r})$ is at an angle λ with AB; its component along AB is therefore obtained by multiplying its magnitude, given by Eq. (6.28), by $\cos\lambda$. That is,

$$|-\boldsymbol{\omega} \times (\boldsymbol{\omega} \times \boldsymbol{r})| \cos\lambda = \omega^2 r \cos^2\lambda.$$

The component of the centrifugal acceleration along the line NS is pointing south in the Northern hemisphere (and north in the Southern hemisphere), and is obtained by multiplying its magnitude by $\sin\lambda$, resulting in

$$|-\boldsymbol{\omega} \times (\boldsymbol{\omega} \times \boldsymbol{r})| \sin\lambda = \omega^2 r \cos\lambda \sin\lambda.$$

The two components are illustrated in Fig. 6–7. According to the definition of $\boldsymbol{g}$ given by Eq. (6.27), the components of $\boldsymbol{g}$ along the radial and horizontal directions

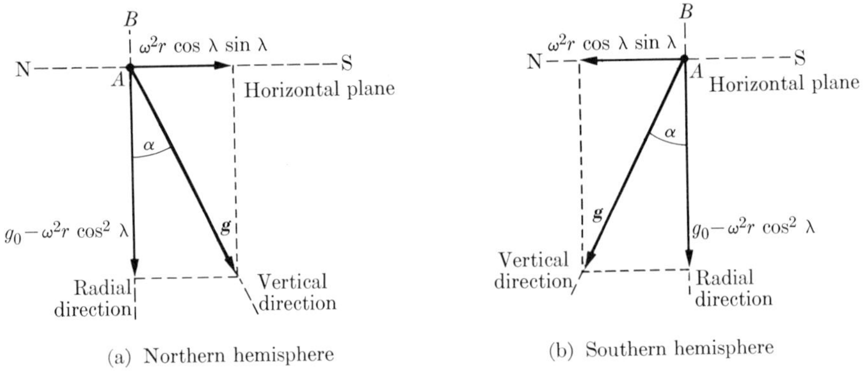

Fig. 6–8. Definition of vertical direction and effective acceleration of free fall.

are as shown in Fig. 6–8. Because of the smallness of the centrifugal term, the angle α is very small and the magnitude of $\boldsymbol{g}$ does not differ appreciably from its component along the radial direction AB. Thus we may write, as a good approximation, that

$$g = g_0 - \omega^2 r \cos^2 \lambda. \tag{6.29}$$

Although the last term is very small, it accounts for the observed increase in the value of the acceleration of gravity with latitude, as reflected in Table 6–1.

The component of the centrifugal acceleration along the NS-direction tends, in the Northern hemisphere, to displace the body slightly toward the south from the radial direction AB and toward the north in the Southern hemisphere. Therefore the path of a falling body will be deviated, as illustrated in Fig. 6–9. The body will thus land at A' instead of landing at A, as would happen if there were no rotation. Because of the small value of α, this deviation is negligible.

Let us consider next the Coriolis term, $-2\boldsymbol{\omega} \times \boldsymbol{V}'$. In the case of a falling body, the velocity $\boldsymbol{V}'$ is essentially pointing downward along the vertical AB (Fig. 6–10) and $\boldsymbol{\omega} \times \boldsymbol{V}'$ points toward the west. Therefore the Coriolis term $-2\boldsymbol{\omega} \times \boldsymbol{V}'$ is

TABLE 6–1 Values of the Acceleration of Gravity, Expressed in m s^{-2}

Location	Latitude	Gravity
North pole	90° 0′	9.8321
Anchorage	61° 10′	9.8218
Greenwich	51° 29′	9.8119
Paris	48° 50′	9.8094
Washington	38° 53′	9.8011
Key West	24° 34′	9.7897
Panama	8° 55′	9.7822
Equator	0° 0′	9.7799

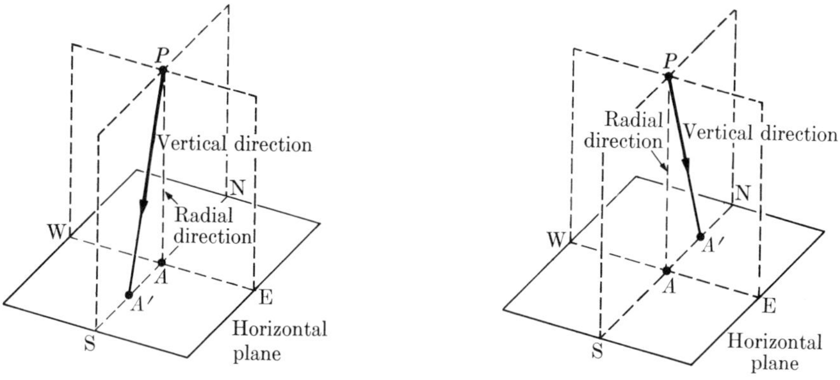

(a) Northern hemisphere (b) Southern hemisphere

Fig. 6–9. Deviation of the direction of a freely falling body due to centrifugal acceleration: southward (northward) in the Northern (Southern) hemisphere.

pointing east, and the falling body will be deviated in that direction, reaching the ground at A'', slightly to the east of A. Combining this Coriolis effect with the centrifugal effect, the body will fall on a point southeast of A in the Northern hemisphere and northeast of A in the Southern hemisphere. This effect, which is negligible in most cases, must be carefully taken into account both in high-altitude bombing and in intercontinental ballistic missiles. Coriolis acceleration also seriously affects the paths of rockets and of satellites, due to their great velocities.

In the case of a body moving in the horizontal plane, the vector $-2\boldsymbol{\omega} \times \boldsymbol{V}'$, perpendicular to $\boldsymbol{\omega}$ and $\boldsymbol{V}'$, makes an angle equal to $\pi/2 - \lambda$ with the horizontal plane. It has a horizontal component $\boldsymbol{a}_H$ and a vertical component $\boldsymbol{a}_V$ (Fig. 6–11).

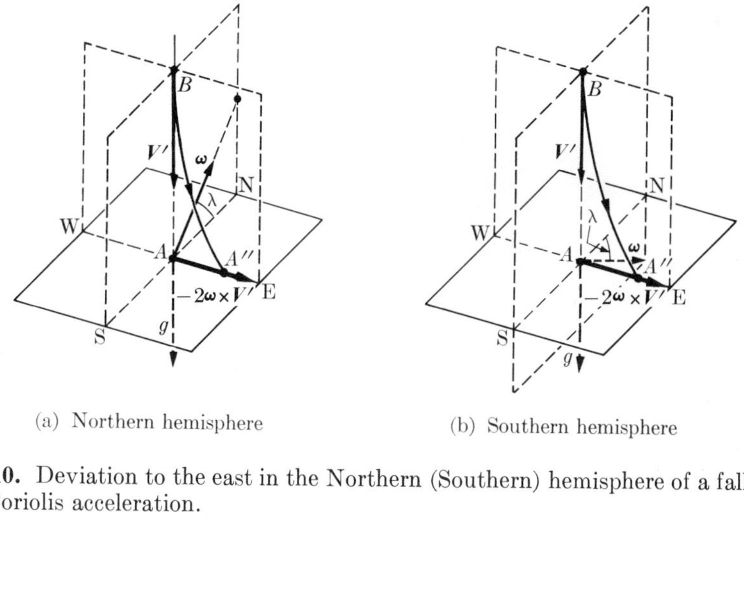

(a) Northern hemisphere (b) Southern hemisphere

Fig. 6–10. Deviation to the east in the Northern (Southern) hemisphere of a falling body due to Coriolis acceleration.

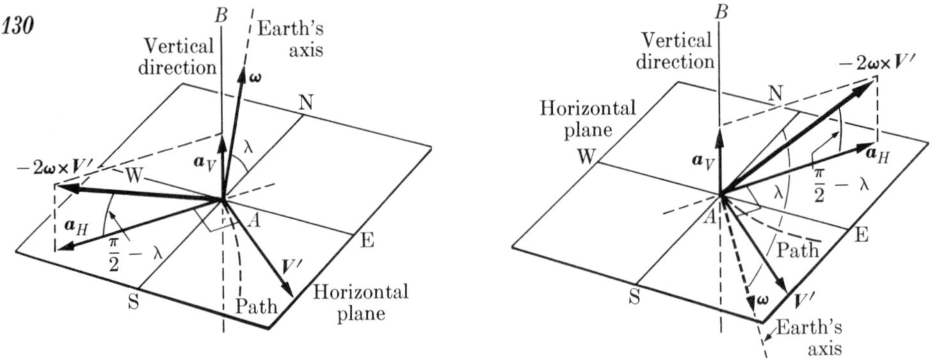

(a) Northern hemisphere (b) Southern hemisphere

Fig. 6–11. Coriolis acceleration. When a body moves in a horizontal plane, the horizontal component of the Coriolis acceleration points to the right (left) of the direction of motion in the Northern (Southern) hemisphere. Here $\boldsymbol{V}'$ is in the horizontal plane, $\boldsymbol{\omega}$ is in the plane defined by AB and NS, and $\boldsymbol{a}_H$ is perpendicular to $\boldsymbol{V}'$.

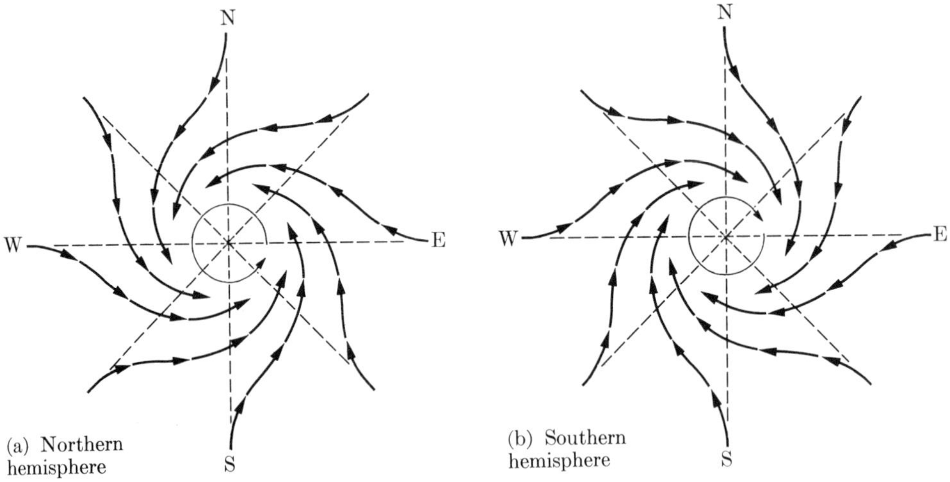

(a) Northern hemisphere

(b) Southern hemisphere

(c)

Fig. 6–12. Counterclockwise (clockwise) whirling of wind in the Northern (Southern) hemisphere resulting from a low pressure center combined with Coriolis acceleration. Part (c) shows a low-pressure disturbance photographed by a Tiros satellite. (Photograph courtesy of NASA/Goddard Space Center.)

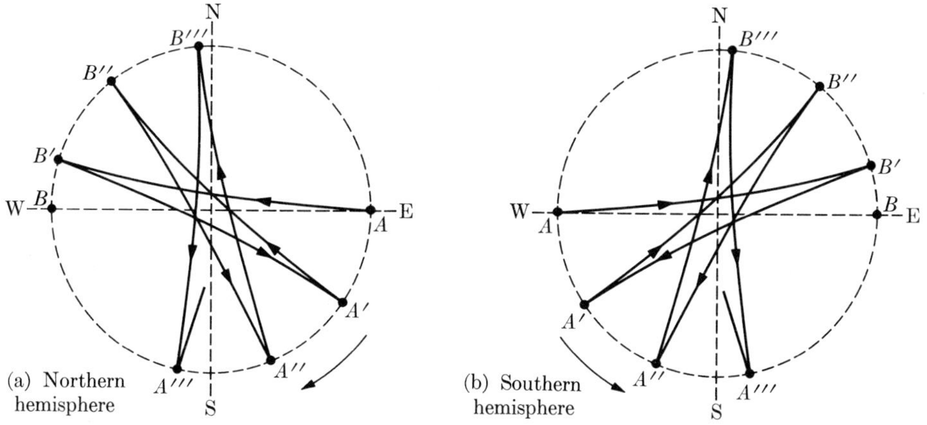

Fig. 6–13. Rotation of plane of oscillation of pendulum as a result of Coriolis acceleration. (Rotation in the Southern hemisphere is in the opposite direction to that in Northern.)

The horizontal component $\boldsymbol{a}_H$ tends to make the path deviate from a straight line, to the right in the Northern hemisphere and to the left in the Southern hemisphere. The component $\boldsymbol{a}_H$ decreases as one moves from the poles toward the equator, where it is zero. Thus at the equator the Coriolis acceleration produces no horizontal effect on the horizontal motion. The vertical effect is small compared with the acceleration of gravity, and in most instances may be neglected.

The horizontal effect may be seen in two common phenomena. One is the whirling of wind in a hurricane. If a low-pressure center develops in the atmosphere, the wind will flow radially toward the center (Fig. 6–12). However, the Coriolis acceleration deviates the air molecules toward the right of their paths in the northern latitudes, resulting in a counterclockwise or whirling motion.* In the Southern hemisphere the rotation is clockwise.

As a second example, let us consider the oscillations of a pendulum. When the amplitude of the oscillations is small, we can assume that the motion of the bob is along a horizontal path. If the pendulum were initially set to oscillate in the east-west direction and were released at A (see Fig. 6–13), it would continue oscillating between A and B if the earth were not rotating. But because of the Coriolis acceleration due to the earth's rotation, the path of the pendulum is deflected continuously to the right in the Northern hemisphere and to the left in the Southern hemisphere. Therefore, at the end of the first oscillation, it reaches B' instead of B. On its return, it goes to A' and not to A. Therefore, in successive complete oscillations, it arrives at A'', A''', etc. In other words, the plane of oscillation of the pendulum rotates clockwise in the Northern hemisphere and counterclockwise in

* The pressure and temperature of the air also have a profound effect on its motion. This effect leads to a phenomenon which is too complicated to be adequately described here. The end result is the cyclonic motion illustrated in Fig. 6–12(c).

the Southern hemisphere. We leave to the student the verification of the fact that the angle through which the plane of oscillation rotates each hour is 15° sin λ. The effect has been much exaggerated in Fig. 6–13; it is maximum at the poles and zero at the equator.

This effect was spectacularly demonstrated by the French physicist Jean Leon Foucault, when in 1851, from the dome of Les Invalides, in Paris, he hung a pendulum 67 m long. During each oscillation, the pendulum's bob dropped sand on a circle, experimentally demonstrating that its plane of oscillation rotated at the rate of 11° 15′ each hour. There is a Foucault pendulum in the lobby of the Smithsonian Institution in Washington, D.C., as well as in the lobby of the United Nations building in New York. Foucault's experiment is an effective proof of the rotation of the earth. Even if the earth had always been covered by clouds, this experiment would have told physicists that the earth was rotating.

EXAMPLE 6.3. Compute the deviation of a falling body due to the Coriolis acceleration. Compare it with the deviation due to the centrifugal term.

Solution: From Fig. 6–10 we see that the velocity $\boldsymbol{V}'$ of a falling body makes an angle $90° + \lambda$ with $\boldsymbol{\omega}$. Thus the magnitude of the Coriolis acceleration $-2\boldsymbol{\omega} \times \boldsymbol{V}'$ is

$$2\omega V' \sin (90° + \lambda) \qquad \text{or} \qquad 2\omega V' \cos \lambda.$$

This is the acceleration d^2x/dt^2 of the falling body with the easterly direction taken as the X-axis. Therefore

$$\frac{d^2x}{dt^2} = 2\omega V' \cos \lambda.$$

For V' we use, as a good approximation, the free-fall value obtained in Chapter 5. That is, $V' = gt$, and

$$\frac{d^2x}{dt^2} = 2\omega gt \cos \lambda.$$

Integrating, and assuming that the body starts falling from rest ($dx/dt = 0$ for $t = 0$), we have

$$\frac{dx}{dt} = \omega gt^2 \cos \lambda.$$

Again integrating and considering that at $t = 0$ the falling body is above A and therefore has $x = 0$, we get

$$x = \tfrac{1}{3}\omega gt^3 \cos \lambda,$$

which gives the eastward displacement in terms of the time of fall. If the body is dropped from the height h we may again write its value for free fall, $h = \frac{1}{2}gt^2$, so that

$$x = \tfrac{1}{3}\omega \left(\frac{8h^3}{g}\right)^{1/2} \cos \lambda = 1.53 \times 10^{-5} h^{3/2} \cos \lambda.$$

For example, for a body falling from a height of 100 m we have $x = 1.53 \times 10^{-2} \cos\lambda$ m, and thus it is a relatively small amount when compared with the distance fallen.

The southward acceleration due to the centrifugal term is $\omega^2 r^2 \cos\lambda \sin\lambda = 3.34 \times 10^{-2} \cos\lambda \sin\lambda$, and the amount of deflection, using $h = \frac{1}{2}gt^2$, is

$$y = \tfrac{1}{2}(\omega^2 r \cos\lambda \sin\lambda)t^2 = \omega^2 r\,(h/g) \cos\lambda \sin\lambda = 0.342h \cos\lambda \sin\lambda \text{ m}.$$

6.6 The Lorentz Transformation

At the end of the nineteenth century, when it was still assumed that space, empty of matter, was filled with "ether," there was a great discussion as to how bodies moved through that ether and how this motion would affect the velocity of light as measured on the earth. Physicists in earlier days had assumed that vibrations of this hypothetical ether were related to light in the same way that vibrations in air are related to sound. Assuming the ether stationary, we find that light moves relative to the ether with a velocity of $c = 2.9974 \times 10^8$ m s^{-1}. If the earth moves through the ether without disturbing it, then the velocity of light relative to the earth should depend on the direction of light propagation. For example, it should be $c - v$ for a ray of light propagating in the same direction the earth is moving and $c + v$ for the opposite direction. However, if the light's path as observed from the earth is perpendicular to the earth's motion, its velocity relative to the earth would be $\sqrt{c^2 - v^2}$. (Remember Example 6.2d for a similar case pertaining to sound.)

In 1881 the American physicists Michelson and Morley started a memorable series of experiments for measuring the velocity of light in different directions relative to the earth. To their great surprise they found that the velocity of light was the same in all directions.* However, Galileo's transformation indicates that no body may have the same velocity relative to two observers in uniform relative motion, and that relative velocity depends on the direction of motion of the observer. This is emphasized particularly by Eqs. (6.9) and (6.10). One possible alternative explanation would be that the earth drags the ether with it, as it drags the atmosphere, and therefore close to the earth's surface the ether should be at rest relative to the earth. This is a rather improbable explanation, since the ether drag would manifest itself in other phenomena connected with light propagation. Such phenomena have never been observed. For the above reasons, the idea of an ether has been discarded by physicists.

The puzzle of the Michelson and Morley experiment was settled in 1905 when Einstein stated his principle of relativity, which will be discussed in more detail in Section 11.3. This principle states that

> *all laws of nature must be the same (i.e., must remain invariant) for all observers in uniform relative translational motion.*

---

* For a critical review of the experiments performed to determine the velocity of light relative to the earth in different directions, consult R. S. Shankland, *et al.*, *Reviews of Modern Physics* **27**, 167 (1955).

Einstein assumed that the velocity of light is a physical invariant, having the same value for all observers. As we shall see later, this is required when we apply the principle of relativity to the laws of electromagnetism. Under this assumption, Galileo's transformation cannot be the correct one. In particular, the fourth equation in (6.8), $t' = t$, can no longer be correct. Since velocity is distance divided by time, we may have to adjust the time as well as the distance if the quotient of the two is to remain the same for observers in relative motion as it does in the case of the velocity of light. In other words, the time interval between two events *does not* have to be the same for observers in relative motion. Therefore we must replace Galileo's transformation by another, so that the speed of light is invariant. As in the case of Galileo's transformation, we shall assume that observers O and O' are moving with relative velocity $\boldsymbol{v}$ and that the X- and X'-axes will point in the direction of their relative motion, the axes YZ and $Y'Z'$ being parallel, respectively (Fig. 6–14). We may also assume that both observers set their clocks so that $t = t' = 0$ when they coincide.

Suppose that at $t = 0$ a flash of light is emitted at their common position. After a time t observer O will note that the light has reached point A and will write $r = ct$, where c is the speed of light. Since

$$r^2 = x^2 + y^2 + z^2,$$

we may also write

$$x^2 + y^2 + z^2 = c^2t^2. \tag{6.30}$$

Similarly, observer O' will note that the light arrives at the same point A in a time t', but also with velocity c. Therefore he writes $r' = ct'$, or

$$x'^2 + y'^2 + z'^2 = c^2t'^2. \tag{6.31}$$

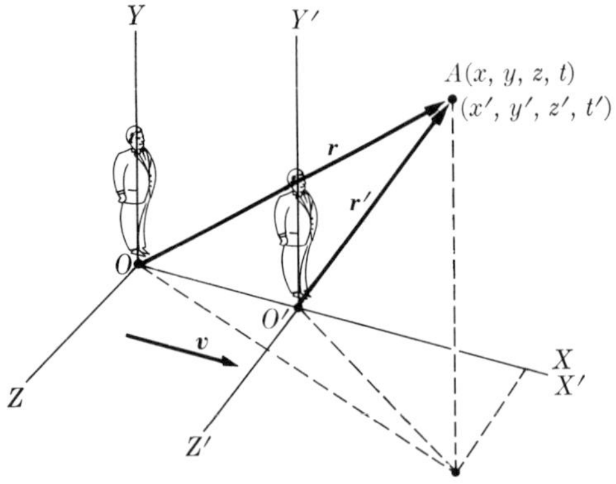

Fig. 6–14. Frames of reference in uniform relative translational motion.

Our next task is to obtain a transformation relating Eqs. (6.30) and (6.31). The symmetry of the problem suggests that $y' = y$ and $z' = z$. Also since $OO' = vt$ for observer O, it must be that $x = vt$ for $x' = 0$ (point O'). This suggests making $x' = k(x - vt)$, where k is a constant to be determined. Since t' is different, we may also assume that $t' = a(t - bx)$, where a and b are constants to be determined (for the Galilean transformation $k = a = 1$ and $b = 0$). Making all these substitutions in Eq. (6.31), we have

$$k^2(x^2 - 2vxt + v^2t^2) + y^2 + z^2 = c^2a^2(t^2 - 2bxt + b^2x^2),$$

or

$$(k^2 - b^2a^2c^2)x^2 - 2(k^2v - ba^2c^2)xt + y^2 + z^2 = (a^2 - k^2v^2/c^2)c^2t^2.$$

This result must be identical to Eq. (6.30). Therefore

$$k^2 - b^2a^2c^2 = 1, \qquad k^2v - ba^2c^2 = 0, \qquad a^2 - k^2v^2/c^2 = 1.$$

Solving this set of equations, we have

$$k = a = \frac{1}{\sqrt{1 - v^2/c^2}} \quad \text{and} \quad b = v/c^2. \tag{6.32}$$

The new transformation, which is compatible with the invariance of the velocity of light, is then

$$\begin{aligned} x' &= k(x - vt) = \frac{x - vt}{\sqrt{1 - v^2/c^2}}, \\ y' &= y, \\ z' &= z, \\ t' &= k(t - bx) = \frac{t - vx/c^2}{\sqrt{1 - v^2/c^2}}. \end{aligned} \tag{6.33}$$

This set of relations is called the *Lorentz transformation* because it was first obtained by the Dutch physicist Hendrik Lorentz, about 1890, in connection with the problem of the electromagnetic field of a moving charge.

When we note that c is a velocity very large compared with the great majority of velocities that we encounter on the earth, so that the ratio v/c is very small, the terms v^2/c^2 and vx/c^2 are, in general, negligible, and k is practically equal to

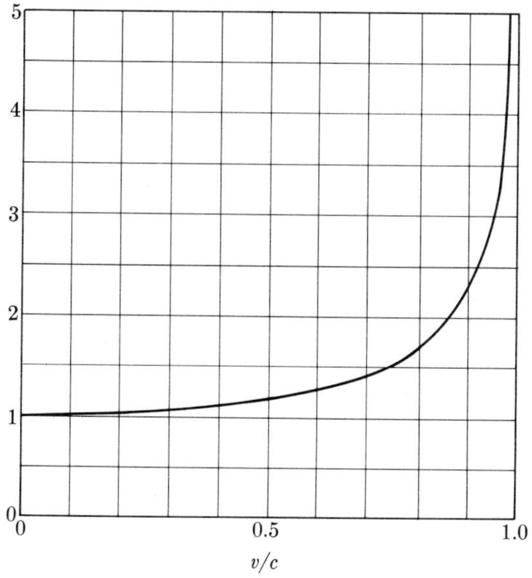

Fig. 6–15. Change of k with v/c.

one (see Fig. 6–15). From the practical point of view, then, there is no difference between Lorentz' and Galileo's transformations, and we may keep using the latter in most of the problems we encounter. However, when we are dealing with very fast particles, such as the electrons in atoms or particles in cosmic rays, we *must* use the Lorentz—or relativistic—transformation.

Even though in the majority of instances the numerical results of the Lorentz transformation do not differ to any great extent from those of the Galilean transformation, from a theoretical point of view the Lorentz transformation represents a most profound conceptual change, especially with regard to space and time.

EXAMPLE 6.4. Obtain the Lorentz transformation that expresses the coordinates x, y, z and the time t measured by O in terms of the coordinates x', y', z' and the time t' measured by O'.

Solution: This is the Lorentz transformation inverse to that expressed by Eq. (6.33). Of course, the second and third relations do not offer any difficulty. A straightforward method of handling the first and fourth equations is to look at them as a set of two simultaneous equations and, by a direct algebraic procedure, solve them for x and t in terms of x' and t'. We shall leave this method as an exercise to the student, however, and proceed along a more physical line of reasoning. From the point of view of observer O', observer O recedes along the $-X'$ direction with a velocity $-\boldsymbol{v}$. Thus O' is entitled to use the same Lorentz transformation to obtain the values x and t measured by O in terms of the values x' and t' which O' measures. For that observer O' has only to replace $\boldsymbol{v}$ by $-\boldsymbol{v}$ in Eq. (6.33) and exchange x, t and x', t'. Thus

$$\begin{aligned} x &= \frac{x' + vt'}{\sqrt{1 - v^2/c^2}}, \\ y &= y', \\ z &= z', \\ t &= \frac{t' + vx'/c^2}{\sqrt{1 - v^2/c^2}}, \end{aligned} \tag{6.34}$$

which give the inverse Lorentz transformation.

6.7 Transformation of Velocities

Next let us obtain the rule for comparing velocities. The velocity of A as measured by O has components

$$V_x = \frac{dx}{dt}, \qquad V_y = \frac{dy}{dt}, \qquad V_z = \frac{dz}{dt}. \tag{6.35}$$

Similarly, the components of the velocity of A as measured by O' are

$$V'_{x'} = \frac{dx'}{dt'}, \qquad V'_{y'} = \frac{dy'}{dt'}, \qquad V'_{z'} = \frac{dz'}{dt'}.$$

Note that we now use dt' and not dt, because t and t' are no longer the same. Differentiating Eqs. (6.33), we have

$$\begin{aligned} dx' &= \frac{dx - v\,dt}{\sqrt{1 - v^2/c^2}} = \frac{V_x - v}{\sqrt{1 - v^2/c^2}}\,dt, \\ dy' &= dy, \\ dz' &= dz, \\ dt' &= \frac{dt - v\,dx/c^2}{\sqrt{1 - v^2/c^2}} = \frac{1 - vV_x/c^2}{\sqrt{1 - v^2/c^2}}\,dt. \end{aligned}$$

In the first and last equations, dx has been replaced by $V_x\,dt$, according to Eq. (6.35). Therefore, dividing the first three of these equations by the fourth, we obtain

$$\begin{aligned} V'_{x'} &= \frac{dx'}{dt'} = \frac{V_x - v}{1 - vV_x/c^2}, \\ V'_{y'} &= \frac{dy'}{dt'} = \frac{V_y\sqrt{1 - v^2/c^2}}{1 - vV_x/c^2}, \\ V'_{z'} &= \frac{dz'}{dt'} = \frac{V_z\sqrt{1 - v^2/c^2}}{1 - vV_x/c^2}. \end{aligned} \tag{6.36}$$

This set of equations gives the law for the Lorentz transformation of velocities; that is, the rule for comparing the velocity of a body as measured by two observers in uniform relative translational motion. Again this reduces to Eq. (6.10) for relative velocities which are very small compared with the velocity of light. For particles moving in the X-direction, we have $V_x = V$, $V_y = V_z = 0$. Therefore, with $V'_{x'} = V'$, since the two other components of V' are zero, Eq. (6.36) becomes

$$V' = \frac{V - v}{1 - vV/c^2}. \tag{6.37}$$

To verify that Eq. (6.37) is compatible with the assumption that the velocity of light is the same for both observers O and O', let us consider the case of a light signal propagating along the X-direction. Then $V = c$ in Eq. (6.37) and

$$V' = \frac{c - v}{1 - vc/c^2} = c.$$

Therefore observer O' also measures a velocity c. Solving Eq. (6.37) for V, we get

$$V = \frac{V' + v}{1 + vV'/c^2}, \tag{6.38}$$

which is the reverse transformation of Eq. (6.37). Note that if V' and v are both smaller than c, then V is also smaller than c. Furthermore, the velocity v cannot be larger than c because the scaling factor $\sqrt{1 - v^2/c^2}$ would become imaginary. We can ascribe no physical meaning at the present time to such a scaling factor. Therefore the velocity of light is the maximum velocity that can be observed.

It must also be noted that Eqs. (6.37) or (6.38) relate the velocity of the *same* body as measured by two observers in relative motion. However, a given observer combines *different* velocities in his own frame of reference according to the rules established in Chapter 3.

EXAMPLE 6.5. Verify the fact that the transformation of velocities, Eq. (6.36), is compatible with the assumption that the velocity of light is the same for both observers by considering a ray of light moving along (a) the Y-axis relative to XYZ, (b) the Y'-axis relative to $X'Y'Z'$.

Solution: (a) In this case we must make $V_x = 0$, $V_y = c$, and $V_z = 0$. Thus Eq. (6.36) becomes

$$V'_{x'} = -v, \qquad V'_{y'} = c\sqrt{1 - v^2/c^2}, \qquad V'_{z'} = 0.$$

Then the velocity relative to $X'Y'Z'$ is

$$V' = \sqrt{V'^2_{x'} + V'^2_{y'}} = \sqrt{v^2 + c^2(1 - v^2/c^2)} = c,$$

and observer O' also measures a velocity c for light, as was required when deriving the Lorentz transformation. Light appears to the moving observer O' to be propagating relative to the $X'Y'Z'$ frame in a direction making an angle with the X'-axis given by

$$\tan \alpha' = \frac{V'_{y'}}{V'_{x'}} = \frac{-c}{v}\sqrt{1 - v^2/c^2}.$$

(b) Let us now consider the case in which the observer O' sees the ray of light propagating along the Y'-axis. Then $V'_{x'} = 0$, and the first two expressions in Eq. (6.36) give

$$0 = \frac{V_x - v}{1 - vV_x/c^2}, \qquad V'_{y'} = \frac{V_y\sqrt{1 - v^2/c^2}}{1 - vV_x/c^2}.$$

From the first equation we get $V_x = v$, which, when placed in the second equation, yields

$$V'_{y'} = \frac{V_y}{\sqrt{1 - v^2/c^2}}.$$

But for observer O, who measures the velocity of light as c, we have

$$c = \sqrt{V_x^2 + V_y^2} = \sqrt{v^2 + V_y^2} \quad \text{or} \quad V_y = \sqrt{c^2 - v^2} = c\sqrt{1 - v^2/c^2},$$

which, when replaced in the previous expressions for $V'_{y'}$, gives $V'_{y'} = c$. Once more we verify that observer O' also measures the velocity of light as c. The direction in which observer O sees the ray of light makes an angle α with the X-axis given by

$$\tan \alpha = \frac{V_y}{V_x} = \frac{c}{v}\sqrt{1 - v^2/c^2}.$$

The results of this problem must be compared with those of Example 6.2 for sound, in which the Galilean transformation was used.

EXAMPLE 6.6. Obtain the relation between the acceleration of a particle as measured by two observers in relative motion. For simplicity, suppose that, at the instant of the comparison, the particle is at rest relative to observer O'.

Solution: The X-component of the acceleration of the particle, as measured by O', is

$$a'_{x'} = \frac{dV'_{x'}}{dt'} = \frac{dV'_{x'}}{dt}\frac{dt}{dt'}.$$

Using the value of $V'_{x'}$ from the first relation of Eq. (6.36) and inserting the appropriate derivatives, we have

$$a'_{x'} = \left[\frac{a_x}{1 - vV_x/c^2} + \frac{(V_x - v)va_x/c^2}{(1 - vV_x/c^2)^2}\right]\frac{\sqrt{1 - v^2/c^2}}{1 - vV_x/c^2} = a_x\frac{(1 - v^2/c^2)^{3/2}}{(1 - vV_x/c^2)^3}.$$

At the moment when the particle is at rest relative to O', $V_x = v$ and

$$a'_{x'} = \frac{a_x}{(1 - v^2/c^2)^{3/2}} = k^3 a_x.$$

By a similar analysis we find that

$$a'_{y'} = \frac{a_y}{1 - v^2/c^2} = k^2 a_y, \qquad a'_{z'} = \frac{a_z}{1 - v^2/c^2} = k^2 a_z.$$

This result differs from Eq. (6.14) for the Galilean transformation, since in this case the acceleration is not the same for both observers in uniform relative motion. In other words, the requirement that the velocity of light be invariant in all frames of reference which are in uniform motion relative to each other destroys the invariance of the acceleration.

It is important to know the relation between the magnitudes of the accelerations observed by O and O'. Now

$$\begin{aligned} a'^2 &= a'^2_{x'} + a'^2_{y'} + a'^2_{z'} \\ &= \frac{a_x^2}{(1 - v^2/c^2)^3} + \frac{a_y^2}{(1 - v^2/c^2)^2} + \frac{a_z^2}{(1 - v^2/c^2)^2} \\ &= \frac{a_x^2 + (a_y^2 + a_z^2)(1 - v^2/c^2)}{(1 - v^2/c^2)^3} \\ &= \frac{a^2 - v^2(a_y^2 + a_z^2)/c^2}{(1 - v^2/c^2)^3}. \end{aligned}$$

But $\boldsymbol{v} = \boldsymbol{u}_x v$ and $\boldsymbol{v} \times \boldsymbol{a} = -\boldsymbol{u}_y v a_z + \boldsymbol{u}_z v a_y$, so that $(\boldsymbol{v} \times \boldsymbol{a})^2 = v^2(a_y^2 + a_z^2)$. Therefore

$$a'^2 = \frac{a^2 - (\boldsymbol{v} \times \boldsymbol{a})^2/c^2}{(1 - v^2/c^2)^3}, \tag{6.39}$$

which is the desired relation. When the acceleration is parallel to the velocity, $\boldsymbol{v} \times \boldsymbol{a} = 0$ and $a' = a/(1 - v^2/c^2)^{3/2}$. This agrees with the result for a_x and $a'_{x'}$. When the acceleration is perpendicular to the velocity, $(\boldsymbol{v} \times \boldsymbol{a})^2 = v^2a^2$ and $a' = a/(1 - v^2/c^2)$, which is the result for a_y, a_z and $a'_{y'}$, $a'_{z'}$.

6.8 Consequences of the Lorentz Transformation

The scaling factor $k = 1/\sqrt{1 - v^2/c^2}$ that appears in Eq. (6.33) suggests that the lengths of bodies and the time intervals between given events may not be the same when measured by observers in relative motion. We shall now discuss this important question.

(1) ***Length Contraction.*** The length of an object may be defined as the distance between its two endpoints. However, if the object is in motion relative to the observer wishing to measure its length, the positions of the two endpoints must be recorded *simultaneously*. Let us consider a bar at rest relative to O' and parallel to the $O'X'$-axis. Designating its two extremes by a and b, its length as measured by O' is $L' = x'_b - x'_a$. Simultaneity is not essential for O' because he sees the bar at rest. However, observer O, who sees the bar in motion, must measure the coordinates x_a and x_b of the endpoints at the same time t, obtaining $L = x_b - x_a$. Applying the first relation in Eq. (6.33), we find that

$$x'_a = \frac{x_a - vt}{\sqrt{1 - v^2/c^2}}$$

and

$$x'_b = \frac{x_b - vt}{\sqrt{1 - v^2/c^2}}.$$

Note that we write the same t in both expressions. Now, subtracting

$$x'_b - x'_a = \frac{x_b - x_a}{\sqrt{1 - v^2/c^2}} \qquad \text{or} \qquad L = \sqrt{1 - v^2/c^2}\, L'. \tag{6.40}$$

Since the factor $\sqrt{1 - v^2/c^2}$ is smaller than unity, we have a situation in which L is smaller than L'; that is, observer O, who sees the object in motion, measures a *smaller* length than observer O', who sees the object at rest. In other words, *objects in motion appear to be shorter;* that is, $L_{\text{motion}} < L_{\text{rest}}$.

(2) ***Time Dilation.*** A *time interval* may be defined as the time elapsed between two events, as measured by an observer. An *event* is a specific occurrence that happens at a particular point in space and at a particular time. Thus, in terms of these definitions, when the bob of a pendulum reaches its highest point during a swing, this constitutes an event. After a certain period of time it will return to this same position; this is a second event. The elapsed time between these two events is then a time interval. Thus a time interval is the time it takes to do something: for a pendulum to oscillate, for an electron to rotate around a nucleus, for a radioactive particle to decay, for a heart to beat, etc.

Let us consider two events that occur at the same place x' relative to an observer O'. The time interval between these events is $T' = t'_b - t'_a$. For an observer O with respect to whom O' is moving at a constant velocity v in the positive X-direction, the time interval is $T = t_b - t_a$. To find the relation between the times at which the two events occurred, as recorded by both observers, we use the last of Eqs. (6.34). This gives us

$$t_a = \frac{t'_a + vx'/c^2}{\sqrt{1 - v^2/c^2}}, \qquad t_b = \frac{t'_b + vx'/c^2}{\sqrt{1 - v^2/c^2}}.$$

Note that we write the same x' in both expressions. Therefore, by subtracting t_a from t_b, we have

$$t_b - t_a = \frac{t'_b - t'_a}{\sqrt{1 - v^2/c^2}} \quad \text{or} \quad T = \frac{T'}{\sqrt{1 - v^2/c^2}}. \tag{6.41}$$

Now T' is the time interval measured by an observer O' *at rest* with respect to the point where the events occurred, and T is the time interval measured by an observer O relative to whom the point is *in motion* when the events occurred. That is, observer O saw the events occur at two different positions in space. Since the factor $1/\sqrt{1 - v^2/c^2}$ is larger than one, Eq. (6.41) indicates that T is greater than T'. Therefore *processes appear to take a longer time when they occur in a body in motion relative to the observer than when the body is at rest relative to the observer; that is,* $T_{\text{motion}} > T_{\text{rest}}$.

It is informative to analyze time dilation and length contraction in greater detail, since these results are so contrary to our *a priori* expectations. We shall show in a more direct way that time dilation and length contraction are direct consequences of the invariance (constancy) of the velocity of light. Let us consider two observers O and O' in relative motion along the X-axis with velocity v. In Fig. 6–16, M' is a mirror at rest relative to O' and at a distance L from the origin along the Y'-axis. This is the same distance as measured by O, since the mirror is at a position perpendicular to the direction of motion. Suppose that, when O and O' are coincident, a light signal is flashed from their common origin toward the mirror. For the system that sees the mirror in motion, the light signal must be sent out at an angle dependent on the velocity of the mirror and the distance L. Let T and T' be the times recorded by O and O' for the light signal to return to O' after it has been reflected from the mirror. In the O'-system, the light will return to the origin, but in the O-system, the light will cross the X-axis at a distance vT from the origin. Relative to O', the path of the light signal is $O'M'O' = 2L$ and the time

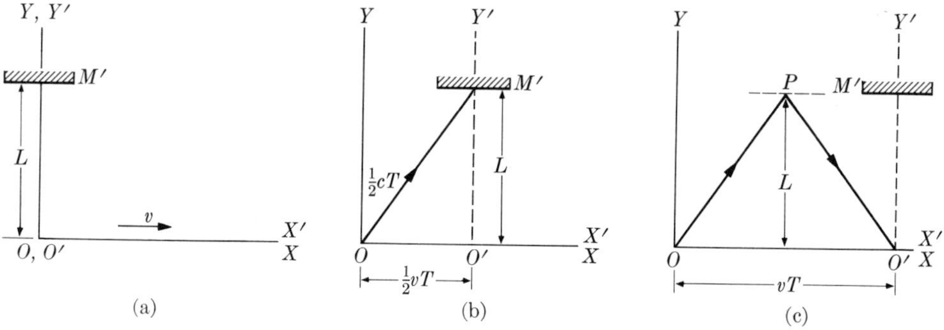

Figure 6–16

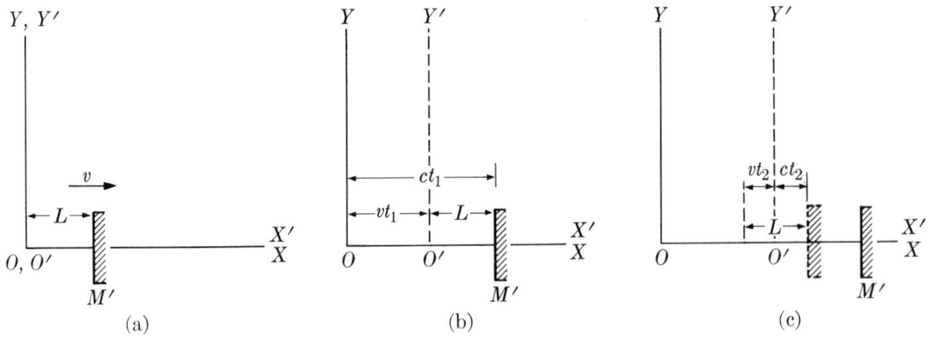

Figure 6–17

elapsed is $T' = 2L/c$, since O' measures the velocity of light as c. This time interval corresponds to two events taking place at the same point (O') relative to O'.

Relative to observer O, who also measures the velocity of light as c, the path of the light signal is OPO', and thus O sees the time relationship (from Fig. 6–16b) as being $(\frac{1}{2}cT)^2 = (\frac{1}{2}vT)^2 + L^2$ or $T = (2L/c)/\sqrt{1 - v^2/c^2}$. Therefore $T = T'/\sqrt{1 - v^2/c^2}$, which is just Eq. (6.41). Note that we have obtained time dilation specifically by requiring that the velocity of light be invariant for all inertial observers.

Next let us consider the mirror M' placed along the X'-axis and oriented perpendicular to it. We place it a distance L' from O' and consider the mirror at rest in the O'-system. The arrangement is shown in Fig. 6–17. Again when O and O' are coincident, a light signal is flashed toward the mirror. The times T and T' for the light to return to O' are again measured. The interval for O', who measures the velocity of light as c, is $T' = 2L'/c$. The distance $O'M'$ may not be the same for observer O, and we therefore call the distance L. Now the time, t_1, for the light to travel from O to the mirror is found from the relation $ct_1 = L + vt_1$ or $t_1 = L/(c - v)$, since M' has advanced the distance vt_1. On reflection, O measures a time t_2 for the light to reach O', who has moved a distance vt_2 in that time (see Fig. 6–17c). Thus $ct_2 = L - vt_2$ or $t_2 = L/(c + v)$. The total time required for the light to reach O', as measured by O, is thus

$$T = t_1 + t_2 = \frac{L}{c - v} + \frac{L}{c + v} = \frac{2L}{c}\frac{1}{1 - v^2/c^2}.$$

But T and T' correspond to two events occurring at the same place, relative to O', and are therefore related by Eq. (6.41). Thus

$$\frac{2L/c}{1 - v^2/c^2} = \frac{2L'/c}{\sqrt{1 - v^2/c^2}} \quad \text{or} \quad L = \sqrt{1 - v^2/c^2}\, L'.$$

This equation is identical to Eq. (6.40), since L' is a length at rest relative to O'. From these two special examples, we see that the constancy of the velocity of light for all inertial observers affects, in a very particular way, the results obtained by observers in relative motion.

EXAMPLE 6.7. *Analysis of the Michelson-Morley experiment.* At the beginning of Section 6.6, we mentioned the Michelson-Morley experiment. We shall describe it briefly now, and analyze the results. The experimental arrangement is shown schematically in Fig. 6–18, where S is a monochromatic source of light and M_1 and M_2 are two mirrors placed at the same distance L' from the glass plate P (as measured by a terrestrial observer). Light coming from S, when it reaches P, is partially transmitted toward M_1 and partially reflected toward M_2. Rays reflected at M_1 and M_2 retrace their paths and eventually reach the observer at O'. Note that the light path drawn in Fig. 6–18 is relative to a frame $X'Y'Z'$ moving with the earth and relative to which the instrument, called an *interferometer*, is at rest. [Drawing the path of light as seen by an observer relative to whom the earth is moving with a velocity v is suggested as an exercise for the student.] The actual experimental arrangement used by Michelson and Morley is illustrated in Fig. 6–19.

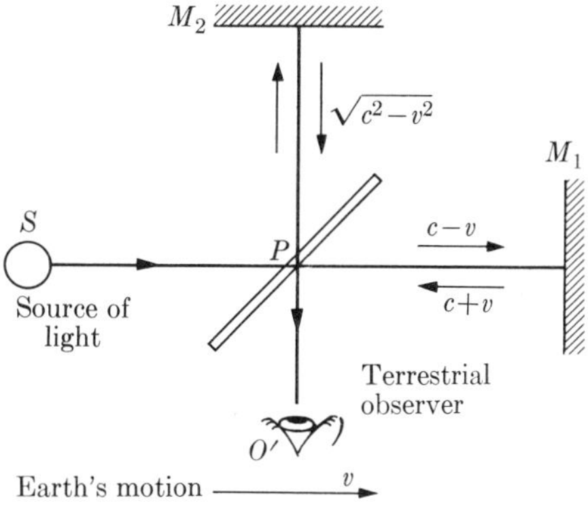

Fig. 6–18. Basic components of the Michelson-Morley experiment.

Solution: Let c be the velocity of light as measured by an observer stationary relative to the ether. Let us call v the velocity of the earth relative to the ether, and orient the interferometer so that the line PM_1 is parallel to the motion of the earth.

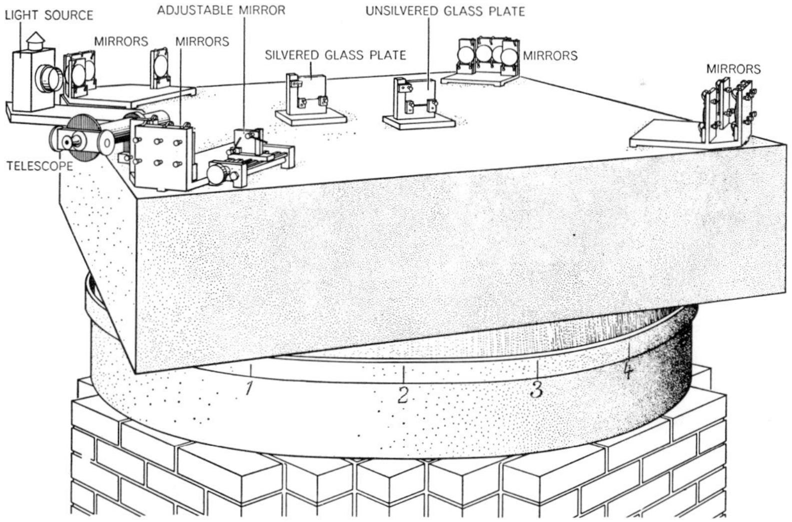

Fig. 6–19. Interferometer used by Michelson and Morley in their measurements of the velocity of light. Sandstone table holding mirrors is fixed to a wooden ring which floats on mercury. The series of mirrors serves to lengthen the total path of light. The unsilvered plate is placed along one path to compensate for the fact that the other path must pass through the glass of the mirror. The telescope permits one to observe the interference fringes. (Drawing courtesy of *Scientific American.*)

When we use the Galilean transformation, we find, following the results of Example 6.2, that, relative to the earth, the velocity of light going from P to M_1 is $c - v$, that from M_1 to P it is $c + v$, and that from P to M_2 or from M_2 to P it is $\sqrt{c^2 - v^2}$. Thus the time required by light to go from P to M_1 and back to P, as measured by the terrestrial observer O', is

$$t'_{\parallel} = \frac{L'}{c - v} + \frac{L'}{c + v} = \frac{2L'c}{c^2 - v^2} = \frac{2L'/c}{1 - v^2/c^2},$$

while the time required to go from P to M_2 and back to P, as measured by O', is

$$t'_{\perp} = \frac{2L'}{\sqrt{c^2 - v^2}} = \frac{2L'/c}{\sqrt{1 - v^2/c^2}}.$$

We note that $t'_{\parallel}$ and $t'_{\perp}$ are different, and therefore the rays that reach observer O' have a certain path difference and (according to the theory presented in Chapter 22) should result in a certain interference pattern. Surprisingly, *no* such interference pattern is observed, as previously indicated in Section 6.6.* This suggests that $t'_{\parallel} = t'_{\perp}$. To solve this puzzle Lorentz, and independently Fitzgerald, proposed that all objects moving through the ether suffer a "real" contraction in the direction of motion, and that this contraction was just enough to make $t'_{\parallel} = t'_{\perp}$. That means that the length that appears in $t'_{\parallel}$ must not be the same as the length in $t'_{\perp}$, because the first is in the direction of the earth's motion and the other is perpendicular to it. Writing L for L' in the expression for $t'_{\parallel}$, we must have

$$t'_{\parallel} = \frac{2L/c}{1 - v^2/c^2}.$$

Equating $t'_{\parallel}$ and $t'_{\perp}$, we obtain, after simplifying,

$$L = \sqrt{1 - v^2/c^2}\, L'. \tag{6.42}$$

This expression relates the lengths PM_1 and PM_2 as measured by an observer O at rest relative to the ether. Observer O' should not notice this contraction, because the measuring stick he uses to measure the distance PM_1 is also contracted to the same degree as PM_1 when placed in the direction of the earth's motion! Thus, to him, the lengths PM_1 and PM_2 are equal. But observer O would laugh at the worries of O', since he realizes that O' is in motion and, according to the Lorentz-Fitzgerald hypothesis, the objects he carries are all shortened in the direction of motion. Thus O concludes that the "real" length of PM_1 is L and that of PM_2 is L', this "real" difference in length being the source of the negative result obtained when the interference of the two light beams was examined.

Of course, an alternative explanation of the negative result of the Michelson-Morley experiment is to assume that the speed of light is always the same in all directions, no matter what the state of motion of the observer. Then observer O' uses c for all paths of Fig. 6–18, and then $t'_{\parallel} = t'_{\perp} = 2L'/c$. This was the position adopted by Albert Einstein when he was formulating his principle of relativity. The student may, however, at this

* In the actual experiment performed by Michelson, the two arms of the interferometer, or to be more precise the optical lengths of both light paths, were slightly different, resulting in an interference pattern. Therefore Michelson, to compensate for this difference and actually increase the precision of his measurement, rotated the instrument (Fig. 6–19). And although the theory, which was based on the Galilean transformation, predicted a shift in the interference pattern as a result of the rotation, no such shift was observed.

moment say that the "real" contraction assumed by Lorentz to explain the negative result of the Michelson-Morley experiment is exactly the same as the contraction we found in Eq. (6.40) by using the Lorentz transformation and the principle of the invariance of the velocity of light. There is, however, a fundamental difference between the two underlying hypotheses used for obtaining these two apparently identical results: (1) The contraction (6.42), obtained by means of the Galilean transformation, is assumed to be a *real* contraction suffered by all bodies moving through the ether, and the v appearing in the formula is the velocity of the object relative to the ether. (2) Contraction (6.40) refers only to the *measured* value of the length of the object in motion relative to the observer, and is a consequence of the invariance of the velocity of light. The v appearing in the formula is the velocity of the object relative to the observer, and thus the contraction is different for different observers. It was the genius of Einstein that led him to realize that the idea of an ether was artificial and unnecessary, and that the logical explanation was the second one. This was the basic postulate which Einstein used to formulate the principle of relativity, as we shall see in Chapter 11.

References

1. "The Coriolis Effect," J. McDonald, *Sci. Am.*, May 1952, page 72
2. "The Speed of Light," J. Rush, *Sci. Am.*, August 1955, page 62
3. "The Clock Paradox," J. Bronowski, *Sci. Am.*, February 1963, page 134
4. "Conversations with Albert Einstein," R. Shankland, *Am. J. Phys.* **31,** 47 (1963).
5. "Michelson-Morley Experiment," R. Shankland, *Am. J. Phys.* **32,** page 16 (1964); *Sci. Am.*, November 1964, page 107
6. "Measurement of the Relativistic Time Dilation Using μ-Mesons," D. Frisch and J. Smith, *Am. J. Phys.* **31,** 342 (1963)
7. "The Geometrical Appearance of Large Objects Moving at Relativistic Speeds," G. D. Scott and M. R. Viner, *Am. J. Phys.* **33,** 534 (1965)
8. "Visual Appearance of Rapidly Moving Objects," V. Weisskopf, *Physics Today*, September 1960, page 24
9. "Resource Letter SRT-1 on Special Relativity Theory," G. Holton, *Am. J. Phys.* **30,** 462 (1962)
10. *An Introduction to the Special Theory of Relativity*, R. Katz. Princeton, N.J.: Momentum Books, D. Van Nostrand Co., 1964
11. *The Special Theory of Relativity*, D. Bohm. New York: W. A. Benjamin, 1964
12. *An Introduction to the Special Theory of Relativity*, W. G. W. Rossen. London: Butterworth & Co., 1964, Chapters 1–4
13. *Special Relativity Theory*, selected reprints from the *Am. J. Phys.*, published by the AIP (335 E. 45th St., New York 17, N.Y.), 1962
14. *Mechanics*, Keith R. Symon. Reading, Mass.: Addison-Wesley, 1960, Sections 7–1 through 7–4
15. *Physical Mechanics*, Robert B. Lindsay. New York: Van Nostrand, 1961, Sections 7–11 and 7–12
16. *Vector Mechanics*, D. E. Christie. New York: McGraw-Hill, 1964, Chapter 14

17. *The Feynman Lectures on Physics,* Volume I, R. P. Feynman, R. B. Leighton, and M. L. Sands. Reading, Mass.: Addison-Wesley, 1963, Chapters 15, 18, and 20

18. *Source Book in Physics,* W. F. Magie. Cambridge, Mass.: Harvard University Press, 1963, page 27 (Huygens); page 369 (Michelson and Morley)

Problems

6.1 Two trains, A and B, are running on parallel tracks at 70 km hr^{-1} and 90 km hr^{-1}, respectively. Calculate the relative velocity of B with respect to A, when: (a) they move in the same direction, (b) they move in opposite directions.

6.2 Solve the previous problem if the tracks are set at an angle of 60° with respect to each other.

6.3 A train leaves city A at 12 noon for city B 400 km away, and maintains a constant speed of 100 km hr^{-1}. Another train leaves city B at 2:00 P.M. and maintains a constant speed of 70 km hr^{-1}. Determine the time at which the trains pass and the distance to city A if (a) the second train heads toward city A, and (b) the second train heads away from city A.

6.4 A man driving through a rainstorm at 80 km hr^{-1} observes that the raindrops make tracks on the side windows that have an angle of 80° with the vertical. When he stops his car, he observes that the rain is actually falling vertically. Calculate the relative velocity of the rain with respect to the car (a) when it is still, and (b) when it is moving at 80 km hr^{-1}.

6.5 Two cars moving along perpendicular roads are traveling north and east, respectively. If their velocities with respect to the ground are 60 km hr^{-1} and 80 km hr^{-1}, calculate their relative velocity. Does the relative velocity depend on the position of the cars on their respective roads? Repeat the problem, assuming that the second car moves west.

6.6 A boat is moving in the direction N 60° W at 4.0 km hr^{-1} relative to the water. The current is in such a direction that the resultant motion relative to the earth is due west at 5.0 km hr^{-1}. Calculate the velocity and direction of the current with respect to the earth.

6.7 The velocity of a speedboat in still water is 55 km hr^{-1}. The driver wants to go to a point located 80 km away at S 20° E. The current is very strong at 20 km hr^{-1} in the direction S 70° W. (a) Calculate which direction the speedboat should be headed so that it travels in a straight line. (b) Determine the length of time for the trip.

6.8 A river flows due north with a velocity of 3 km hr^{-1}. A boat is going east with a velocity relative to the water of 4 km hr^{-1}. (a) Calculate the velocity of the boat relative to the earth. (b) If the river is 1 km wide, calculate the time necessary for a crossing. (c) What is the northward deviation of the boat when it reaches the other side of the river?

6.9 Two places, A and B, are 1 km apart and located on the bank of a rectilinear (perfectly straight) river section. A man goes from A to B and back to A in a rowboat that is rowed at 4 km hr^{-1} relative to the river. Another man walks along the bank from A to B and back again at 4 km hr^{-1}. If the river flows at 2 km hr^{-1}, calculate the time taken by each man to make the round trip.

6.10 Using the data of the previous problem, determine the speed of the river so that the time difference for the two round trips is 6 min.

6.11 A river is 1 km wide. The current is 2 km hr^{-1}. Determine the time it would take a man to row a boat directly across the river and back again. Compare this time with the time it would take a man to row 1 km upstream and back again. The rowboat moves with a constant velocity of 4 km hr^{-1} with respect to the water.

6.12 Using the data of the previous problem, determine the current velocity if the time difference between the two round trips is 10 minutes.

6.13 Given a coordinate system fixed with respect to the earth (assume the earth flat and "motionless"). Consider a bullet that has a muzzle velocity of 800 ft s^{-1} fired from the tail gun of an airplane moving with a velocity of 700 ft s^{-1} (approximately 440 mi hr^{-1}). Describe the motion of the bullet (a) in the earth's coordinate system, (b) in the coordinate system attached to the plane. (c) Calculate the angle at which the gunner must point the gun so that the bullet has no horizontal component of velocity in the earth's coordinate system.

6.14 The position of a particle Q in a coordinate system O is measured as $\boldsymbol{r} = \boldsymbol{u}_x(6t^2 - 4t) + \boldsymbol{u}_y(-3t^3) + \boldsymbol{u}_z 3$ m. (a) Determine the constant relative velocity of system O' with respect to O if the position of Q is measured as $\boldsymbol{r}' = \boldsymbol{u}_x(6t^2 + 3t) + \boldsymbol{u}_y(-3t^3) + \boldsymbol{u}_z 3$ m. (b) Show that the acceleration of the particle is the same in both systems.

6.15 A train passes through a station at 30 m s^{-1}. A ball is rolling along the floor of the train with a velocity of 15 m s^{-1} directed (a) along the direction of the train's motion, (b) in the opposite direction, and (c) perpendicular to the motion. Find, in each case, the velocity of the ball relative to an observer standing on the station platform.

6.16 A particle with a velocity of 500 m s^{-1} relative to the earth is heading due south at latitude 45° N. (a) Compute the centrifugal acceleration of the particle. (b) Compute the Coriolis acceleration of the particle. (c) Repeat the problem for the position latitude 45° S.

6.17 A body falls from a height of 200 m at a point whose latitude is 41° N. Find the eastward deviation with respect to the point directly (radially) below. Repeat this problem for a point at latitude 41° S.

6.18 A river is flowing southward (northward) at a rate of 9 km/hr at 45° latitude N (S). Find the Coriolis acceleration. Show that in the Northern (Southern) hemisphere it pushes the water against the right (left) bank. This effect produces a somewhat larger erosion on the right (left) bank that has been noticed in some cases.

6.19 You are flying along the equator due east in a jet plane at 450 m s^{-1} (about 1000 mi hr^{-1}). What is your Coriolis acceleration?

6.20 The planet Jupiter rotates on its axis once in 9 hr and 51 min, has a radius of approximately 7×10^4 km, and the acceleration due to gravity at its surface is 26.5 m s^{-2}. What is the maximum deviation of the plumb line from the radial direction on the surface of Jupiter?

6.21 Compare the values of the acceleration of gravity given in Table 6–1 with the theoretical values predicted by Eq. (6.29).

6.22 A body is thrown vertically upward with a velocity v_0. Prove that it will fall back on a point displaced to the west by a distance equal to $(\frac{4}{3})\omega \cos \lambda \sqrt{8h^3/g}$, where $h = v_0^2/2g$.

6.23 Obtain the expressions for the velocity and acceleration of a point as recorded by two observers O and O' moving with relative angular velocity $\boldsymbol{\omega}$, when $\boldsymbol{\omega}$ is not constant. Consider this problem when the origins coincide and then when they are displaced.

6.24 Observers O and O' are in relative translational motion with $v = 0.6c$. (a) Observer O sees that a stick, aligned parallel to the motion, is at rest relative to him and measures 2.0 m. How long is the stick according to O'? (b) If the same stick is at rest in O', and is aligned parallel to the motion, how long is the stick according to O and O'?

6.25 Determine the relative velocity of a stick which has a measured length equal to $\frac{1}{2}$ of its rest length.

6.26 By what amount does the earth appear shortened along its diameter to an observer at rest relative to the sun? (The orbital velocity of the earth relative to the sun is 30 km s^{-1}, and the radius of the earth is given in Table 13–1.)

6.27 A rocket ship heading toward the moon passes the earth with a relative velocity of $0.8c$. (a) How long does the trip from the earth to the moon take, according to an observer on the earth? (b) What is the earth–moon distance, according to a passenger on the rocket? (c) How long does the trip take, according to the passenger?

6.28 The average lifetime of a neutron, as a free particle at rest, is 15 min. It disintegrates spontaneously into an electron, proton, and neutrino. What is the average minimum velocity with which a neutron must leave the sun in order to reach the earth before breaking up?

6.29 A μ-meson is an unstable particle whose mean life is 2×10^{-6} s as measured by an observer at rest relative to the meson. What will be its mean life to an observer who sees the meson moving with a velocity of $0.9c$? If a large burst of such mesons is produced at a certain point in the atmosphere, but only 1% reach the earth's surface, estimate the height of the point where the burst originated.

6.30 A radioactive nucleus is moving with a velocity of $0.1c$ relative to the laboratory when it emits an electron with a velocity of $0.8c$ relative to the nucleus. What is the velocity and direction of the electron relative to the laboratory if, relative to the frame of reference attached to the decaying nucleus, the electron is emitted (a) in the direction of motion, (b) in the opposite direction, (c) in the perpendicular direction?

6.31 Observers O and O' are in relative translational motion, with $v = 0.6c$. They coincide at $t = t' = 0$. When five years have passed, according to O, how long does it take a light signal to get from O to O'? With this information known by both O and O', how much time has elapsed according to O' since O and O' coincided? A light placed at O is turned on for one year. How long is the light on, according to O'?

6.32 Answer the previous problem when the relative translation motion is $0.9c$.

6.33 A rocket, whose rest length is 60 m, is moving directly away from the earth. The ship is fitted with mirrors at each end. A light signal, sent from the earth, is reflected back from the two mirrors. The first light signal is received after 200 s and the second 1.74 μs later. Find the distance of the rocket from the earth and its velocity relative to the earth.

6.34 An astronaut wishes to go to a star five light years away. Calculate the velocity of his rocket relative to the earth so that the time, as measured by the astronaut's own clock, is one year. What will be the time for this mission as recorded by a terrestrial observer?

6.35 A student is given an examination to be completed in one hour, as measured by the professor's clock. The professor moves at a velocity of $0.97c$ relative to the student and sends back a light signal when his clock reads one hour. The student stops writing when the light signal reaches him. How much time did the student have for the examination?

6.36 A scientist wishes to use the Michelson-Morley method to measure wind velocity, by sending out sound signals on two perpendicular paths. He assumes the velocity of sound to be 300 m s^{-1} and the path length to be 100 m. What minimum wind velocity can he detect if he can measure a time difference $\Delta t \geq 0.001$ s?

6.37 Prove that the general Lorentz transformation when the coordinate axes used by O and O' are not parallel to the relative velocity is

$$\boldsymbol{r}' = \boldsymbol{r} + (k - 1)\frac{(\boldsymbol{r} \cdot \boldsymbol{v})\boldsymbol{v}}{v^2} - k\boldsymbol{v}t,$$

$$t' = k(t - \boldsymbol{r} \cdot \boldsymbol{v}/c^2).$$

[*Hint:* Resolve vectors $\boldsymbol{r}$ and $\boldsymbol{r}'$ into components parallel and perpendicular to $\boldsymbol{v}$; note that $\boldsymbol{r}' = \boldsymbol{r}'_{\parallel} + \boldsymbol{r}'_{\perp}$ and $\boldsymbol{r}_{\parallel} = (\boldsymbol{r} \cdot \boldsymbol{v})\boldsymbol{v}/v^2$.]

6.38 Prove that if V and V' are the magnitudes of the velocity of a particle as measured by observers O and O' moving along the X-axis with relative velocity v, then

$$\sqrt{1 - V'^2/c^2} = \frac{\sqrt{(1 - v^2/c^2)(1 - V^2/c^2)}}{1 - vV_x/c^2}$$

and

$$\sqrt{1 - V^2/c^2} = \frac{\sqrt{(1 - v^2/c^2)(1 - V'^2/c^2)}}{1 + vV'_x/c^2}.$$

6.39 Prove that the general transformation for the acceleration of a particle as measured by O and O', when the particle moves with velocity V relative to O, is

$$a'_x = \frac{a_x(1 - v^2/c^2)^{3/2}}{(1 - vV_x/c^2)^3},$$

$$a'_y = \frac{1 - v^2/c^2}{(1 - vV_x/c^2)^2}\left(a_y + a_x\frac{vV_y/c^2}{1 - vV_x/c^2}\right),$$

$$a'_z = \frac{1 - v^2/c^2}{(1 - vV_x/c^2)^2}\left(a_z + a_x\frac{vV_z/c^2}{1 - vV_x/c^2}\right).$$

6.40 Prove that when v is almost equal to c, then $k \approx 1/\sqrt{2(1 - v/c)}$, and that when v is very small compared with c, then $k \approx 1 + v^2/2c^2$.

6.41 A cubical box, of side L_0 as measured by an observer O' at rest with it, moves with velocity v parallel to one side relative to another observer O. Prove that the volume measured by O is $L_0^3\sqrt{1 - v^2/c^2}$.

6.42 A particle moves relative to an observer O so that its position at time t is $x = vt$, $y = \frac{1}{2}at^2$ and its path is a parabola. Describe its motion relative to an observer O' who moves relative to O with a velocity v. In particular, find its path and its acceleration.

6.43 A meter stick is held at an angle of 45° with respect to the direction of motion in a moving coordinate system. What is its length and its orientation, measured in the laboratory system, if the moving system has a velocity of $0.8c$?

6.44 *Discussion of simultaneity.* (a) Prove that if two events occur relative to observer O at times t_1 and t_2 and at places x_1 and x_2, and if $T = t_2 - t_1$, $L = x_2 - x_1$, the events appear to observer O' (moving relative to O with velocity v along the X-axis) at times t'_1 and t'_2 such that, if

$$T' = t'_2 - t'_1,$$

then

$$T' = k(T - vL/c^2).$$

(b) In general, are events that appear as simultaneous to O also simultaneous to O'? Under what conditions are events that appear simultaneous to O also simultaneous to all other observers in uniform relative motion? (c) Obtain the relation between L and T such that the order in which two events, as observed by O', is reversed for O. (d) Suppose that events (x_1, t_1) and (x_2, t_2) observed by O are related causally [that is, (x_2, t_2) is the result of some signal transmitted from (x_1, t_1) with velocity $V = L/T$, by necessity smaller than or equal to c]. Can the order of the events appear reversed to O'? [Note that if the answer is yes, then the theory requires that $V > c$.]

6.45 Prove that the law of transformation of velocities can be written in vector form as

$$\boldsymbol{V}' = \frac{1}{k(1 - \boldsymbol{V}\cdot\boldsymbol{v}/c^2)}\left[\boldsymbol{V} + (k-1)\frac{\boldsymbol{V}\cdot\boldsymbol{v}}{v^2}\boldsymbol{v} - k\boldsymbol{v}\right].$$

6.46 Prove that the law of transformation of accelerations can be written in vector form as

$$\boldsymbol{a}' = \frac{1}{k^3(1 - \boldsymbol{V}\cdot\boldsymbol{v}/c^2)^3}\left[\boldsymbol{a} + \left(\frac{1}{k} - 1\right)\frac{\boldsymbol{a}\cdot\boldsymbol{v}}{v^2}\boldsymbol{v} - \frac{1}{c^2}\boldsymbol{v}\times(\boldsymbol{a}\times\boldsymbol{V})\right].$$

7
DYNAMICS OF A PARTICLE

7.1 Introduction

In Chapter 5, which dealt with kinematics, we discussed the elements that enter into the "description" of the motion of a particle. Let us now investigate the reasons *why* particles move the way they do. Why do bodies near the surface of the earth fall with constant acceleration? Why does the earth move around the sun in an elliptical orbit? Why do atoms bind together to form molecules? Why does a spring oscillate when it is stretched? We want to understand these and many other motions that we continually observe around us. This understanding is important not only to our basic knowledge of nature, but also for engineering and practical applications. Understanding how motions in general are produced enables us to design machines and other practical devices that move as we desire. The study of the relationship between the motion of a body and the causes for this motion is called *dynamics*.

From daily experience we know that the motion of a body is a direct result of its *interactions* with the other bodies around it. When a batter hits a ball, he is interacting with it and modifying its motion. The path of a projectile is but a result of its interaction with the earth. The motion of an electron around a nucleus is the result of its interactions with the nucleus and perhaps with other electrons. Interactions are conveniently described by a mathematical concept called *force*. The study of dynamics is basically the analysis of the relation between force and the changes in motion of a body.

The laws of motion which we shall present in the following discussion are generalizations arising from a careful analysis of the motions we observe around us and the extrapolation of our observations to certain ideal or simplified experiments.

7.2 The Law of Inertia

A *free particle* is one that is not subject to any interaction. Strictly speaking, there is no such thing, because each particle is subject to interactions with the rest of the particles in the world. Therefore a free particle should either be completely isolated, or else be the only particle in the world. But then it would be impossible to observe it because, in the process of observation, there is always an interaction between the observer and the particle. In practice, however, there are some particles which may be considered free, either because they are sufficiently far away from others for their interactions to be negligible, or because the interactions with the other particles cancel, giving a zero net interaction.

Let us now consider the *law of inertia*, which states that

> *a free particle always moves with constant velocity, or* (which amounts to the same thing) *without acceleration.*

That is, a free particle either moves in a straight line with constant speed or is at rest (zero velocity). This statement is also called *Newton's first law*, because it was stated initially by Sir Isaac Newton (1642–1727). It is the first of three "laws" which he enunciated in the seventeenth century.

We recall from Chapters 5 and 6 that motion is relative. Therefore, when we state the law of inertia we must indicate to whom or what the motion of the free particle is referred. We assume that the motion of the particle is relative to an observer who is himself a free particle or system; i.e., who is not subject to interactions with the rest of the world. Such an observer is called an *inertial observer*, and the frame of reference he uses is called an *inertial frame of reference*. We assume that inertial frames of reference are not rotating, because the existence of rotations would imply that there are accelerations (or changes in velocity due to changes in direction), and therefore that there are interactions, which would be contrary to our definition of the inertial observer as being a "free particle," or one without acceleration. According to the law of inertia, different inertial observers may be in motion, relative to each other, with constant velocity. Therefore their observations are correlated through either the Galilean or the Lorentz transformation, depending on the magnitude of their relative velocities.

Because of its daily rotation and its interaction with the sun and the other planets, the earth is *not* an inertial frame of reference. However, in many cases the effects of the earth's rotation and interaction are negligible, and the frames of reference attached to our terrestrial laboratories can, without great error, be considered inertial. Nor is the sun an inertial frame of reference. Because of its interactions with the other bodies in the galaxy, it describes a curved orbit about the center of the galaxy (Fig. 7–1). However, since the sun's motion is more nearly rectilinear and uniform than that of the earth (the orbital acceleration of the earth is 15 million times that of the sun), the sun's resemblance to an inertial frame is much greater.

Let us illustrate some experiments performed in our terrestrial laboratories that support the law of inertia. A spherical ball resting on a smooth horizontal surface will remain at rest unless acted upon. That is, its velocity remains constant, with value equal to zero. We assume that the surface on which the ball is resting balances the interaction between the ball and the earth, and hence that the ball is essentially free of interactions. When the ball is hit, as in billiards, it momentarily suffers an interaction and gains velocity, but afterward is free again, moving in a straight line with the velocity it acquired when it was struck. If the ball is rigid and perfectly spherical, and the surface perfectly horizontal and smooth, we may

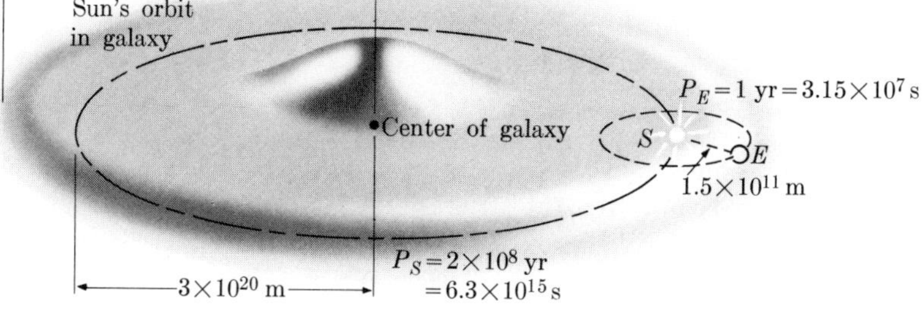

Fig. 7–1. A coordinate system attached to the earth is not inertial because of its daily rotation and its accelerated motion around the sun. Nor is the sun an inertial frame because of its motion about the center of the galaxy. However, for practical purposes, either of these two bodies may be used to define an inertial frame.

assume that the ball will continue moving that way indefinitely. In practice this is not the case, for the ball slows down and eventually stops. We say that there has been an additional interaction between the ball and the surface. This interaction, called *friction,* will be discussed later.

7.3 Linear Momentum

In Section 2.3 we gave an operational definition of *mass* by saying that it is a number we attach to each particle or body and that it is obtained by comparing the body with a standard body, using the principle of an equal arm balance. Mass, therefore, is a coefficient that distinguishes one particle from another. Our operational definition of mass gives us its value, assuming that the particle is at rest. However, we do not know from that definition whether the mass will be the same when the particle is in motion; therefore, to be precise, we should use the term *rest mass.* But let us assume, for the time being, that the mass is independent of the state of motion and call it simply mass. Later on, in Chapter 11, we shall make a more careful analysis of this important aspect and verify that our assumption is a good approximation so long as the velocity of the particle is very small compared with the velocity of light.

The *linear momentum* of a particle is defined as the product of its mass and its velocity. Designating it by $\boldsymbol{p}$, we write

$$\boldsymbol{p} = m\boldsymbol{v}. \tag{7.1}$$

Linear momentum is a vector quantity, and it has the same direction as the velocity. It is a very important physical concept because it combines the two elements that characterize the dynamical state of a particle: its mass and its velocity. Henceforth we shall write the word *momentum* instead of "linear momentum." In the MKSC system, momentum is expressed in m kg s^{-1} (no special name has been given to this unit).

That momentum is a more informative dynamical quantity than velocity alone can be seen from several simple experiments. For example, a loaded truck in motion is more difficult to stop or to speed up than an empty one, even if the velocity is the same for each, because the momentum of the loaded one is greater.

We may now restate the law of inertia by saying that

a free particle always moves with constant momentum.

7.4 Principle of Conservation of Momentum

One immediate consequence of the law of inertia is that an inertial observer recognizes that a particle is not free (i.e., that it is interacting with other particles) when he observes that the velocity or the momentum of the particle fails to remain constant; or in other words, when the particle experiences an acceleration.

Let us now consider an ideal situation. Suppose that, instead of observing one isolated particle in the universe, as assumed in the law of inertia, we observe two particles which are subject only to their mutual interaction and are otherwise isolated from the rest of the world. As a result of their interaction, their individual velocities are not constant but change with time, and their paths in general are curved, as indicated in Fig. 7–2 by curves (1) and (2). At a particular time t, particle 1 is at A with velocity $\boldsymbol{v}_1$ and particle 2 is at B with velocity $\boldsymbol{v}_2$. At a later time t', the particles are at A' and B' with velocities $\boldsymbol{v}_1'$ and $\boldsymbol{v}_2'$, respectively. Denoting the masses of the particles by m_1 and m_2, we say that the total momentum of the system at time t is

$$\boldsymbol{P} = \boldsymbol{p}_1 + \boldsymbol{p}_2 = m_1\boldsymbol{v}_1 + m_2\boldsymbol{v}_2. \tag{7.2}$$

At a later time t', the total momentum of the system is

$$\boldsymbol{P}' = \boldsymbol{p}_1' + \boldsymbol{p}_2' = m_1\boldsymbol{v}_1' + m_2\boldsymbol{v}_2'. \tag{7.3}$$

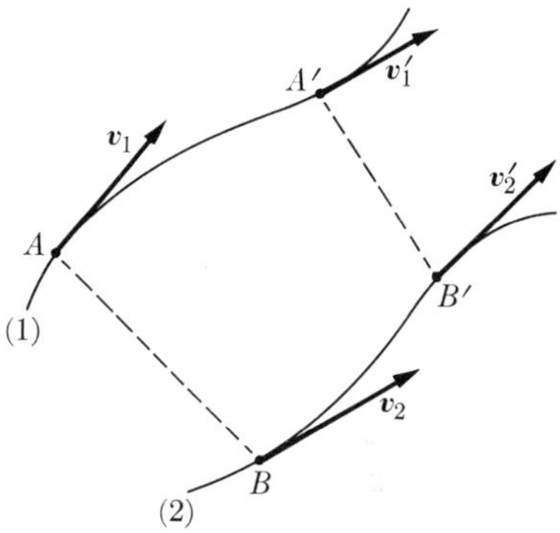

Fig. 7–2. Interaction between two particles.

In writing this equation we have maintained our assumption that the masses of the particles are independent of their states of motion; thus we have used the same masses as in Eq. (7.2). Otherwise we would have to write $\boldsymbol{P}' = m_1'\boldsymbol{v}_1' + m_2'\boldsymbol{v}_2'$. The important result of our experiment is that no matter what the times t and t' are, we always find, as a result of our observation, that $\boldsymbol{P} = \boldsymbol{P}'$. In other words,

the total momentum of a system composed of two particles which are subject only to their mutual interaction remains constant.

This result constitutes the *principle of the conservation of momentum,* one of the most fundamental and universal principles of physics. For example, consider a hydrogen atom, composed of an electron revolving around a proton, and let us assume that it is isolated so that only the interaction between the electron and the proton has to be considered. Then the sum of the momenta of the electron and the proton relative to an inertial frame of reference is constant. Similarly, consider the system composed of the earth and the moon. If it were possible to neglect the interactions due to the sun and the other bodies of the planetary system, then the sum of the momenta of the earth and the moon, relative to an inertial frame of reference, would be constant.

Although the above-stated principle of the conservation of momentum considers only two particles, this principle holds also for any number of particles forming an isolated system; i.e., particles which are subject only to their own mutual interactions and not to interactions with other parts of the world. Therefore, the principle of conservation of momentum in its general form says that

the total momentum of an isolated system of particles is constant.

For example, consider a hydrogen molecule composed of two hydrogen atoms (therefore of two electrons and two protons). If the molecule is isolated, so that only the interactions among these four particles have to be considered, the sum of their momenta relative to an inertial frame of reference will be constant. Similarly, consider our planetary system, composed of the sun, the planets, and their satellites. If we could neglect the interactions with all other heavenly bodies, the total momentum of the planetary system relative to an inertial frame of reference would be constant.

No exceptions to this general principle of conservation of momentum are known. In fact, whenever this principle seems to be violated in an experiment, the physicist immediately looks for some unknown or hidden particle which he has failed to notice and which may be responsible for the apparent lack of conservation of momentum. It is this search which has led physicists to identify the neutron, the neutrino, the photon, and many other elementary particles. Later on we shall have to reformulate the principle of conservation of momentum in a slightly different way; but for the great majority of the problems we shall discuss, we may use it in the form in which it has been stated here.

The conservation of momentum may be expressed mathematically by writing the following equation:

$$\boldsymbol{P} = \textstyle\sum_i \boldsymbol{p}_i = \boldsymbol{p}_1 + \boldsymbol{p}_2 + \boldsymbol{p}_3 + \cdots = \text{const}, \tag{7.4}$$

which implies that, in an isolated system, the change of momentum of a particle during a particular interval of time is equal to the negative of the change of momentum of the rest of the system during the same time interval. So, for example, in the case of an isolated hydrogen molecule, the change of momentum of one of the electrons is equal and opposite to the sum of the changes of momenta of the other electron and the two protons.

For the particular case of two particles,

$$\boldsymbol{p}_1 + \boldsymbol{p}_2 = \text{const} \tag{7.5}$$

or

$$\boldsymbol{p}_1 + \boldsymbol{p}_2 = \boldsymbol{p}'_1 + \boldsymbol{p}'_2. \tag{7.6}$$

Note, from Eq. (7.6), that

$$\boldsymbol{p}'_1 - \boldsymbol{p}_1 = \boldsymbol{p}_2 - \boldsymbol{p}'_2 = -(\boldsymbol{p}'_2 - \boldsymbol{p}_2). \tag{7.7}$$

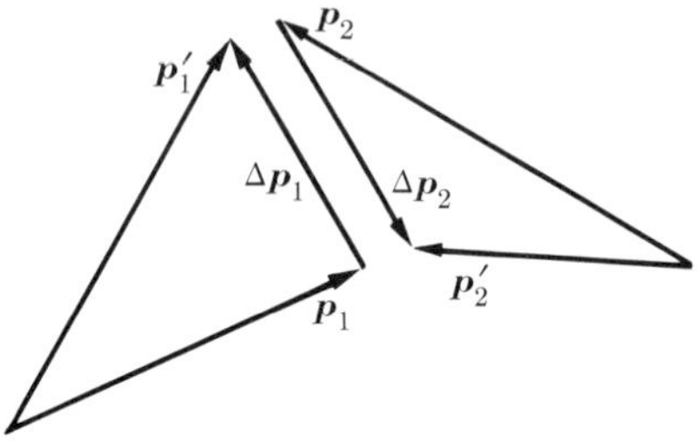

Fig. 7-3. Momentum exchange as a result of the interaction between two particles.

Or, calling $\boldsymbol{p}' - \boldsymbol{p} = \Delta\boldsymbol{p}$ the change in momentum between times t and t', we can write

$$\Delta\boldsymbol{p}_1 = -\Delta\boldsymbol{p}_2. \tag{7.8}$$

This result indicates that, for two interacting particles, the change in momentum of one particle in a certain time interval is equal and opposite to the change in momentum of the other during the same time interval (Fig. 7–3). Thus the above result may also be expressed by saying that

an interaction produces an exchange of momentum,

so that the momentum "lost" by one of the interacting particles is equal to the momentum "gained" by the other particle.

The law of inertia stated in Section 7.2 is just one particular case of the principle of conservation of momentum. Because if we have only one isolated particle instead of several, Eq. (7.4) has only one term and becomes $\boldsymbol{p} =$ const or its equivalent, $\boldsymbol{v} =$ const, which is the law of inertia.

We continually find around us examples of the principle of conservation of momentum. The recoil of a firearm is one. Initially the system of gun plus bullet is at rest, and the total momentum is zero. When the gun is fired, it recoils to compensate for the forward momentum gained by the bullet. When a nucleus disintegrates, emitting (for example) an electron and a neutrino, the total momentum of the electron, the neutrino, and the resultant nucleus must add to zero, since initially the system was at rest with respect to an inertial frame attached to the laboratory. Similarly, if a grenade or bomb explodes in flight, the total momentum of all the fragments immediately after the explosion must add to a value equal to the momentum of the grenade immediately before exploding (Fig. 7–4).

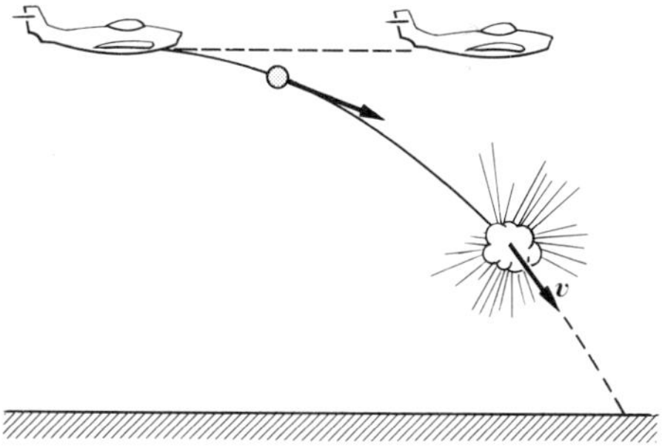

Fig. 7–4. Momentum is conserved in the explosion of a grenade.

EXAMPLE 7.1. A gun whose mass is 0.80 kg fires a bullet whose mass is 0.016 kg with a velocity of 700 m s^{-1}. Compute the velocity of the gun's recoil.

Solution: Initially both the gun and the bullet are at rest and their total momentum is zero. After the explosion the bullet is moving forward with a momentum

$$p_1 = m_1 v_1 = (0.016 \text{ kg}) \times (700 \text{ m s}^{-1}) = 11.20 \text{ m kg s}^{-1}.$$

The gun must then recoil with an equal but opposite momentum. Therefore we must have also

$$p_2 = 11.20 \text{ m kg s}^{-1} = m_2 v_2$$

or, since $m_2 = 0.80$ kg,

$$v_2 = \frac{11.20 \text{ m kg s}^{-1}}{0.80 \text{ kg}} = 14.0 \text{ m s}^{-1}.$$

EXAMPLE 7.2. Analysis of conservation of momentum in interactions between atomic particles.

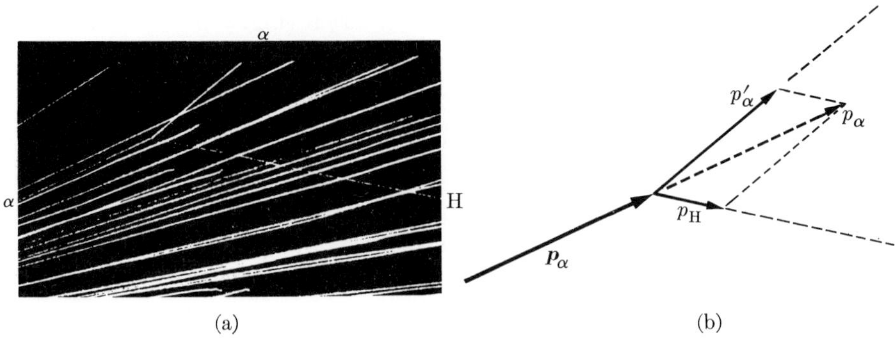

Fig. 7–5. Momentum conservation in the collision of an α-particle (helium nucleus) and a proton (hydrogen nucleus).

Solution: The cloud-chamber photograph in Fig. 7–5(a) shows an incoming alpha particle (or helium nucleus) interacting with an atom of hydrogen which was initially at rest, and which was part of the gas in the chamber. The alpha particle is deflected from its original direction and the atom of hydrogen is set in motion. If we know the respective masses, which in this case are in the ratio of 4 to 1, and measure their velocities (by special techniques devised to analyze cloud-chamber photographs), we can draw the momentum diagram of Fig. 7–5(b). When, after the interaction, the two momenta are added, the result is equal to the momentum of the incoming alpha particle; that is, $\boldsymbol{p}_\alpha = \boldsymbol{p}'_\alpha + \boldsymbol{p}_H$. So far conservation of momentum has been observed to hold in all atomic and nuclear interactions.

7.5 Redefinition of Mass

Using definition (7.1) of momentum, and assuming that the mass of a particle is constant, we may express the change in momentum of the particle in a time Δt as

$$\Delta \boldsymbol{p} = \Delta(m\boldsymbol{v}) = m\,\Delta \boldsymbol{v}.$$

Hence Eq. (7.8) reads $m_1\,\Delta \boldsymbol{v}_1 = -m_2\,\Delta \boldsymbol{v}_2$ or, considering only the magnitudes, we have

$$\frac{m_2}{m_1} = \frac{|\Delta \boldsymbol{v}_1|}{|\Delta \boldsymbol{v}_2|}, \tag{7.9}$$

which indicates that the ratio of the masses of the particles is inversely proportional to the magnitude of the changes of velocity. This result allows us to define mass dynamically. In fact, if particle 1 is our "standard" particle, its mass m_1 may be defined as unity. By letting any other particle—let us call it 2—interact with the standard particle and applying Eq. (7.9), we may obtain its mass m_2. This result indicates that our previous operational definition of mass in Section 2.3 can be replaced by this new operational definition, derived from the principle of conservation of momentum and the assumption that mass does not change with velocity.

7.6 Newton's Second and Third Laws; Concept of Force

In many cases we observe the motion of only one particle, either because we have no way of observing the other particles with which it interacts or because we purposely ignore them. In this situation it is rather difficult to use the principle of conservation of momentum. However, there is a practical way of circumventing this difficulty, by introducing the concept of *force*. The corresponding mathematical theory is called *dynamics of a particle.*

Equation (7.8) relates the changes in momentum of particles 1 and 2 during the time interval $\Delta t = t' - t$. Dividing both sides of this equation by Δt, we may write

$$\frac{\Delta \boldsymbol{p}_1}{\Delta t} = -\frac{\Delta \boldsymbol{p}_2}{\Delta t}, \tag{7.10}$$

which indicates that the average rates of (vector) change of momentum of the particles in a time interval Δt are equal in magnitude and opposite in direction. If we make Δt very small, i.e., if we find the limit of Eq. (7.10) as $\Delta t \to 0$, we get

$$\frac{d\boldsymbol{p}_1}{dt} = -\frac{d\boldsymbol{p}_2}{dt}, \tag{7.11}$$

so that the instantaneous rates of (vector) change of momentum of the particles, at any time t, are equal and opposite. Thus, using our previous examples, we can see that the rate of change of momentum of the electron in an isolated hydrogen atom is equal and opposite to the rate of change of momentum of the proton. Or, if we assume that the earth and the moon constitute an isolated system, the rate of change of momentum of the earth is equal and opposite to the rate of change of momentum of the moon.

We shall designate the time rate of change of momentum of a particle by the name "force." That is, the force "acting" on a particle is

$$\boldsymbol{F} = \frac{d\boldsymbol{p}}{dt}. \tag{7.12}$$

The word "acting" is somewhat misleading because it suggests the idea of something applied to the particle. Force is a mathematical concept which, by definition, is equal to the time rate of change of momentum of a given particle, which in turn is due to the interaction of the particle with other particles. Therefore, physically, we may consider force as an expression of an interaction. If the particle is free, $\boldsymbol{p} = \text{const}$ and $\boldsymbol{F} = d\boldsymbol{p}/dt = 0$. Hence we can say that no force acts on a free particle.

Expression (7.12) is *Newton's second law of motion;* but, as we can see, it is more a definition than a law, and is a direct consequence of the principle of conservation of momentum.

Using the concept of force, we can write Eq. (7.11) in the form

$$\boldsymbol{F}_1 = -\boldsymbol{F}_2, \tag{7.13}$$

where $\boldsymbol{F}_1 = d\boldsymbol{p}_1/dt$ is the force on particle 1 due to its interaction with particle 2 and $\boldsymbol{F}_2 = d\boldsymbol{p}_2/dt$ is the force on particle 2 due to its interaction with particle 1. Then we conclude that

when two particles interact, the force on one particle is equal and opposite to the force on the other.

This is *Newton's third law of motion,* again a consequence of the definition of force and the principle of the conservation of momentum. It is sometimes called the *law of action and reaction.*

In numerous problems $\boldsymbol{F}_1$ (and of course also $\boldsymbol{F}_2$) can be expressed as a function of the relative position vector of the two particles, $\boldsymbol{r}_{12}$, and perhaps also as a function of their relative velocity. According to Eq. (7.9), if m_2 is very massive compared with m_1, the change in velocity of m_2 is very small compared with that of m_1, and we may assume that particle 2 remains practically at rest in some inertial frame of reference. Then we may speak of the motion of particle 1 under the action of the force $\boldsymbol{F}_1$ (Fig. 7–6), and $\boldsymbol{F}_1$ can be considered as a function of the position or the velocity of m_1 only. It is in these cases that Eq. (7.12) is particularly useful. For example, this is the case for terrestrial bodies moving under the gravitational action of the earth, or an electron moving relative to a nucleus in an atom.

The determination of $\boldsymbol{F}(\boldsymbol{r}_{12})$ for the many interactions found in nature is one of the most important problems of physics. It is precisely because the physicist has been able to associate specific functional forms of $\boldsymbol{F}(\boldsymbol{r}_{12})$ with different interactions observed in nature that the concept of force has been so useful to him.

Remembering the definition (7.1) of momentum, we may write Eq. (7.12) in the form

$$\boldsymbol{F} = \frac{d(m\boldsymbol{v})}{dt}, \tag{7.14}$$

and if m is constant, we have

$$\boldsymbol{F} = m\frac{d\boldsymbol{v}}{dt} \qquad \text{or} \qquad \boldsymbol{F} = m\boldsymbol{a}. \tag{7.15}$$

We may express Eq. (7.15) in words by saying:

Force is equal to mass times acceleration, if the mass is constant.

Note that in this case the force has the same direction as the acceleration. From Eq. (7.15) we see that if the force is constant, the acceleration, $\boldsymbol{a} = \boldsymbol{F}/m$, is also constant and the motion is uniformly accelerated. This is what happens to bodies falling near the earth's surface: All bodies fall toward the earth with the same acceleration $\boldsymbol{g}$, and thus the force of gravitational attraction of the earth, called *weight,* is

$$\boldsymbol{W} = m\boldsymbol{g}. \tag{7.16}$$

(Strictly speaking, we should write $\boldsymbol{W} = m\boldsymbol{g}_0$, where $\boldsymbol{g}$ and $\boldsymbol{g}_0$ are related by Eq. 6.27.)

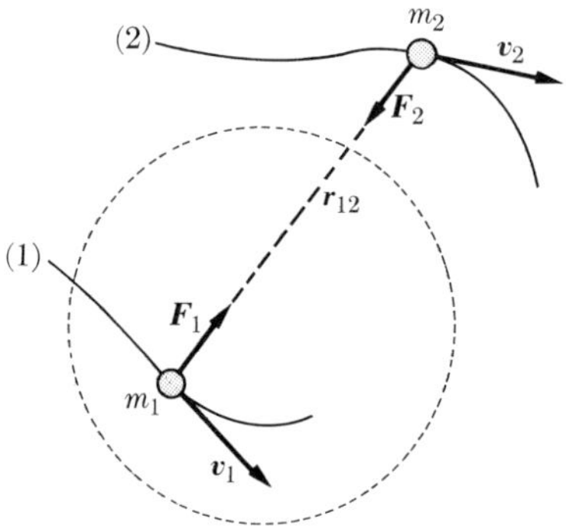

Fig. 7–6. As a result of momentum conservation, action and reaction are equal and opposite.

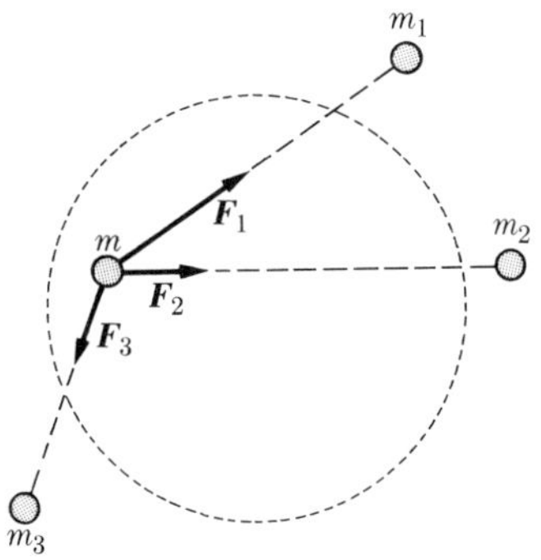

Fig. 7–7. Resultant force on the particle.

In writing Eq. (7.12) we have assumed that the particle interacts with only one other particle, as follows from the discussion preceding Eq. (7.12), and illustrated in Fig. 7–6. However, if particle m interacts with particles $m_1, m_2, m_3, \ldots$ (Fig. 7–7), each one produces a change in the momentum of m that is characterized by the respective forces $\boldsymbol{F}_1$, $\boldsymbol{F}_2$, $\boldsymbol{F}_3$, ..., according to Eq. (7.12). Then the *total* rate of change of momentum of particle m is

$$\frac{d\boldsymbol{p}}{dt} = \boldsymbol{F}_1 + \boldsymbol{F}_2 + \boldsymbol{F}_3 + \cdots = \boldsymbol{F}.$$

The vector sum on the right-hand side is called the *resultant* force $\boldsymbol{F}$ acting on m. This rule for computing the resultant force has already been applied in Chapter 4. In Fig. 7–7 we have not indicated the possible interactions between m_1 and m_2, m_1 and m_3, m_2 and m_3, etc., because these interactions are irrelevant to our present purpose. Also we have implicitly assumed that the interaction between m and m_1, for example, is not altered by the presence of $m_3, m_4, \ldots$; in other words, we have assumed that there are no interference effects.

In succeeding sections of this chapter, in which we shall discuss the motion of a particle, we shall assume that the resultant force $\boldsymbol{F}$ is a function of the coordinates of the particle only, thus ignoring the motion of the other particles with which it interacts. This very useful approximation, as we said before, constitutes what is known as the *dynamics of a particle.* In later chapters we shall consider the motions of systems of particles and the forces associated with the different interactions known to the physicist.

7.7 Critique of the Concept of Force

Let us now present a critical appraisal of the concept of force. We introduced this concept (that is, $\boldsymbol{F} = d\boldsymbol{p}/dt$) in Eq. (7.12) as a mathematical concept which is convenient for describing the rate of change of the momentum of a particle due to its interactions with other particles. However, in daily life we have a somewhat different image of the concept of force. We "feel" a force (actually an interaction) when a batter hits a ball, a hammer drives a nail, a boxer jabs at the face of his opponent, or a weight pulls on a string. And obviously it is difficult to reconcile this sensory image of force with the force or interaction between the sun and the earth. In both cases, however, we have an interaction between two bodies. The student may say: yes, but there is a very large distance between the sun and the earth, while the batter "touches" the ball. And this is precisely the point at which things are not so different as they may seem. No matter how compact a solid may appear, its atoms are all separated and held in position by interactions in the same way that the planets are held in position as a result of their interactions with the sun. The bat is never in contact with the ball in the microscopic sense, although its molecules do come very close to those of the ball, producing a temporary disturbance in their arrangement as a result of their interactions. Thus all forces in nature correspond to interactions between bodies a certain distance apart. In some cases the distance is so small by human standards that we tend to extrapolate and think it is zero. In other cases the distance is very large by human standards. However, from the physical point of view, there is no essential difference in the two kinds of forces. Hence we must apply such sensory or macroscopic concepts as "contact" very carefully when we are dealing with processes on an atomic scale.

The fact that two particles interact when they are separated a certain distance means that we must consider a mechanism for the transmission of the interaction. This mechanism will be considered in later chapters; we shall only state here that our discussion will require a revision of Eq. (7.5). In the form in which it is written, Eq. (7.5) presumes that the interaction between two particles is instantaneous. However, interactions propagate with a finite velocity presumably equal to that of light, as will be discussed in later chapters. In order to take into account the retardation in the interaction due to the finite velocity of propagation, an additional term will have to be incorporated into Eq. (7.5). When this is done, the concept of force passes into a secondary role and the law of action and reaction loses its meaning. However, so long as the particles move very slowly compared with the velocity of light, or interact very weakly, Eq. (7.5) and the theory developed from it constitute an excellent approximation for describing the physical situation.

7.8 Units of Force

From Eqs. (7.12) or (7.15), we see that the unit of force must be expressed in terms of the units of mass and acceleration. Thus in the MKSC system the force is measured in m kg s^{-2}, a unit that is called a *newton* and is denoted by N; that is, N = m kg s^{-2}. Accordingly, we define the newton as the force that is applied to a body whose mass is one kg to produce an acceleration of 1 m s^{-2}.

Still in frequent use is the cgs unit of force called a *dyne*, and defined as the force applied to a body whose mass is one gram, to produce an acceleration of 1 cm s^{-2}; that is, dyne = cm g s^{-2}. Noting that 1 kg = 10^3 g and 1 m = 10^2 cm, we see that N = m kg s^{-2} = (10^2 cm)(10^3 g) s^{-2} = 10^5 dynes.

The British unit of force, very seldom used, is the *poundal*, defined as the force acting on a body whose mass is one pound and whose acceleration is 1 ft s^{-2}, and abbreviated pdl; that is, poundal $=$ ft lb s^{-2}. Recalling that 1 lb $=$ 0.4536 kg and that 1 ft $=$ 0.3048 m, we may write poundal $=$ (0.3048 m)(0.4536 kg) s^{-2} $=$ 0.1383 N.

Two other units are used frequently by engineers. They are based on Eq. (7.16), which defines the weight of a body. One is the *kilogram force*, abbreviated kgf, defined as a force equal to the weight of a mass equal to one kilogram. Thus, setting $m = 1$ kg in Eq. (7.16), we have kgf $= g$ N $\simeq$ 9.807 N. Similarly the *pound force*, abbreviated lbf, is defined as a force equal to the weight of a mass equal to one pound. Thus, setting $m = 1$ lb in Eq. (7.16), we have lbf $= g$ pdl $\simeq$ 32.17 pdl $=$ 4.448 N.

Note that mass measured in kilograms or pounds and weight measured in kilograms force or pounds force are expressed by the same number. So a mass of 7.24 lb weighs 7.24 lbf or 238.7 poundals. The introduction of kgf and lbf for measuring forces requires the definition of new units of mass if we want to use these units of force in conjunction with the equation of motion $F = ma$. For example, in the British system we would have that

$$\text{lbf} = (\text{new mass unit}) \times (\text{ft s}^{-2}).$$

Calling the new mass unit a *slug*, we see that

$$\text{slug} = \frac{\text{lbf}}{\text{ft s}^{-2}} = \frac{32.17 \text{ pdl}}{\text{ft s}^{-2}} = 32.17 \text{ lb},$$

or 1 lb $=$ 0.0311 slug. A slug is thus the mass of a body whose acceleration is 1 ft s^{-2} when acted on by a force of 1 lbf.

Although weight, being a force, should be expressed in N or poundals, it is customary, especially in engineering and household uses, to express it in kilograms force or pounds force. In practice, however, one speaks of a force of so many pounds and not pounds force.

EXAMPLE 7.3. An automobile whose mass is 1000 kg moves uphill along a street inclined 20°. Determine the force which the motor must produce if the car is to move (a) with uniform motion, (b) with an acceleration of 0.2 m s^{-2}. Find also in each case the force exerted on the automobile by the street.

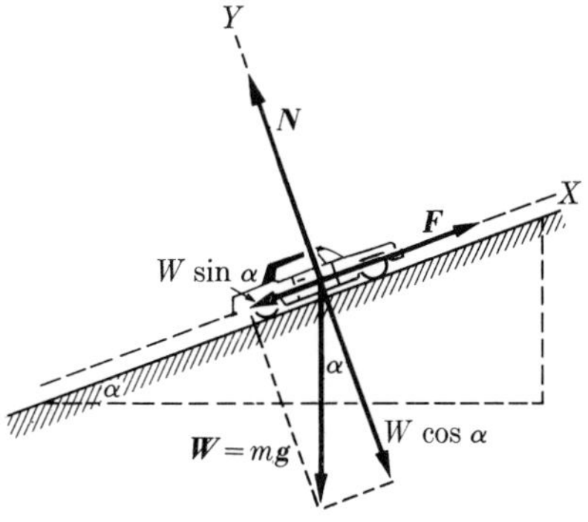

Figure 7–8

Solution: We designate the mass of the automobile by m; the forces acting on it are illustrated in Fig. 7–8. They are its weight $\boldsymbol{W} = m\boldsymbol{g}$, pointing downward, the force $\boldsymbol{F}$ due to the motor, pointing uphill, and the force $\boldsymbol{N}$ due to the street and perpendicular to it. Using a set of axes as indicated in the figure, and employing Eq. (7.15), we find that the motion along the X-direction satisfies the equation

$$F - mg \sin \alpha = ma \qquad \text{or} \qquad F = m(a + g \sin \alpha).$$

The car has no motion along the Y-axis, and thus

$$N - mg \cos \alpha = 0 \qquad \text{or} \qquad N = mg \cos \alpha.$$

We note that the force N due to the street is independent of the acceleration of the car and, to introduce numerical values, is equal to 9210 N. But the force F due to the motor does depend on the acceleration of the car. When the car moves with uniform motion, $a = 0$ and $F = mg \sin \alpha$; in our example it is 3350 N. When it moves with the acceleration of 0.2 m s^{-2}, then $F = 3550$ N.

We suggest that the student solve the problem again, this time for a car moving downhill.

EXAMPLE 7.4. Determine the acceleration with which the masses m and m' of Fig. 7–9 move. Assume that the wheel can rotate freely around O and disregard any possible effects due to the mass of the wheel (these effects will be considered later, in Chapter 10).

Solution: Let us assume that the motion is in the direction shown by the arrow, so that mass m is falling and mass m' rising. Both masses move with the same acceleration a if the string is inextensible, as we may assume. The masses interact through the string, the equal and opposite forces they exert on each other being designated by F. Then the downward motion of m with acceleration a is $mg - F = ma$, and the upward motion of m' with the same acceleration a is $F - m'g = m'a$.

Thus, by adding the two equations, we eliminate F, and obtain

$$a = \frac{m - m'}{m + m'} g$$

for their common acceleration. Then the tension in the string is

$$F = \frac{2mm'}{m + m'} g.$$

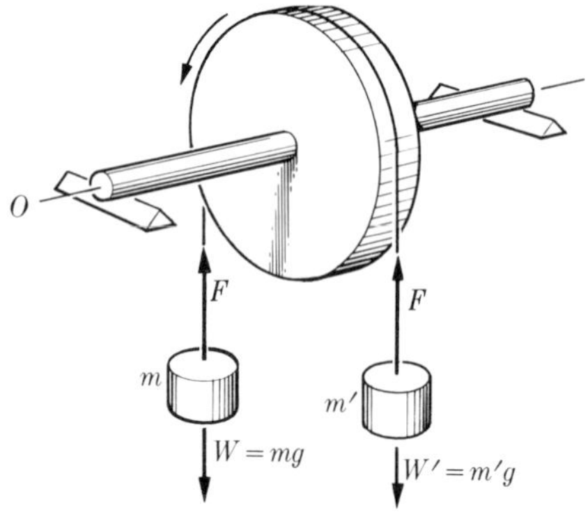

Figure 7–9

A device similar to the arrangement of Fig. 7–9, and which is called *Atwood's machine*, is sometimes used to study the laws of uniformly accelerated motion. One advantage of using it is that, by setting m very close to m', we can make the acceleration a very small, which makes it easier to observe the motion.

EXAMPLE 7.5. A particle of mass 10 kg, subject to a force $F = (120t + 40)$ N, moves in a straight line. At time $t = 0$ the particle is at $x_0 = 5$ m, with a velocity $v_0 = 6$ m s^{-1}. Find its velocity and position at any later time.

Solution: Using Eq. (7.15), we obtain

$$120t + 40 = 10a \qquad \text{or} \qquad a = (12t + 4)\ \text{m s}^{-2}.$$

From now on we proceed as in Example 5.2. Since for rectilinear motion $a = dv/dt$,

$$\frac{dv}{dt} = 12t + 4.$$

Integrating, we have

$$\int_6^v dv = \int_0^t (12t + 4)\,dt \qquad \text{or} \qquad v = (6t^2 + 4t + 6)\ \text{m s}^{-1}.$$

Now, setting $v = dx/dt$ and integrating again, we have

$$\int_5^x dx = \int_0^t v\,dt = \int_0^t (6t^2 + 4t + 6)\,dt$$

or

$$x = (2t^3 + 2t^2 + 6t + 5)\ \text{m},$$

which allows us to find the position at any later time.

7.9 Frictional Forces

Whenever there are two bodies in contact, such as in the case of a book resting on a table, there is a resistance which opposes the relative motion of the two bodies. For example, suppose that we push the book along the table, giving it some velocity. After we release it, it slows down and eventually stops. This loss of momentum is indicative of a force opposing the motion; the force is called *sliding friction*. It is due to the interaction between the molecules of the two bodies, sometimes referred to as *cohesion* or *adhesion* depending on whether the two bodies are of the same or different materials. The phenomenon is rather complex and depends on many factors such as the condition and nature of the surfaces, the relative velocity, etc. We can experimentally verify that the force of friction $\boldsymbol{F}_f$ has a magnitude that, for most practical purposes, may be considered as proportional to the normal force $\boldsymbol{N}$ pressing one body against the other (Fig. 7–10). The constant of proportionality is called the *coefficient of friction*, and is designated by f. That is, in magnitude,

$$F_f = \text{sliding friction} = fN. \tag{7.17}$$

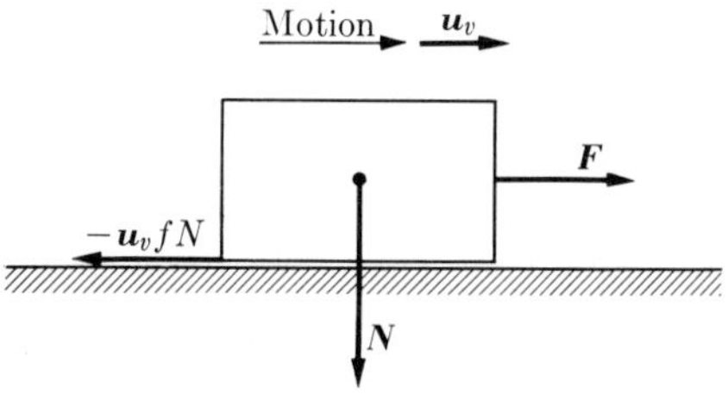

Fig. 7–10. The force of friction opposes the motion and depends on the normal force.

The force of sliding friction always opposes the motion of the body, and so has a direction opposite to the velocity. We can write Eq. (7.17) in vector form by recognizing

TABLE 7–1 Coefficients of Friction (All Surfaces Dry)*

Material	f_s	f_k
Steel on steel (hard)	0.78	0.42
Steel on steel (mild)	0.74	0.57
Lead on steel (mild)	0.95	0.95
Copper on steel (mild)	0.53	0.36
Nickel on nickel	1.10	0.53
Cast iron on cast iron	1.10	0.15
Teflon on Teflon (or on steel)	0.04	0.04

* These values must be considered as only average, since the coefficients of friction are macroscopic quantities that depend on microscopic properties of both materials, and fluctuate greatly.

that a unit vector in the direction of motion is obtained by dividing the velocity vector by the velocity magnitude, $\boldsymbol{u}_v = \boldsymbol{v}/v$. This allows us to write Eq. (7.17) in the vector form $\boldsymbol{F}_f = -\boldsymbol{u}_v fN$. For example, in the case of Fig. 7–10, if $\boldsymbol{F}$ is the applied force moving the body to the right (possibly a pull on an attached string), the resultant horizontal force to the right is $\boldsymbol{F} - \boldsymbol{u}_v fN$, and the equation of motion of the body, applying Eq. (7.15), is

$$m\boldsymbol{a} = \boldsymbol{F} - \boldsymbol{u}_v fN.$$

In general there are two kinds of coefficient of friction. The *static* coefficient of friction, f_s, when multiplied by the normal force, gives the minimum force required to set in relative motion two bodies that are initially in contact and at relative rest. The *kinetic* coefficient of friction, f_k, when multiplied by the normal force, gives the force required to maintain the two bodies in uniform relative motion. It has been found experimentally that f_s is larger than f_k for all materials so far tested. Table 7–1 lists representative values of f_s and f_k for several materials.

Friction is a statistical concept, since the force F_f represents the sum of a very large number of interactions between the molecules of the two bodies in contact. It is, of course, impossible to take into account the individual molecular interactions; hence they are determined in a collective way by some experimental method and represented approximately by the coefficient of friction.

In the following examples we illustrate how to handle dynamical problems involving friction between solids.

EXAMPLE 7.6. A body whose mass is 0.80 kg is on a plane inclined 30°. What force must be applied on the body so that it moves (a) uphill and (b) downhill? In both cases assume that the body moves with uniform motion and with an acceleration of 0.10 m s^{-2}. The coefficient of sliding friction with the plane is 0.30.

Solution: Let us first consider the body moving uphill. The forces acting on the body are illustrated in Fig. 7–11(a). They are the weight $W = mg$, pointing downward, the

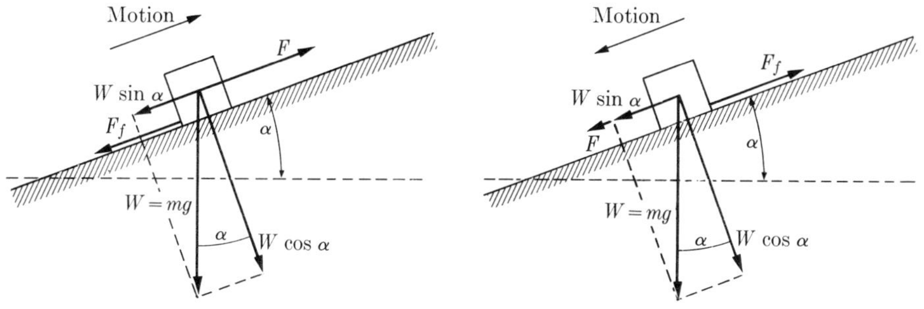

(a) Body moving uphill (b) Body moving downhill

Figure 7–11

applied force F (which we assume uphill), and the force of friction F_f, which is always *against* the motion and thus in this case must be downhill.* When we separate the weight into its component along the plane and its component perpendicular to the plane, the motion of the body along the plane, using Eq. (7.15), is

$$F - mg\sin\alpha - F_f = ma.$$

Now, according to Eq. (7.17), we must write $F_f = fN$. But from Fig. 7–11(a) we see that the normal force pressing the body against the plane is $mg\cos\alpha$. Thus $F_f = f\,mg\cos\alpha$. And the equation of motion becomes

$$F - mg(\sin\alpha + f\cos\alpha) = ma.$$

This equation serves two purposes. If we know the acceleration a, we can find the applied force F. Conversely, if we know the force F we can find the acceleration. In the first case we have

$$F = m[a + g(\sin\alpha + f\cos\alpha)].$$

For example, if the motion is uniform, $a = 0$, and when we insert the corresponding numerical values, $F = 5.95$ N. When the body is moving with an acceleration of 0.10 m s^{-2}, we obtain $F = 6.03$ m s^{-2}.

When the body moves downhill, the forces are as illustrated in Fig. 7–11(b). Now we have assumed that F is downhill, but we could also have made the opposite assumption. However, the force of friction F_f must be uphill to oppose the motion. Taking downhill as the positive direction, the student may verify that the equation of motion is now

$$F + mg(\sin\alpha - f\cos\alpha) = ma$$

or

$$F = m[a - g(\sin\alpha - f\cos\alpha)].$$

If the motion is uniform ($a = 0$), when we insert numerical values, we obtain $F = -1.88$ N, while if it slides down with an acceleration of 0.10 m s^{-2}, we get $F = -1.80$ N.

---

* Another force that has not been shown in the figure is the force exerted by the plane on the body. We need not consider this force in this problem.

The negative sign in each case means that the force F is uphill instead of downhill, as we had assumed.

We suggest that the student determine the motion of the body if no force F is applied, and in view of the result obtained, justify the negative sign for F obtained previously.

7.10 Frictional Forces in Fluids

When a body moves through a fluid, such as a gas or a liquid, at a relatively low velocity, the force of friction may be approximated by assuming that it is proportional to the velocity, and opposed to it. We therefore write

$$\boldsymbol{F}_f = \text{fluid friction} = -K\eta \boldsymbol{v}. \tag{7.18}$$

The coefficient K depends on the shape of the body. For example, in the case of a sphere of radius R, laborious calculation indicates that

$$K = 6\pi R, \tag{7.19}$$

a relation known as *Stokes' law*. The coefficient η depends on the internal friction of the fluid (i.e., the frictional force between different layers of the fluid moving with different velocities). This internal friction is also called *viscosity* and η is called the *coefficient of viscosity*.* The coefficient of viscosity in the MKSC system is expressed in $\mathrm{N\,s\,m^{-2}}$. This can be seen as follows. From Stokes' law, Eq. (7.19), we see that K is expressed in meters (the same applies to bodies of different shapes). Thus, according to Eq. (7.18), η must be expressed in $\mathrm{N/m(m\ s^{-1})}$, which is the same as the unit indicated above. Remembering that $\mathrm{N = m\ kg\ s^{-2}}$, we may also express viscosity in $\mathrm{m^{-1}\ kg\ s^{-1}}$. Viscosity may also be expressed in $\mathrm{cm^{-1}\ g\ s^{-1}}$, a unit called the *poise*, and abbreviated P. The poise is equal to one-tenth of the MKSC unit for viscosity, since

$$1\ \mathrm{m^{-1}\ kg\ s^{-1}} = (10^2\ \mathrm{cm})^{-1}\ (10^3\ \mathrm{g})\ \mathrm{s^{-1}} = 10\ \mathrm{cm^{-1}\ g\ s^{-1}} = 10\ \mathrm{P}.$$

The coefficient of viscosity of liquids decreases with an increase of temperature while, in the case of gases, the coefficient of viscosity increases with increasing temperature. Table 7–2 presents the coefficients of viscosity of several fluids.

When a body moves through a viscous fluid under the action of a force $\boldsymbol{F}$, the resultant force is $\boldsymbol{F} - K\eta\boldsymbol{v}$ and the equation of motion is

$$m\boldsymbol{a} = \boldsymbol{F} - K\eta\boldsymbol{v}. \tag{7.20}$$

Assuming the force $\boldsymbol{F}$ constant, the acceleration $\boldsymbol{a}$ produces a continuous increase in $\boldsymbol{v}$ and a corresponding increase in fluid friction, so that eventually the right-hand side becomes zero. At that moment the acceleration is also zero and there is no further increase in velocity, the fluid friction being exactly balanced by the applied

* In Chapter 24, a more general definition of coefficient of viscosity will be given.

TABLE 7–2 Coefficients of Viscosity, in Poises*

Liquids	$\eta \times 10^2$	Gases	$\eta \times 10^4$
Water (0°C)	1.792	Air (0°C)	1.71
Water	1.005	Air	1.81
Water (40°C)	0.656	Air (40°C)	1.90
Glycerine	833	Hydrogen	0.93
Castor oil	9.86	Ammonia	0.97
Alcohol	0.367	Carbon dioxide	1.46

* All at 20°C, except where noted.

force. The particle continues moving in the direction of the force with a constant velocity, called the *limiting* or *terminal velocity,* which is given by

$$\boldsymbol{v}_L = \frac{\boldsymbol{F}}{K\eta}. \tag{7.21}$$

Therefore the limiting velocity depends on η and K; that is, on the viscosity of the fluid and the shape of the body. In free fall under the influence of gravity, $\boldsymbol{F} = m\boldsymbol{g}$, and Eq. (7.21) becomes

$$\boldsymbol{v}_L = \frac{m\boldsymbol{g}}{K\eta}. \tag{7.22}$$

Equation (7.22) has to be corrected for the buoyant force exerted by the fluid, which, according to Archimedes' principle, is equal to the weight of the fluid displaced by the body. If m_f is the mass of fluid displaced by the body, its weight is $m_f\boldsymbol{g}$, so that the upward buoyant force is $\boldsymbol{B} = -m_f\boldsymbol{g}$, and the net downward force will be $m\boldsymbol{g} - m_f\boldsymbol{g} = (m - m_f)\boldsymbol{g}$. This yields, instead of Eq. (7.22),

$$\boldsymbol{v}_L = \frac{(m - m_f)\boldsymbol{g}}{K\eta}. \tag{7.23}$$

The three forces acting on the body in this case are illustrated in Fig. 7–12. For large bodies and large velocities, the fluid friction is proportional to a higher power of the velocity, and the discussion of the previous paragraphs is insufficient to describe physical events.

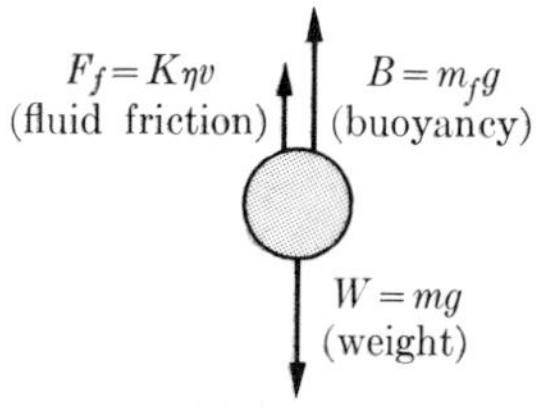

Fig. 7–12. Forces acting on a body falling through a fluid.

EXAMPLE 7.7. Find the limiting velocity of a raindrop. Assume a diameter of 10^{-3} m. The density of air relative to water is 1.30×10^{-3}.

Solution: Assuming that raindrops are spherical, of radius r, we find, using Eq. (1.1), that their masses are

$$m = \rho V = \tfrac{4}{3}\pi r^3 \rho,$$

where ρ is the density of water. Also if ρ_f is the density of the fluid (in this case air), we have that

$$m_f = \rho_f V = \tfrac{4}{3}\pi r^3 \rho_f,$$

so that

$$m - m_f = \tfrac{4}{3}\pi r^3(\rho - \rho_f).$$

Also, using Eq. (7.19), $K = 6\pi r$ because the drops are spherical. By applying Eq. (7.23), we find that the limiting velocity is given by

$$v_L = \frac{2(\rho - \rho_f)r^2 g}{9\eta}.$$

Substituting numerical values, including $\eta = 1.81 \times 10^{-5}$ N s m^{-2} and $\rho = 10^3$ kg m^{-3}, we find that $v_L = 30$ m s^{-1}, or about 107 km hr^{-1} or 66 mi hr^{-1}! A larger drop will *not* have a very different terminal velocity, due to the considerations mentioned in the paragraph previous to this example.

EXAMPLE 7.8. Obtain the velocity of a particle moving through a viscous fluid as a function of time, assuming that Eq. (7.20) holds with a constant force, and that the motion is in a straight line.

Solution: Since the motion is in a straight line, we may write Eq. (7.20) (remembering that $a = dv/dt$) as

$$m\frac{dv}{dt} = F - K\eta v,$$

so that

$$\frac{dv}{dt} = -\frac{K\eta}{m}\left(v - \frac{F}{K\eta}\right).$$

Separating variables and integrating, we have

$$\int_{v_0}^{v} \frac{dv}{v - F/K\eta} = -\frac{K\eta}{m}\int_0^t dt,$$

or

$$\ln\left(v - \frac{F}{K\eta}\right) - \ln\left(v_0 - \frac{F}{K\eta}\right) = -\frac{K\eta}{m}t.$$

Or, using Eq. (M.18), in which $\ln e^x = x$, we obtain

$$v = \frac{F}{K\eta} + \left(v_0 - \frac{F}{K\eta}\right)e^{-(K\eta/m)t}.$$

The second term decreases very rapidly, soon becoming negligible, so that the velocity becomes constant, and equal to $F/K\eta$, in agreement with Eq. (7.21). In other words, the terminal velocity is independent of the initial velocity. If $v_0 = 0$,

$$v = \frac{F}{K\eta}(1 - e^{-(K\eta/m)t}).$$

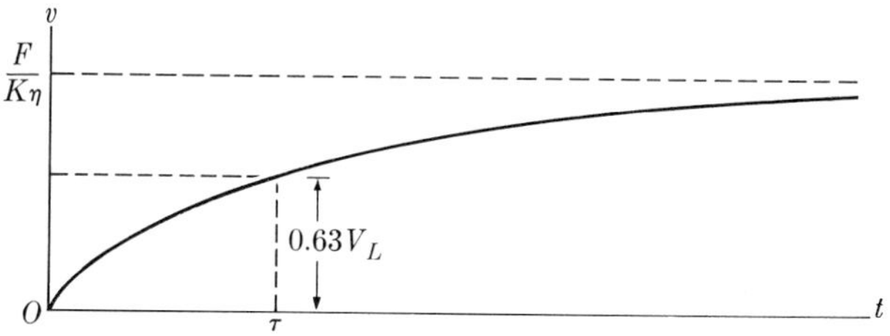

Fig. 7–13. Velocity as a function of time for a body falling through a viscous fluid.

The variation of v with t is illustrated in Fig. 7–13. The relaxation time is defined as $\tau = m/K\eta$. This is the time at which v is 63% of v_L, as the student may verify directly. We suggest that the student proceed one step further and, using the previous result for v, obtain by integration the distance moved in terms of the time. Also find the distance corresponding to the time τ.

7.11 Systems with Variable Mass

The great majority of systems we encounter in physics may be considered as having constant mass. However, in certain cases the mass is variable. The simplest example is that of a raindrop. While it falls, moisture may condense on its surface or water may evaporate, resulting in a change of mass. Suppose that the mass of the drop is m when it is moving with velocity $\boldsymbol{v}$ and that moisture, whose velocity is $\boldsymbol{v}_0$, condenses on the drop at the rate dm/dt. The total rate of change of momentum is the sum of $m\, d\boldsymbol{v}/dt$, corresponding to the acceleration of the drop, and $(dm/dt)(\boldsymbol{v} - \boldsymbol{v}_0)$, corresponding to the rate of gain of momentum of the moisture. Thus the equation of motion of the drop, using Eq. (7.14), is

$$\boldsymbol{F} = m\frac{d\boldsymbol{v}}{dt} + \frac{dm}{dt}(\boldsymbol{v} - \boldsymbol{v}_0).$$

To solve this equation it is necessary to make some assumptions as to how the mass varies with time.

A conveyor on which material is dropped at one end and/or discharged at the other end is another example of variable mass. Let us consider, for example, the conveyor system of Fig. 7–14, where material is dropped continuously on the moving belt at the rate of dm/dt kg s^{-1}. The conveyor is moving at the constant velocity v and a force F is applied to move it. If M is the mass of the belt and m is the mass of the material already dropped at time t, the total momentum of the system at that time is $P = (m + M)v$. Therefore the force applied to the belt is

$$F = \frac{dP}{dt} = v\frac{dm}{dt}.$$

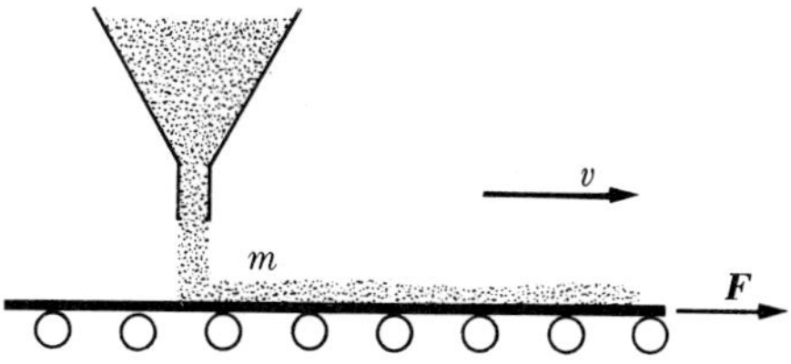

Figure 7–14

Note that the force in this case is entirely due to the change in mass and not to the change in velocity.

Perhaps the most interesting example is that of a rocket, whose mass decreases because it consumes the fuel it carries. In the following example we shall analyze the dynamics of a rocket.

EXAMPLE 7.9. Discuss the motion of a rocket.

Solution: A rocket is a missile which, instead of receiving an initial impulse from the expansion of gases in a gun barrel, is acted on by a continuous force derived from the exhaust produced in the combustion chamber within the missile itself. The rocket at takeoff has a certain amount of fuel which it uses gradually, and therefore its mass decreases.

Let us call $\boldsymbol{v}$ the velocity of the rocket relative to an inertial system, which we shall assume with good approximation to be the earth, and $\boldsymbol{v}'$ the exhaust velocity of the gases, also relative to the earth. Then the exhaust velocity of the gases relative to the rocket is

$$\boldsymbol{v}_e = \boldsymbol{v}' - \boldsymbol{v}.$$

This velocity is always opposed to $\boldsymbol{v}$, and is usually constant. Let m be the mass of the rocket, including its fuel, at any time. During a very small time interval dt, the mass of the system experiences a small change dm, which is negative because the mass decreases. In the same time interval the velocity of the rocket changes by $d\boldsymbol{v}$. The momentum of the system at time t is $\boldsymbol{p} = m\boldsymbol{v}$. The momentum at time $t + dt$, since $-dm$ is the positive value of the mass of the expelled gases, is

$$\boldsymbol{p}' = \underbrace{(m + dm)(\boldsymbol{v} + d\boldsymbol{v})}_{\text{Rocket}} + \underbrace{(-dm)\boldsymbol{v}'}_{\text{Gases}} = m\boldsymbol{v} + m\,d\boldsymbol{v} - (\boldsymbol{v}' - \boldsymbol{v})\,dm$$

or

$$\boldsymbol{p}' = m\boldsymbol{v} + m\,d\boldsymbol{v} - \boldsymbol{v}_e\,dm,$$

where we have neglected the second-order term $dm\,d\boldsymbol{v}$. The change in momentum in the time dt is

$$d\boldsymbol{p} = \boldsymbol{p}' - \boldsymbol{p} = m\,d\boldsymbol{v} - \boldsymbol{v}_e\,dm,$$

and the change of momentum of the system per unit time is

$$\frac{d\boldsymbol{p}}{dt} = m\frac{d\boldsymbol{v}}{dt} - \boldsymbol{v}_e\frac{dm}{dt}.$$

If $\boldsymbol{F}$ is the external force acting on the rocket, the equation of motion, according to Eq. (7.12), is

$$m\frac{d\boldsymbol{v}}{dt} - \boldsymbol{v}_e\frac{dm}{dt} = \boldsymbol{F}. \tag{7.24}$$

The second term on the left in Eq. (7.24) is often designated as the *thrust* of the rocket, since it is equal to the "force" due to the escaping exhaust. To solve this equation we must make some assumption about $\boldsymbol{v}_e$. In general it is assumed that $\boldsymbol{v}_e$ is constant. Also, neglecting air resistance and the variation of gravity with altitude, we may write $\boldsymbol{F} =$

mg, so that Eq. (7.24) becomes

$$\frac{dv}{dt} - \frac{v_e}{m}\frac{dm}{dt} = g. \qquad (7.25)$$

To simplify, consider that the motion is vertical. Then v is directed upward and v_e and g downward, and Eq. (7.25) becomes

$$\frac{dv}{dt} + \frac{v_e}{m}\frac{dm}{dt} = -g.$$

Multiplying by dt and integrating from the beginning of the motion ($t = 0$), when the velocity is v_0 and the mass is m_0, up to an arbitrary time t, we have

$$\int_{v_0}^{v} dv + v_e \int_{m_0}^{m} \frac{dm}{m} = -g \int_0^t dt.$$

Then

$$v - v_0 + v_e \ln \frac{m}{m_0} = -gt,$$

or

$$v = v_0 + v_e \ln \left(\frac{m_0}{m}\right) - gt. \qquad (7.26)$$

If t is the time required for burning all the fuel, then, in Eq. (7.26), m is the final mass and v is the maximum velocity attained by the rocket. In general $v_0 = 0$, and the last term (in many cases) is negligible. For example, if a rocket has an initial mass of 3000 tons, a final mass of 2780 tons after the fuel is burned, and the gases are expelled at a rate of 2840 lb s^{-1} (or 1290 kg s^{-1}), then $t = 155$ s. If we assume an exhaust velocity of 55,000 m s^{-1} and $v_0 = 0$, the maximum velocity of this stage of the rocket will be

$$\begin{aligned} v &= 55{,}000 \ln \frac{3000}{2780} \text{ m s}^{-1} - (9.8 \text{ m s}^{-2})(155 \text{ s}) \\ &= (55{,}000 \ln 1.08 - 1520) \text{ m s}^{-1} = 2710 \text{ m s}^{-1}. \end{aligned}$$

This speed is almost 9000 ft s^{-1}, or approximately 6000 mi hr^{-1}. These figures refer to the Centaur rocket, which has five engines, each of which is capable of developing 1.5 million lbf of thrust at takeoff.

7.12 Curvilinear Motion

In the examples given so far, we have discussed rectilinear motion. Let us now consider the case of curvilinear motion. If the force has the same direction as the velocity, the motion is in a straight line. To produce curvilinear motion, the resultant force must be at an angle with respect to the velocity, so that the acceleration has a component perpendicular to the velocity which will account for the change in the direction of the motion. On the other hand, we recall that (if the mass is constant) the force is parallel to the acceleration. The relation of all these vectors in curvilinear motion is illustrated in Fig. 7–15.

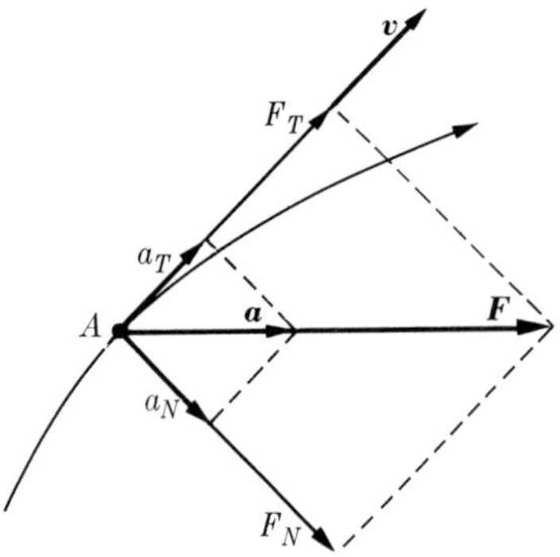

Fig. 7-15. Relationship between the tangential and normal components of the force and the acceleration in curvilinear motion.

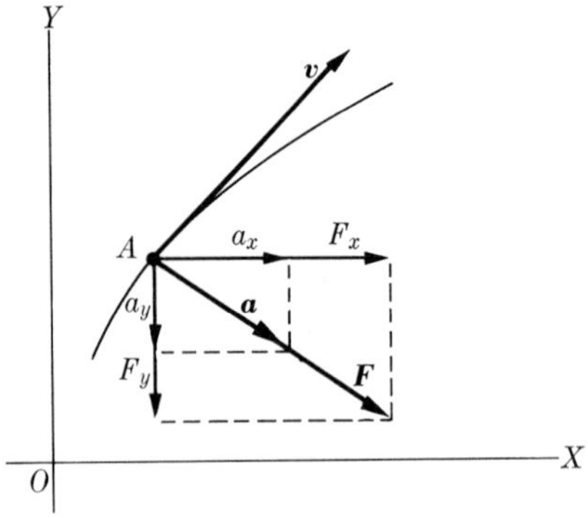

Fig. 7-16. Relationship between the rectangular components of the force and the acceleration in curvilinear motion.

From the relation $\boldsymbol{F} = m\boldsymbol{a}$ and both Eqs. (5.44), we conclude that the component of the force tangent to the path, or the *tangential force*, is

$$F_T = ma_T \qquad \text{or} \qquad F_T = m\frac{dv}{dt}, \tag{7.27}$$

and the component of force perpendicular to the path, or the *normal* or *centripetal force*, is

$$F_N = ma_N \qquad \text{or} \qquad F_N = \frac{mv^2}{\rho}, \tag{7.28}$$

where ρ is the radius of curvature of the path. The centripetal force is always pointing toward the center of curvature of the trajectory. The tangential force is responsible for the change in the magnitude of the velocity, and the centripetal force is responsible for the change in the direction of the velocity. If the tangential force is zero, there is no tangential acceleration and the motion is uniform circular motion. If the centripetal force is zero, there is no normal acceleration and the motion is rectilinear.

In the particular case of circular motion, ρ is the radius R of the circle and $v = \omega R$, so that the force is also

$$F_N = m\omega^2 R. \tag{7.29}$$

For uniform circular motion the only acceleration is a_N, which can be written, using Eq. (5.58), in vector form: $\boldsymbol{a} = \boldsymbol{\omega} \times \boldsymbol{v}$. Therefore $\boldsymbol{F} = m\boldsymbol{a} = m\boldsymbol{\omega} \times \boldsymbol{v} = \boldsymbol{\omega} \times (m\boldsymbol{v})$, and since $\boldsymbol{p} = m\boldsymbol{v}$,

$$\boldsymbol{F} = \boldsymbol{\omega} \times \boldsymbol{p}. \tag{7.30}$$

This is a useful mathematical relation between the force, the angular velocity, and the linear momentum of a particle in uniform circular motion.

Sometimes it may be more convenient to use the rectangular components of $\boldsymbol{F}$ (Fig. 7–16). For example, in the case of plane motion, the vector equation $\boldsymbol{F} = m\boldsymbol{a}$ may be split into the following two equations:

$$F_x = ma_x \quad \text{and} \quad F_y = ma_y$$

or

$$F_x = m\frac{dv_x}{dt} \quad \text{and} \quad F_y = m\frac{dv_y}{dt}. \tag{7.31}$$

By integrating these equations, we may obtain the velocity and the position of the particle at any time.

In general, when we include the case in which the mass is variable, we must use $\boldsymbol{F} = d\boldsymbol{p}/dt$. But $\boldsymbol{p}$, being parallel to the velocity, is tangent to the path. Thus we may write $\boldsymbol{p} = \boldsymbol{u}_T p$ and, using Eq. (5.42), we have

$$\boldsymbol{F} = \frac{d\boldsymbol{p}}{dt} = \boldsymbol{u}_T\frac{dp}{dt} + \frac{d\boldsymbol{u}_T}{dt}p = \boldsymbol{u}_T\frac{dp}{dt} + \boldsymbol{u}_N\frac{vp}{\rho}.$$

Therefore, instead of Eqs. (7.27) and (7.28), we have

$$F_T = \frac{dp}{dt} \quad \text{and} \quad F_N = \frac{pv}{\rho}.$$

EXAMPLE 7.10. Railroad tracks and highways are banked at curves to produce the centripetal force required by a vehicle moving along a curve. Find the angle of banking in terms of the velocity of the vehicle along the curve.

Solution: Figure 7–17 illustrates banking, although the angle has been exaggerated. The forces acting on the car are its weight $W = mg$ and the normal force N due to the tracks. Their resultant F_N must be enough to produce the centripetal force given by

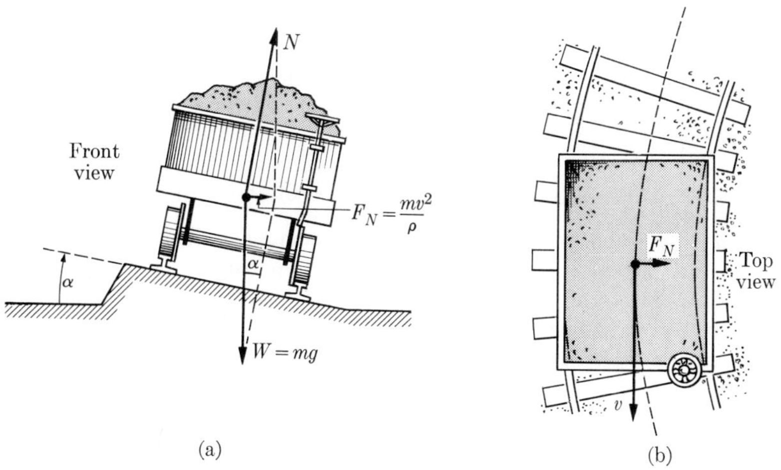

Fig. 7–17. Banking of curves to produce a centripetal force.

Eq. (7.28). Thus $F_N = mv^2/\rho$, where ρ is the radius of the curve. Then from the figure we have that

$$\tan\alpha = \frac{F_N}{W} = \frac{v^2}{\rho g}.$$

The result is thus independent of the mass of the body. Since α is fixed once the tracks have been laid, this formula gives the correct speed to traverse the curve so that there will be no sidewise forces acting on the vehicle. For smaller or somewhat larger speeds there is no great problem with the curve, because the tracks provide the balancing force necessary. However, for much larger speeds the car will tend to jump off the curve.

EXAMPLE 7.11. A mass m suspended from a fixed point by a string of length L is made to rotate around the vertical with angular velocity ω. Find the angle of the string with the vertical. This arrangement is called a *conical pendulum.*

Solution: The system has been illustrated in Fig. 7–18. The mass A moves around the vertical OC, describing a circle of radius $R = CA = OA \sin\alpha = L \sin\alpha$. The forces acting on A are its weight $W = mg$ and the tension F of the string. Their resultant F_N must be just the centripetal force required to describe the circle. Thus, using Eq. (7.29), we have

$$F_N = m\omega^2 R = m\omega^2 L \sin\alpha.$$

From the figure we see that

$$\tan\alpha = \frac{F_N}{W} = \frac{\omega^2 L \sin\alpha}{g}$$

or, since $\tan\alpha = \sin\alpha/\cos\alpha$,

$$\cos\alpha = \frac{g}{\omega^2 L}.$$

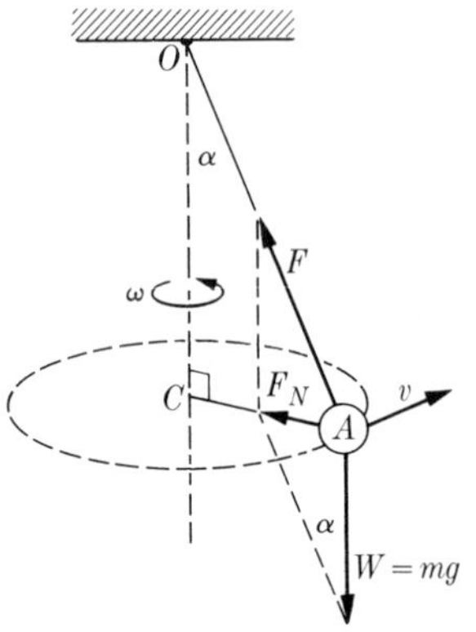

Fig. 7–18. Conical pendulum.

Therefore the larger the angular velocity ω, the larger the angle α, as experiment shows. For this reason the conical pendulum has long been used as a speed regulator for engines; it closes the steam-intake valve when the velocity goes above a prefixed limit and opens it when it falls below.

EXAMPLE 7.12. Analyze the effect of the earth's rotation on the weight of a body.

Solution: In Section 6.5 we discussed, from a kinematical point of view, the motion of a body relative to a frame of reference rotating with the earth. In this example we shall look at the same problem dynamically.

Figure 7–19 shows a particle A on the earth's surface. The gravitational force due to the earth's attraction is designated by $\boldsymbol{W}_0$. If the earth were not rotating, the acceleration of a body near the earth's surface would be $\boldsymbol{g}_0 = \boldsymbol{W}_0/m$. However, due to the earth's rotation, part of this force must be used to produce the centripetal force $\boldsymbol{F}_N$ required for A to move in a circle of radius $CA = r\cos\lambda$ with angular velocity ω. That is, using Eq. (7.29), we have $F_N = m\omega^2 r \cos\lambda$. The difference $\boldsymbol{W}_0 - \boldsymbol{F}_N$ gives the net force $\boldsymbol{W}$, which produces a downward pull on the particle. Thus the effective acceleration of gravity is

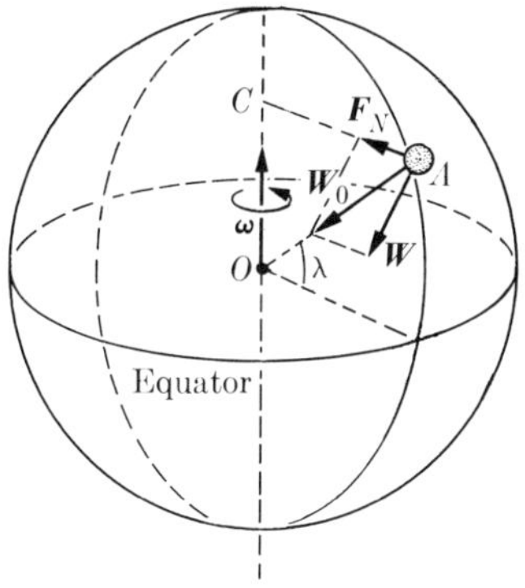

Fig. 7–19. Effect of earth's rotation on the weight of a body.

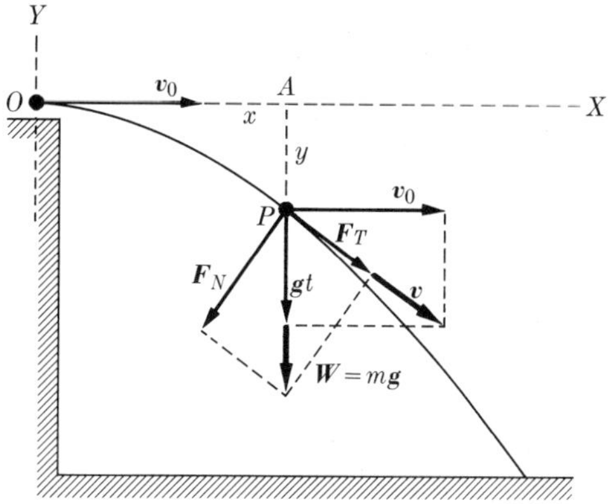

Figure 7–20

$g = W/m$. If the particle A is suspended from a point by means of a string (as with a plumb line), the string will lie in the same direction as $\boldsymbol{W}$. Also, the upward pull on A produced by the string must be equal to $\boldsymbol{W}$. Therefore, when a spring is used to determine the weight of a body, it is the force $\boldsymbol{W}$ that is measured. Only at the poles and along the equator do $\boldsymbol{W}_0$ and $\boldsymbol{W}$ have the same direction, and only in those places is a plumb line along the radial line.

EXAMPLE 7.13. Calculate the tangential and normal forces acting on a projectile thrown horizontally from the top of a building.

Solution: If the projectile is thrown with an initial horizontal velocity v_0 (Fig. 7–20), then at point P its horizontal velocity is still v_0 but its vertical velocity is gt, where t is the time required for the projectile to drop the distance y, or travel the horizontal distance $x = v_0t$. Therefore the total velocity of the projectile is

$$v = \sqrt{v_0^2 + g^2t^2}.$$

Thus Eq. (7.27) gives the tangential force as

$$F_T = m\frac{dv}{dt} = \frac{mg^2t}{\sqrt{v_0^2 + g^2t^2}}.$$

To find the centripetal force we could use Eq. (7.28), but that would require the previous calculation of the radius of curvature of the path, which is a parabola. We can circumvent it in this case because we know that the resultant force is

$$W = mg = \sqrt{F_T^2 + F_N^2}.$$

Therefore

$$F_N = \sqrt{W^2 - F_T^2} = \frac{mgv_0}{\sqrt{v_0^2 + g^2t^2}}.$$

7.13 Angular Momentum

The angular momentum around point O (Fig. 7–21) of a particle of mass m moving with velocity $\boldsymbol{v}$ (and therefore having momentum $\boldsymbol{p} = m\boldsymbol{v}$) is defined by the vector product

$$\boldsymbol{L} = \boldsymbol{r} \times \boldsymbol{p}$$

or (7.32)

$$\boldsymbol{L} = m\boldsymbol{r} \times \boldsymbol{v}.$$

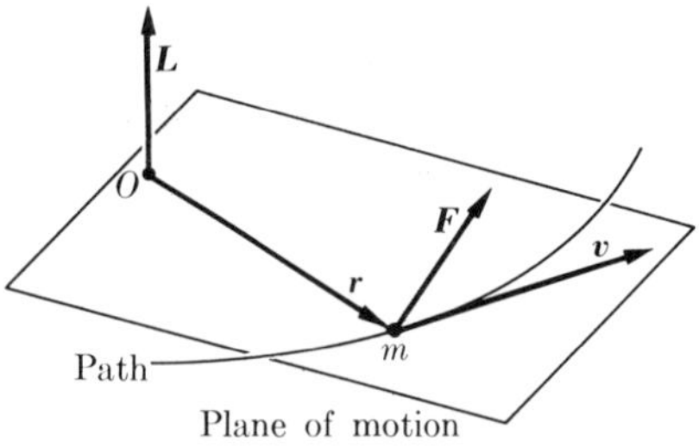

Fig. 7–21. Angular momentum of a particle.

The angular momentum is therefore a vector perpendicular to the plane determined by $\boldsymbol{r}$ and $\boldsymbol{v}$. The angular momentum of the particle in general changes in magnitude and direction while the particle moves. However, if a particle moves in a plane, and the point O lies in the plane, the direction of the angular momentum remains the same, that is, perpendicular to the plane, since both $\boldsymbol{r}$ and $\boldsymbol{v}$ are in the plane. In the case of circular motion (Fig. 7–22), when O is the center of the circle, the vectors $\boldsymbol{r}$ and $\boldsymbol{v}$ are perpendicular, and $v = \omega r$, so that

$$L = mrv = mr^2\omega. \tag{7.33}$$

The direction of $\boldsymbol{L}$ is the same as that of $\boldsymbol{\omega}$, so that Eq. (7.33) can be written vectorially as

$$\boldsymbol{L} = mr^2\boldsymbol{\omega}. \tag{7.34}$$

If the plane motion is not circular, but curvilinear, we can decompose the velocity into its radial and transverse components, as explained in Section 5.11; that is, $\boldsymbol{v} = \boldsymbol{v}_r + \boldsymbol{v}_\theta$ (Fig. 7–23). Then we may write the angular momentum as

$$\boldsymbol{L} = m\boldsymbol{r} \times (\boldsymbol{v}_r + \boldsymbol{v}_\theta) = m\boldsymbol{r} \times \boldsymbol{v}_\theta,$$

since $\boldsymbol{r} \times \boldsymbol{v}_r = 0$ (the two vectors are parallel). Then, for the magnitude of $\boldsymbol{L}$, we have $L = mrv_\theta$. Or, since $v_\theta = r(d\theta/dt)$ according to Eq. (5.64), we may write

$$L = mr^2 \frac{d\theta}{dt}\cdot \tag{7.35}$$

This expression is identical to Eq. (7.33) for circular motion, since $\omega = d\theta/dt$, but in the general case r is not constant. Remembering Eq. (3.26) for the vector product, we may write the angular momentum of a particle as

$$\boldsymbol{L} = \boldsymbol{r} \times \boldsymbol{p} = \begin{vmatrix} \boldsymbol{u}_x & \boldsymbol{u}_y & \boldsymbol{u}_z \\ x & y & z \\ p_x & p_y & p_z \end{vmatrix}$$

or, in terms of the components,

$$L_x = yp_z - zp_y, \qquad L_y = zp_x - xp_z, \qquad L_z = xp_y - yp_x. \tag{7.36}$$

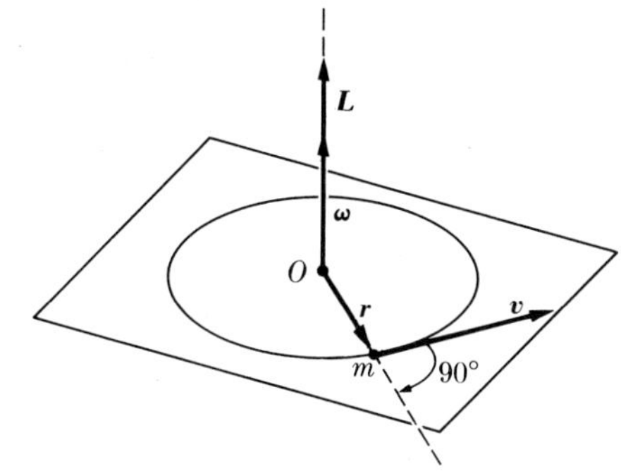

Fig. 7–22. Vector relation between angular velocity and angular momentum in circular motion.

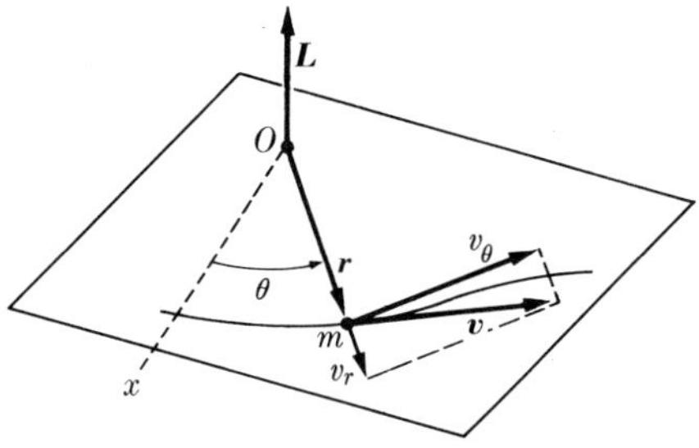

Fig. 7–23. Relation between angular momentum and the transverse component of the velocity.

We may note that for motion in a plane, let us say the XY-plane, we have $z = 0$ and $p_z = 0$, so that $L_x = L_y = 0$, and only the L_z-component remains. That is, the angular momentum is perpendicular to the plane, as we have indicated previously, using a different logic.

Let us now take the time derivative of Eq. (7.32). This gives

$$\frac{d\boldsymbol{L}}{dt} = \frac{d\boldsymbol{r}}{dt} \times \boldsymbol{p} + \boldsymbol{r} \times \frac{d\boldsymbol{p}}{dt}. \tag{7.37}$$

But $d\boldsymbol{r}/dt = \boldsymbol{v}$, and $\boldsymbol{p} = m\boldsymbol{v}$ is always parallel to $\boldsymbol{v}$, so that

$$\frac{d\boldsymbol{r}}{dt} \times \boldsymbol{p} = \boldsymbol{v} \times \boldsymbol{p} = m\boldsymbol{v} \times \boldsymbol{v} = 0.$$

On the other hand, $d\boldsymbol{p}/dt = \boldsymbol{F}$ according to Eq. (7.12). Therefore, Eq. (7.37) becomes $d\boldsymbol{L}/dt = \boldsymbol{r} \times \boldsymbol{F}$. Or, when we remember that according to definition (4.5), the torque of $\boldsymbol{F}$ around O is $\boldsymbol{\tau} = \boldsymbol{r} \times \boldsymbol{F}$, we finally obtain

$$\frac{d\boldsymbol{L}}{dt} = \boldsymbol{\tau}. \tag{7.38}$$

The student must note that this equation is correct only if $\boldsymbol{L}$ and $\boldsymbol{\tau}$ are measured relative to the same point.

Equation (7.38), which bears a great resemblance to Eq. (7.12), with the linear momentum $\boldsymbol{p}$ replaced by the angular momentum $\boldsymbol{L}$, and the force $\boldsymbol{F}$ replaced by the torque $\boldsymbol{\tau}$, is fundamental to the discussion of rotational motion. It simply states that

> *the time rate of change of the angular momentum of a particle is equal to the torque of the force applied to it.*

This implies that the change $d\boldsymbol{L}$ in the angular momentum in a short interval dt is parallel to the torque $\boldsymbol{\tau}$ applied to the particle.

7.14 Central Forces

If the torque on a particle is zero ($\boldsymbol{\tau} = \boldsymbol{r} \times \boldsymbol{F} = 0$), then according to Eq. (7.38), we must have $d\boldsymbol{L}/dt = 0$ or $\boldsymbol{L} =$ constant vector. Thus the angular momentum of a particle is constant if the torque is zero. This condition is fulfilled if $\boldsymbol{F} = 0$; that is, if the particle is free. From Fig. 7–24, we have $L = mvr \sin \theta = mvd$, where $d = r \sin \theta$. This quantity remains a constant because all factors involved are also constants, since the path of the free particle is in a straight line and the velocity does not change.

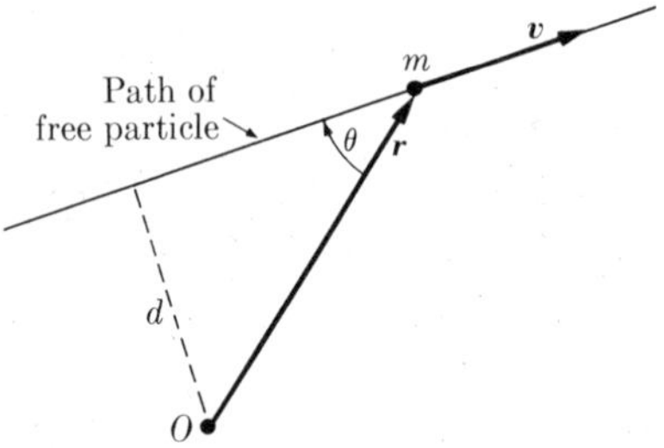

Fig. 7–24. Angular momentum is constant for a free particle.

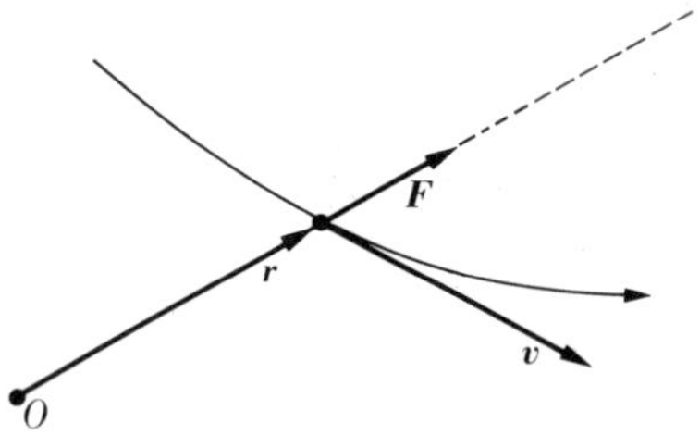

Fig. 7–25. Angular momentum is constant for motion under a central force.

The condition $\boldsymbol{r} \times \boldsymbol{F} = 0$ is also fulfilled if $\boldsymbol{F}$ is parallel to $\boldsymbol{r}$; in other words, if the direction of $\boldsymbol{F}$ passes through the point O. A force whose direction always passes through a fixed point is called a *central force* (Fig. 7–25). Therefore, when a body moves under the action of a central force its angular momentum remains constant, the converse being also true. Another way of stating this is to say that

> *when the force is central, the angular momentum relative to the center of force is a constant of motion, and conversely.*

This result is very important because many forces in nature are central. For example, the earth moves around the sun under the influence of a central force whose direction is always through the center of the sun. The earth's angular momentum relative to the sun is thus constant. The electron in a hydrogen atom essentially moves under the central force due to the electrostatic interaction with the nucleus, with the direction of the force being always pointed toward the nucleus. Thus the angular momentum of the electron relative to the nucleus is constant.

In atoms having many electrons, the force on each electron is not rigorously central because, in addition to the central interaction with the nucleus, there are also the interactions with the other electrons. However, in general, the average force on the electron may be considered as central. Also, in certain nuclei, we may assume as a first approximation that their components (protons and neutrons) move under average central forces.

In a molecule, on the other hand, the force on an electron is not central, because it is the result of the attraction produced by the different nuclei and the repulsion of the other electrons. Therefore the angular momentum of the electrons is not constant. In a diatomic molecule, an interesting situation arises (Fig. 7–26). An electron e revolves around the two nuclei P_1 and P_2, subject to their forces $\boldsymbol{F}_1$ and $\boldsymbol{F}_2$, whose resultant $\boldsymbol{F} = \boldsymbol{F}_1 + \boldsymbol{F}_2$ always lies in the plane determined by $\overrightarrow{Oe} = \boldsymbol{r}$ and the line through the two nuclei, or the Z-axis. The resultant torque on the electron relative to the center of mass O of the molecule (if we neglect all other electron interactions) is

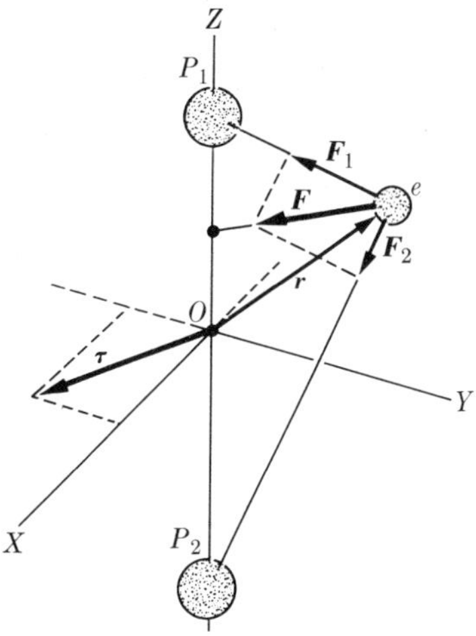

Fig. 7–26. For motion under an axial force, the component of the angular momentum along the axis is constant.

$$\boldsymbol{\tau} = \boldsymbol{r} \times (\boldsymbol{F}_1 + \boldsymbol{F}_2) = \boldsymbol{r} \times \boldsymbol{F}.$$

From Fig. 7–26 we see that this torque is perpendicular to the plane determined by the position vector $\boldsymbol{r}$ and the Z-axis. Thus the torque is in the XY-plane, or $\tau_z = 0$. Accordingly, Eq. (7.38) gives $dL_z/dt = 0$ or $L_z = \text{const}$. Thus, although the angular momentum of the electron is not constant, its component along the molecular or Z-axis is constant. This result is valid not only for a diatomic molecule but for any linear molecule, or in a more general form, for motion under a force that always passes through a fixed axis. Such a force is called an *axial force*. Therefore,

when the force is axial, the component of the angular momentum along the axis is constant.

This result is very useful when we study the structure of atoms and molecules.

The motion due to a central force is always in a plane because $\boldsymbol{L}$ is constant. Therefore, using Eq. (7.35), we have

$$r^2 \frac{d\theta}{dt} = \text{const.} \tag{7.39}$$

When the particle moves from P to P' (Fig. 7–27), the radius vector $\boldsymbol{r}$ sweeps out the shaded area, corresponding to the triangle OPP'. Therefore

$$dA = \text{area } \Delta OPP' = \tfrac{1}{2}r^2\, d\theta,$$

and the area swept out in unit time is

$$\frac{dA}{dt} = \tfrac{1}{2}r^2 \frac{d\theta}{dt}.$$

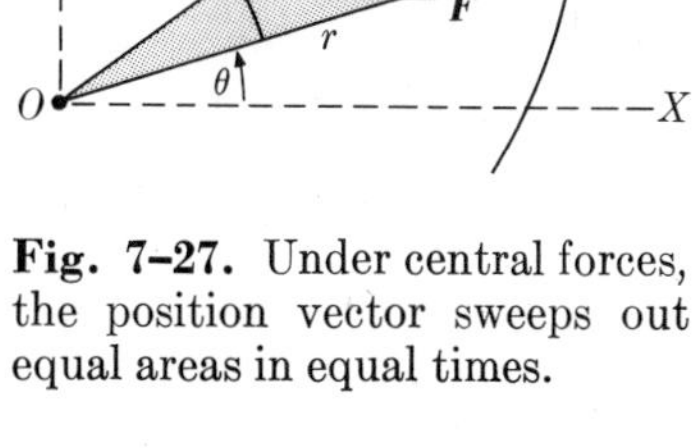

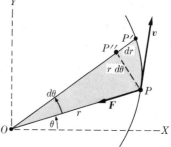

Fig. 7–27. Under central forces, the position vector sweeps out equal areas in equal times.

Comparing this result with Eq. (7.39), we see that $dA/dt = \text{const}$, indicating that *in the motion under central forces, the radius vector of the particle sweeps out equal areas in equal times.* This result is of historical interest in connection with the discovery of the laws of planetary motion, and is known as *Kepler's second law.* We shall refer to it in more detail in Chapter 13, when we discuss planetary motion.

EXAMPLE 7.14. In the case of the projectile of Example 7.13, find the angular momentum and the torque around O. Then verify that Eq. (7.38) holds.

Solution: When we set our X- and Y-axes as indicated in Fig. 7–20, the coordinates of point P are $x = OA = v_0t$, $y = AP = -\frac{1}{2}gt^2$, and the components of the velocity of P are $v_x = v_0$, $v_y = -gt$. Recalling that $\boldsymbol{p} = m\boldsymbol{v}$ and using the third equation of (7.36), we may write

$$L_z = xp_y - yp_x = m(xv_y - yv_x) = -\tfrac{1}{2}mgv_0t^2.$$

Also the components of the force applied to P are $F_x = 0$, $F_y = -mg$. Thus, using Eq. (4.8), we obtain

$$\tau_z = xF_y - yF_x = -mgv_0t.$$

The student may verify that in this case $dL_z/dt = \tau_z$, so that Eq. (7.38) holds.

EXAMPLE 7.15. Estimate the angular momentum of the earth around the sun, and that of an electron around the nucleus in a hydrogen atom. In both cases assume, for simplicity, that the orbit is circular, so that the relations of Fig. 7–22 apply.

Solution: The mass of the earth is 5.98×10^{24} kg and its mean distance from the sun is 1.49×10^{11} m. Also, from our definition of the second given in Section 2.3, we conclude that the period of revolution of the earth around the sun is 3.16×10^7 s. Thus the average angular velocity of the earth around the sun is, from Eq. (5.51),

$$\omega = \frac{2\pi}{P} = \frac{2\pi}{3.16 \times 10^7\ \text{s}} = 1.98 \times 10^{-7}\ \text{s}^{-1}.$$

Therefore, from Eq. (7.33), the angular momentum of the earth relative to the sun is

$$\begin{aligned} L = mr^2\omega &= (5.98 \times 10^{24}\ \text{kg})(1.49 \times 10^{11}\ \text{m})^2(1.98 \times 10^{-7}\ \text{s}^{-1}) \\ &= 2.67 \times 10^{40}\ \text{m}^2\ \text{kg}\ \text{s}^{-1}. \end{aligned}$$

On the other hand, an electron in a hydrogen atom has a mass of 9.11×10^{-31} kg, its mean distance to the nucleus is 5.29×10^{-11} m, and its angular velocity is $4.13 \times 10^{16}\ \text{s}^{-1}$. Thus, again using Eq. (7.33), we find the angular momentum of the electron around the nucleus to be

$$\begin{aligned} L = mr^2\omega &= (9.11 \times 10^{-31}\ \text{kg})(5.29 \times 10^{-11}\ \text{m})^2(4.13 \times 10^{16}\ \text{s}^{-1}) \\ &= 1.05 \times 10^{-34}\ \text{m}^2\ \text{kg}\ \text{s}^{-1}. \end{aligned}$$

This numerical value constitutes one of the most important constants in physics, and is designated by the symbol $\hbar$, read h-bar. The angular momentum of atomic and fundamental particles is usually expressed in units of $\hbar$. The quantity $h = 2\pi\hbar$ is called *Planck's constant.*

The student must realize the tremendous disparity in the values of the physical quantities that enter into the two situations we have worked out, and he may wonder if the same laws apply in both cases. We may answer here by saying that in both cases, since the forces are central, the angular momentum is constant. However, in the electron's case, when we refer to an atomic particle, a certain revision of our methods will be required; the new technique is called quantum mechanics, but we shall not take up this subject at this time. We may state in advance, however, that the result we shall obtain will essentially agree with the one we have obtained in this example.

EXAMPLE 7.16. Scattering of a particle by a central repulsive inverse-square force.

Solution: Let us look at the deviation or scattering that a particle suffers when it is subject to a repulsive force which is inversely proportional to the square of the distance from the moving particle to a fixed point or center of force. This problem is of special interest because of its application in atomic and nuclear physics. For example, when a proton, accelerated by a machine such as a cyclotron, passes near a nucleus of the target material, it is deflected or scattered under the action of a force of this kind, due to the electrostatic repulsion of the nucleus.

Let O be the center of the force and A a particle thrown against O from a great distance with velocity v_0 (Fig. 7–28). The distance b, called the *impact parameter*, is the perpendicular distance between the line of action of $\boldsymbol{v}_0$ and a line drawn through O parallel to it. Assuming that the force between A and O is repulsive and central, the particle will follow the path AMB. The form of the curve depends on how the force varies with the distance. If the force is inversely proportional to the square of the distance, that is, if

$$F = k/r^2, \qquad (7.40)$$

the path is a hyperbola, as will be proved in Section 13.5. When the particle is at A its angular momentum is mv_0b. In any position such as M, its angular momentum, according to Eq. (7.35), is $mr^2\,(d\theta/dt)$. Therefore, since the angular momentum must remain constant because the force is central,

$$mr^2 \frac{d\theta}{dt} = mv_0b. \qquad (7.41)$$

The equation of motion in the Y-direction is obtained by combining Eq. (7.40) with the second of Eqs. (7.31); that is,

$$m\frac{dv_y}{dt} = F_y = F\sin\theta = \frac{k\sin\theta}{r^2}.$$

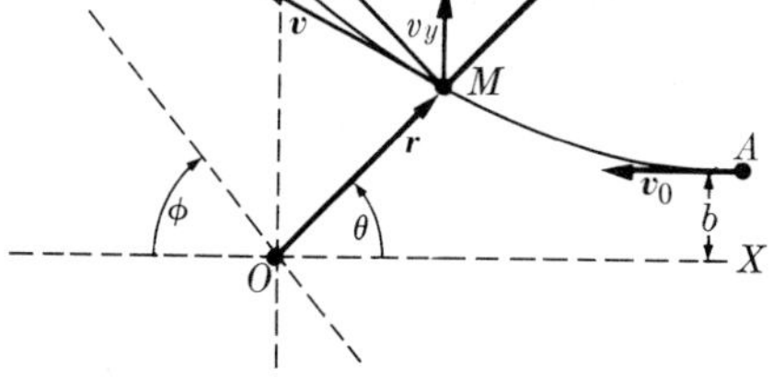

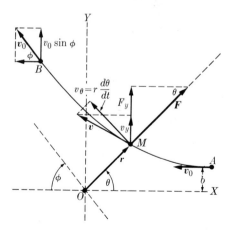

Fig. 7–28. Scattering of a particle under an inverse-square central force.

Eliminating r^2 by using Eq. (7.41), we may write

$$\frac{dv_y}{dt} = \frac{k}{mv_0 b} \sin\theta \frac{d\theta}{dt}.$$

To find the deflection of the particle, we must integrate this equation from one extreme of the path to the other. At A the value of v_y is zero because the initial motion is parallel to the X-axis, and also $\theta = 0$. At B we have $v_y = v_0 \sin\phi$ and $\theta = \pi - \phi$. Note that at B the velocity is again v_0 because, by symmetry, the velocity lost when the particle approaches O must be regained when it recedes from O. (The principle of conservation of energy, to be discussed in the next chapter, also verifies this.) Then

$$\int_0^{v_0 \sin\phi} dv_y = \frac{k}{mv_0 b} \int_0^{\pi-\phi} \sin\theta \, d\theta$$

or

$$v_0 \sin\phi = \frac{k}{mv_0 b} (1 + \cos\phi).$$

Remembering that $\cot \frac{1}{2}\phi = (1 + \cos\phi)/\sin\phi$, we finally get

$$\cot \tfrac{1}{2}\phi = \frac{mv_0^2}{k} b. \tag{7.42}$$

This relation gives the scattering angle ϕ in terms of the impact parameter b.

In Section 14.7 we shall apply this equation to the scattering of charged particles by nuclei. Note that result (7.42) is valid only for an inverse-square force. If the force depends on the distance in a different manner, the angle of scattering satisfies a different equation. Therefore, scattering experiments are very useful when we wish to determine the law of force in interactions between particles.

In nuclear physics laboratories, scattering experiments are performed by accelerating electrons, protons, or other particles by means of a cyclotron, a Van de Graaff accelerator, or some other similar device, and observing the angular distribution of the scattered particles.

7.15 Equilibrium and Rest

We conclude this chapter with a brief review of the concepts of rest and equilibrium. A particle is *at rest* relative to an inertial observer when its velocity, as measured by the observer, is zero. A particle is in *equilibrium* relative to an inertial observer when its acceleration is zero ($\boldsymbol{a} = 0$). Then, from Eq. (7.15), we conclude that $\boldsymbol{F} = 0$; that is, a particle is in equilibrium when the resultant of all the forces acting on it is zero. This definition was used in Chapter 4.

A particle may be at rest relative to an inertial observer, but may not be in equilibrium. For example, when we throw a stone vertically upward, the stone is momentarily at rest when it reaches its maximum height. However, it is not in equilibrium because it is subject to the unbalanced downward pull of the earth. For that reason the stone immediately begins to fall.

Also, a particle may be in equilibrium and yet not be at rest relative to an inertial observer. An example of this is a free particle. Since no forces act on it, there is no acceleration and the particle is in equilibrium. However, the particle may not be at rest relative to many inertial observers. The most common situation one encounters is that of a particle which is both at rest and in equilibrium at the same time. For that reason many people erroneously consider the two concepts synonymous. Of course a particle in equilibrium may always be at rest in some inertial frame of reference.

References

1. "Inertia," D. Sciama, *Sci. Am.*, February 1957, page 99
2. "Galileo and the Law of Inertia," S. Drake, *Am. J. Phys.* **32,** 601 (1964)
3. "Isaac Newton," I. Cohen, *Sci. Am.*, December 1955, page 73
4. "Resource Letter PhM-1 on the Philosophical Foundation of Classical Mechanics," M. Hesse, *Am. J. Phys.* **32,** 905 (1964)
5. "The Conservation Laws of Physics," G. Feinberg and M. Goldharber, *Sci. Am.*, October 1963, page 36
6. "Friction," F. Palmer, *Sci. Am.*, February 1951, page 54
7. "Resource Letter F-1 on Friction," E. Rabinowicz, *Am. J. Phys.* **31,** 897 (1963)
8. "The Shape of Raindrops," J. McDonald, *Sci. Am.*, February 1954, page 64
9. "Billiard-Ball Collision Experiment," J. Bayes and W. Scott, *Am. J. Phys.* **31,** 197 (1963)
10. "Duration of Atomic Collisions," O. Oldenberg, *Am. J. Phys.* **25,** 94 (1957)
11. *Concepts of Mass in Classical and Modern Physics*, M. Jammer. Cambridge, Mass.: Harvard University Press, 1961
12. *Mechanics*, Keith R. Symon. Reading, Mass.: Addison-Wesley, second edition, 1960, Sections 2–4, 4–4, and 4–5
13. *Physical Mechanics*, Robert B. Lindsay. Princeton, N.J.: D. Van Nostrand, 1963, Sections 1–6 through 1–10, 3–10, 3–6, 3–7
14. *Introduction to Engineering Mechanics*, John V. Huddleston. Reading, Mass.: Addison-Wesley, 1961, Chapter 19
15. *Vector Mechanics*, D. Christie. New York: McGraw-Hill, 1964, Chapters 6 and 12; Sections 7.1 through 7.5
16. *The Feynman Lectures on Physics*, Volume I, R. P. Feynman, R. B. Leighton, and M. L. Sands. Reading, Mass.: Addison-Wesley, 1963, Chapters 9, 10, and 18
17. *Source Book in Physics*, W. F. Magie. Cambridge, Mass.: Harvard University Press, 1963, page 1, Galileo; page 30, Newton
18. *Foundations of Modern Physical Science*, Gerald Holton and D. H. D. Roller. Reading, Mass.: Addison-Wesley, 1958, Chapters 16 and 17

Problems

7.1 A particle of mass 3.2 kg is moving due west with a velocity of 6.0 m s^{-1}. Another particle of mass 1.6 kg is moving due north with a velocity of 5.0 m s^{-1}. The two particles are interacting. After 2 s the first particle is moving in the direction N 30° E with a velocity of 3.0 m s^{-1}. Find: (a) the magnitude and direction of the velocity of the other particle, (b) the total momentum of the two particles, both at the beginning and after the 2 s have elapsed, (c) the change in momentum of each particle, (d) the change in velocity of each particle, and (e) the magnitudes of these changes in velocity; verify Eq. (7.9).

7.2 A log whose mass is 45 kg is floating downstream at a constant velocity of 8 km hr^{-1}. A 10-kg swan attempts to land on the log while flying at a rate of 8 km hr^{-1} in the upstream direction. The swan slides the length of the log and falls off the end with a velocity of 2 km hr^{-1}. Calculate the final velocity of the log. Neglect water friction. Is it necessary to convert the velocities to m s^{-1}?

7.3 In the chemical reaction H + Cl → HCl, the H atom initially was moving to the right with a velocity of 1.57×10^5 m s^{-1}, while the Cl atom was moving in a perpendicular direction with a velocity of 3.4×10^4 m s^{-1}. Find the magnitude and direction (relative to the original motion of the H atom) of the resulting HCl molecule. Use the atomic masses of Table A–1.

7.4 Write an equation expressing the conservation of momentum in the chemical reaction A + BC → AB + C.

7.5 A particle whose mass is 0.2 kg is moving at 0.4 m s^{-1} along the X-axis when it collides with another particle, of mass 0.3 kg, which is at rest. After the collision the first particle moves at 0.2 m s^{-1} in a direction making an angle of 40° with the X-axis. Determine (a) the magnitude and direction of the velocity of the second particle after the collision, and (b) the change in the velocity and the momentum of each particle. (c) Verify relation (7.9).

7.6 Find the momentum acquired by a mass of 1 gm, 1 kg, and 10^6 kg when each falls through a distance of 100 m. Since the momentum acquired by the earth is equal and opposite, determine the velocity (upward) acquired by the earth. The mass of the earth is listed in Table 13–1. Determine the magnitude of the force in each case.

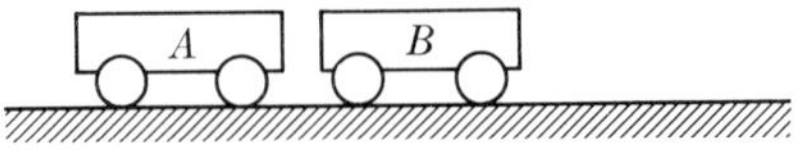

Figure 7–29

7.7 Two carts, A and B, are pushed toward each other (Fig. 7–29). Initially B is at rest, while A moves to the right at 0.5 m s^{-1}. After they collide, A rebounds at 0.1 m s^{-1}, while B moves to the right at 0.3 m s^{-1}. In a second experiment, A is loaded with a mass of 1 kg and pushed against B with a velocity of 0.5 m s^{-1}. After the collision, A remains at rest, while B moves to the right at 0.5 m s^{-1}. Find the mass of each cart.

7.8 Consider the earth-moon system (ignore the motion of this system around the sun). In 28 days, the moon rotates about the earth in a circle of radius 4.0×10^8 m. (a) What is the change in the momentum of the moon in 14 days? (b) What must be the change in momentum of the earth in 14 days? (c) Is the earth stationary in the earth-moon system? (d) The mass of the earth is 80 times that of the moon. What is the change in velocity of the earth in 14 days?

7.9 Two objects, A and B, which are moving without friction in a horizontal line, interact. The momentum of A is $p_A = p_0 - bt$, where p_0 and b are constants and t is the time. Find the momentum of B as a function of time if: (a) B is initially at rest and (b) the initial momentum of B was $-p_0$.

7.10 A grenade moving horizontally at 8 km s^{-1} relative to the earth explodes into three equal fragments. One continues to move horizontally at 16 km s^{-1}, another moves upward at an angle of 45° and the third moves at an angle of 45° below the horizontal. Find the magnitude of the velocities of the second and third fragment.

7.11 A satellite is moving "horizontally" at a velocity of 8 km s^{-1} relative to the earth. We wish to drop a 50-kg load straight down toward the earth by ejecting it horizontally from the satellite. Calculate the velocity of the satellite after the ejection of the load if the total mass (including the load) is 450 kg. (What is the load's velocity, relative to the earth, immediately after ejection?)

7.12 An empty railroad car of mass 10^5 kg coasts with a velocity of 0.5 m s^{-1} beneath a stationary coal hopper. If 2×10^5 kg of coal are dumped into the car as it passes beneath the hopper, then: (a) What is the car's final velocity? (b) What will be the car's velocity if the coal is allowed to leave the car through bottom hoppers and the coal falls straight down relative to the car? (c) Suppose that it were possible to throw all the coal at one time out the rear of the car so that the coal would be at rest relative to the earth. Calculate the resultant velocity of the car under such circumstances. (d) Under what conditions would the result be the same as in (c) if the coal were thrown off at an angle relative to the car's motion?

7.13 A cart having a mass of 1.5 kg moves along its track at 0.20 m s^{-1} until it runs into a fixed bumper at the end of the track. What is its change in momentum and the average force exerted on the cart if, in 0.1 s, it: (a) is brought to rest, (b) rebounds with a velocity of 0.10 m s^{-1}? Discuss the conservation of momentum in the collision.

7.14 What constant force is needed in order to increase the momentum of a body from 2300 kg m s^{-1} to 3000 kg m s^{-1} in 50 s?

7.15 An automobile has a mass of 1500 kg and its initial speed is 60 km hr^{-1}. When the brakes are applied to produce a constant deceleration, the car stops in 1.2 min. Determine the force applied to the car.

7.16 How long a time should a constant force of 80 N act on a body of 12.5 kg in order to stop it, providing that the initial velocity of the body is 72 km hr^{-1}?

7.17 A body with a mass of 10 g falls from a height of 3 m onto a pile of sand. The body penetrates the sand a distance of 3 cm before stopping. What force has the sand exerted on the body?

7.18 Two mules are pulling a barge up a canal by ropes tied to the prow of the barge. The angle between the ropes is 40° and the tension in the ropes is 2500 N and 2000 N, respectively. (a) Given that the mass of the barge is 1700 kg, what would its acceleration be if the water offered no resistance? (b) If the barge moves with uniform motion, what is the resistance of the water?

7.19 A man is standing on the flat bed of a truck moving at the speed of 36 km hr^{-1}. At what angle, and in which direction, should the man lean to avoid falling if, in 2 s, the speed of the truck changes to (a) 45 km hr^{-1}, (b) 9 km hr^{-1}?

7.20 An elevator whose mass is 250 kg is carrying three persons whose masses are 60 kg, 80 kg, and 100 kg, and the force exerted by the motor is 5000 N. With what acceleration will the elevator rise? Starting from rest, how high will it go in 5 s?

7.21 Suppose that the 100-kg man in the previous problem is standing on a scale. How much does he "weigh" as the elevator accelerates?

7.22 An empty elevator having a mass of 5000 kg is moving vertically downward with a constant acceleration. Starting from rest, it moves 100 ft during the first 10 s. Calculate the tension in the cable holding the elevator.

7.23 A boy whose mass is 60 kg is standing on a scale. If he suddenly pushes himself up with an acceleration of 245 cm s^{-2}, what will the scale read? Discuss the effect associated with this problem as it applies to a machine that measures the acceleration of the body by measuring the force exerted. (Such a machine, called an *accelerometer*, is an extremely useful tool in industry and research laboratories.)

7.24 A 200-gm mass is moving with a constant velocity $\boldsymbol{v} = \boldsymbol{u}_x\, 50$ cm s^{-1}. When the mass is at $\boldsymbol{r} = -\boldsymbol{u}_x\, 10$ cm, a constant force $\boldsymbol{F} = -\boldsymbol{u}_x\, 400$ dyn is applied to the body. Determine: (a) the time for the mass to stop, and (b) the position of the mass at the instant it stops.

7.25 A man whose mass is 90 kg is in an elevator. Determine the force the floor exerts on him when: (a) the elevator goes *up* with uniform speed, (b) the elevator goes *down* with uniform speed, (c) the elevator *accelerates upward* at 3 m s^{-2}, (d) the elevator *accelerates downward* at 3 m s^{-2}, and (e) the cable breaks and the elevator falls freely.

7.26 A body whose mass is 2 kg is moving on a smooth horizontal surface under the action of a horizontal force $F = 55 + t^2$, where F is in newtons and t in seconds. Calculate the velocity of the mass when $t = 5$ s (the body was at rest when $t = 0$).

7.27 A body of mass m is moving along the X-axis according to the law $x = A \cos(\omega t + \phi)$, where A, ω, and ϕ are constants. Calculate the force acting on the body as a function of its position. What is the direction of the force when x is (a) positive, (b) negative?

7.28 The resultant force on an object of mass m is $F = F_0 - kt$, where F_0 and k are constants and t is the time. Find the acceleration. By integration, find the velocity and position equations.

7.29 A particle of mass m, initially at rest, is acted on by a force $F = F_0[1 - (t - T)^2/T^2]$ during the interval $0 \leq t \leq 2T$. Prove that the velocity of the particle at the end of the interval is $4F_0T/3m$. Note that it depends only on the product $F_0(2T)$ and, if T is made smaller, the same velocity is attained by making F_0 proportionately larger. Make a plot of F against t. Can you think of some physical situation of which this problem could be an adequate description?

7.30 A body which is initially at rest at x_0 moves in a straight line under the action of a force $F = -K/x^2$. Show that its velocity at x is $v^2 = 2(K/m)(1/x - 1/x_0)$. This method can be used to determine the velocity of a body falling toward the earth from a great height.

7.31 Repeat Example 7.3 for the case of a car moving downhill.

7.32 A body with a mass of 1.0 kg is on a smooth plane inclined at an angle of 30° with the horizontal. With what acceleration will the body move if there is a force of 8.0 N applied parallel to the plane and directed (a) upward, (b) downward.

7.33 A truck of mass 5000 kg is traveling north at 30 m s^{-1} when, in 20 s, it turns into a road N 70° E. Find (a) its change in momentum, (b) the magnitude and direction of the average force exerted on the truck.

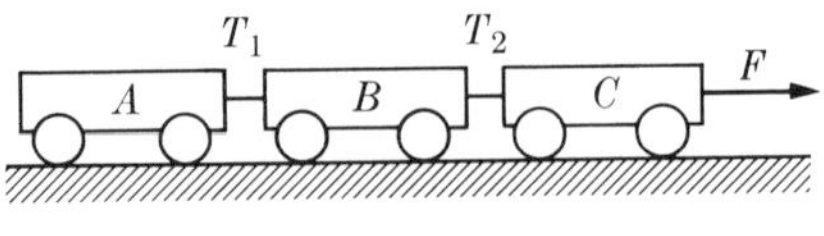

Figure 7–30

7.34 The bodies in Fig. 7–30 have masses 10 kg, 15 kg, and 20 kg, respectively. A force F, equal to 50 N, is applied to C. Find the acceleration of the system and the tensions in each cable. Discuss the same problem when the system moves vertically instead of horizontally.

7.35 Calculate the acceleration of the bodies in Fig. 7–31 and the tension in the string. First solve the problem algebraically and apply to the case $m_1 = 50$ g, $m_2 = 80$ g, and $F = 10^5$ dyn.

7.36 The bodies in Fig. 7–32 are connected by a string as shown. Assuming that the pulleys are smooth, calculate the accelera-

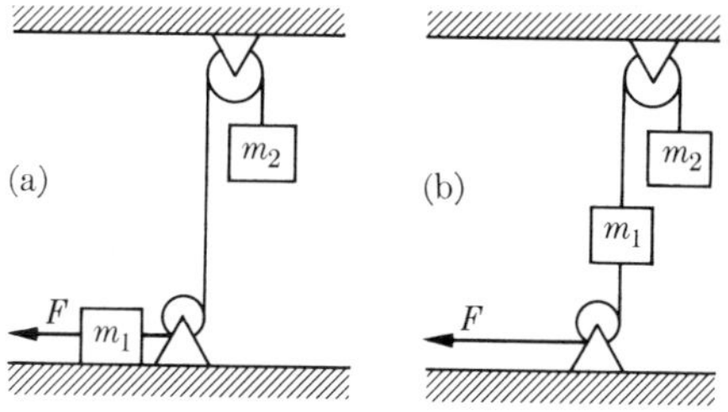

Figure 7–31

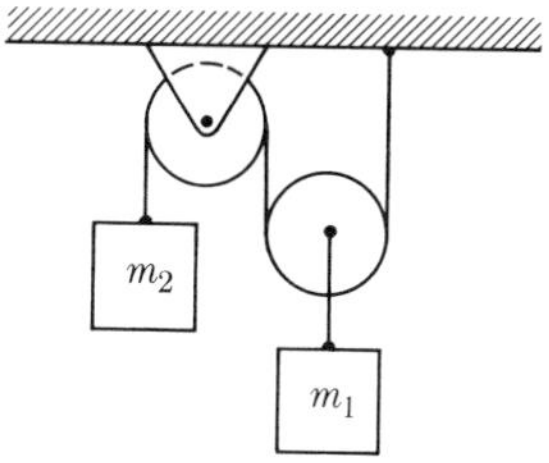

Figure 7–32

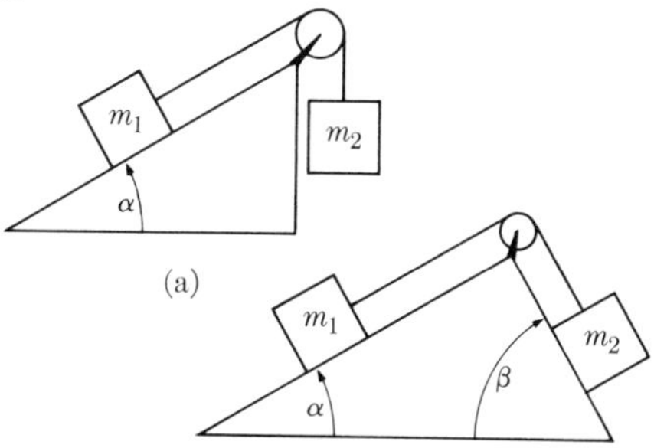

Figure 7–33 (b)

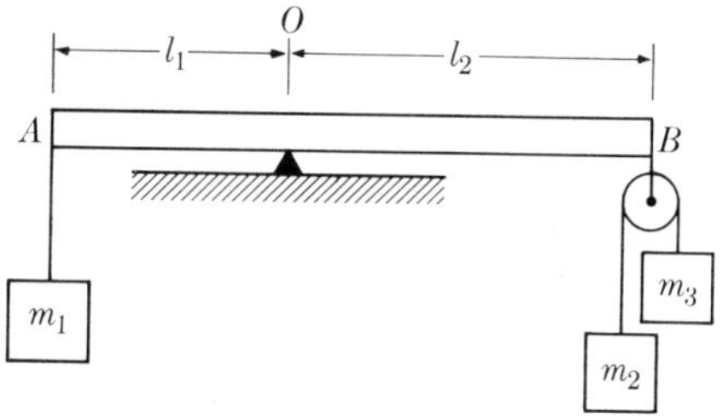

Figure 7–34

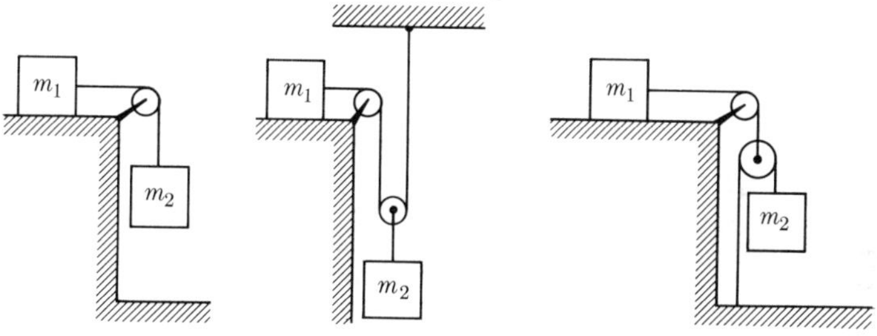

Figure 7–35 (a) (b) (c)

tion of the bodies and the tension in the string. Solve the problem algebraically first, and apply to the case $m_1 = 8$ kg, $m_2 = 2$ kg.

7.37 Determine the acceleration with which the bodies in Fig. 7–33(a) and (b) move, and also the tensions in the strings. Assume that the bodies slide without friction. Solve the problem generally first, and then apply to the case $m_1 = 200$ g, $m_2 = 180$ g, $\alpha = 30°$, $\beta = 60°$.

7.38 Repeat the above problem when there is friction, with coefficients f_1 on the first surface and f_2 on the second. Discuss all possible motions.

7.39 (a) Prove that the beam AB in Fig. 7–34 will be in equilibrium under the condition that the following equation holds:

$$m_1(m_2 + m_3)l_1 = 4m_2m_3l_2.$$

(b) Find the force that the pivot point exerts on the bar.

7.40 Calculate the acceleration of the bodies m_1 and m_2 and the tension in the ropes (Fig. 7–35). All pulleys are weightless and frictionless and the bodies slide without friction. Which device may accelerate m_1 faster than in free fall? Solve first algebraically; then apply to the case $m_1 = 4$ kg, $m_2 = 6$ kg.

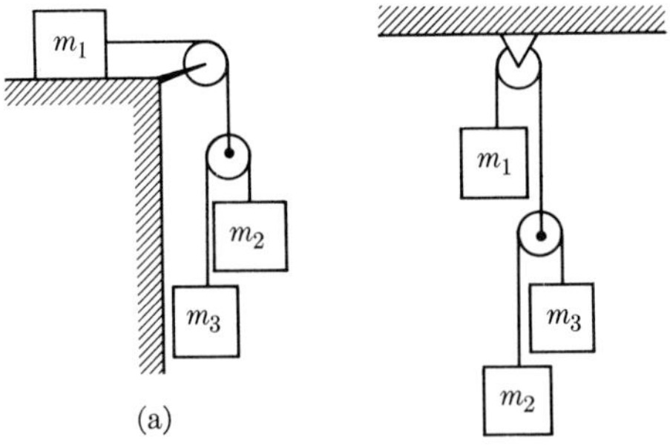

(a) (b)

Figure 7–36

7.41 Show that the accelerations of the bodies in Fig. 7–36, with

$$P = g/(m_1m_2 + m_1m_3 + 4m_2m_3),$$

are

$$\begin{aligned}
\text{(a)}\ a_1 &= 4m_2m_3P,\\
a_2 &= (m_1m_3 - m_1m_2 - 4m_2m_3)P,\\
a_3 &= (m_1m_3 - m_1m_2 + 4m_2m_3)P;\\
\text{(b)}\ a_1 &= (4m_2m_3 - m_1m_2 - m_1m_3)P,\\
a_2 &= (3m_1m_3 - m_1m_2 - 4m_2m_3)P,\\
a_3 &= (m_1m_3 - 3m_1m_2 + 4m_2m_3)P.
\end{aligned}$$

7.42 The masses of A and B in Fig. 7–37 are 3 kg and 1 kg, respectively. If an upward force $F = 5t^2$N is applied to the pulley, find the acceleration of A and B as functions of t. What happens after B reaches the pulley?

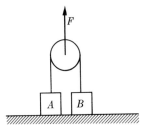

Figure 7–37

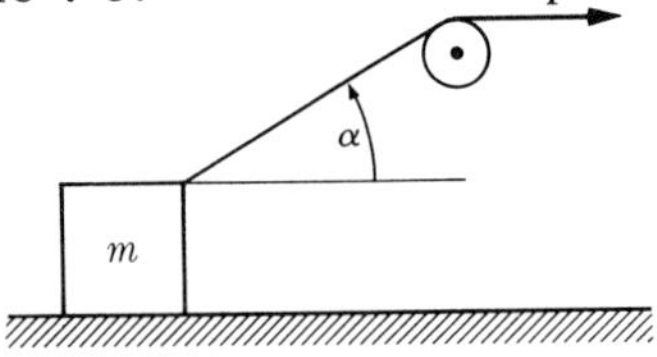

Figure 7–39

7.43 The masses of A and B in Fig. 7–38 are, respectively, 10 kg and 5 kg. The coefficient of friction of A with the table is 0.20. Find the minimum mass of C that will prevent A from moving. Compute the acceleration of the system if C is lifted up.

7.44 Determine the frictional force exerted by the air on a body whose mass is 0.4 kg if it falls with an acceleration of 9.0 m s^{-2}.

7.45 Repeat Example 7.6 for a case in which there is no applied force. The initial velocity of the body is 2 m s^{-1} up the plane. How far up the plane will the body move before it stops? What is the *least* value for the coefficient of static friction so that the body, once stopped, will not come back down?

7.46 A block of mass 0.2 kg starts up a plane inclined 30° with the horizontal with a velocity of 12 m s^{-1}. If the coefficient of sliding friction is 0.16, determine how far up the plane the block travels before stopping. What is the block's speed when (if) it returns to the bottom of the plane?

7.47 A train having a mass of 100 tons is going up an incline that rises 1 ft per 224 ft of length. The traction of the train is 9000 lbf and its acceleration is 1 ft s^{-2}. Calculate the force of friction.

7.48 Find the acceleration of m in Fig. 7–39 if the coefficient of friction with the floor is

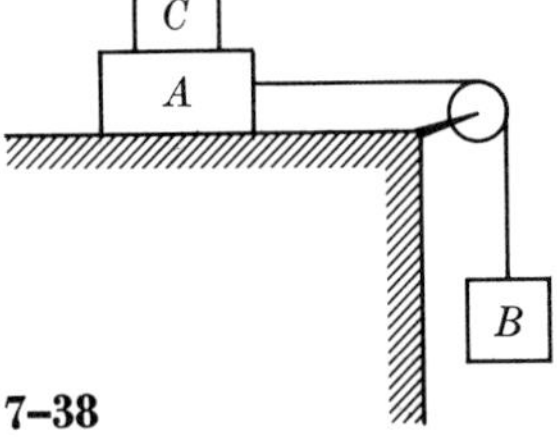

Figure 7–38

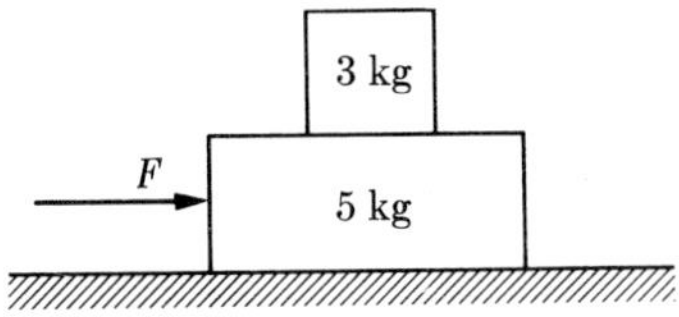

Figure 7–40

f. Find also the force exerted by the floor on the body. Apply to $m = 2.0$ kg, $f = 0.2$, and $F = 1.5$ N.

7.49 A block of mass 3 kg is placed on top of another block of mass 5 kg (Fig. 7–40). Assume that there is no friction between the 5-kg block and the surface on which it rests. The coefficients of static and sliding friction between the blocks are 0.2 and 0.1, respectively. (a) What is the maximum force that may be applied to either block to slide the system and still keep the blocks together? (b) What is the acceleration when the maximum force is applied? (c) What is the acceleration of the 3-kg block if the force is larger than the above maximum force and is applied to the 5-kg block? What if it is applied to the 3-kg block?

7.50 Find the limiting velocity of a sphere having a radius of 2 cm and a density 1.50 g cm^{-3} falling through glycerine (density = 1.26 g cm^{-3}). Also find the velocity of the sphere when its acceleration is 100 cm s^{-2}.

7.51 A body having a mass of 45 kg is launched vertically with an initial velocity of 60 m s^{-1}. The body encounters an air resistance $F = -3v/100$, where F is in newtons and v is the velocity of the body in m s^{-1}. Calculate the time from launch to the maximum altitude. What is the maximum altitude?

7.52 A body falls from a height of 108 m in 5 s, starting from rest. Find its limiting velocity if the resistance is proportional to the velocity.

7.53 Using the results of Example 7.8, find the time it takes the raindrops of Example 7.7 to reach 0.50 and 0.63 of its limiting velocity. Also find the distance covered in the time τ.

7.54 Plot the velocity of a body falling through a viscous fluid as a function of t when the initial velocity is not zero. Consider both when v_0 is smaller and larger than $F/K\eta$. What happens when $v_0 = F/K\eta$?

7.55 The electron in a hydrogen atom revolves around the proton, following an almost circular path of radius 0.5×10^{-10} m with a velocity which is estimated to be about 2.2×10^6 m s^{-1}. Estimate the magnitude of the force between the electron and the proton.

7.56 A stone whose mass is 0.4 kg is tied to the end of an 0.8-m rope. If the stone is spun in a circle at the rate of 80 rev/min, what is the magnitude of the force the rope exerts on the stone? If the rope breaks when the tension is greater than 50 kgf, what is the largest possible angular velocity of the stone?

7.57 A small block with a mass of 1 kg is tied to a rope 0.6 m and is spinning at 60 rev/min in a vertical circle. Calculate the tension in the rope when the block is (a) at the highest point of the circle, (b) at the lowest point, (c) when the rope is horizontal. (d) Calculate the linear velocity the block must have at the highest point in order for the tension in the rope to be zero.

7.58 A train rounds a banked curve at 63 km hr^{-1}. The radius of the curve is 300 m. Calculate: (a) the degree of banking the curve must have in order that the train will experience no sideways forces, (b) the angle a chain hanging from the ceiling of one of the cars makes with the vertical.

7.59 A highway is 24 ft wide. Calculate the difference in level between the external and internal edges of the road in order for a car to be able to travel at 50 mi hr^{-1} (without experiencing sideways forces) around a curve whose radius is 2000 ft.

7.60 A highway curve whose radius is 1000 ft is *not* banked. Assume that the coefficient of friction between rubber and dry asphalt is 0.75, between rubber and wet asphalt is 0.50, and between rubber and ice is 0.25. Determine the maximum safe speed for traversing the curve on (a) dry days, (b) rainy days, (c) icy days. Why are these values independent of the car's mass?

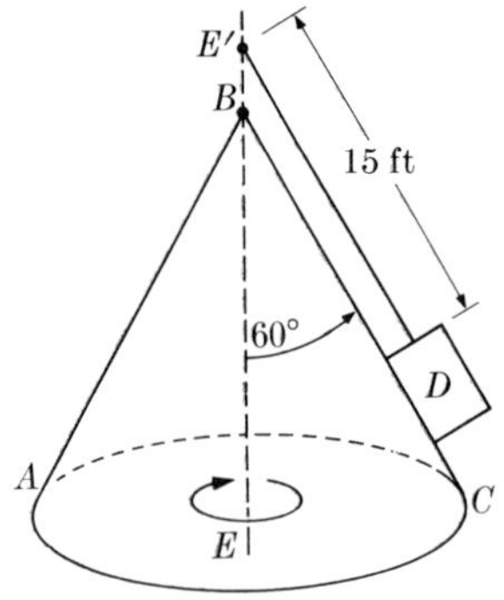

Figure 7–41

7.61 A body D which has a mass of 12 lb (Fig. 7–41) is on a smooth conical surface ABC, and is spinning about the axis EE' with an angular velocity of 10 rev/min. Calculate: (a) the linear velocity of the body, (b) the reaction of the surface on the body, (c) the tension in the thread, and (d) the angular velocity necessary to reduce the reaction of the plane to zero.

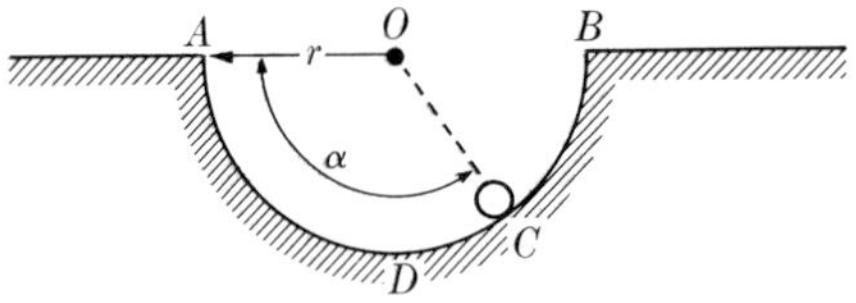

Figure 7–42

7.62 A small ball of mass m, initially at A, slides on the smooth circular surface ADB (Fig. 7–42). When the ball is at the point C, show that the angular velocity and the force exerted by the surface are $\omega = \sqrt{2g \sin \alpha / r}$, $F = mg(1 + 2 \sin \alpha)$.

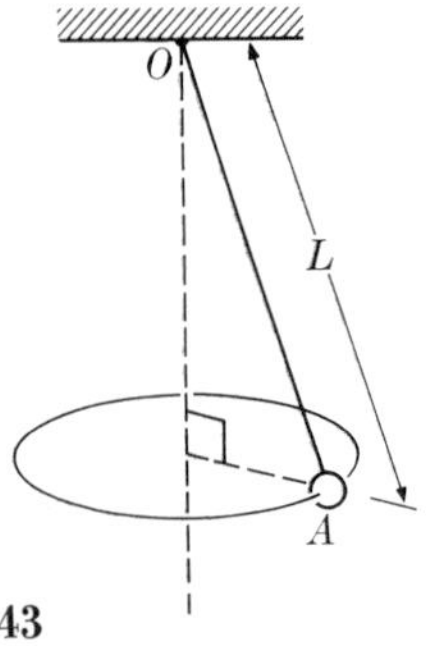

Figure 7–43

7.63 Referring to the conical pendulum of Fig. 7–43 rotating in a horizontal circle with an angular velocity ω, calculate the tension in the rope and its angle with respect to the vertical for the case when $M = 12$ kg, $L = 1.16$ m and $\omega = 30$ rad s^{-1}.

7.64 Show that the periods of two conical pendulums hung from the same ceiling and having different lengths, but moving so that both bobs are at the same height above the floor, are equal.

7.65 A particle of density ρ_1 is suspended in a rotating liquid of density ρ_2. Prove that the particle will spiral outward (inward) if ρ_1 is greater (smaller) than ρ_2.

7.66 Prove that if a body moves under the action of a force $F = k\boldsymbol{u} \times \boldsymbol{v}$, where $\boldsymbol{u}$ is an arbitrary unit vector, the motion is circular with angular velocity $\boldsymbol{\omega} = k\boldsymbol{u}$ or, in a more general case, a spiral parallel to $\boldsymbol{u}$.

7.67 At $t = 0$, a body of mass 3.0 kg is located at $\boldsymbol{r} = \boldsymbol{u}_x\, 4$ m, with a velocity $\boldsymbol{v} = (\boldsymbol{u}_x + \boldsymbol{u}_y\, 6)$ m s^{-1}. If a constant force $\boldsymbol{F} = \boldsymbol{u}_y\, 5$ N acts on the particle, find (a) the change in the (linear) momentum of the body after 3 s, (b) the change in the angular momentum of the body after 3 s.

7.68 A ball of mass 200 gm is moving due north with a velocity of 300 cm s^{-1}. When a force of 2000 dyn in the due-east direction is applied, obtain the equation of the trajectory and calculate after 40 s: (a) the magnitude and direction of the velocity, (b) the distance from the initial point, (c) the displacement from the initial point.

7.69 A particle moving with a velocity v_0 along the X-axis is acted on by a force F parallel to the Y-axis while moving in the region $0 \leq x \leq L$. Find the change in its direction of motion. At what distance from the X-axis will the particle strike a wall placed at $x = L$?

7.70 A point mass is moving in the XY-plane under the action of a constant force whose components are $F_x = 6$ N and $F_y =$

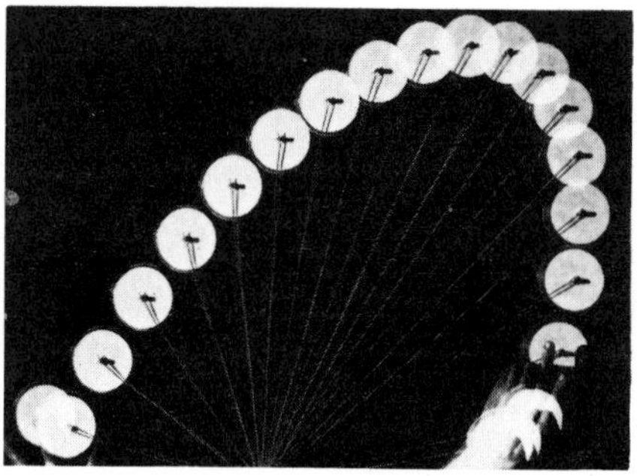

Figure 7–44

-7 N. When $t = 0$ s, $x = 0$, $y = 0$, $v_x = -2$ m s^{-1}, and $v_y = 0$; find the position and velocity when $t = 2$ s. Assume that the mass of the particle is 16 kg.

7.71 The position vector of a body of mass 6 kg is given as: $\boldsymbol{r} = \boldsymbol{u}_x(3t^2 - 6t) + \boldsymbol{u}_y(-4t^3) + \boldsymbol{u}_z(3t + 2)$ m. Find: (a) the force acting on the particle, (b) the torque, with respect to the origin, acting on the particle, (c) the momentum and angular momentum of the particle with respect to the origin. (d) Verify that $\boldsymbol{F} = d\boldsymbol{p}/dt$ and $\boldsymbol{\tau} = d\boldsymbol{L}/dt$.

7.72 At $t = 0$ s, a 3-kg mass is located at $\boldsymbol{r} = \boldsymbol{u}_x\, 5$ m and has a velocity of $\boldsymbol{u}_y$ 10 m s^{-1}. There are no forces acting on the mass. Determine the angular momentum of the mass with respect to the origin at (a) $t = 0$ s and (b) $t = 12$ s.

7.73 One end of a rubber band has a disk attached to it; the other end of the band is fixed. The disk can move on a frictionless horizontal table. If the rubber band is extended and the disk is pushed at an angle, it describes the path shown in the multiflash photograph in Fig. 7–44 (the time interval between flashes is 0.5 s). By actual measurement on the photograph, show that the law of areas holds for this motion. From the physical situation described, is the force on the disk central?

7.74 A 1-kg mass rests on a 10-kg mass, which in turn rests on a horizontal surface, as shown in Fig. 7–45. The force F varies with time t (measured in seconds), such that $F = 0.2t$ N. If the coefficient of static friction is 0.2 and the coefficient of sliding friction is 0.15 between all surfaces, find the motion of each block as a function of time.

7.75 When the earth is at aphelion (the position at which it is farthest away from the sun), June 21, its distance is 1.52×10^{11} m and its orbital velocity is 2.93×10^4 m s^{-1}. Find its orbital velocity at perihelion (the position at which it is closest to the sun) about six months later, when its distance from the sun is 1.47×10^{11} m. Do these variations in velocity affect the duration of the solar day? Also find the angular velocity of the earth about the sun for both cases. [*Hint:* both at aphelion and at perihelion the velocity is perpendicular to the radius vector.]

7.76 A 10^3-kg rocket is set vertically on its launching pad. The propellant is expelled at the rate of 2 kg s^{-1}. Find the minimum velocity of the exhaust gases so that the rocket just begins to rise. Also find the rocket's velocity 10 s after ignition, assuming the minimum exhaust velocity.

7.77 A rocket, launched vertically, expels mass at a constant rate equal to $5 \times 10^{-2} m_0$ kg s^{-1}, where m_0 is its initial mass.

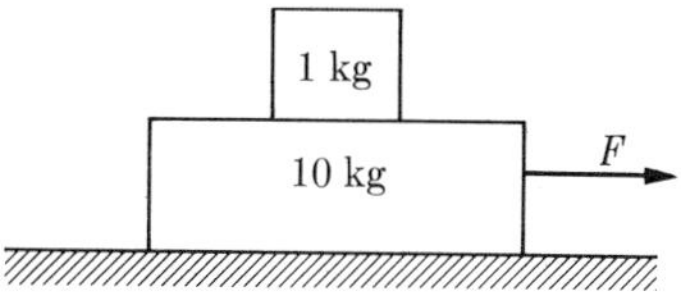

Figure 7–45

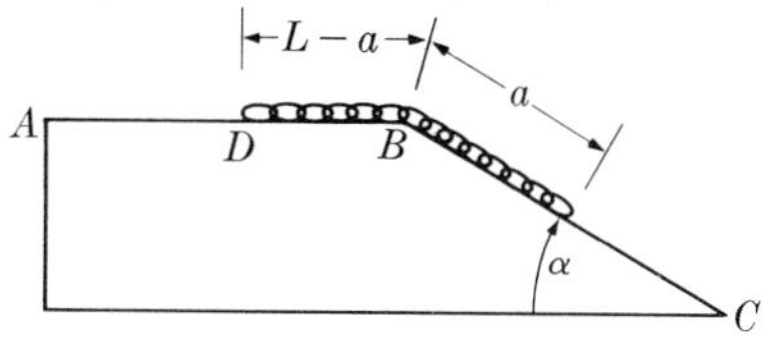

Figure 7–46

The exhaust velocity of the gases relative to the rocket is 5×10^3 m s^{-1}. Find the velocity and the height of the rocket after 10 s.

7.78 A flexible chain of length L and weight W (Fig. 7–46) is initially placed at rest on a smooth frictionless surface ABC, with D the distance $L - a$ from B. Prove that when the end D arrives at the point B the velocity of the chain is $v = \sqrt{(g/L)(L^2 - a^2)\sin\alpha}$.

7.79 A uniform rope of mass M and length L (Fig. 7–47) passes over a smooth peg of very small radius. When the motion starts, $BC = b$. Show that the acceleration and velocity when $BC = \frac{2}{3}L$ are $a = g/3$, $v = \sqrt{2g/L(\frac{8}{3}L^2 + 2bL - b^2)}$. Apply your results to $L = 12$ ft, $b = 7$ ft.

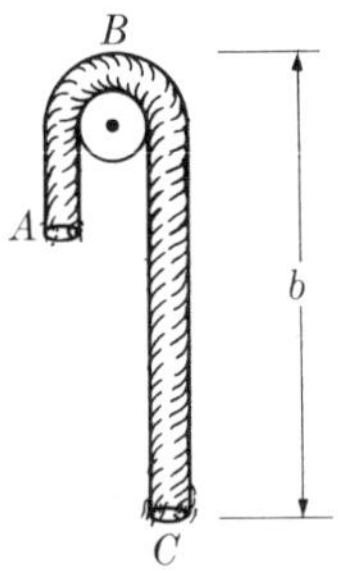

Figure 7–47

7.80 A mass M, attached to an end of a very long chain having a mass m per unit length, is thrown vertically upward with an initial velocity v_0. Show that the maximum height reached by M is $h = (M/m)[\sqrt[3]{1 + 3mv_0^2/2Mg} - 1]$, and that the velocity of M when it returns to the ground is $v = \sqrt{2gh}$.

7.81 Water vapor condenses on a raindrop at the rate of m mass units per unit time; the drop initially has a mass M and starts from rest. Show that the distance it falls in time t is $\frac{1}{2}g\{\frac{1}{2}t^2 + (M/m)t - (M^2/m^2)\ln[1 + (m/M)t]\}$. Neglect the resistance due to the air.

7.82 A particle moves under a constant force through a fluid resisting the motion with a force proportional to the velocity. Show that, if the force is cut off after the particle reaches the limiting velocity, the velocity at time t will be $v = v_L e^{-(k/m)t}$ and the distance moved will be $x = (m/k)v_L[1 - e^{-(k/m)t}]$. Verify that the distance moved before stopping is $v_L(m/k)$. Show that the velocity of the particle will reduce to $1/e$ of its value after the time $t = m/k$.

7.83 A body moves under the action of a constant force F through a fluid which opposes the motion with a force proportional to the square of the velocity; that is, $F_f = -kv^2$. Show that the limiting velocity is $v_L = \sqrt{F/k}$. Prove that the relationship between the velocity and the distance is $v^2 = (F/k) + [v_0^2 - (F/k)]e^{-2(k/m)x}$. Plot v^2 against x for $v_0 = 0$. If the force is suppressed after the body reaches the limiting velocity, show that the velocity of the particle will fall to $1/e$ of the limiting velocity after traversing the distance m/k.

7.84 Prove that when a body is in motion under a resisting force proportional to the square of the velocity, the velocity at time t is:

$$v = v_L \frac{(v_0 + v_L)e^{(kv_L/m)t} + (v_0 - v_L)e^{-(kv_L/m)t}}{(v_0 + v_L)e^{(kv_L/m)t} - (v_0 - v_L)e^{-(kv_L/m)t}}.$$

8
WORK AND ENERGY

8.1 Introduction

In this chapter we shall continue to discuss various aspects of the dynamics of a particle. Accordingly, we shall observe only one particle, and reduce its interactions with the rest of the universe to a single term which we have called *force.* When we are solving the fundamental equation of the dynamics of a particle (that is, $\boldsymbol{F} = d\boldsymbol{p}/dt$), we can always perform a first integration if we know the force as a function of time, because from this equation we obtain by integration

$$\int_{\boldsymbol{p}_0}^{\boldsymbol{p}} d\boldsymbol{p} = \int_{t_0}^{t} \boldsymbol{F}\, dt$$

or

$$\boldsymbol{p} - \boldsymbol{p}_0 = \int_{t_0}^{t} \boldsymbol{F}\, dt = \boldsymbol{I}. \tag{8.1}$$

The quantity $\boldsymbol{I} = \int_{t_0}^{t} \boldsymbol{F}\, dt$ appearing on the right is called the *impulse.* Therefore, Eq. (8.1) tells us that

the change in momentum of the particle is equal to the impulse.

Since impulse is essentially force multiplied by time, a very strong force acting through a short time may produce the same change in momentum as a weaker force acting for a longer time. For example, when a batter hits a ball he produces a large force during a very short time, resulting in an appreciable change in the momentum of the ball. However, gravity, to produce an equivalent change in momentum, would have to act on the ball for a much longer time.

When we replace $\boldsymbol{p}$ by its equivalent $m\boldsymbol{v}$, it is possible to integrate again and obtain the position of the particle as a function of time. That is,

$$m\boldsymbol{v} - m\boldsymbol{v}_0 = \boldsymbol{I} \qquad \text{or} \qquad \boldsymbol{v} = \boldsymbol{v}_0 + \frac{1}{m}\boldsymbol{I}.$$

Recalling that $\boldsymbol{v} = d\boldsymbol{r}/dt$, we may write

$$\int_{\boldsymbol{r}_0}^{\boldsymbol{r}} d\boldsymbol{r} = \int_{t_0}^{t} \left(\boldsymbol{v}_0 + \frac{1}{m}\boldsymbol{I}\right) dt \qquad \text{or} \qquad \boldsymbol{r} = \boldsymbol{r}_0 + \boldsymbol{v}_0 t + \frac{1}{m}\int_{t_0}^{t} \boldsymbol{I}\, dt,$$

which gives $\boldsymbol{r}$ in terms of t, and thus formally solves the dynamical problem. In fact, in Example 7.5 we solved a problem of this type for the case of rectilinear motion.

However, in the important problems encountered in physics, the force on a particle is not known as a function of time but as a function of position given by $\boldsymbol{r}$ or x, y, z; that is, $\boldsymbol{F}(\boldsymbol{r})$ or $\boldsymbol{F}(x, y, z)$. Hence we cannot evaluate the integral appearing in Eq. (8.1) until we know x, y, and z as functions of time; that is, until we have solved the problem that we attempt to solve with Eq. (8.1)! To circumvent this apparent vicious circle we must resort to other mathematical techniques which will lead us to the definition of two new concepts: *work* and *energy.* These powerful methods will enable us to solve problems even in cases in which we do not know the force, but can make reasonable assumptions about its properties.

EXAMPLE 8.1. A ball whose mass is 0.1 kg is allowed to fall from a height of 2 m and, after hitting the floor, it bounces back up to a height of 1.8 m. Determine the impulse it received from gravity while it was falling and the impulse it received when it struck the floor.

Solution: We first use Eq. (5.12) to find the velocity of the particle when it arrives at the floor; that is, $v_1 = \sqrt{2gh_1}$, where $h_1 = 2$ m. Thus $v_1 = 6.26$ m s^{-1}. Since the velocity is directed downward, we must write $\boldsymbol{v}_1 = -\boldsymbol{u}_y(6.26 \text{ m s}^{-1})$. The initial momentum is zero, and thus the total change in momentum during the fall is $m\boldsymbol{v}_1 - 0 = -\boldsymbol{u}_y(0.626 \text{ kg m s}^{-1})$. This is the impulse due to gravity. We may also compute this impulse directly by using the definition $\boldsymbol{I} = \int_{t_0}^{t} \boldsymbol{F}\, dt$. In this case $t_0 = 0$ and $t = v_1/g = 0.639$ s. Also $\boldsymbol{F} = m\boldsymbol{g} = -\boldsymbol{u}_y mg = -\boldsymbol{u}_y(0.98 \text{ N})$. Thus direct calculation again gives $-\boldsymbol{u}_y(0.626 \text{ kg m s}^{-1})$ for the impulse due to gravity during the fall.

But when the ball hits the ground a new force acts during a very short time. We do not know the force, but we may obtain the impulse by computing the momentum of the ball when it bounces back. Since it goes to a height $h_2 = 1.8$ m, the velocity when it bounces back is $v_2 = \sqrt{2gh_2} = 5.94$ m s^{-1}, or in vector form $\boldsymbol{v}_2 = \boldsymbol{u}_y(5.94 \text{ m s}^{-1})$, since the body is moving upward. Thus the change in momentum is expressed by

$$\boldsymbol{p}_2 - \boldsymbol{p}_1 = m\boldsymbol{v}_2 - m\boldsymbol{v}_1 = \boldsymbol{u}_y(1.221 \text{ kg m s}^{-1}),$$

which also gives the impulse. Comparing this value with the result for free fall, and noting that the collision with the ground takes place in a very short time interval, we conclude that the force acting in this second case is much stronger. If we could measure the time interval, we could obtain the average force on the ball.

8.2 Work

Let us consider a particle A moving along a curve C under the action of a force $\boldsymbol{F}$ (Fig. 8–1). In a very short time dt it moves from A to A', the displacement being $\overrightarrow{AA'} = d\boldsymbol{r}$. The *work* done by the force $\boldsymbol{F}$ during that displacement is defined by the scalar product

$$dW = \boldsymbol{F} \cdot d\boldsymbol{r}. \tag{8.2}$$

Designating the magnitude of $d\boldsymbol{r}$ (that is, the distance moved) by ds, we may also write Eq. (8.2) in the form

$$dW = F\, ds \cos\theta, \tag{8.3}$$

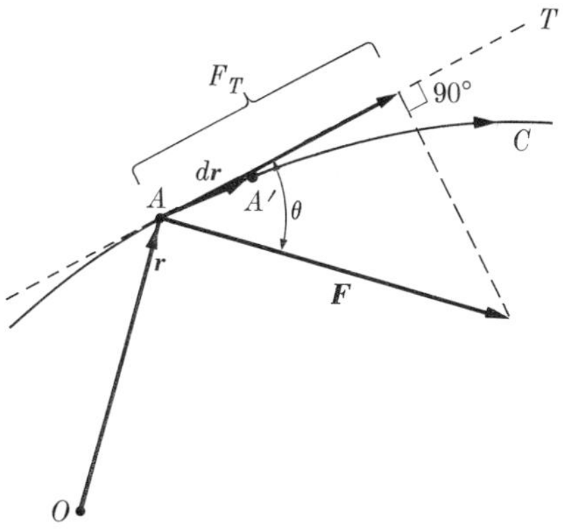

Fig. 8–1. Work is equal to displacement multiplied by the component of the force along the displacement.

where θ is the angle between the direction of the force $\boldsymbol{F}$ and the displacement $d\boldsymbol{r}$. Now $F \cos\theta$ is the component F_T of the force along the tangent to the path, so that

$$dW = F_T\, ds. \tag{8.4}$$

In words, we may express this by saying that

> *work is equal to the displacement times the component of the force along the displacement.*

Let us note that if a force is perpendicular to the displacement ($\theta = 90°$), the work done by the force is zero. For example, this is the case for the centripetal force $\boldsymbol{F}_N$ in circular motion (Fig. 8–2a), or the force of gravity mg when a body is moved on a horizontal plane (Fig. 8–2b).

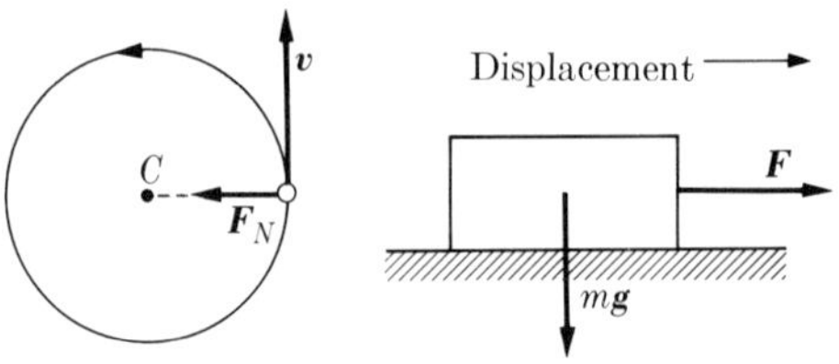

(a) (b)

Fig. 8–2. Forces that do no work.

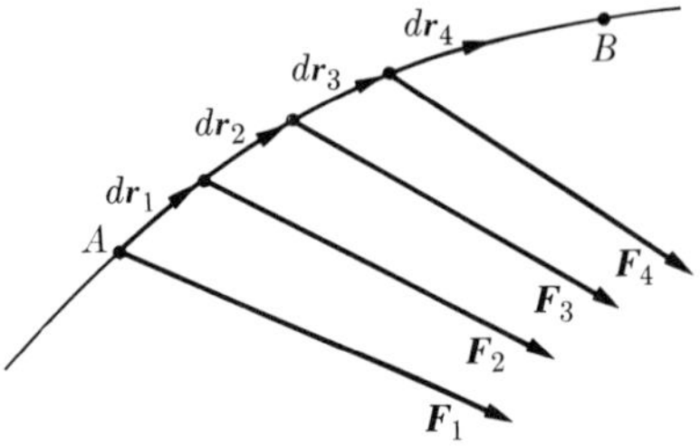

Fig. 8–3. The total work is the sum of many infinitesimal works.

Equation (8.2) gives the work for an infinitesimal displacement. The total work done on the particle when moving from A to B (Fig. 8–3) is the sum of all the infinitesimal works done during successive infinitesimal displacements. That is,

$$W = \boldsymbol{F}_1 \cdot d\boldsymbol{r}_1 + \boldsymbol{F}_2 \cdot d\boldsymbol{r}_2 + \boldsymbol{F}_3 \cdot d\boldsymbol{r}_3 + \cdots$$

or

$$W = \int_A^B \boldsymbol{F} \cdot d\boldsymbol{r} = \int_A^B F_T \, ds. \tag{8.5}^*$$

Before we can perform the integral that appears in Eq. (8.5), we must know $\boldsymbol{F}$ as a function of x, y, and z. Also, in general, we must know the equation of the path along which the particle moves. Alternatively, we must know $\boldsymbol{F}$, x, y, and z as functions of time or some other variable.

Sometimes it is convenient to represent F_T graphically. In Fig. 8–4 we have plotted F_T as a function of the distance s. The work $dW = F_T \, ds$ done during a small displacement ds corresponds to the area of the narrow rectangle. Thus we

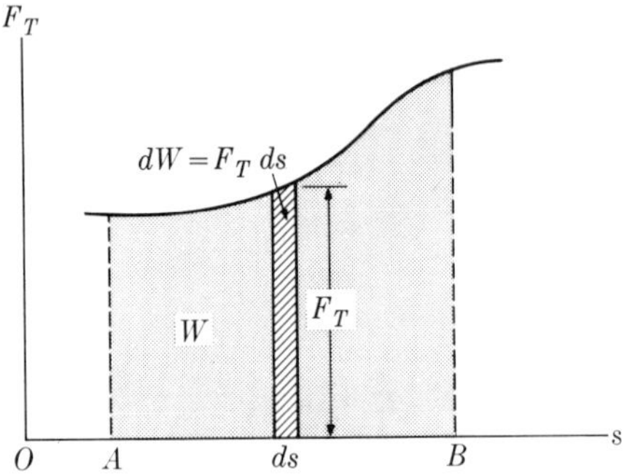

Fig. 8–4. The total work done in going from A to B is equal to the area under the curve.

---

* For any vector $\boldsymbol{V}$ which is a function of position, an integral of the form $\int_A^B \boldsymbol{V} \cdot d\boldsymbol{r}$ along some path joining points A and B is called the *line integral* of $\boldsymbol{V}$. It will appear many times in this book.

can find the total work done on the particle in Fig. 8–3 in order to move it from A to B by first dividing the whole shaded area in Fig. 8–4 into narrow rectangles and then adding their areas. That is, the work done is given by the total shaded area in Fig. 8–4.

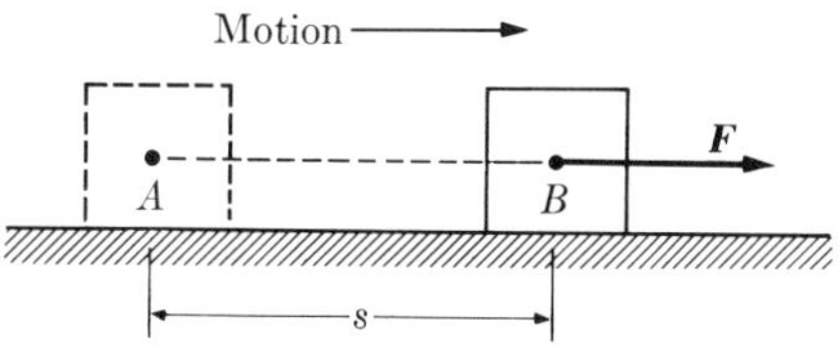

Fig. 8–5. Work of a force that is constant in magnitude and direction.

An interesting particular case is that in which the force is constant in magnitude and direction and the body moves in a straight line in the direction of the force (Fig. 8–5). Then $F_T = F$ and Eq. (8.5) yields

$$W = \int_A^B F\,ds = F\int_A^B ds = Fs, \tag{8.6}$$

or work = force × distance, which is the expression normally found in elementary textbooks.

If F_x, F_y, and F_z are the rectangular components of $\boldsymbol{F}$ and dx, dy, and dz are the rectangular components of $d\boldsymbol{r}$ (Fig. 8–6), application of Eq. (3.20) indicates that

$$W = \int_A^B (F_x\,dx + F_y\,dy + F_z\,dz). \tag{8.7}$$

When the particle is acted on by several forces $\boldsymbol{F}_1, \boldsymbol{F}_2, \boldsymbol{F}_3, \ldots$, the work done by each force during a displacement $\overrightarrow{AA'} = d\boldsymbol{r}$ (Fig. 8–7) is $dW_1 = \boldsymbol{F}_1 \cdot d\boldsymbol{r}$, $dW_2 = \boldsymbol{F}_2 \cdot d\boldsymbol{r}$, $dW_3 = \boldsymbol{F}_3 \cdot d\boldsymbol{r}$, and so forth. Note that $d\boldsymbol{r}$ is the same for all forces because all are acting on the same particle. The total work dW done on the

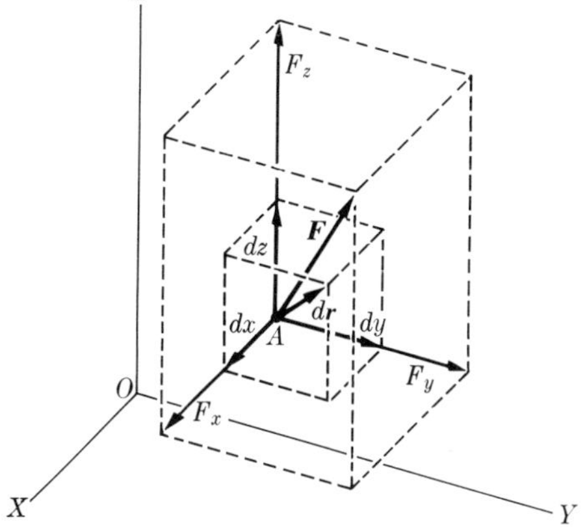

Fig. 8–6. The work done by a force is equal to the sum of the works done by its rectangular components.

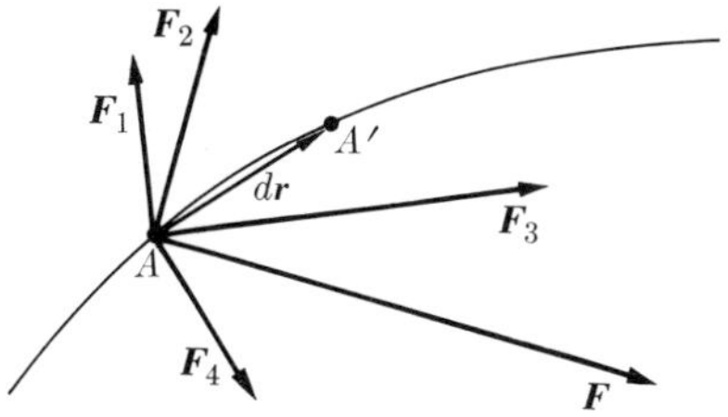

Fig. 8–7. When several forces act on a particle, the work of the resultant is the sum of the works done by the components.

particle is obtained by adding the infinitesimal works $dW_1, dW_2, dW_3, \ldots,$ done by each of the forces. Thus

$$\begin{aligned} dW &= dW_1 + dW_2 + dW_3 + \cdots \\ &= \boldsymbol{F}_1 \cdot d\boldsymbol{r} + \boldsymbol{F}_2 \cdot d\boldsymbol{r} + \boldsymbol{F}_3 \cdot d\boldsymbol{r} + \cdots \\ &= (\boldsymbol{F}_1 + \boldsymbol{F}_2 + \boldsymbol{F}_3 + \cdots) \cdot d\boldsymbol{r} \\ &= \boldsymbol{F} \cdot d\boldsymbol{r}, \end{aligned} \tag{8.8}$$

where $\boldsymbol{F} = \boldsymbol{F}_1 + \boldsymbol{F}_2 + \boldsymbol{F}_3 + \cdots$ is the resultant force. But the last result in Eq. (8.8) is the work done by the resultant force acting on the particle. This proves then that the work of the resultant of several forces applied to the same particle is equal to the sum of the works of the component forces.

8.3 Power

In practical applications, especially in connection with machines and engineering, it is important to know the rate at which work is done. The *instantaneous power* is defined by

$$P = \frac{dW}{dt}. \tag{8.9}$$

That is, power is defined as the work done per unit time during a very small time interval dt. Using Eqs. (8.2) and (5.17), we may also write

$$P = \boldsymbol{F} \cdot \frac{d\boldsymbol{r}}{dt} = \boldsymbol{F} \cdot \boldsymbol{v}, \tag{8.10}$$

and thus power can also be defined as force times velocity. The *average power* during a time interval t is obtained by dividing the total work W, as given in Eq. (8.5), by the time t, yielding $P_{\text{ave}} = W/t$.

From the engineering point of view, the concept of power is very important because, when an engineer designs a machine, it is the *rate* at which it can do work that matters, rather than the total amount of work the machine can do.

8.4 Units of Work and Power

From Eqs. (8.2) or (8.6), we see that work must be expressed as the product of a unit of force and a unit of distance. In the MKSC system, work is expressed in newton meters, a unit called the *joule*, abbreviated J. Thus one joule is the work done by a force of one newton when it moves a particle one meter in the same direction as the force. Recalling that $\text{N} = \text{m kg s}^{-2}$, we have that $\text{J} = \text{N m} = \text{m}^2 \text{ kg s}^{-2}$. The name joule was chosen to honor James Prescott Joule (1816–1869), a British scientist famous for his research on the concepts of heat and energy.

In the cgs system, work is expressed in dynes centimeters, a unit called an *erg*. Thus: erg = dyn cm. Recalling that $1 \text{ N} = 10^5$ dyn and $1 \text{ m} = 10^2$ cm, we have that $1 \text{ J} = (10^5 \text{ dyn})(10^2 \text{ m}) = 10^7$ ergs. For the unit of work in the British system, called the *foot-pound*, and abbreviated ft-lb, we refer the student to Problem 8.4.

According to definition (8.9), power must be expressed as the ratio between a unit of work and a unit of time. In the MKSC system power is expressed in *joules per second*, a unit called a *watt*, abbreviated W. One watt is the power of a machine that does work at the rate of one joule every second. Recalling that $J = m^2\,kg\,s^{-2}$, we have that $W = J\,s^{-1} = m^2\,kg\,s^{-3}$. The name watt was chosen in honor of the British engineer James Watt (1736–1819), who improved the steam engine with his inventions. Two multiples of the watt generally used are the *kilowatt* (kW) and the *megawatt* (MW), defined by: 1 kW $= 10^3$ W and 1 MW $= 10^6$ W. A unit of power commonly used by engineers is the *horsepower*, abbreviated hp, and defined as 550 ft lb per second, or 746 W.

Another unit used to express work is the *kilowatt-hour*. The kilowatt-hour is equal to the work done during one hour by an engine having a power of one kilowatt. Thus: 1 kilowatt-hour $= (10^3\text{ W})\,(3.6 \times 10^3\text{ s}) = 3.6 \times 10^6$ J.

EXAMPLE 8.2. An automobile having a mass of 1200 kg moves up a long hill inclined 5° with a constant velocity of 36 km per hour. Calculate the work the engine does in 5 minutes and the power developed by it. Neglect all frictional effects.

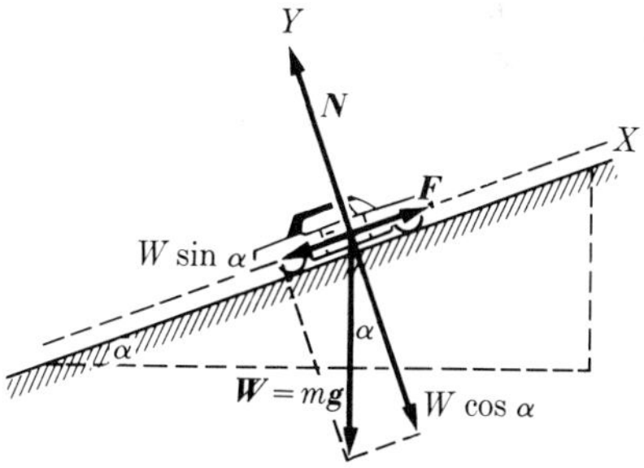

Figure 8–8

Solution: The motion of the automobile along the hill is due to the force F, exerted by the engine, and to the force $W \sin \alpha$, due to the weight of the automobile (Fig. 8–8). Thus we must write, using $W = mg$,

$$F - mg \sin \alpha = ma.$$

Since the motion is uniform, $a = 0$, and $F = mg \sin \alpha = 1.023 \times 10^3$ N. The velocity of the automobile is $v = 36\text{ km hr}^{-1} = 36(10^3\text{ m})(3.6 \times 10^3\text{ s})^{-1} = 10\text{ m s}^{-1}$, and in 5 minutes (or 300 s) it moves the distance $s = (10\text{ m s}^{-1})(300\text{ s}) = 3 \times 10^3$ m. Therefore, if we use Eq. (8.6), the work done by the engine is

$$W = Fs = (1.023 \times 10^3\text{ N})(3 \times 10^3\text{ m}) = 3.069 \times 10^6\text{ J}.$$

The average power can be computed in two different ways. First we may say that

$$P = \frac{W}{t} = \frac{3.069 \times 10^6\text{ J}}{3 \times 10^2\text{ s}} = 1.023 \times 10^4\text{ W}.$$

Alternatively, we may say that

$$P = Fv = (1.023 \times 10^3\text{ N})(10\text{ m s}^{-1}) = 1.023 \times 10^4\text{ W}.$$

EXAMPLE 8.3. Calculate the work required to expand the spring of Fig. 8–9 a distance of 2 cm without acceleration. It is known that when a body whose mass is 4 kg is hung from the spring, the spring's length increases by 1.50 cm.

Solution: When no body is hanging from the spring, the spring's length extends from O to the horizontal level A. It has been verified experimentally that to extend a spring a small distance x without acceleration, a force proportional to the distance is required; that is, $F = kx$. If the spring is extended without acceleration, it produces an equal and opposite force. This is the principle of the spring balance or *dynamometer*, commonly used for measuring forces. To determine the proportionality constant k, we use the fact that when the body m exerts the force of its weight on the spring, the spring expands the distance $x = 1.50$ cm $= 1.50 \times 10^{-2}$ m. The force F is, in this case, the weight $mg = 39.2$ N. Thus, making $mg = kx$, we obtain

$$k = \frac{39.2 \text{ N}}{1.50 \times 10^{-2} \text{ m}} = 2.61 \times 10^3 \text{ N m}^{-1}.$$

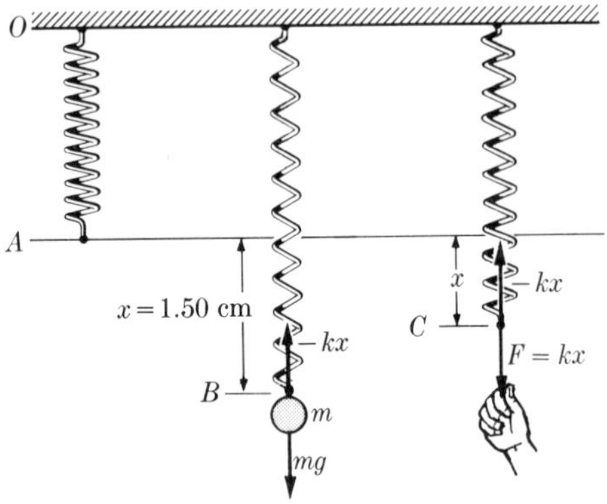

Fig. 8–9. Work done in stretching a spring.

To extend the spring a distance x, without acceleration, we now apply a force $F = kx$. This can be accomplished by slowly pulling on a cord attached to the spring. The force necessarily increases steadily as x increases. To find the work done, we must use Eq. (8.5), which yields

$$W = \int_0^x F\,dx = \int_0^x kx\,dx = \tfrac{1}{2}kx^2.$$

This is the work done for any displacement x. Introducing corresponding numerical values for x and k, we obtain the work required to extend the spring by 2 cm, which is $W = 5.22 \times 10^{-1}$ J.

EXAMPLE 8.4. A force $F = 6t$ N acts on a particle whose mass is 2 kg. If the particle starts from rest, find the work done by the force during the first 2 s.

Solution: In the preceding example it was easy to calculate the work because we knew the force as a function of the position ($F = kx$). But in this example we know the force only as a function of the time ($F = 6t$). Thus we cannot directly calculate the work by $W = \int F\,dx$. Instead we must first find the displacement in terms of the time, using the equation of motion, $F = ma$. Thus $a = F/m = 3t$ m s^{-2}. Using Eq. (5.6), with $v_0 = 0$ because the particle starts from rest, we may write

$$v = \int_0^t (3t)\,dt = 1.5t^2 \text{ m s}^{-1}.$$

Now, if we use Eq. (5.3) with $x_0 = 0$, and if we place our origin of coordinates at the starting point, we obtain

$$x = \int_0^t (1.5t^2)\,dt = 0.5t^3 \text{ m}.$$

Now that we have the position x as a function of time t, we may proceed in two different ways.

(a) Solving for t, we get $t = (x/0.5)^{1/3} = 1.260x^{1/3}$, and the force in terms of position is then $F = 6t = 7.560x^{1/3}$ N. Using Eq. (8.5), we then have

$$W = \int_0^x (7.560x^{1/3})\, dx = 5.670x^{4/3}.$$

When $t = 2$, we have that $x = 0.5(2)^3 = 4$ m, and thus $W = 36.0$ J.

(b) We may also proceed in a different way: From $x = 0.5t^3$, we have $dx = 1.5t^2\, dt$. Then, using for the force its expression in terms of time, $F = 6t$, we may write

$$W = \int_0^t (6t)(1.5t^2\, dt) = 2.25t^4 \text{ J},$$

and if we make $t = 2$ s, then $W = 36.0$ J, in agreement with the previous result.

This second method is the one we normally must use when we know the force as a function of time, because even after solving the equation of motion it may be, in general, difficult to express force as a function of position.

8.5 Kinetic Energy

From Eq. (7.27), we have that the tangential force is $F_T = m\, dv/dt$. Therefore

$$F_T\, ds = m \frac{dv}{dt}\, ds = m\, dv \frac{ds}{dt} = mv\, dv,$$

since $v = ds/dt$, according to Eq. (5.23). Therefore the integral appearing in Eq. (8.5) for the total work is

$$W = \int_A^B F_T\, ds = \int_A^B mv\, dv = \tfrac{1}{2}mv_B^2 - \tfrac{1}{2}mv_A^2, \tag{8.11}$$

where v_B is the particle's velocity at B and v_A is the particle's velocity at A. The result (8.11) indicates that no matter what the functional form of the force $\boldsymbol{F}$ and the path followed by the particle, the value of the work W done by the force is always equal to the difference of the quantity $\frac{1}{2}mv^2$ evaluated at the end and at the beginning of the path. This important quantity, called *kinetic energy*, is designated by E_k. Therefore

$$E_k = \tfrac{1}{2}mv^2 \quad \text{or} \quad E_k = \frac{p^2}{2m}, \tag{8.12}$$

since $p = mv$. Equation (8.11) can then be expressed in the form

$$W = E_{k,B} - E_{k,A}, \tag{8.13}$$

which can be expressed in words as:

the work done on a particle is equal to the change in its kinetic energy,

and is a result which is valid in general, no matter what the nature of the force.

We can see that, in view of Eq. (8.13), kinetic energy is obviously measured in the same units as work; i.e., in joules in the MKSC system and in ergs in the cgs system. This can also be verified by noting, from Eq. (8.12), that E_k in the MKSC system must be expressed in $\mathrm{m^2\,kg\,s^{-2}}$, which is the dimensional expression for joules in terms of the fundamental units.

Let us mention in passing that another unit of energy widely used by physicists to describe chemical and nuclear processes is the *electron volt*, abbreviated eV, whose precise definition will be given in Section 14.9 (Vol. II). Its equivalence is: $\mathrm{eV} = 1.60210 \times 10^{-19}$ J. A useful multiple of the electron volt is the MeV, which is equal to 10^6 eV or 1.60210×10^{-13} J.

Result (8.13), relating the change in kinetic energy E_k of a particle to the work W done by the force, bears a great resemblance to Eq. (8.1), relating the change in momentum $\boldsymbol{p}$ of a particle to the impulse $\boldsymbol{I}$ of the force. The difference is that the impulse, since it is a *time* integral, is useful only when we know the force as a function of time. But work, since it is a *space* integral, can easily be computed when we know the force as a function of position. We usually do know the force as a function of position, and it is for this reason that the concepts of work and energy play such an important role in physics.

Let us remind the student that these concepts of work and energy, as used in physics, have very precise meanings that must be understood thoroughly, and must not be confused with the same terms as they are loosely used in daily life.

EXAMPLE 8.5. Using the data of Example 8.4, compute directly the kinetic energy which the particle gains in a time t.

Solution: We recall from the solution of Example 8.4 that the velocity at time t is $v = 1.5t^2\ \mathrm{m\,s^{-1}}$, and thus the kinetic energy of the particle is

$$E_k = \tfrac{1}{2}mv^2 = \tfrac{1}{2}(2\ \mathrm{kg})(1.5t^2\ \mathrm{m\,s^{-1}})^2 = 2.25t^4\ \mathrm{J}.$$

The particle's initial kinetic energy, at $t = 0$, is zero, and therefore the gain in kinetic energy of the particle in the time interval t is $E_k - E_{k,0} = 2.25t^4$ J, which is just equal to the work W done on the particle, according to the second result of Example 8.4.

EXAMPLE 8.6. The spring of Example 8.3 is placed in horizontal position, as shown in Fig. 8–10. The mass m is moved to the right the distance a, and then released. Calculate its kinetic energy when it is at distance x from the equilibrium position.

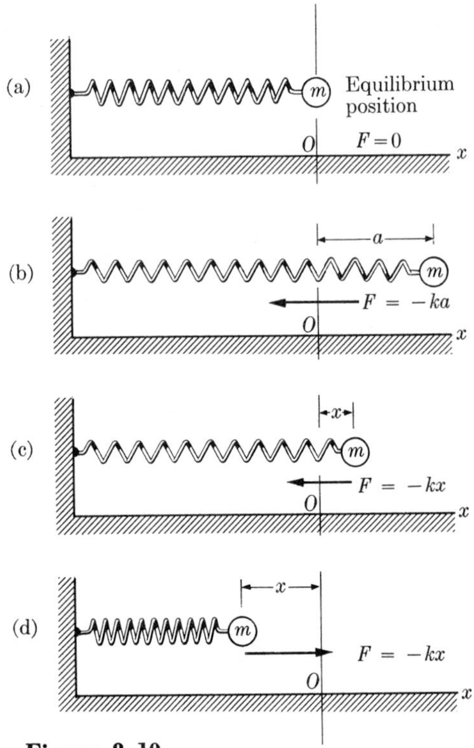

Figure 8–10

Solution: According to our explanation in Example 8.3, the spring will exert a force $F = -kx$ on the mass m when it is at distance x from the unextended position. (The minus sign indicates that the force produced by the spring is to the left when the body is displaced to the right.) At the equilibrium position $x = 0$, and thus $F = 0$. At position (b), when the mass is about to be released, $x = a$, $F = -ka$, and the velocity is zero ($v_0 = 0$) resulting in an initial kinetic energy of zero. Let us call v the velocity at the intermediate position x. Then, using Eq. (8.11), we find that

$$\tfrac{1}{2}mv^2 = \int_a^x F\,dx = \int_a^x (-kx)\,dx = \tfrac{1}{2}k(a^2 - x^2)$$

or

$$v = \sqrt{(k/m)(a^2 - x^2)},$$

which gives us the velocity of the particle in terms of the position. Note that the velocity depends on the square of x. What is the physical meaning of this dependence? With what velocity does the particle reach the position $x = 0$? Should we put a $\pm$ sign in front of the square root in the expression for v? Is there any limitation on the possible values of x? Can the student arrive at a pictorial representation of the resulting motion?

8.6 Work of a Force Constant in Magnitude and Direction

Consider a particle m moving under the action of a force $\boldsymbol{F}$ which is constant in magnitude and direction (Fig. 8–11). There may be other forces acting on the particle that may or may not be constant, but we do not wish to be concerned with them now. The work of $\boldsymbol{F}$ when the particle moves from A to B along path (1) is

$$W = \int_A^B \boldsymbol{F} \cdot d\boldsymbol{r} = \boldsymbol{F} \cdot \int_A^B d\boldsymbol{r} = \boldsymbol{F} \cdot (\boldsymbol{r}_B - \boldsymbol{r}_A). \tag{8.14}$$

One important conclusion derived from Eq. (8.14) is that the work in this case is independent of the path joining points A and B. For example, if the particle, instead of moving along path (1), moves along path (2), which also joins A and B, the work will be the same because the vector difference $\boldsymbol{r}_B - \boldsymbol{r}_A = \overrightarrow{AB}$ is still

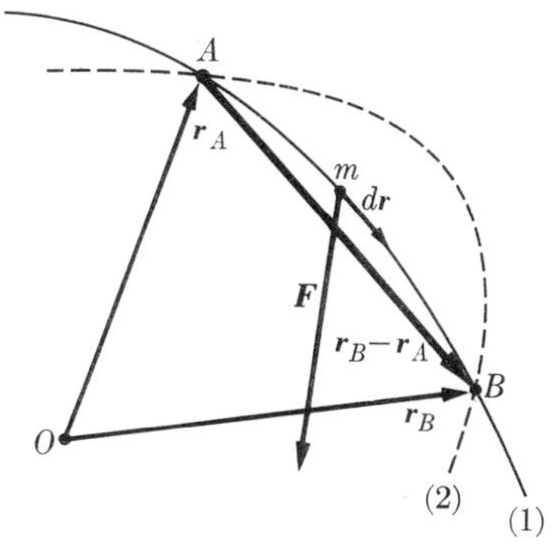

Fig. 8–11. Work done by a force which is constant in magnitude and direction.

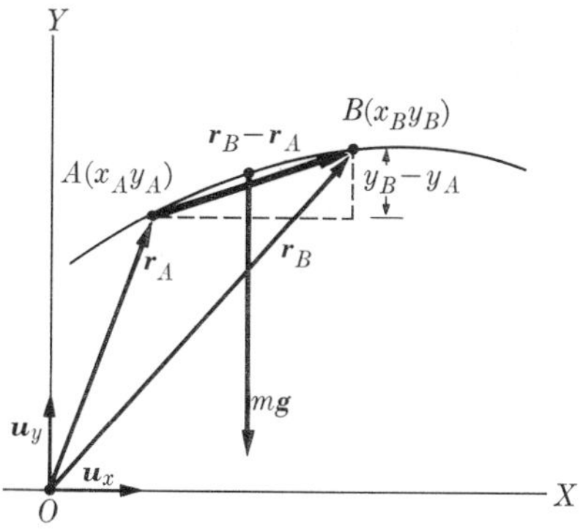

Fig. 8–12. Work done by gravity.

the same. Note that Eq. (8.14) can also be written in the form

$$W = \boldsymbol{F} \cdot \boldsymbol{r}_B - \boldsymbol{F} \cdot \boldsymbol{r}_A, \tag{8.15}$$

and is therefore equal to the difference between the quantity $\boldsymbol{F} \cdot \boldsymbol{r}$ evaluated at one end of the path and at the other.

An important application of Eq. (8.14) is to be found in the work done by the force of gravity (Fig. 8–12). In this case $\boldsymbol{F} = m\boldsymbol{g} = -\boldsymbol{u}_y mg$ and $\boldsymbol{r}_B - \boldsymbol{r}_A = \boldsymbol{u}_x(x_B - x_A) + \boldsymbol{u}_y(y_B - y_A)$. Therefore, substituting in Eq. (8.14) and using Eq. (3.19) for the scalar product, we have

$$W = -mg(y_B - y_A) = mgy_A - mgy_B. \tag{8.16}$$

Obviously in Eq. (8.16) there is no reference to the path, and the work depends only on the difference $y_B - y_A$ between the heights of the two endpoints.

EXAMPLE 8.7. A mass of 2 kg attached to a string one meter long is displaced an angle 30° with the vertical and released. Find its velocity when the string forms an angle of 10° with the vertical, on the same side and on the opposite side.

Solution: A mass hanging from a string is commonly called a *pendulum*. When the string is pulled out to an angle θ_0 (Fig. 8–13) and released, its initial velocity is zero. Under the action of its weight mg and the pull $\boldsymbol{F}_N$ of the string, it describes an arc of a circle while approaching point A. After passing point A it moves to the left until it reaches a symmetrical position. From then on the motion continues back and forth, resulting in the well-known oscillation of a pendulum. (Oscillatory motion will be discussed in detail in Chapter 12.)

In order to obtain v by using the principle of energy, Eq. (8.11), we should compute first the work done by the forces acting on the particle. The centripetal force $\boldsymbol{F}_N$ does no work, because at each position it is perpendicular to the velocity. And the work of the force of gravity mg can be computed with the aid of Eq. (8.16); that is, $W = mgy_0 - mgy = mg(y_0 - y)$. Now, measuring the height from an arbitrary horizontal level, we obtain $y_0 - y = B'C' = OC' - OB'$. But $OB' = l\cos\theta_0$ and $OC' = l\cos\theta$. Thus $y_0 - y = l(\cos\theta - \cos\theta_0)$ and

$$W = mg(y_0 - y) = mgl(\cos\theta - \cos\theta_0).$$

The kinetic energy at position C is $E_k = \frac{1}{2}mv^2$, and at B is zero. Thus, using Eq. (8.13), we obtain

$$\tfrac{1}{2}mv^2 = mgl(\cos\theta - \cos\theta_0)$$

or

$$v = \sqrt{2gl(\cos\theta - \cos\theta_0)}.$$

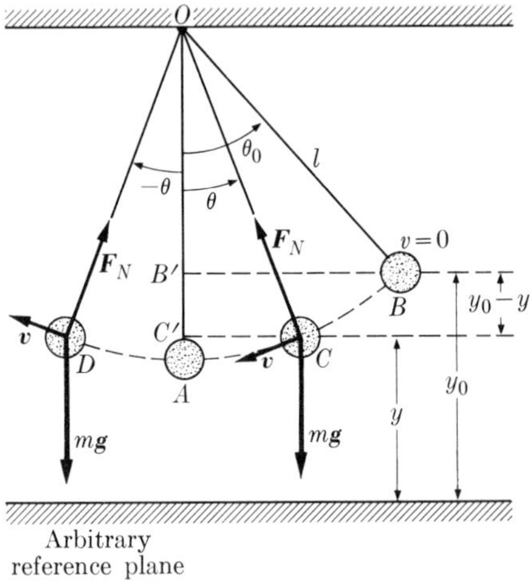

Fig. 8–13. Energy relations in motion of a pendulum.

We note that the result is independent of the mass. Introducing the numerical values, we have

$$v = \sqrt{2(9.8 \text{ m s}^{-2})(1 \text{ m})(\cos 10° - \cos 30°)} = 1.526 \text{ m s}^{-1}.$$

Note that at the symmetric position D, which makes an angle of $-10°$ with the vertical, we get the same result, since $\cos(-\theta) = \cos\theta$.

8.7 Potential Energy

The situation illustrated in the previous section is just one example of a large and important class of forces, which are called *conservative forces*, for reasons to be explained in later sections of this chapter.

A force is conservative if its dependence on the position vector $\boldsymbol{r}$ or on the coordinates x, y, z of the particle is such that the work W can always be expressed as the difference between a quantity $E_p(x, y, z)$ evaluated at the initial and at the final points. The quantity $E_p(x, y, z)$ is called the *potential energy*, and is afunction of the coordinates of the particles. Then, if $\boldsymbol{F}$ is a conservative force,

$$W = \int_A^B \boldsymbol{F} \cdot d\boldsymbol{r} = E_{p,A} - E_{p,B}. \tag{8.17}$$

Note that we write $E_{p,A} - E_{p,B}$ and not $E_{p,B} - E_{p,A}$; that is, the work done is equal to E_p at the starting point minus E_p at the endpoint. In other words,

> *potential energy is a function of the coordinates such that the difference between its value at the initial and final positions is equal to the work done on the particle to move it from the initial to the final position.*

Strictly speaking, the potential energy E_p must depend on the coordinates of the particle considered, as well as on the coordinates of all the other particles of the world which interact with it. However, as we mentioned in Chapter 7 when we were dealing with the dynamics of a particle, we assume the rest of the world essentially fixed, and thus only the coordinates of the particle under consideration appear in E_p.

The student must realize, comparing Eq. (8.17) with the kinetic energy relation (8.12), that Eq. (8.12) is generally valid no matter what the force $\boldsymbol{F}$ may be. It is always true that $E_k = \frac{1}{2}mv^2$, while the form of the function $E_p(x, y, z)$ depends on the nature of the force $\boldsymbol{F}$, and not all forces may satisfy the condition set by Eq. (8.17). Only those satisfying it are called *conservative*. For example, comparing Eq. (8.17) with Eq. (8.16), we note that the force of gravity is conservative, and the potential energy due to gravity is

$$E_p = mgy. \tag{8.18}$$

Similarly, from Eq. (8.15), we see that the potential energy corresponding to a constant force is

$$E_p = -\boldsymbol{F} \cdot \boldsymbol{r}. \tag{8.19}$$

Potential energy is always defined within an arbitrary constant, because, for example, if we write $mgy + C$ instead of Eq. (8.18), Eq. (8.16) still remains the same, since the constant C, appearing in the two terms, cancels out. Because of this arbitrariness, we can define the zero or reference level of potential energy wherever it best suits us. For example, for problems of falling bodies, the earth's surface is the most convenient reference level, and so the potential energy due to gravity is taken as zero at the earth's surface. For a satellite, either natural or man-made, the zero of potential energy is usually defined at an infinite distance.

The work done by conservative forces is independent of the path.

We can see this from the defining Eq. (8.17) since, no matter what the path joining points A and B, the difference $E_{p,A} - E_{p,B}$ remains the same because it depends only on the coordinates of A and B. In particular, if the path is *closed* (Fig. 8–14) so that the final point coincides with the initial point (that is, A and B are the same point), then $E_{p,A} = E_{p,B}$ and the work is zero ($W = 0$). This means that during part of the path the work is positive and during the other part it is negative by the same amount, giving a zero net result. When the path is closed, the integral appearing in Eq. (8.17) is written $\oint$. The circle on the integral sign indicates that the path is closed. Therefore, for conservative forces,

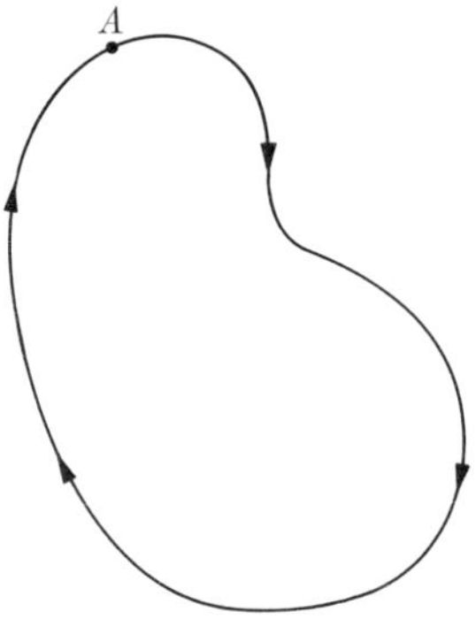

Fig. 8–14. The work done by a conservative force along a closed path is zero.

$$W_{\bigcirc} = \oint \boldsymbol{F} \cdot d\boldsymbol{r} = 0. \qquad (8.20)^*$$

Conversely, it can be proved that the condition expressed by Eq. (8.20) may be adopted as the definition of a conservative force. In other words, if a force $\boldsymbol{F}$ satisfies Eq. (8.20) for any closed path arbitrarily chosen, then it can be proved that Eq. (8.17) is correct.

To satisfy Eq. (8.17) it is necessary that

$$\boldsymbol{F} \cdot d\boldsymbol{r} = -dE_p, \qquad (8.21)$$

because then

$$\begin{aligned} W &= \int_A^B \boldsymbol{F} \cdot d\boldsymbol{r} = -\int_A^B dE_p \\ &= -(E_{p,B} - E_{p,A}) = E_{p,A} - E_{p,B}, \end{aligned}$$

in agreement with Eq. (8.17). Note that the negative sign appearing in Eq. (8.21) is necessary if we are to obtain $E_{p,A} - E_{p,B}$ instead of $E_{p,B} - E_{p,A}$.

* For any vector $\boldsymbol{V}$ which is a function of the position, an integral of the form $\oint \boldsymbol{V} \cdot d\boldsymbol{r}$ along a closed path is called the *circulation* of $\boldsymbol{V}$. It will appear many times in this book.

Since $\boldsymbol{F} \cdot d\boldsymbol{r} = F\,ds \cos\theta$, where θ is the angle between the force and the displacement, we may write instead of Eq. (8.21)

$$F \cos\theta = -\frac{dE_p}{ds}. \tag{8.22}$$

Now, as explained in connection with Fig. 8–1, $F \cos\theta$ is the component of the force in the direction of the displacement ds; therefore if we know $E_p(x, y, z)$, we may obtain the component of $\boldsymbol{F}$ in any direction by computing the quantity $-dE_p/ds$ which is the negative of the space rate of change of E_p in that direction. This is called the *directional derivative* of E_p. When a vector is such that its component in any direction is equal to the directional derivative of a function in that direction, the vector is called the *gradient* of the function. Thus we say that $\boldsymbol{F}$ is the negative of the gradient of E_p, and write Eq. (8.22) in the general form:

$$\boldsymbol{F} = -\text{grad } E_p,$$

where "grad" stands for gradient. When we are interested in the rectangular components of $\boldsymbol{F}$ along the X-, Y-, and Z-axes, $F \cos\theta$ in Eq. (8.22) becomes F_x, F_y, and F_z, and the displacement ds becomes dx, dy, and dz, respectively, so that

$$F_x = -\frac{\partial E_p}{\partial x}, \qquad F_y = -\frac{\partial E_p}{\partial y}, \qquad F_z = -\frac{\partial E_p}{\partial z}, \tag{8.23}$$

or

$$\boldsymbol{F} = -\text{grad } E_p = -\boldsymbol{u}_x \frac{\partial E_p}{\partial x} - \boldsymbol{u}_y \frac{\partial E_p}{\partial y} - \boldsymbol{u}_z \frac{\partial E_p}{\partial z}. \tag{8.24}$$

Note that when we write Eq. (8.24) we use the symbol for partial derivative for the first time in this book. This terminology is necessary because the potential energy $E_p(x, y, z)$ is, in general, a function of all three variables x, y, and z. But when a particle is displaced a distance dx along the X-axis, for example, the coordinates y and z remain unchanged. Thus, instead of writing dE_p/dx, we must use the notation $\partial E_p/\partial x$ adopted by the mathematicians for these cases.

If the motion is in a plane and the coordinates r, θ are used (Fig. 8–15), the displacement along the radius vector $\boldsymbol{r}$ is dr and the displacement perpendicular to the radius vector is $r\,d\theta$. Thus the radial and transverse components of the force are

$$F_r = -\frac{\partial E_p}{\partial r}, \qquad F_\theta = -\frac{1}{r}\frac{\partial E_p}{\partial \theta}. \tag{8.25}$$

Note that again we use the partial derivative notation.

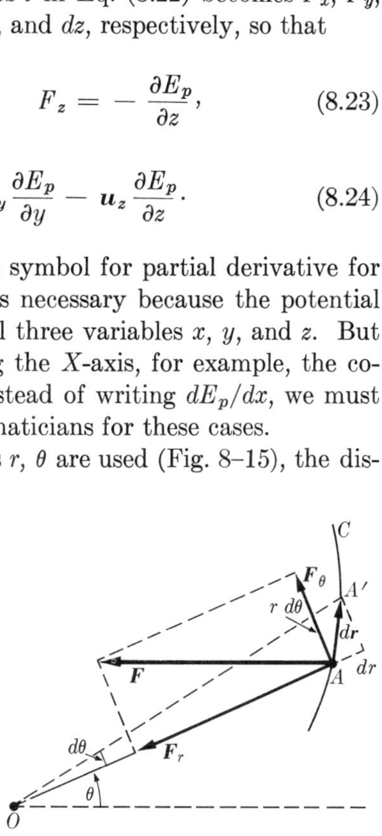

Figure 8–15

An important case is that in which the potential energy E_p depends on the distance r but not on the angle θ; that is, instead of $E_p(r, \theta)$, we have $E_p(r)$. Then $\partial E_p/\partial\theta = 0$ and, according to Eq. (8.25), $F_\theta = 0$. The force then does not have a transverse component, but only a radial one, so that the force is central, and its line of action always passes through the center. Conversely, if the force is central there is only a radial component, and $F_\theta = 0$, yielding $\partial E_p/\partial\theta = 0$, which implies that E_p is independent of θ. As a result, a central force depends only on the distance of the particle from the center. This important result can be stated by saying that

the potential energy associated with a central force depends only on the distance of the particle from the force center, and conversely.

When the forces are not central, there is a torque around point O given by $\tau = F_\theta r$, since the radial force does not contribute to the torque. Using the second relation in Eq. (8.25), we have that the torque around O is

$$\tau = -\frac{\partial E_p}{\partial\theta}. \tag{8.26}$$

This is a general expression that gives the torque in a direction perpendicular to the plane on which the angle θ is measured. Therefore, since a torque produces a corresponding change in angular momentum [cf. Eq. (7.38)], we conclude that

whenever the potential energy depends on an angle, a torque is applied to the system, resulting in a change in the angular momentum in a direction perpendicular to the plane of the angle.

Note on the concept of gradient. We shall often encounter expressions in physics similar to Eq. (8.24); therefore it is important to have a clear understanding of the meaning of gradient. Let us consider a function $V(x, y, z)$ that depends on the three coordinates of a point. We draw the surfaces

$$V(x, y, z) = C_1 \qquad \text{and} \qquad V(x, y, z) = C_2$$

(Fig. 8–16). In moving from a point A on C_1 to any point B on C_2, the function V always experiences a change $C_2 - C_1$. If C_1 and C_2 differ by an infinitesimal amount, we may write $dV = C_2 - C_1$. The change in V per unit length, or the "directional derivative" of V, is

$$dV/ds = (C_2 - C_1)/ds.$$

Let us consider the case when A and B are along a normal N common to the two surfaces. The directional derivative along the normal AN is dV/dn. But from Fig. 8–16, we see that $dn = ds\cos\theta$. Thus

$$\frac{dV}{ds} = \frac{dV}{dn}\frac{dn}{ds} = \frac{dV}{dn}\cos\theta,$$

which relates the directional derivative along the normal with the directional derivative along any other direction. Since $\cos\theta$ has its maximum value for $\theta = 0$, we conclude that dV/dn gives the maximum directional derivative of V. Introducing the unit vector $\boldsymbol{u}_N$, perpendicular to the surface at A, we define the gradient of V by

$$\text{grad } V = \boldsymbol{u}_N \frac{dV}{dn},$$

and thus the gradient is a vector perpendicular to the surface $V(x, y, z) = \text{const}$, and is equal to the maximum directional derivative of $V(x, y, z)$. Then we may write

$$\frac{dV}{ds} = |\text{grad } V| \cos\theta,$$

which indicates that the space rate of change in the direction AD, or the directional derivative of $V(x, y, z)$, is equal to the component of the vector grad V in that direction. This is the relation that was used to go from Eq. (8.22) to Eqs. (8.23) and (8.24). A differential operator, identified by the symbol ∇, read "del," has been introduced to shorten notation. It is expressed as:

$$\nabla = \boldsymbol{u}_x \frac{\partial}{\partial x} + \boldsymbol{u}_y \frac{\partial}{\partial y} + \boldsymbol{u}_z \frac{\partial}{\partial z}.$$

In terms of this operator, the gradient may be written as

$$\text{grad } V = \nabla V.$$

For further information concerning the gradient of a function, the student is referred to *Calculus and Analytic Geometry* (third edition), by G. B. Thomas. Reading, Mass.: Addison-Wesley, 1962.

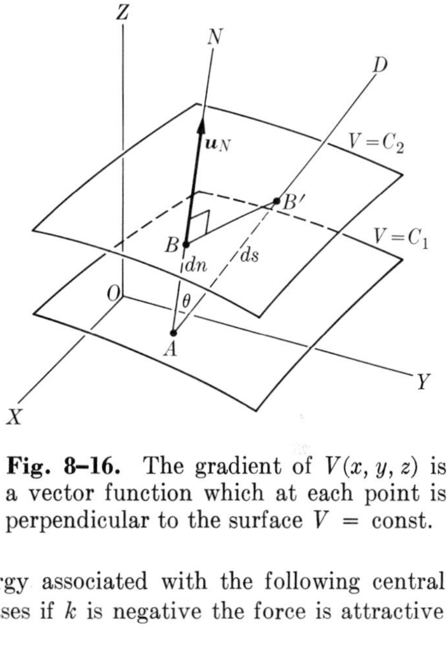

Fig. 8–16. The gradient of $V(x, y, z)$ is a vector function which at each point is perpendicular to the surface $V = \text{const}$.

EXAMPLE 8.8. Compute the potential energy associated with the following central forces: (a) $F = kr$, (b) $F = k/r^2$. In both cases if k is negative the force is attractive and if k is positive the force is repulsive.

Solution: Using Eq. (8.25), for case (a), we have $F = -\partial E_p/\partial r = kr$ or $dE_p = -kr\,dr$. Integrating, we obtain

$$E_p = \int -kr\,dr = -\tfrac{1}{2}kr^2 + C.$$

The constant of integration C is determined by assigning a value of E_p to a given position. In this case it is customary to make $E_p = 0$ at $r = 0$, so that $C = 0$ and $E_p = -\frac{1}{2}kr^2$. Considering that $r^2 = x^2 + y^2 + z^2$, we may also write $E_p = -\frac{1}{2}k(x^2 + y^2 + z^2)$. Using Eq. (8.23), we find that the rectangular components of the force are

$$F_x = -\frac{\partial E_p}{\partial x} = kx, \qquad F_y = -\frac{\partial E_p}{\partial y} = ky, \qquad F_z = -\frac{\partial E_p}{\partial z} = kz,$$

a result that was to be expected, since the central force $F = kr$ in vector form is $\boldsymbol{F} = k\boldsymbol{r} = k(\boldsymbol{u}_x x + \boldsymbol{u}_y y + \boldsymbol{u}_z z)$.

For case (b) we have $F = -\partial E_p/\partial r = k/r^2$ or $dE_p = -k(dr/r^2)$. Integrating, we have

$$E_p = \int -k\frac{dr}{r^2} = \frac{k}{r} + C.$$

For inverse-r forces, it is customary to determine C by making $E_p = 0$ at $r = \infty$, so that $C = 0$ and $E_p = k/r$. What are the rectangular components of the force in this case?

8.8 Conservation of Energy of a Particle

When the force acting on a particle is conservative, we may combine Eq. (8.17) with the general Eq. (8.13), which gives us $E_{k,B} - E_{k,A} = E_{p,A} - E_{p,B}$ or

$$(E_k + E_p)_B = (E_k + E_p)_A. \tag{8.27}$$

The quantity $E_k + E_p$ is called the *total energy* of the particle, designated by E; that is, the total energy of a particle is equal to the sum of its kinetic energy and its potential energy, or

$$E = E_k + E_p = \tfrac{1}{2}mv^2 + E_p(x, y, z). \tag{8.28}$$

Equation (8.27) indicates that

> *when the forces are conservative the total energy E of the particle remains constant,*

since states designated by A and B are arbitrary. Thus we may write for any position of the particle,

$$E = E_k + E_p = \text{const.} \tag{8.29}$$

In other words, *the energy of the particle is conserved.* This is the reason why we say that when there is a potential energy, the forces are conservative. For example, in the case of a falling body we have seen (Eq. 8.18) that $E_p = mgy$, and the conservation of energy gives

$$E = \tfrac{1}{2}mv^2 + mgy = \text{const.} \tag{8.30}$$

If initially the particle is at height y_0 and its velocity is zero, the total energy is mgy_0, and we have $\frac{1}{2}mv^2 + mgy = mgy_0$, or $v^2 = 2g(y_0 - y) = 2gh$, where $h = y_0 - y$ is the height through which it has fallen. This result is the well-known formula for the velocity acquired in free fall through a height h. We must note, however, that Eq. (8.30) is not restricted to vertical motion; it is equally valid for the motion of any projectile moving at an angle with the vertical.

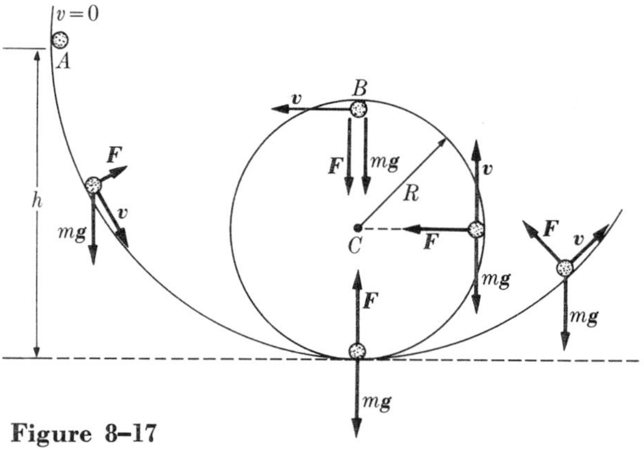

Figure 8–17

It should be noted that, for a given total energy, the magnitude of the velocity (irrespective of the direction of the motion) at a given point is fixed by Eq. (8.29). This is particularly clear in the case of motion under gravity, as shown in Eq. (8.30).

EXAMPLE 8.9. Determine the minimum height at which a ball should start in order to successfully complete the loop shown in Fig. 8–17. Assume that the ball slides without rolling and without friction.

Solution: We assume that the ball is released at point A at a height h above the base of the circle in Fig. 8–17. The ball gains velocity while moving down and starts losing velocity when moving up the circle. At any point on the track, the forces acting on the particle are its weight mg and the force $\boldsymbol{F}$ due to the track. (The force $\boldsymbol{F}$ points toward the center of the loop, since the track "pushes" but does not "pull.") At the highest point on the loop, both mg and $\boldsymbol{F}$ point toward the center O, and according to Eq. (7.28) we must have

$$F + mg = \frac{mv^2}{R},$$

where R is the radius of the track. Since F cannot be negative, the minimum velocity of the ball at B if it is to describe the circle must correspond to $F = 0$ or $mg = mv^2/R$, which gives

$$v^2 = gR.$$

If the velocity is less than $\sqrt{gR}$, the downward pull of the weight is larger than the required centripetal force, and the ball will separate from the circle before it reaches point B, and will describe a parabola until it falls back on the circle.

To obtain the corresponding height h, we note that at point A the total energy is $E_A = (E_k + E_p)_A = mgh$, since $v = 0$. At B, where $y = 2R$ and $v^2 = gR$,

$$E_B = (E_k + E_p)_B = \tfrac{1}{2}m(gR) + mg(2R) = \tfrac{5}{2}mgR.$$

Thus, equating the values of E_A and E_B, we get $h = \frac{5}{2}R$, which is the minimum height of the starting point of the ball if it is to successfully describe the circle. This result is correct so long as we can neglect frictional forces. If the ball rolls, the methods to be introduced in Chapter 10 must be used.

8.9 Rectilinear Motion under Conservative Forces

In the general case of rectilinear motion the potential energy depends on only one coordinate, let us say x, and Eq. (8.28) for the conservation of energy becomes

$$E = \tfrac{1}{2}mv^2 + E_p(x), \tag{8.31}$$

where E, the total energy, is a constant. This equation will show us the practical usefulness of the energy concept. For rectilinear motion $v = dx/dt$, and Eq. (8.31) becomes

$$E = \tfrac{1}{2}m\left(\frac{dx}{dt}\right)^2 + E_p(x). \tag{8.32}$$

Solving for dx/dt, we obtain

$$\frac{dx}{dt} = \left\{\frac{2}{m}[E - E_p(x)]\right\}^{1/2}. \tag{8.33}$$

Under the present conditions we may write this equation in a form in which the variables x and t are separated; that is, the x-variable appears on only one side of the equation and the t-variable appears only on the other side. For our equation, we do this by writing

$$\frac{dx}{\{(2/m)[E - E_p(x)]\}^{1/2}} = dt.$$

Integrating (and setting $t_0 = 0$ for convenience), we have

$$\int_{x_0}^{x} \frac{dx}{\{(2/m)[E - E_p(x)]\}^{1/2}} = \int_0^t dt = t. \tag{8.34}$$

This equation allows us to obtain a relation between x and t, and thus to solve the problem of the rectilinear motion of the particle. Therefore, whenever we can find the potential energy function [and this is relatively easy if we know the force as a function of x, because we simply utilize Eq. (8.23) to obtain $E_p(x)$], the conservation of energy expressed by Eq. (8.34) gives us directly the solution of the problem of rectilinear motion.

EXAMPLE 8.10. Use Eq. (8.34) to solve the problem of rectilinear motion under constant force.

Solution: In this case F is constant. If we take the X-axis along the direction of the force, the first of Eqs. (8.23) gives us $F = -dE_p/dx$ or $dE_p = -F\,dx$. Integrating, we obtain $E_p = -Fx + C$, and setting $E_p = 0$ at $x = 0$, we get $C = 0$. Thus

$$E_p = -Fx$$

is the expression for the potential energy associated with a constant force. This agrees with Eq. (8.19) if we make $\boldsymbol{F} = \boldsymbol{u}_x F$; that is, the force $\boldsymbol{F}$ is in the X-direction. Using

Eq. (8.34), with $x_0 = 0$ for simplicity, we now have

$$\frac{1}{(2/m)^{1/2}} \int_0^x \frac{dx}{(E + Fx)^{1/2}} = t$$

or

$$\frac{2}{F}(E + Fx)^{1/2} - \frac{2}{F}E^{1/2} = \left(\frac{2}{m}\right)^{1/2} t.$$

Solving for x, we get

$$x = \frac{1}{2}\left(\frac{F}{m}\right)t^2 + \left(\frac{2E}{m}\right)^{1/2} t.$$

But $F/m = a$, and since $E = \frac{1}{2}mv^2 + Fx$ is the total energy, we have that at $t = 0$, when $x = 0$, the energy E is all kinetic and is equal to $\frac{1}{2}mv_0^2$. Thus $2E/m = v_0^2$, and we finally obtain for x, $x = \frac{1}{2}at^2 + v_0t$, which is the same expression we obtained before, in Eq. (5.11), with $x_0 = 0$ and $t_0 = 0$. This problem is sufficiently simple for it to be more easily solved by the methods of Chapter 5. We have presented it here mainly as an illustration of the techniques for solving the equation of motion using the principle of energy.

8.10 Motion under Conservative Central Forces

In the case of a central force, when E_p depends only on the distance r, Eq. (8.28) becomes

$$E = \tfrac{1}{2}mv^2 + E_p(r), \tag{8.35}$$

from which it is possible to determine the velocity at any distance. In many cases the function $E_p(r)$ decreases in absolute value when r increases. Then, at very large distances from the center, $E_p(r)$ is negligible and the magnitude of the velocity is constant and is independent of the direction of motion. This is the principle we applied in Example 7.16 when, in Fig. 7–28, we indicated that the final velocity of the receding particle at B was the same as its initial velocity at A.

Note that, when we are dealing with motion under the influence of central forces, there are two conservation theorems. One is the conservation of angular momentum, discussed in Section 7.13, and the other is the conservation of energy, expressed by Eq. (8.35). When we use polar coordinates r and θ, and remember that the components of the velocity are $v_r = dr/dt$ and $v_\theta = r\,d\theta/dt$, we may write, according to Eq. (5.63),

$$v^2 = v_r^2 + v_\theta^2 = \left(\frac{dr}{dt}\right)^2 + r^2\left(\frac{d\theta}{dt}\right)^2.$$

But from the principle of conservation of angular momentum, using Eq. (7.35), $L = mr^2\,d\theta/dt$, we have that

$$r^2\left(\frac{d\theta}{dt}\right)^2 = \frac{L^2}{(mr)^2},$$

where L is the constant angular momentum. Therefore

$$v^2 = \left(\frac{dr}{dt}\right)^2 + \frac{L^2}{(mr)^2}.$$

Introducing this result into Eq. (8.35), we have

$$E = \tfrac{1}{2}m\left(\frac{dr}{dt}\right)^2 + \frac{L^2}{2mr^2} + E_p(r). \tag{8.36}$$

This expression closely resembles Eq. (8.32) for rectilinear motion, with velocity dr/dt, if we assume that, insofar as the radial motion is concerned, the particle moves under an "effective" potential energy

$$E_{p,\,\mathrm{eff}}(r) = \frac{L^2}{2mr^2} + E_p(r). \tag{8.37}$$

The first term is called the *centrifugal* potential, $E_{p,c}(r) = L^2/2mr^2$, because the "force" associated with it, using Eq. (8.25), is $F_c = -\partial E_{p,c}/\partial r = L^2/mr^3$ and, being positive, is pointing away from the origin; that is, it is centrifugal. Of course no centrifugal force is acting on the particle, except the one that may be due to the real potential $E_p(r)$, in the event that it is repulsive and the centrifugal "force" F_c is just a useful mathematical concept. Physically this concept describes the tendency of the particle, according to the law of inertia, to move in a straight line and thus avoid moving in a curve. Introducing Eq. (8.37) into Eq. (8.36), we have

$$E = \tfrac{1}{2}m\left(\frac{dr}{dt}\right)^2 + E_{p,\,\mathrm{eff}}(r),$$

and solving for dr/dt, we obtain

$$\frac{dr}{dt} = \left\{\frac{2}{m}\left[E - E_{p,\,\mathrm{eff}}(r)\right]\right\}^{1/2}, \tag{8.38}$$

which is formally identical to Eq. (8.33) for rectilinear motion. Separating the variables r and t and integrating (setting $t_0 = 0$ for convenience), we obtain

$$\int_{r_0}^{r} \frac{dr}{\{(2/m)[E - E_{p,\,\mathrm{eff}}(r)]\}^{1/2}} = \int_0^t dt = t, \tag{8.39}$$

which gives us the distance r as a function of time [that is, $r(t)$], and therefore we have the solution of our dynamical problem corresponding to radial motion.

When we solve the expression for the angular momentum, $L = mr^2\, d\theta/dt$ for $d\theta/dt$, we have

$$\frac{d\theta}{dt} = \frac{L}{mr^2}. \tag{8.40}$$

Then when we introduce $r(t)$ as obtained from Eq. (8.39) into Eq. (8.40), we express L/mr^2 as a function of time, and when we integrate we have

$$\int_{\theta_0}^{\theta} d\theta = \int_0^t \frac{L}{mr^2}\,dt \qquad \text{or} \qquad \theta = \theta_0 + \int_0^t \frac{L}{mr^2}\,dt. \tag{8.41}$$

This gives θ as a function of time; that is, $\theta(t)$. In this way we can solve the problem completely, giving both the radial and the angular motions as functions of time.

Sometimes, however, we are more interested in the equation of the path. Combining Eqs. (8.38) and (8.40) through division, we may write

$$\frac{dr}{d\theta} = \frac{\{(2/m)[E - E_{p,\mathrm{eff}}(r)]\}^{1/2}}{L/mr^2} \tag{8.42}$$

or, separating the variables r and θ and integrating,

$$\int_{r_0}^{r} \frac{dr}{(m/L)r^2\{(2/m)[E - E_{p,\mathrm{eff}}(r)]\}^{1/2}} = \int_{\theta_0}^{\theta} d\theta = \theta - \theta_0. \tag{8.43}$$

This expression relating r to θ gives the equation of the path in polar coordinates. Conversely, if we know the equation of the path, so that we can compute $dr/d\theta$, Eq. (8.42) allows us to compute the potential energy and then the force.

This section has illustrated how the principles of conservation of angular momentum and of energy allow us to solve for the motion of a particle acted on by a central force. By now the student will have recognized the fact that these principles are not mathematical curiosities, but real and effective tools for solving dynamical problems. We must note that when the motion is due to a central force, the conservation of energy is not enough to solve the problem. It is also necessary to use the conservation of angular momentum. In the case of rectilinear motion, the conservation of energy *is* sufficient to solve the problem. This is because energy is a scalar quantity, and may not be used to determine the direction of motion, while in rectilinear motion, the direction is fixed from the outset.

Finally, let us make it especially clear that the principles of conservation of angular momentum and of energy, as used in this chapter, are properties associated with an individual particle under the special circumstances of its motion, and there is no direct relation to the possible conservation of total energy of the universe. This subject will be discussed in more detail in the next chapter.

8.11 Discussion of Potential Energy Curves

The graphs representing $E_p(x)$ versus x in rectilinear or one-dimensional problems and $E_p(r)$ versus r in central force problems are very useful in helping one to understand the motion of a particle, even without solving the equation of motion. In Fig. 8–18 we have illustrated a possible potential energy curve for one-dimensional motion. When we use the first of Eqs. (8.23), the force on the particle for any value of x is given by $F = -dE_p/dx$.* Now dE_p/dx is the slope of the curve $E_p(x)$. The slope is positive whenever the curve is increasing or upward, and negative whenever the curve is decreasing or downward. Therefore, the force F (i.e., the negative of the slope), is negative or directed to the left whenever the potential energy is increasing, and positive or directed to the right whenever the potential energy is decreasing. This situation has been indicated in Fig. 8–18 by the horizontal arrows and the different regions marked below the figure.

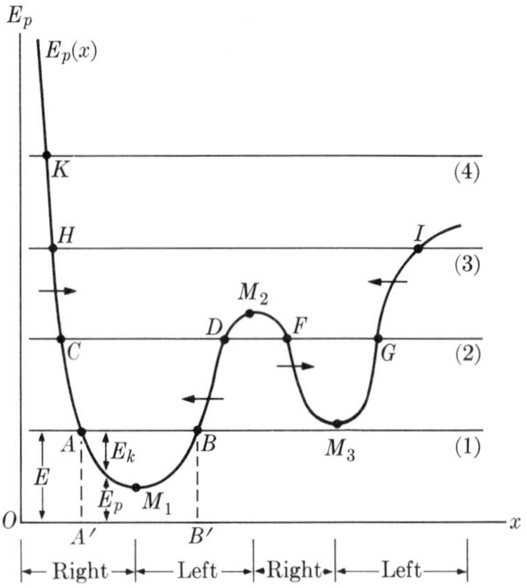

Fig. 8–18. Relation between motion in straight line and potential energy.

At the points where the potential energy is minimum or maximum, such as M_1, M_2, and M_3, we have $dE_p/dx = 0$, and therefore $F = 0$; that is, they are positions of equilibrium. Those positions where $E_p(x)$ is a *minimum* are of *stable* equilibrium because, when the particle is displaced slightly from its equilibrium position, it is acted on by a force that tends to restore it to that position. Where $E_p(x)$ is *maximum*, the equilibrium is *unstable*, since a slight displacement from the equilibrium position causes the particle to experience a force that tends to move it even further away.

Consider now a particle having total energy E, as indicated by the horizontal line (1) of Fig. 8–18. At any position x the potential energy E_p is given by the ordinate of the curve and the kinetic energy, $E_k = E - E_p$, is given by the distance from curve $E_p(x)$ to the E line. Now the E line intersects curve $E_p(x)$ at points A and B. To the left of A and to the right of B the energy E is less than the potential energy $E_p(x)$, and therefore in that region the kinetic energy $E_k = E - E_p$ would be negative. But that is impossible because $E_k = \frac{1}{2}mv^2$ is necessarily positive. Therefore the motion of the particle is limited to the interval AB and the particle oscillates between $x = A'$ and $x = B'$. At these points the velocity becomes zero and the particle reverses its motion. These points are called *turning* points.

If the particle has a higher energy, such as that corresponding to line (2), it has two possible regions of motion. One is oscillating between C and B and the other oscillating between F and G. However, if the particle is in one region it can never jump to the other, because that would require passing through the region DF where the kinetic energy would be negative and is therefore forbidden. We say

* It is not necessary to use the partial derivative notation in this case because E_p depends on only one variable, x.

that the two regions where the motion is allowed are separated by a *potential barrier*. At energy level (3), the motion is oscillatory between H and I. Finally at energy level (4) the motion is no longer oscillatory and the particle moves between K and infinity. For example, if the particle is moving initially to the left, when it reaches K it "bounces" back, receding toward the right and never returning again. When we consider the motion of atomic particles, so that quantum mechanics applies, the description we have given requires some modification.

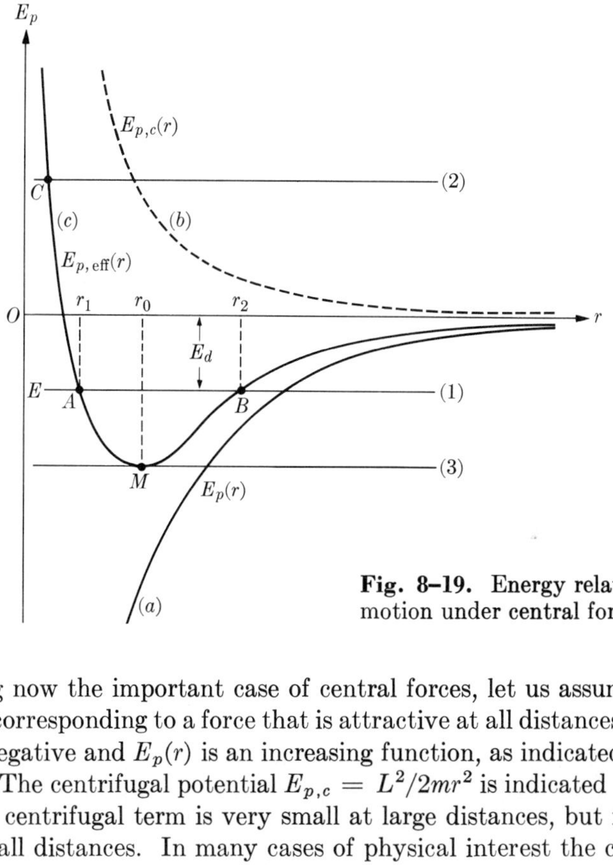

Fig. 8–19. Energy relations for motion under central forces.

Considering now the important case of central forces, let us assume a potential energy $E_p(r)$ corresponding to a force that is attractive at all distances, that is, $F = -\partial E_p/\partial r$ is negative and $E_p(r)$ is an increasing function, as indicated by curve (a) of Fig. 8–19. The centrifugal potential $E_{p,c} = L^2/2mr^2$ is indicated by the dashed line (b). The centrifugal term is very small at large distances, but increases very rapidly at small distances. In many cases of physical interest the centrifugal potential is the dominant term at small distances, resulting in an effective potential energy $E_{p,\text{eff}} = E_{p,c} + E_p(r)$ with the shape indicated by curve (c).

If the total energy E of the particle is indicated by horizontal line (1), the radius of the orbit will oscillate between the minimum and maximum values r_1 and r_2, and the orbit will have the shape illustrated in Fig. 8–20. But if the energy corresponds to a value such as line (2) of Fig. 8–19, the orbit is not bound, and the particle comes from infinity up to the point C of closest approach at distance r_{min}, and then recedes again without ever returning, as shown in Fig. 8–21. If the energy

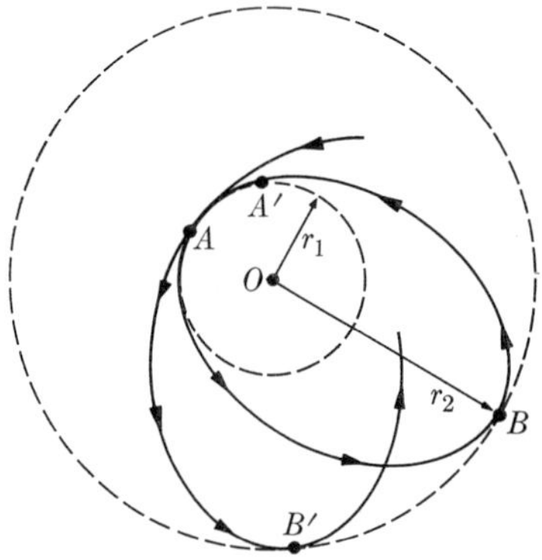

Fig. 8–20. General shape of path for motion under central forces.

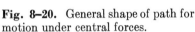

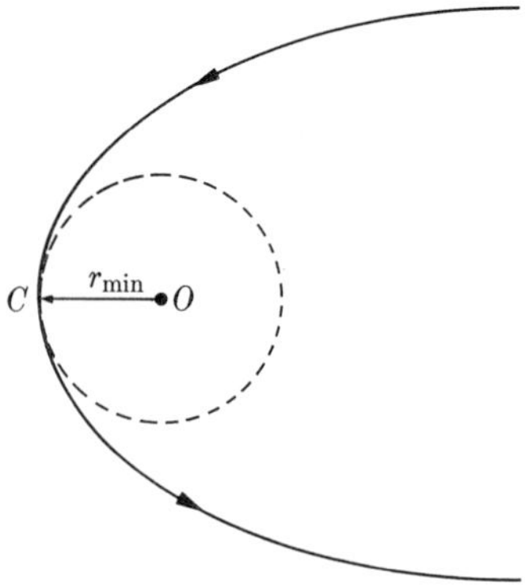

Fig. 8–21. Distance of closest approach.

corresponds to the minimum M of $E_{p,\mathrm{eff}}$, as indicated by line (3), there is only one intersection and the distance to the center remains constant, the particle describing a circular path of radius r_0. Note that the distance of closest approach increases with increasing value of the angular momentum, due to the effect of the centrifugal potential energy $E_{p,c}(r)$.

If, by some mechanism, a particle that has energy equal to level (1) of Fig. 8–19 can absorb energy and thereby "jump" to energy level (2), it will fly away from the center of force; that is, it "dissociates" from the center of force. The minimum energy a particle requires to dissociate from energy level (1) has been indicated in Fig. 8–19 by E_d. On the other hand, if the particle initially in energy level (2) by some process loses energy when it passes near the center of force, it may jump into energy level (1), and then remain in a bound orbit. We say that it has been "captured" by the center of force. This situation is found, for example, in molecular formation and dissociation.

In the case of a diatomic molecule such as H_2 or CO, the potential energy E_p for the interaction between the two atoms already has the shape of (*c*) in Fig. 8–19. Such a potential energy, illustrated by curve (*a*) of Fig. 8–22, corresponds to attraction at large distances and repulsion at short distances, thus preventing the two atoms from coalescing into one single unit even in the absence of the centrifugal effect. The effect of the centrifugal potential $E_{p,c}$ given by the dashed curve (*b*) is to raise the curve to the shape (*c*). We may therefore picture the atoms in the molecule with an energy E in a state of relative oscillation between P_1 and P_2. If the molecule absorbs energy in a proper amount, it may then dissociate and separate into two component atoms which move apart.

EXAMPLE 8.11. The potential energy for the interaction between two gas molecules can be approximated by the expression

$$E_p(r) = -E_{p,0}\left[2\left(\frac{r_0}{r}\right)^6 - \left(\frac{r_0}{r}\right)^{12}\right],$$

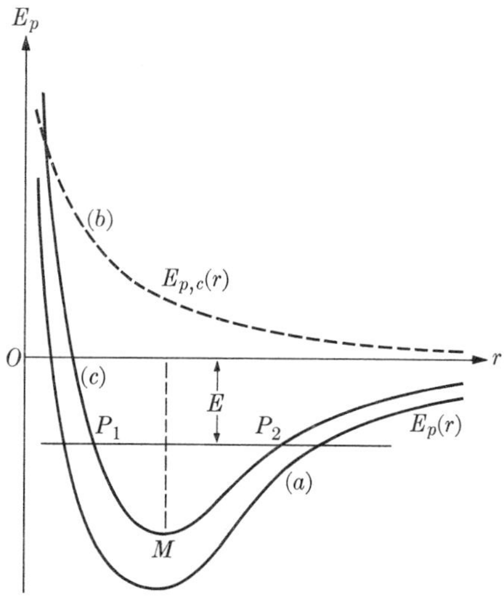

Fig. 8–22. Intermolecular potential.

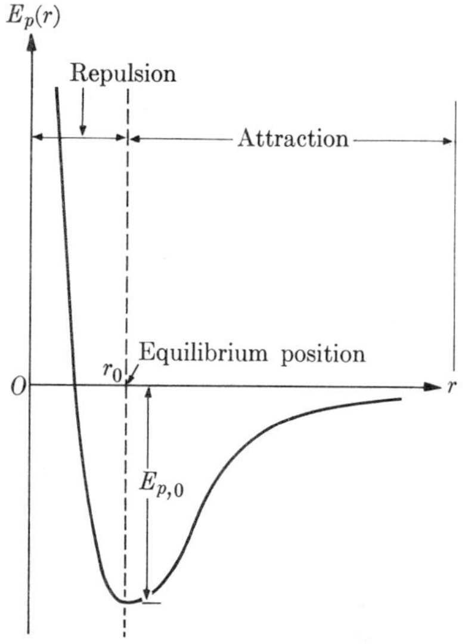

Fig. 8–23. Lennard-Jones intermolecular potential.

where $E_{p,0}$ and r_0 are positive constants and r is the separation between the molecules. This model for molecular potential energies was introduced by the English scientist J. Lennard-Jones. Find the equilibrium position and the value of the potential energy there. The graph of $E_p(r)$ is shown in Fig. 8–23.

Solution: At the equilibrium position, $F = -\partial E_p/\partial r = 0$. Thus

$$\frac{\partial E_p}{\partial r} = -E_{p,0}\left[-12\frac{r_0^6}{r^7} + 12\frac{r_0^{12}}{r^{13}}\right] = 0$$

or $r = r_0$. Setting $r = r_0$ in $E_p(r)$, we have $E_p = -E_{p,0}$ for the potential energy at the point of equilibrium. For distances less than r_0, the intermolecular force is repulsive [$E_p(r)$ is a decreasing function] and for distances larger than r_0 it is attractive [$E_p(r)$ is an increasing function].

Which is the dominant term in $E_p(r)$ at small distances, and which at large distances? We suggest that the student plot the force as a function of the separation r and determine the separation for which the attractive force is maximum. Also we suggest that he look in the literature for values of $E_{p,0}$ and r_0.

8.12 Nonconservative Forces

At first sight we find some forces in nature that are not conservative. One example is friction. Sliding friction always opposes the displacement. Its work will depend on the path followed, and although the path may be closed, the work is not zero, so that Eq. (8.20) does not hold. Similarly, fluid friction opposes the velocity, and depends on velocity but not on position. A particle may thus be subject to conservative and to nonconservative forces at the same time.

For example, a particle falling through a fluid is subject to the conservative gravitational force and to the nonconservative fluid friction. Calling E_p the potential energy corresponding to the conservative forces and W' the work done by the nonconservative forces (work which, in general, is negative because frictional forces oppose the motion), the total work done on the particle when moving from A to B is $W = E_{p,A} - E_{p,B} + W'$. Using Eq. (8.13), we then write

$$E_{k,B} - E_{k,A} = E_{p,A} - E_{p,B} + W'$$

or

$$(E_k + E_p)_B - (E_k + E_p)_A = W'. \tag{8.44}$$

In this case the quantity $E_k + E_p$ does not remain constant but decreases (increases) if W' is negative (positive). But on the other hand, we *cannot* call $E_k + E_p$ the total energy of the particle, because this concept is not applicable in this case, since it does not include all the forces present. The concept of total energy of a particle is meaningful only when *all* the forces are conservative. However, Eq. (8.44) is useful when we wish to make a comparison between the case in which only the conservative forces act (so that $E_k + E_p$ is the total energy) and the case in which there are additional nonconservative forces. Then we say that Eq. (8.44) gives the gain or loss of energy due to the nonconservative forces.

The existence of nonconservative forces such as friction must not be considered as necessarily implying that there may exist nonconservative interactions between fundamental particles. We must recall that frictional forces do not correspond to an interaction between two particles but are really statistical concepts (recall the discussion of Section 7.9). Sliding friction, for example, is the result of many individual interactions between the molecules of the two bodies in contact. *Each* of these interactions can be expressed by a conservative force. However, the macroscopic effect is not conservative for the following reason: Although the body, when it completes a closed orbit, is macroscopically at its original position, the individual molecules have not returned to their original condition. Hence the final state is not microscopically identical to the initial one, nor is it even equivalent, in a statistical sense.

The nonconservative work W' thus represents an energy transfer that, because it corresponds to molecular motion, is in general irreversible. The reason it cannot be recovered is the difficulty, even from a statistical standpoint, of restoring all the molecular motions to the initial state. In some cases, however, the molecular motions can be statistically returned to the original conditions. That is, even if the final state is not microscopically identical to the initial one, they are statistically equivalent. This is the case, for example, when a gas expands very slowly while it is doing work. If after the expansion the gas is very slowly compressed back to the original physical conditions, the final state is statistically equivalent to the initial state. The work done during the compression is the negative of the expansion work, and the total work done is therefore zero.

EXAMPLE 8.12. A body is falling through a viscous fluid starting from rest at a height y_0. Calculate the rate of dissipation of its kinetic and gravitational potential energy.

Solution: When the body is at height y falling with velocity v, its kinetic plus its gravitational potential energy is $\frac{1}{2}mv^2 + mgy$. The rate of dissipation of energy (or energy lost per unit time) due to the action of the nonconservative viscous forces is thus

$$\frac{d}{dt}(E_k + E_p) = \frac{d}{dt}(\tfrac{1}{2}mv^2 + mgy).$$

Let us first suggest that the student, using the results of Example 7.7, express v^2 and y as functions of time. Then, by evaluating the above derivative, he can solve the problem.

We propose, however, to show how the problem may be solved by a different procedure. According to Eq. (8.44), if points A and B are very close, we may write the equation $d(E_k + E_p) = dW' = F'\,dx$, where F' is the nonconservative force. In our example F' is due to the fluid friction, and has the form $F_f = -K\eta v$ given in Eq. (7.18). Thus

$$\frac{d}{dt}(E_k + E_p) = F'\frac{dx}{dt} = (-K\eta v)v = -K\eta v^2.$$

For v we take the result obtained in Example 7.8,

$$v = \frac{F}{K\eta}[1 - e^{-(K\eta/m)t}],$$

where $F = mg$ is the weight of the particle (corrected for the buoyancy due to the fluid). Thus

$$\frac{d}{dt}(E_k + E_p) = -\frac{m^2g^2}{K\eta}[1 - e^{-(K\eta/m)t}]^2.$$

The negative sign for the rate of energy dissipation indicates that the body is losing kinetic and gravitational potential energy. However, this energy is not "lost," but transferred to the molecules of the fluid in a form that is practically impossible to recover. After a certain length of time the exponential is essentially zero. Hence we may write

$$\frac{d}{dt}(E_k + E_p) = -\frac{m^2g^2}{K\eta},$$

and thus show that energy is lost at a constant rate. The physicist calls this a steady-state condition.

It is interesting to look at this result from a different angle. We saw in Example 7.8 that after a long time the velocity becomes constant and equal to $F/K\eta$, where $F = mg$. Thus the kinetic energy E_k remains constant and only the potential energy $E_p = mgy$ is changing. We may therefore write

$$\frac{d}{dt}(E_k + E_p)_{ss} = \frac{dE_p}{dt} = \frac{d}{dt}(mgy) = mg\frac{dy}{dt},$$

where the subscript ss means that this is a steady-state problem. But dy/dt is the limiting velocity given in Eq. (7.21), and we may write $dy/dt = -F/K\eta = -mg/K\eta$. The reason for the negative sign is that y is measured upward and the limiting velocity is pointing downward. Substituting this value in the previous expression, we obtain

$$\frac{d}{dt}(E_k + E_p)_{ss} = mg\left(-\frac{mg}{K\eta}\right) = -\frac{m^2g^2}{K\eta},$$

which is the same result obtained before. We note, then, that after a certain length of time, all the gravitational potential energy lost by the body is dissipated into molecular agitation of the fluid. This is a different way of saying that the downward force of gravity is balanced by the opposing force due to the viscosity of the fluid.

8.13 The Virial Theorem for a Single Particle

This theorem (although not so important as the conservation of angular momentum under a central force or the conservation of energy under a conservative force) is useful for obtaining some practical results.

Consider a particle of mass m moving under the action of a force $\boldsymbol{F}$. Define the scalar quantity $A = m\boldsymbol{v} \cdot \boldsymbol{r}$, where $\boldsymbol{r}$ is the position vector of the particle and $\boldsymbol{v}$ its velocity. Taking the time derivative of A, we have

$$\frac{dA}{dt} = m\frac{d\boldsymbol{v}}{dt} \cdot \boldsymbol{r} + m\boldsymbol{v} \cdot \frac{d\boldsymbol{r}}{dt} = m\boldsymbol{a} \cdot \boldsymbol{r} + mv^2,$$

since $\boldsymbol{a} = d\boldsymbol{v}/dt$ and $\boldsymbol{v} = d\boldsymbol{r}/dt$. The last term, according to Eq. (8.12), is twice the kinetic energy of the particle and in the first term we may write $m\boldsymbol{a} = \boldsymbol{F}$. Thus

$$\frac{dA}{dt} = \boldsymbol{F} \cdot \boldsymbol{r} + 2E_k.$$

If we take the time average of this equation, we have

$$\left(\frac{dA}{dt}\right)_{\text{ave}} = (\boldsymbol{F} \cdot \boldsymbol{r})_{\text{ave}} + 2(E_k)_{\text{ave}}. \tag{8.45}$$

The time average, over an interval τ, of any quantity $f(t)$ that depends on the time is defined by

$$f(t)_{\text{ave}} = \frac{1}{\tau}\int_0^\tau f(t)\, dt.$$

In our case, then,

$$\left(\frac{dA}{dt}\right)_{\text{ave}} = \frac{1}{\tau}\int_0^\tau \frac{dA}{dt}\, dt = \frac{1}{\tau}\int_0^\tau dA = \frac{A - A_0}{\tau}. \tag{8.46}$$

If the time τ is very large and if A does not increase indefinitely with time, the quantity $(A - A_0)/\tau$ can be so small (if τ is sufficiently large) that it can be considered as zero. This is the case when the particle moves in a bounded region. For example, an electron in an atom moves in a limited region of space and its values of $\boldsymbol{r}$ and $\boldsymbol{v}$, the quantities that enter into the definition of A, always remain within certain values. The same may be said of the earth in its motion around the sun.

Therefore, setting $(dA/dt)_{\text{ave}} = 0$ in Eq. (8.45), we find that

$$(E_k)_{\text{ave}} = -\tfrac{1}{2}(\boldsymbol{F} \cdot \boldsymbol{r})_{\text{ave}}. \tag{8.47}$$

This is the *virial theorem* for a particle. The quantity $-\frac{1}{2}(\boldsymbol{F} \cdot \boldsymbol{r})_{\text{ave}}$ is called the *virial of the particle.*

The virial theorem adopts a special form when the forces are central and conservative. If $E_p(r)$ is the potential energy, then $\boldsymbol{F} = -\boldsymbol{u}_r\, \partial E_p/\partial r$ and $\boldsymbol{F} \cdot \boldsymbol{r} = -r\, \partial E_p/\partial r$ because $\boldsymbol{u}_r \cdot \boldsymbol{r} = r$. Thus Eq. (8.47) becomes

$$(E_k)_{\text{ave}} = \frac{1}{2}\left(r\,\frac{\partial E_p}{\partial r}\right)_{\text{ave}}. \tag{8.48}$$

Suppose that the potential energy is of the form $E_p = -k/r^n$. Then

$$\frac{\partial E_p}{\partial r} = n\,\frac{k}{r^{n+1}} = -\,\frac{nE_p}{r},$$

and Eq. (8.48) becomes

$$(E_k)_{\text{ave}} = -\tfrac{1}{2}n(E_p)_{\text{ave}}. \tag{8.49}$$

With this result, we obtain a relation between the time averages of the kinetic and potential energies of the particle.

8.14 Critique of the Concept of Energy

In this chapter we have seen how we can use the concept of energy in a very effective way to solve certain problems in the dynamics of a particle when we know the force as a function of position. This is one of the basic reasons for introducing the concept of energy in physics.

Our immediate experience leads us to recognize that the bodies around us are in motion. We attribute these motions to the interactions among the bodies, and describe the motions by means of the concepts of force or energy. These concepts have only one purpose: to provide useful methods for analyzing and predicting the motions we observe. The great usefulness of the concept of potential energy, like the concept of force, is that it has enabled us to associate specific forms of potential energy with specific interactions observed in nature. This result is not surprising, since the force $\boldsymbol{F}$ is related to the potential energy E_p according to Eq. (8.24). It is this relationship between potential energy and the interaction that really gives physical meaning to the idea of potential energy.

Once we know the potential as a function of position, we can describe the motion qualitatively as indicated in Section 8.11, or quantitatively as explained in Sections 8.9 and 8.10. In future chapters we shall discuss the fact that the interaction between two bodies can be described as an exchange of energy or as an exchange of momentum. Either of these descriptions provides a convenient and useful pictorial representation of an interaction. The student should realize that throughout the rest of the book we shall describe the processes we observe in nature almost solely by means of the concepts of momentum and energy.

References

1. "Energy," S. Schurr, *Sci. Am.*, September 1963, page 110
2. "Newton's Law of Motion and the 17th Century Laws of Impact," A. Arons and A. Bork, *Am. J. Phys.* **32,** 313 (1964)
3. *Mechanics* (second edition), by K. Symon. Reading, Mass.: Addison-Wesley, 1964, Sections 2–1, 2–5, 3–7, and 3–12
4. *Physical Mechanics* (third edition), by R. Lindsay. Princeton, N.J.: Van Nostrand, 1963, Chapter 4
5. *Introduction to Engineering Mechanics*, by J. Huddleston. Reading, Mass.: Addison-Wesley, 1961, Chapters 20 and 21
6. *Vector Mechanics*, by D. Christie. New York: McGraw-Hill, 1964, Chapters 7 and 17; Sections 12.6 through 12.8
7. *A Source Book of Physics*, W. F. Magie. Cambridge, Mass.: Harvard University Press, 1963, page 59 (Young)
8. *Foundations of Modern Physical Science*, by G. Holton and D. H. D. Roller. Reading, Mass.: Addison-Wesley, 1958, Chapter 18
9. "Resource Letter EEC-1 on the Evolution of Energy Concepts from Galileo to Helmholtz," T. Brown; *Am. J. Phys.* **33,** 759 (1965)

Problems

8.1 A force F that lasts 20 s is applied to a body of mass 500 kg. The body, which is initially at rest, is given a sideways velocity of 0.5 m s^{-1} as a result of the force. If the force increases from zero linearly with time for 15 s and then decreases to zero linearly for 5 s, (a) find the impulse on the body caused by the force, (b) find the maximum force exerted on the body and (c) make a graph of F versus t, and find the area under the curve. Does this area agree with the result of (a)? Assume that F is the only force which is acting on the body.

8.2 Calculate the work of a constant force of 12 N when its point of application moves 7 m if the angle between the directions of the force and the displacement is (a) 0°, (b) 60°, (c) 90°, (d) 145°, (e) 180°.

8.3 Calculate the work done by a man who drags a 65-kg bushel of flour 10 m along the floor with a force of 25 kgf and then lifts it up to a truck whose platform is 75 cm high. What is the average power developed if it took 2 min for the whole process?

8.4 A *foot-pound* is defined as the work done by a force of 1 lbf when it moves a body a distance of 1 ft in its own direction. Verify that 1 ft-lb is equal to 1.356 J, and that 1 hp is equal to 746 W. Show that when the mass is given in slugs and the velocity is in ft s^{-1}, kinetic energy is expressed in ft-lb.

8.5 A body with a mass of 4 kg moves upward on a plane inclined 20° with the horizontal. The following forces are acting on the body: an 80-N horizontal force, a 100-N force parallel to the plane favoring the motion, and a constant 10-N force of friction that opposes the motion. The body slides 20 m on the plane. Calculate the total work done by the system of forces acting on the body, as well as the work done by each force.

8.6 The ring m of mass 5.0 kg slides on a smooth metallic arc ABC (Fig. 8–24) shaped as an arc of a circle with a 4-ft radius. Acting on the body are two forces F and F' whose magnitudes are, respectively, 40 N and 150 N. The force F remains tangent to the circle. The force F' is acting in a constant direction forming a 30° angle with the horizontal. Calculate the total work done by the system of forces acting on the body when it moves from A to B and from A to C.

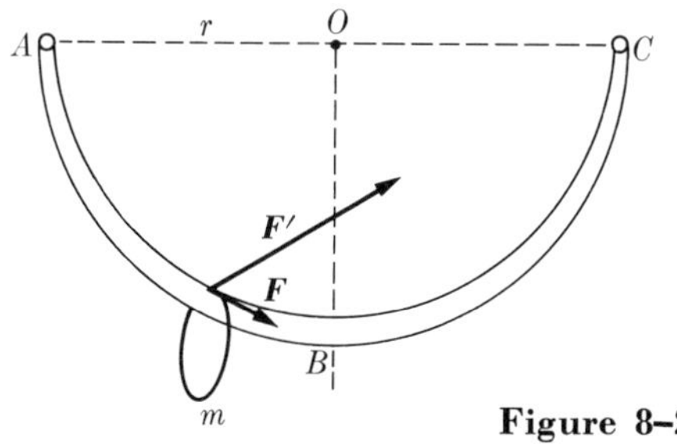

Figure 8–24

8.7 A body with a mass of 0.10 kg falls through a height of 3 m onto a sand pile. If the body penetrates a distance of 3 cm before stopping, what constant force has the sand exerted on the body?

8.8 A body having a mass of 1000 kg falls through a height of 10 m onto a metal pile which is standing upright with one end buried in the ground. The pile is driven 1 cm further into the ground. Calculate the average resistance force exerted by the ground on the pile. (Assume that all the kinetic energy of the body is transformed into work for driving the pile.)

8.9 A man whose mass is 80 kg goes up an inclined plane forming a 10° angle with the horizontal at a velocity of 6 km hr^{-1}. Calculate the power developed.

8.10 An elevator lifts 10 passengers 80 m in 3 min. Each passenger has a mass of 80 kg, and the elevator has a mass of 1000 kg. Calculate the horsepower of its motor.

8.11 An automobile goes up a road inclined 3° with a constant velocity of 45 km hr^{-1}. The mass of the automobile is 1600 kg. What is the power developed by the motor? What is the work done in 10 s? Neglect frictional forces.

8.12 An automobile which weighs 2000 lbf and is moving on a horizontal path reaches a maximum velocity of 100 ft s^{-1} when the motor develops its maximum power, 50 hp. Calculate the maximum velocity of the automobile when it is going up a hill whose slope is 5%. Assume that the resistance of the air is constant.

8.13 Solve the previous problem for an automobile which is going down the hill.

8.14 A constant force of 60 dyn acts during 12 s on a body whose mass is 10 g. The body has an initial velocity of 60 cm s^{-1} in the same direction as the force. Calculate (a) the work done by the force, (b) the final kinetic energy, (c) the power developed, and (d) the increase of the kinetic energy.

8.15 Repeat the previous problem for a force which is perpendicular to the initial velocity.

8.16 (a) What constant force must be exerted by the motor of an automobile whose mass is 1500 kg in order to increase the speed of the automobile from 4.0 km hr^{-1} to 40 km hr^{-1} in 8 s? (b) Determine the variation of the momentum and kinetic energy. (c) Determine the impulse received and the work done by the force. (d) Compute the average power of the motor.

8.17 A small steel ball of mass 1 kg is tied to the end of a wire 1 m long spinning in a vertical circle about the other end with a constant angular velocity of 120 rad s^{-1}. Calculate the kinetic energy. If the total energy instead of the angular velocity of the ball remains constant, what is the change in the kinetic energy and angular velocity between the top and the bottom of the circle? Assume that the value given for the angular velocity is for the top of the circle.

8.18 A body of mass m is moving with velocity $\boldsymbol{V}$ relative to an observer O and with velocity $\boldsymbol{V}'$ relative to O'. The relative velocity of O and O' is $\boldsymbol{v}$. Find the relation between the kinetic energies E_k and E'_k of the particle as measured by O and O'.

8.19 Express, in eV, the kinetic energy of an electron (mass $= 9.109 \times 10^{-31}$ kg) moving at a velocity of 10^6 m s^{-1}. Repeat for a proton (mass $= 1.675 \times 10^{-27}$ kg).

8.20 Find the velocity of an electron in a television tube which hits the screen with an energy of 1.8×10^4 eV.

8.21 Find the velocity of a proton which emerges from a particle accelerator with an energy of 3×10^5 eV.

8.22 When E_k is the kinetic energy in eV and v is the velocity in m s^{-1}, prove that their relationship is $E_k = 2.843 \times 10^{-12}v^2$ for the electron and $E_k = 5.228 \times 10^{-9}v^2$ for a proton.

8.23 The force acting on a body of mass 10 kg is $\boldsymbol{F} = \boldsymbol{u}_x(10 + 2t)$ N, where t is in seconds. (a) Determine the change in momentum and velocity of the body after 4 s, as well as the impulse given the body. (b) How long should the force act on the body so that its impulse is 200 N s? Answer both questions for a body which is initially at rest and for one which has an initial velocity of $-\boldsymbol{u}_y(6)$ m s^{-1}.

8.24 A 10-kg mass moves under the force $\boldsymbol{F} = [\boldsymbol{u}_x(5t) + \boldsymbol{u}_y(3t^2 - 1)]$ N. At $t = 0$ the body is at rest at the origin. (a) Find the momentum and the kinetic energy of the body at $t = 10$ s. (b) Compute the impulse and the work done by the force from $t = 0$ to $t = 10$ s. Check with the answers in (a).

8.25 A 20-kg mass moves under the influence of the force $\boldsymbol{F} = \boldsymbol{u}_x(100t)$ N, where t is measured in seconds. If, at $t = 2$, $\boldsymbol{v} = \boldsymbol{u}_x(3)$ m s^{-1}, determine (a) the impulse delivered to the particle during the time interval 2 s $< t <$ 10 s, and (b) the momentum of the mass at $t = 10$ s. (c) Prove that the impulse is equal to the change in the momentum of the mass for the given time interval. (d) Find the work done on the particle, and (e) its kinetic energy at $t = 10$ s. (f) Prove that the change in kinetic energy is equal to the work done.

8.26 Repeat the previous problem when $\boldsymbol{v} = \boldsymbol{u}_y(3t)$ m s^{-1} at $t = 2$ s.

8.27 A particle is subject to a force $\boldsymbol{F} = \boldsymbol{u}_x(y^2 - x^2) + \boldsymbol{u}_y(3xy)$. Find the work done by the force when the particle is moved from the point (0, 0) to the point (2, 4) along each of the following paths: (a) along the X-axis from (0, 0) to (2, 0) and parallel to the Y-axis up to (2, 4); (b) along the Y-axis from (0, 0) to (0, 4) and parallel to the X-axis up to (2, 4); (c) along the straight line passing through both points; (d) along the parabola $y = x^2$. Is the force conservative?

8.28 Repeat the previous problem when the force is $\boldsymbol{F} = [\boldsymbol{u}_x(2xy) + \boldsymbol{u}_y(x^2)]$.

8.29 Given $\boldsymbol{F} = [\boldsymbol{u}_x(7) - \boldsymbol{u}_y(6)]$ N. (a) Compute the work done when a particle goes from the origin to $\boldsymbol{r} = \boldsymbol{u}_x(-3) + \boldsymbol{u}_y(4) + \boldsymbol{u}_z(16)$ m. Is it necessary to specify the path followed by the particle? (b) Compute the average power if it took 0.6 s to go from one place to the other. Express your answer in watts and horsepower. (c) If the mass of the particle is 1.0 kg, calculate the change in kinetic energy.

8.30 The force in the previous problem is conservative, since it is constant. Calculate the potential energy difference between the two points. Determine the potential energy at the point $\boldsymbol{r} = \boldsymbol{u}_x(7) + \boldsymbol{u}_y(16) + \boldsymbol{u}_z(-42)$ m.

8.31 A particle moves under an attractive inverse-square force, $F = -k/r^2$. The path is a circle of radius r. Show that the total energy is $E = -k/2r$, that the velocity is $v = (k/mr)^{1/2}$, and that the angular momentum is $L = (mkr)^{1/2}$.

8.32 An inclined plane is 13 m long and its base 12 m long. A body of mass 0.80 kg slides from the top with an initial velocity of 100 cm s^{-1}. What is the velocity and the kinetic energy when it reaches the bottom of the plane?

8.33 Plot the kinetic and potential energies as a function of (a) time and (b) height, as a body falls from rest from a height h. Verify that the curves in each case always add to the same constant value.

8.34 A body of mass 20 kg is launched vertically upward with an initial velocity of 50 m s^{-1}. Calculate (a) the initial E_k, E_p, and E, (b) E_k and E_p after 3 s, (c) E_k and E_p at 100 m altitude, and (d) the body's altitude when E_k is reduced to 80% of the initial value.

8.35 A 0.40-kg ball is launched horizontally from the top of a hill 120 m high with a velocity of 6 m s^{-1}. Calculate (a) the ball's initial kinetic energy, (b) its initial potential energy, (c) its kinetic energy when it hits the ground, and (d) its velocity when it hits the ground.

8.36 A bomb, with a mass of 10 kg, is dropped from a plane flying horizontally at 270 km hr^{-1}. If the plane is at 100 m altitude, calculate (a) the bomb's initial kinetic energy, (b) its initial potential energy, (c) its total energy, (d) its velocity when it hits the ground, and (e) its kinetic and potential energies 10 s after it is dropped.

8.37 Using only energy conservation, calculate the velocity of the bomb in the previous problem when it is 50 m above the ground and its altitude when its kinetic energy has increased by 30% of the initial value.

8.38 Solve Problem 8.34 for a case in which the body is launched in a direction forming a 70° angle with the horizontal.

8.39 A boy of mass m is seated on a hemispherical mound of ice as shown in Fig. 8–25. If he starts sliding from rest (assume the ice to be frictionless), where is the point P at which the boy leaves the mound?

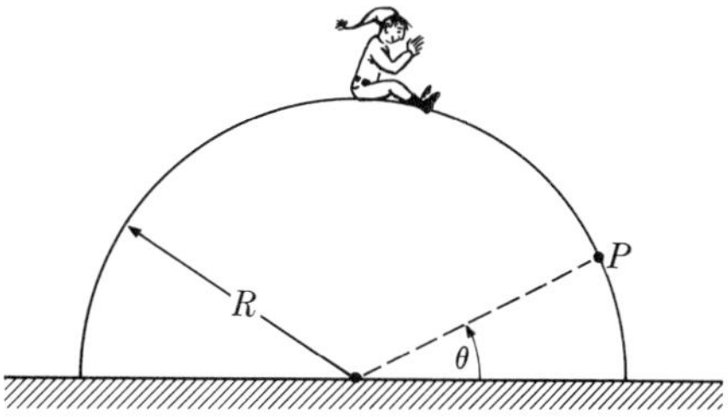

Figure 8–25

8.40 Three guns fire bullets with the same initial velocity (Fig. 8–26) in such a manner that the bullets all pass through the same point A (not necessarily at the same time). Copy Fig. 8–26, and draw their velocity vectors. Basing your calculations on energy considerations, determine the relationship between the magnitudes of the velocities of the bullets at A. Do you conclude from your answers that, by using the conservation of energy alone, you can determine the direction of motion? Why?

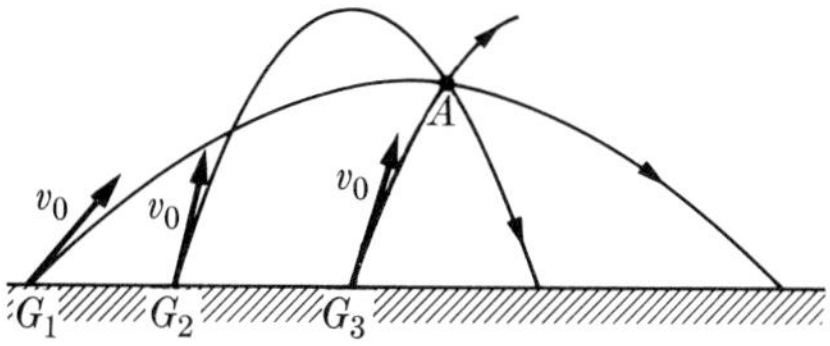

Figure 8–26

8.41 A body of mass 0.5 kg is dropped from a height of 1 m onto a small vertical spring which is in an upright position on the floor and becomes attached to it. The constant of the spring is $k = 2000$ N m^{-1}. Calculate the maximum deformation of the spring.

8.42 The body A in Fig. 8–27 has a mass of 0.5 kg. Starting from rest, it slides 3 m on a smooth plane forming a 45° angle with

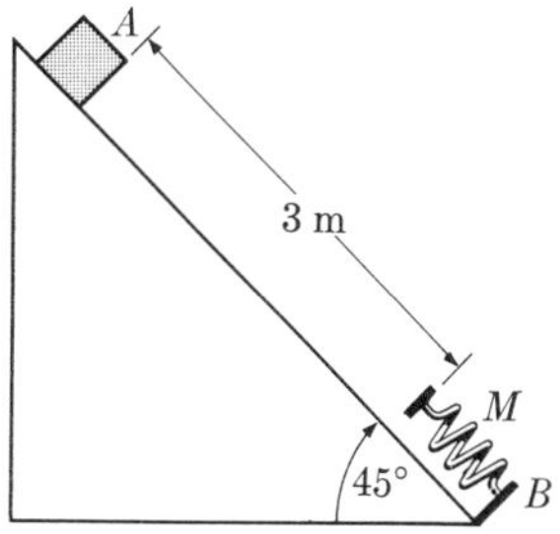

Figure 8–27

the horizontal, until it hits the spring M whose end B is fixed to the far end of the plane. The constant of the spring is k = 400 N m^{-1}. Calculate the maximum deformation of the spring.

8.43 A body of mass 5 kg is hung from a spring whose elastic constant is 2×10^3 N m^{-1}. If the spring is allowed to expand very slowly, how far will the body fall? The body is released so that it may fall freely. Find (a) its initial acceleration and (b) its acceleration and its velocity when it has fallen a distance of 0.010 m, 0.0245 m, and 0.030 m. How far will the body go in this case? Use energy considerations whenever possible.

8.44 In the NH_3 molecule the N atom occupies the vertex of a tetrahedron with the three H atoms at the base (see Fig. 2–3). It is clear that the N atom has two symmetric stable equilibrium positions. Draw a schematic potential-energy curve for the N atom as a function of its distance to the base of the tetrahedron and discuss its possible motion in terms of its total energy.

8.45 In the ethane molecule (C_2H_6), the two CH_3 groups are tetrahedra with the C atom at one vertex (Fig. 8–28). The two CH_3 groups may rotate relative to each other around the line joining the two carbon atoms. Symmetry suggests that there are two sets of positions of equilibrium for this motion; one set consists of stable positions and the other consists of unstable ones. Determine these positions and make a schematic plot of the potential energy as a function of the angle ϕ between 0 and 2π. Discuss the possible rotational motion for different values of the total energy.

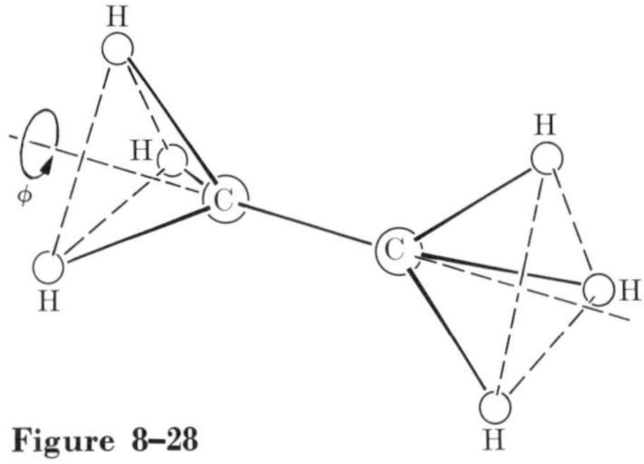

Figure 8–28

8.46 Make a plot, similar to Fig. 8–19, of $E_{p,\text{eff}}$ for $E_p(r) = -1/r$ and (a) $E_{p,c} = \frac{1}{2}r^2$, (b) $E_{p,c} = 2/r^2$, where all energies are given in J and r is in m. Determine the position of the minima of $E_{p,\text{eff}}$ in each case. Measure the energy necessary to go from the minimum of the first curve to the minimum of the second curve.

8.47 A sled with a mass of 20 kg slides on a hill, starting at an altitude of 20 m. The sled starts from rest and has a velocity of 16 m s^{-1} when it reaches the bottom of the slope. Calculate the loss of energy due to friction.

8.48 A ball of mass 0.5 kg which is launched vertically upward with an initial velocity of 20 m s^{-1} reaches an altitude of 15 m. Calculate the loss of energy due to air resistance.

8.49 A train starting from rest travels 300 m down a 1% slope. With the impetus thus acquired, it goes 60 m up a 2% slope and comes to rest. Calculate the force of resistance to the motion of the train. (Assuming that α and β are the slopes of the two planes, $\tan \alpha = 0.01$ and $\tan \beta = 0.02$.)

8.50 A body of mass m slides downward along a plane inclined at an angle α. The coefficient of friction is f. Find the rate at which kinetic plus gravitational potential energy is dissipated.

8.51 Solve Example 8.12 by substituting the appropriate values for v and y as functions of t (obtained from Example 7.8) into the expression $d/dt(E_k + E_p) = d/dt(\frac{1}{2}mv^2 + mgy)$. Show that the result is the same as discussed in Example 8.12.

8.52 A body of mass 8 kg rests on a horizontal plane in such a way that it is in contact with the end of a horizontal spring having an elastic constant of 10^3 N m^{-1}.

The other end of the spring is attached to a vertical wall. When the body is pushed toward the wall, the spring is compressed by 15 cm. When the body is released, it is projected horizontally by the action of the spring. The force of friction between the body and the plane is constant, with a value of 5 N. Calculate (a) the velocity of the body at the time the spring returns to its original length, and (b) the distance traveled by the body before it comes to rest, assuming that the action of the spring on the body stops when the spring returns to its normal length. Discuss the variation of the kinetic energy and the potential energy of the body-spring system during the whole process.

8.53 Apply the virial theorem to obtain the total energy of a body in motion under an attractive inverse-square force $F = -k/r^2$. Compare the answer with the results of Problem 8.31.

8.54 A particle moves under a force field described by one of the following potential energy functions: (a) $E_p(x) = ax^n$, (b) $E_p = by^n$, (c) $E_p = cxy$, (d) $E_p = cxyz$, (e) $E_p = k(x^2 + y^2 + z^2)$. In each case, express the force field in vector form.

8.55 A particle is subject to a force associated with the potential energy $E_p(x) = 3x^2 - x^3$. (a) Make a plot of $E_p(x)$. (b) Determine the direction of the force in each appropriate range of the variable x. (c) Discuss the possible motions of the particle for different values of its total energy. Find its position of equilibrium (stable and unstable).

8.56 The interaction between two nucleons can be represented with some degree of accuracy by the *Yukawa potential* $E_p(r) = -V_0(r_0/r)e^{-r/r_0}$, where V_0 is about 50 MeV and r_0 is about 1.5×10^{-15} m. Find the force between the two nucleons as a function of their separation. Find the value of the force at $r = r_0$. Estimate the value of r at which the force is 1% of its value at $r = r_0$.

8.57 Instead of the Yukawa interaction, consider an interaction of the form $E_p(r) = -V_0(r_0/r)$, and repeat the same calculations as before. What do you conclude about the effect of the factor e^{-r/r_0} on the range of the force?

8.58 Prove that when a force is conservative, then $\partial F_x/\partial y = \partial F_y/\partial x$, $\partial F_y/\partial z = \partial F_z/\partial y$, and $\partial F_z/\partial x = \partial F_x/\partial z$. It can be proved that the converse is also true, and therefore this provides an important test for determining whether a force field is conservative. On this basis, verify which of the following forces are conservative: (a) $\boldsymbol{u}_x x^n$, (b) $\boldsymbol{u}_x y^n$, (c) $\boldsymbol{u}_x(x^2 - y^2) + \boldsymbol{u}_y(3xy)$, (d) $\boldsymbol{u}_x(2xy) + \boldsymbol{u}_y(x^2)$, (e) $\boldsymbol{u}_x yz + \boldsymbol{u}_y zx + \boldsymbol{u}_z xy \cdot x$, (f) $\boldsymbol{u}_x x + \boldsymbol{u}_y y + \boldsymbol{u}_z z$.

8.59 Show that if the force applied to a body is $\boldsymbol{F} = k\boldsymbol{u} \times \boldsymbol{v}$, where $\boldsymbol{u}$ is an arbitrary unit vector, its kinetic energy remains constant. What is the work done by the force? Describe the nature of the resulting motion.

9
DYNAMICS OF A SYSTEM OF PARTICLES

9.1 Introduction

In the last two chapters we have discussed the theory of the dynamics of a particle. In that theory, we ignored the rest of the universe and represented it by either a *force* or a *potential energy*, depending only on the coordinates of the particle. Now we shall consider the more realistic and important problem of several particles. In fact, it was with a system of particles that we started our discussion of dynamics, when we stated the principle of conservation of momentum in Chapter 7. Three main results will be discussed in the first part of this chapter: the motion of the center of mass, the conservation of angular momentum, and the conservation of energy. In the second half of this chapter we shall consider systems composed of a very large number of particles, which require some considerations of a statistical nature. Throughout this chapter we shall assume that the masses of the particles are constant.

I. FUNDAMENTAL RELATIONS

9.2 Motion of the Center of Mass of a System of Particles

Let us consider a system composed of particles of masses $m_1, m_2, \ldots$, and velocities $\boldsymbol{v}_1, \boldsymbol{v}_2, \ldots$, relative to an inertial frame of reference. We shall define the *center-of-mass velocity* by

$$\boldsymbol{v}_{\text{CM}} = \frac{m_1\boldsymbol{v}_1 + m_2\boldsymbol{v}_2 + \cdots}{m_1 + m_2 + \cdots} = \frac{\sum_i m_i\boldsymbol{v}_i}{M}. \tag{9.1}$$

If the masses of the particles are independent of the velocities, $\boldsymbol{v}_{\text{CM}}$ corresponds to the velocity of the point defined in Section 4.8 as the center of mass, and given by the position vector

$$\boldsymbol{r}_{\text{CM}} = \frac{m_1\boldsymbol{r}_1 + m_2\boldsymbol{r}_2 + \cdots}{m_1 + m_2 + \cdots} = \frac{\sum_i m_i\boldsymbol{r}_i}{M}. \tag{9.2}$$

We can see this by taking the time derivative of Eq. (9.2),

$$\frac{d\boldsymbol{r}_{\text{CM}}}{dt} = \frac{1}{M}\sum_i m_i\frac{d\boldsymbol{r}_i}{dt} = \frac{\sum_i m_i\boldsymbol{v}_i}{M} = \boldsymbol{v}_{\text{CM}}.$$

Noting that $\boldsymbol{p}_i = m_i\boldsymbol{v}_i$, we can also write Eq. (9.1) as

$$\boldsymbol{v}_{\text{CM}} = \frac{1}{M}\sum_i \boldsymbol{p}_i = \frac{\boldsymbol{P}}{M} \qquad \text{or} \qquad \boldsymbol{P} = M\boldsymbol{v}_{\text{CM}}, \tag{9.3}$$

where $\boldsymbol{P} = \sum_i \boldsymbol{p}_i$ is the total momentum of the system. This suggests that the momentum of the system is the same as it would be if all the mass were concentrated at the center of mass, moving with velocity $\boldsymbol{v}_{\text{CM}}$. For that reason, $\boldsymbol{v}_{\text{CM}}$ is sometimes called the *system velocity.* Thus when we speak of the velocity of a moving body composed of many particles, such as an airplane or an automobile, the earth or the moon, or even a molecule or a nucleus, we actually refer to its center-of-mass velocity $\boldsymbol{v}_{\text{CM}}$.

If the system is isolated, we know from the principle of conservation of momentum that $\boldsymbol{P}$ is constant. Therefore

> *the center of mass of an isolated system moves with constant velocity in any inertial system (assuming that the masses of the particles are independent of the velocity).*

In particular, we may attach an inertial frame of reference to the center of mass of an isolated system and, relative to this inertial frame, the center of mass is at rest ($\boldsymbol{v}_{\mathrm{CM}} = 0$). This is called *the center-of-mass frame of reference or C-frame of reference.* In view of Eq. (9.3), the total momentum of a system of particles referred to the C-frame of reference is always zero:

$$\boldsymbol{P}_{\mathrm{CM}} = \textstyle\sum_i \boldsymbol{p}_i = 0 \qquad \text{(in CM-frame of reference).} \tag{9.4}$$

For that reason the C-frame is sometimes called the *zero-momentum frame.* This C-frame is important because many experiments that we perform in our laboratory or frame of reference L can be more simply analyzed in the CM-frame of reference.

Next we consider what happens when a system S is not isolated; in other words, when the components of S are interacting with other particles in the world that do not belong to the system S. Let us suppose that our system S is composed of the particles within the dashed line in Fig. 9–1, and that the particles in S interact with all those outside the dashed line, comprising another system S'. We may also assume that S and S' together form an isolated system. To consider some concrete examples, our system S may be our galaxy and S' the rest of the universe. Or S may be the solar system and S' may be the rest of the universe. We may even consider an isolated molecule, and group the atoms composing it into two systems S and S'.

We designate the particles that belong to S by the subscript i, and those that belong to S' by the subscript j. The principle of conservation of momentum for the complete isolated system $S + S'$ is

$$\boldsymbol{P} = \underbrace{\textstyle\sum_i \boldsymbol{p}_i}_{\text{System } S} + \underbrace{\textstyle\sum_j \boldsymbol{p}_j}_{\text{System } S'} = \text{const}$$

or

$$\boldsymbol{P} = \boldsymbol{P}_S + \boldsymbol{P}_{S'} = \text{const.} \tag{9.5}$$

Then any change in the momentum of S must be accompanied by an equal and opposite change in the momentum of S'. That is,

$$\Delta \boldsymbol{P}_S = -\Delta \boldsymbol{P}_{S'}$$

or

$$\textstyle\sum_i \Delta \boldsymbol{p}_i = -\sum_j \Delta \boldsymbol{p}_j. \tag{9.6}$$

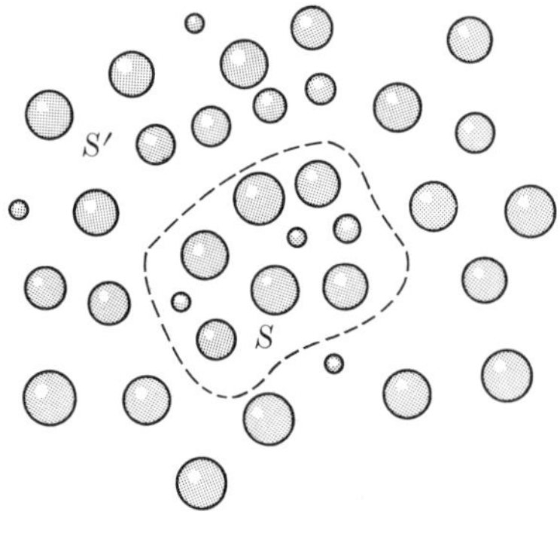

Fig. 9–1. Interaction between a system S and its surroundings S'.

Therefore the interaction between systems S and S' can be described as an exchange of momentum. The student should compare Eqs. (9.5) and (9.6) with Eqs. (7.5) and (7.8) for the particular case of two particles, and note the similarity.

Taking the time derivative of Eq. (9.5), we have

$$\frac{d\boldsymbol{P}_S}{dt} = -\frac{d\boldsymbol{P}_{S'}}{dt}. \tag{9.7}$$

We call the time rate of change of momentum of system S the *external force* exerted on S; that is,

$$\frac{d\boldsymbol{P}_S}{dt} = \boldsymbol{F}_{\text{ext}} \quad \text{or} \quad \frac{d}{dt}\left(\textstyle\sum_i \boldsymbol{p}_i\right) = \boldsymbol{F}_{\text{ext}}. \tag{9.8}$$

We say external force because the time rate of change of momentum of S is due to its interaction with S'. The *internal forces* existing in S due to the interactions among its component particles do not produce any change in its total momentum, as required by the principle of conservation of momentum. Then if $\boldsymbol{F}'_{\text{ext}}$ is the external force on system S', Eq. (9.7) requires that $\boldsymbol{F}_{\text{ext}} = -\boldsymbol{F}'_{\text{ext}}$, which is the law of action and reaction for the interactions between systems S and S'.

Since, by Eq. (9.3), the velocity of the center of mass of S is $\boldsymbol{v}_{\text{CM}} = \boldsymbol{P}_S/M$, we have from Eq. (9.8) that

$$\boldsymbol{F}_{\text{ext}} = M\frac{d\boldsymbol{v}_{\text{CM}}}{dt} = M\boldsymbol{a}_{\text{CM}}. \tag{9.9}$$

Comparing this result with Eq. (7.15), we see that

> *the center of mass of a system of particles moves as if it were a particle of mass equal to the total mass of the system and subject to the external force applied to the system.*

The results expressed by Eqs. (9.6), (9.7), (9.8), and (9.9) clearly indicate that the interaction between two systems of particles can be formally described in terms identical to those introduced in Chapter 7 for two single particles. This justifies, *a posteriori*, the loose way in which we illustrated the application of the principles of dynamics in Chapter 7 (where bodies and not particles were involved) in such cases as the interaction between the earth and the moon, between two molecules, or in the motion of a rocket or an automobile.

It is interesting to obtain the relation between $\boldsymbol{F}_{\text{ext}}$ and the forces acting on the individual particles. For simplicity let us consider that our system S is composed of two particles (Fig. 9–2). Let us call $\boldsymbol{F}_{12}$ the

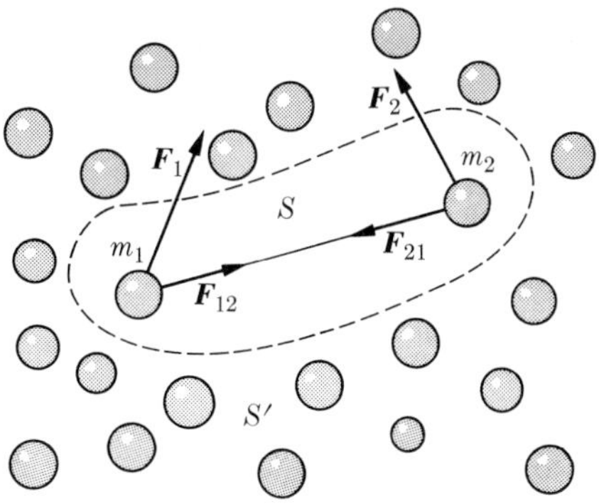

Fig. 9–2. External and internal forces on a system S.

internal force on particle m_1 due to its interaction with m_2, and $\boldsymbol{F}_{21}$ the *internal* force on m_2 due to its interaction with m_1. The law of action and reaction requires that

$$\boldsymbol{F}_{12} = -\boldsymbol{F}_{21}. \tag{9.10}$$

Let $\boldsymbol{F}_1$ be the resultant *external* force on m_1 due to its interaction with other particles and $\boldsymbol{F}_2$ the *external* force on m_2. To obtain the equation of motion of each particle under the action of *all* the forces acting on it, we apply Eq. (7.12):

$$\frac{d\boldsymbol{p}_1}{dt} = \boldsymbol{F}_1 + \boldsymbol{F}_{12}, \qquad \frac{d\boldsymbol{p}_2}{dt} = \boldsymbol{F}_2 + \boldsymbol{F}_{21}.$$

Adding these two equations and using Eq. (9.10) so that $\boldsymbol{F}_{12} + \boldsymbol{F}_{21} = 0$, we find that

$$\frac{d\boldsymbol{P}}{dt} = \frac{d}{dt}(\boldsymbol{p}_1 + \boldsymbol{p}_2) = \boldsymbol{F}_1 + \boldsymbol{F}_2. \tag{9.11}$$

Therefore the total rate of change of momentum of the system composed of m_1 and m_2 is equal to the sum of the *external* forces applied on m_1 and m_2. In general, for a system composed of an arbitrary number of particles,

$$\frac{d\boldsymbol{P}}{dt} = \frac{d}{dt}(\textstyle\sum_i \boldsymbol{p}_i) = \sum_i \boldsymbol{F}_i, \tag{9.12}$$

where $\boldsymbol{F}_i$ is the *external* force acting on particle m_i. Comparison with Eq. (9.8) indicates that

> *the external force on a system of particles is the sum of the external forces on each of its component particles.*

Let us consider some examples. Figure 9–3(a) shows the earth in its motion around the sun. The center of mass of the earth moves in a way which corresponds to a particle having a mass equal to that of the earth and subject to a force equal to the sum of the forces exerted by the sun (and the other heavenly bodies) on all the particles composing the earth. Figure 9–3(b) depicts a water molecule. Supposing, for example, that the molecule is subject to external electrical forces. Its center of mass moves as if it were a particle of mass equal to that of the molecule and subject to a force equal to the sum of the forces acting on all the charged particles composing the molecule. Figure 9–3(c) illustrates the motion of a chain thrown into the air. The center of mass of the chain moves as if it were a particle of mass equal to that of the chain and subject to a force equal to the weight of the chain, and therefore the center of mass describes a parabolic path. Finally, in Fig. 9–3(d), we have the case of a grenade exploding in the air; the center of mass of the fragments will continue moving on the original parabola, since the center of mass behaves like a particle of mass identical to the grenade and subject to the total weight of all fragments. The weight of the fragments does not change with the explosion because the force of gravity is practically independent of position at points near the surface of the earth. We must note, however, that if the field of force were not constant, but depended on position, the fragments resulting from the explosion

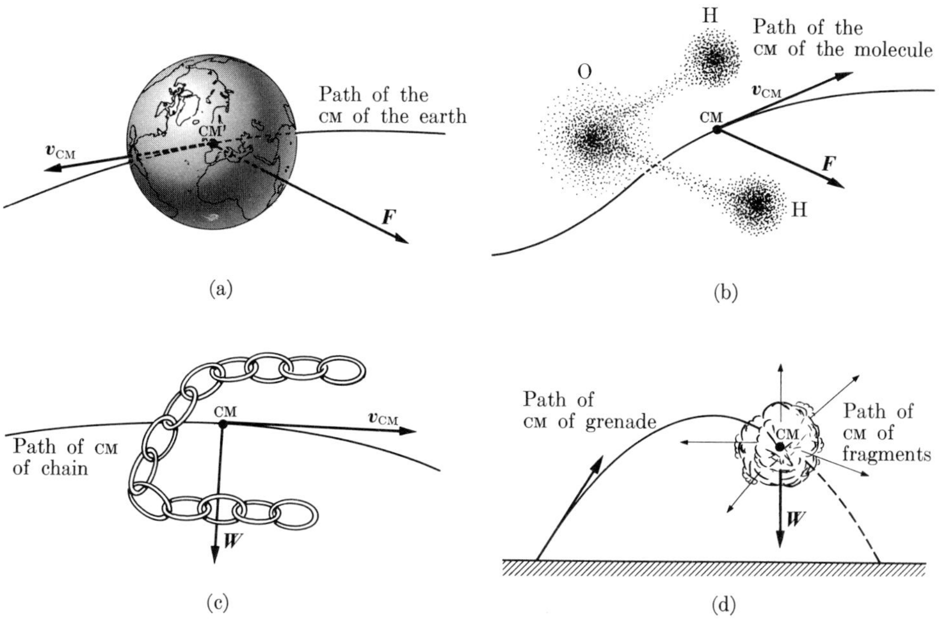

Fig. 9–3. The CM of a system of particles follows a path due to the total external force on the system.

would be subject to forces different from those along the original path. The path of the center of mass would not then continue to be the same as before the explosion because the sum of the external forces would be different. For example, if (due to some cosmic cataclysm) a planet in the solar system should break into fragments, the center of mass of the fragments would not follow the original elliptical path of the planet because the forces on the fragments would be different.

EXAMPLE 9.1. A grenade that is falling vertically explodes into two equal fragments when it is at a height of 2000 m and has a downward velocity of 60 m s^{-1}. Immediately after the explosion one of the fragments is moving downward at 80 m s^{-1}. Find the position of the center of mass of the system 10 s after the explosion.

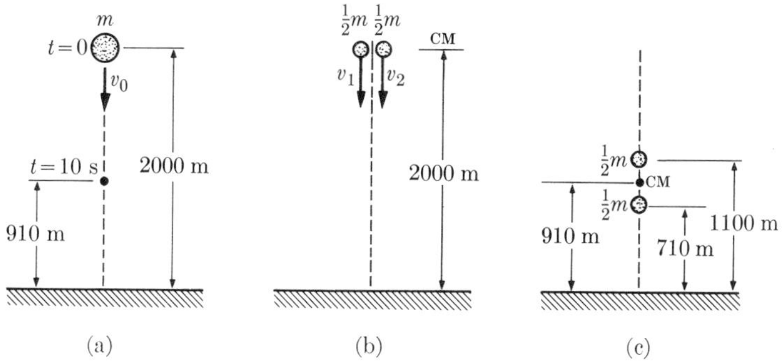

Figure 9–4

Solution: We may follow one of two methods (see Fig. 9–4). Since we know that as a result of the explosion the external forces have not changed, we may assume that the center of mass continues moving as if there had not been any explosion. Thus, after the explosion, the center of mass will be at a height given by $z = z_0 + v_0 t + \frac{1}{2}gt^2$, where $z_0 = 2000$ m, $v_0 = -60$ m s^{-1}, and $g = -9.8$ m s^{-2}. Therefore at $t = 10$ s, $z = 910$ m.

As an alternate method, we directly compute the position of the center of mass from the positions of the fragments 10 s after the explosion. Since momentum is conserved in the explosion, we have that $mv_0 = m_1v_1 + m_2v_2$. But $m_1 = m_2 = \frac{1}{2}m$; thus $2v_0 = v_1 + v_2$. Now $v_0 = -60$ m s^{-1} and $v_1 = -80$ m s^{-1}. Therefore $v_2 = -40$ m s^{-1} and the second fragment initially moves downward also. After 10 s the position of the first fragment is $z_1 = z_0 + v_1 t + \frac{1}{2}gt^2 = 710$ m and the second fragment has the position $z_2 = z_0 + v_2 t + \frac{1}{2}gt^2 = 1110$ m. Applying Eq. (9.2), we find that the position of the center of mass is

$$z_{\rm CM} = \frac{(\frac{1}{2}m)z_1 + (\frac{1}{2}m)z_2}{m} = \tfrac{1}{2}(z_1 + z_2) = 910 \text{ m},$$

which is in agreement with the previous result.

EXAMPLE 9.2. A nozzle which has a cross section a is throwing a stream of gas against a wall with a velocity $\boldsymbol{v}$ much larger than the thermal agitation of the molecules. The wall deflects the molecules without changing the magnitude of their velocity. Find the force exerted on the wall.

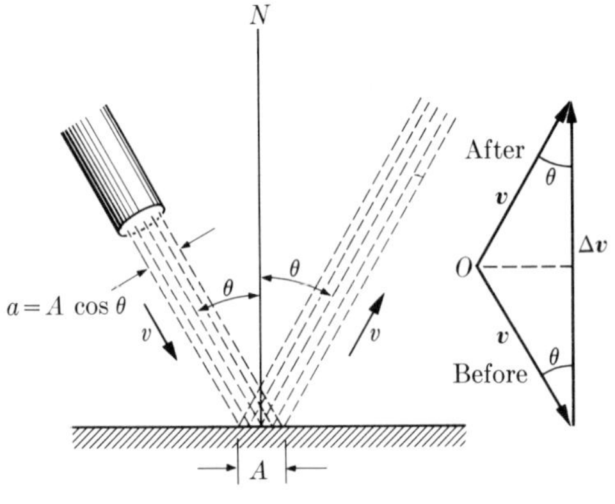

Fig. 9–5. Change of momentum of a stream of gas striking a wall.

Solution: When the molecules are moving toward the wall (Fig. 9–5), their velocity is downward. After they strike the wall they begin to move upward. In both cases they make an angle θ with the normal N. Each molecule, as a result of its impact on the wall, suffers a change $\Delta \boldsymbol{v}$ in its velocity which is parallel to the normal N because that is the direction of the force exerted by the wall. The magnitude of the change is $|\Delta \boldsymbol{v}| = 2v \cos \theta$. The change in momentum of a molecule is $|\Delta \boldsymbol{p}| = m|\Delta \boldsymbol{v}| = 2mv \cos \theta$ in the direction of the normal N. Let n be the number of molecules per unit volume. The number of molecules arriving at the wall per unit time are those in a volume whose length is equal to the velocity v and whose cross section is a. Thus this number is $n(av)$. Each molecule suffers a change of momentum equal to $2mv \cos \theta$. Therefore the change of momentum of the stream of gas per unit time is

$$F = (nav)(2mv \cos \theta) = 2anmv^2 \cos \theta.$$

Let A be the area of the wall that suffers the impact of the gas. We see from the figure that $a = A \cos \theta$, and our previous result becomes

$$F = 2Anmv^2 \cos^2 \theta.$$

This, according to Eq. (9.8), is the force exerted by the wall on the stream of gas, and in view of Eq. (9.10), the stream of gas produces an equal and opposite force on the area A of the wall. [The wind's force on the sails of a sailboat is given by this equation. It also gives the force exerted by the wind blowing against a wall during a storm. In Example 9.16 we shall see another application.]

Since the total force is not applied to a single particle of the wall, but rather over an area, we may introduce a useful concept, already known to the student; that is, *pressure*, defined as the force of the gas per unit area of the wall. Thus

$$p = \frac{F}{A}. \tag{9.13}$$

In the particular case of this example, the gas exerts a pressure on the wall equal to $2nmv^2 \cos^2 \theta$.

9.3 Reduced Mass

Consider now the case of two particles which are subject only to their mutual interaction; that is, there are no external forces acting on them (Fig. 9–6). The two particles could be, for example, an electron and a proton in an isolated hydrogen atom. The mutual internal forces $\boldsymbol{F}_{12}$ and $\boldsymbol{F}_{21}$ satisfy the relation (9.10). We have drawn these forces along the line $\boldsymbol{r}_{12}$. Let us now discuss the *relative* motion of the two particles. The equation of motion for each particle relative to an inertial observer O is $m_1(d\boldsymbol{v}_1/dt) = \boldsymbol{F}_{12}$ and $m_2(d\boldsymbol{v}_2/dt) = \boldsymbol{F}_{21}$ or

$$\frac{d\boldsymbol{v}_1}{dt} = \frac{\boldsymbol{F}_{12}}{m_1}, \qquad \frac{d\boldsymbol{v}_2}{dt} = \frac{\boldsymbol{F}_{21}}{m_2}.$$

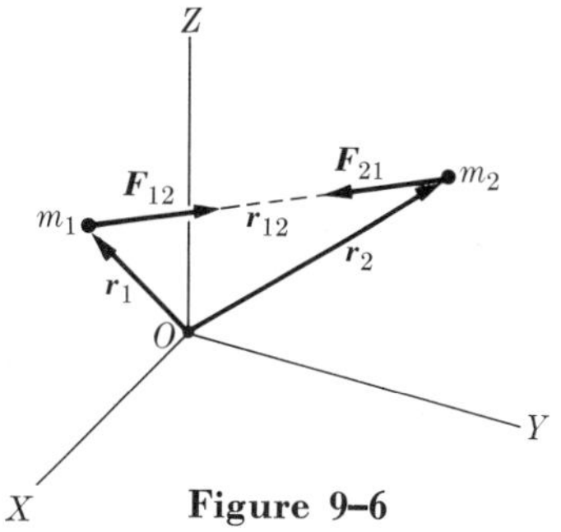

Figure 9–6

Subtracting these equations, we have

$$\frac{d\boldsymbol{v}_1}{dt} - \frac{d\boldsymbol{v}_2}{dt} = \frac{\boldsymbol{F}_{12}}{m_1} - \frac{\boldsymbol{F}_{21}}{m_2}.$$

We use Eq. (9.10), in which $\boldsymbol{F}_{12} = -\boldsymbol{F}_{21}$, and rewrite the preceding result as

$$\frac{d}{dt}(\boldsymbol{v}_1 - \boldsymbol{v}_2) = \left(\frac{1}{m_1} + \frac{1}{m_2}\right)\boldsymbol{F}_{12}. \tag{9.14}$$

Now $\boldsymbol{v}_1 - \boldsymbol{v}_2 = \boldsymbol{v}_{12}$ is the velocity of m_1 *relative* to m_2, and therefore

$$\frac{d}{dt}(\boldsymbol{v}_1 - \boldsymbol{v}_2) = \frac{d\boldsymbol{v}_{12}}{dt} = \boldsymbol{a}_{12}$$

is the acceleration of m_1 *relative* to m_2. Let us introduce a quantity called the *reduced mass* of the two-particle system, designated by μ, and defined by

$$\frac{1}{\mu} = \frac{1}{m_1} + \frac{1}{m_2} = \frac{m_1 + m_2}{m_1 m_2} \quad \text{or} \quad \mu = \frac{m_1 m_2}{m_1 + m_2}. \tag{9.15}$$

Equation (9.14) can then be written in the form

$$\boldsymbol{a}_{12} = \frac{\boldsymbol{F}_{12}}{\mu} \quad \text{or} \quad \boldsymbol{F}_{12} = \mu \boldsymbol{a}_{12}. \tag{9.16}$$

This important result expresses the fact that

> *the relative motion of two particles subject only to their mutual interaction is equivalent to the motion, relative to an inertial observer, of a particle of mass equal to the reduced mass under a force equal to their interaction.*

For example, we can reduce the motion of the moon relative to the earth to a single-particle problem by using the reduced mass of the system earth-moon and a force equal to the attraction of the earth on the moon. Similarly, when we talk about the motion of an electron around the nucleus, we may assume the system reduced to a particle with a mass equal to the reduced mass of the electron-nucleus system and moving under the force between the electron and the nucleus. Therefore, in describing the motion of two particles under their mutual interaction, we may separate the motion of the system into the motion of the center of mass, whose velocity is constant, and the relative motion of the two particles, given by Eq. (9.16), which is referred to a frame of reference attached to their center of mass.

Note that if one of the particles, say m_1, has a much smaller mass than the other, the reduced mass may be written as

$$\mu = \frac{m_1}{1 + m_1/m_2} \cong m_1 \left(1 - \frac{m_1}{m_2}\right), \tag{9.17}$$

where we have divided both terms in Eq. (9.15) by m_2 and used the approximation $(1 + x)^{-1} \approx 1 - x$, according to Eq. (M.28). Hence this results in a reduced mass approximately equal to the mass of the lighter particle. For example, when we discuss the motion of an artificial satellite around the earth we may use, with very good approximation, the mass of the satellite and not the reduced mass of the earth-satellite system. On the other hand, if the two particles have the same mass ($m_1 = m_2$), we have then $\mu = \frac{1}{2}m_1$. This is the situation when two protons interact. This also holds, with very good approximation, for a system formed by one neutron and one proton, as in the deuteron.

EXAMPLE 9.3. Calculate the reduced mass of the following systems: (a) electron-proton in a hydrogen atom, (b) proton-neutron in a deuteron nucleus. In each case compare the result with the mass of the lighter particle.

Solution: (a) For the electron-proton system, which comprises a hydrogen atom, we have that $m_e = 9.1091 \times 10^{-31}$ kg and $m_p = 1.6725 \times 10^{-27}$ kg. Thus, since m_e is much smaller than m_p, we may write, using Eq. (9.17),

$$\mu_{ep} = m_e\left(1 - \frac{m_e}{m_p}\right) = 9.1031 \times 10^{-31} \text{ kg}.$$

So μ differs from m_e by about 0.06%. In spite of the small difference, it produces detectable results in many atomic processes.

(b) For the neutron-proton system in the deuteron, we have that $m_n = 1.6748 \times 10^{-27}$ kg, which is almost the same as m_p. Then we must use the exact formula, Eq. (9.15), which yields

$$\mu_{np} = \frac{m_p m_n}{m_p + m_n} = 0.8368 \times 10^{-27} \text{ kg},$$

which is approximately equal to one-half the mass of either particle.

EXAMPLE 9.4. An observer measures the velocities of two particles of masses m_1 and m_2 and obtains, respectively, the values $\boldsymbol{v}_1$ and $\boldsymbol{v}_2$. Determine the velocity of the center of mass relative to the observer and the velocity of each particle relative to the center of mass.

Solution: From Eq. (9.1) we have (Fig. 9–7)

$$\boldsymbol{v}_{CM} = \frac{m_1\boldsymbol{v}_1 + m_2\boldsymbol{v}_2}{m_1 + m_2}.$$

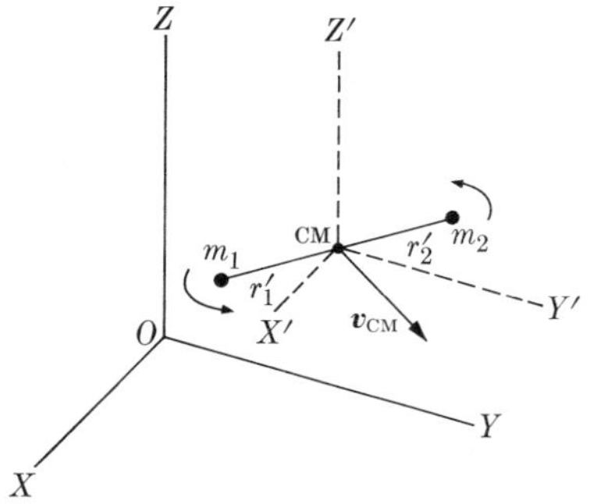

Fig. 9–7. Motion relative to the CM.

The velocity of each particle relative to the center of mass, using the Galilean transformation of velocities given by Eq. (6.9), is

$$\boldsymbol{v}_1' = \boldsymbol{v}_1 - \boldsymbol{v}_{CM} = \boldsymbol{v}_1 - \frac{m_1\boldsymbol{v}_1 + m_2\boldsymbol{v}_2}{m_1 + m_2} = \frac{m_2(\boldsymbol{v}_1 - \boldsymbol{v}_2)}{m_1 + m_2} = \frac{m_2\boldsymbol{v}_{12}}{m_1 + m_2};$$

$$\boldsymbol{v}_2' = \boldsymbol{v}_2 - \boldsymbol{v}_{CM} = \frac{m_1(\boldsymbol{v}_2 - \boldsymbol{v}_1)}{m_1 + m_2} = -\frac{m_1\boldsymbol{v}_{12}}{m_1 + m_2},$$

where $\boldsymbol{v}_{12} = \boldsymbol{v}_1 - \boldsymbol{v}_2$ is the relative velocity of the two particles. Thus, in frame C, the two particles appear to be moving in opposite directions. The momentum of particle 1 relative to the center of mass is

$$\boldsymbol{p}_1' = m_1\boldsymbol{v}_1' = \frac{m_1 m_2}{m_1 + m_2}\boldsymbol{v}_{12} = \mu\boldsymbol{v}_{12}.$$

Therefore the momentum of particle 1 in the CM-frame of reference is equal to the reduced mass of the system multiplied by the relative velocity. Similarly, for particle 2,

$$\boldsymbol{p}_2' = m_2\boldsymbol{v}_2' = \mu\boldsymbol{v}_{21} = -\mu\boldsymbol{v}_{12}.$$

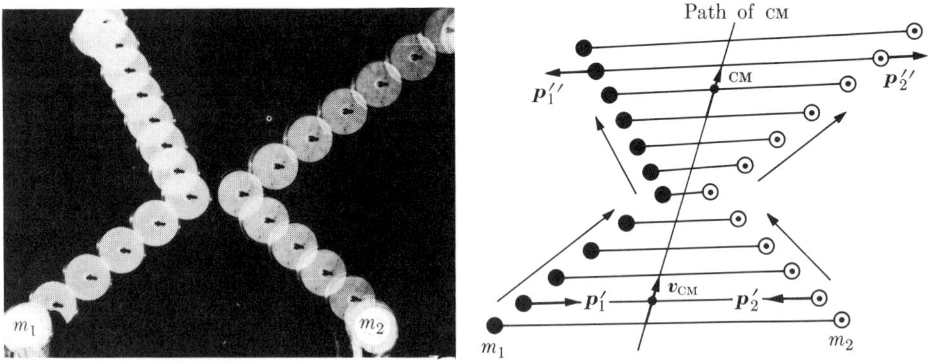

(a) (b)

Fig. 9–8. Collision between two bodies ($m_1 = 2$ kg, $m_2 = 1.5$ kg). The interaction applies only when they are very close. (a) Multiflash photograph of the motion of the two bodies. (b) Graphical analysis of the photograph, showing that the CM has moved in a straight line with constant velocity relative to the laboratory.

Thus we verify that *in the* CM*-frame of reference the two particles move with equal and opposite momenta,* and that the total momentum is $\boldsymbol{p}_1' + \boldsymbol{p}_2' = 0$, as it should be according to Eq. (9.4). This is illustrated in the photograph in Fig. 9–8(a) and its analysis in Fig. 9–8(b).

The relations we have derived in this example are very important in scattering experiments in nuclear physics. In these experiments the velocities of the particles are measured relative to a frame of reference L attached to the laboratory. But the theoretical expressions for the scattering are simpler when they are related to the CM-frame of reference. Thus the relationships between both sets of measurements must be known, and in order to determine these, we must use the formulas derived above.

9.4 Angular Momentum of a System of Particles

Next let us discuss the angular momentum of a system of particles. In Eq. (7.32) we defined the angular momentum of a particle relative to a given point as the vector quantity

$$\boldsymbol{L} = \boldsymbol{r} \times \boldsymbol{p} = m(\boldsymbol{r} \times \boldsymbol{v}), \tag{9.18}$$

and obtained in Eq. (7.38) a relation between $\boldsymbol{L}$ and the torque $\boldsymbol{\tau} = \boldsymbol{r} \times \boldsymbol{F}$ of the applied force. That is,

$$\frac{d\boldsymbol{L}}{dt} = \boldsymbol{\tau}. \tag{9.19}$$

Now let us look at a similar situation, in which not one but several particles are present. For simplicity let us consider first the case of only two particles. Equation (9.19) applied to particles 1 and 2 becomes

$$\frac{d\boldsymbol{L}_1}{dt} = \boldsymbol{\tau}_1 \quad \text{and} \quad \frac{d\boldsymbol{L}_2}{dt} = \boldsymbol{\tau}_2.$$

Adding the two equations, we obtain

$$\frac{d}{dt}(\boldsymbol{L}_1 + \boldsymbol{L}_2) = \boldsymbol{\tau}_1 + \boldsymbol{\tau}_2. \tag{9.20}$$

Let us assume that each particle, in addition to having a mutual interaction with the other particle, is acted on by an external force (Fig. 9–9). Then the force on particle 1 is $\boldsymbol{F}_1 + \boldsymbol{F}_{12}$ and on particle 2 is $\boldsymbol{F}_2 + \boldsymbol{F}_{21}$, and

$$\boldsymbol{\tau}_1 = \boldsymbol{r}_1 \times (\boldsymbol{F}_1 + \boldsymbol{F}_{12}) = \boldsymbol{r}_1 \times \boldsymbol{F}_1 + \boldsymbol{r}_1 \times \boldsymbol{F}_{12},$$

$$\boldsymbol{\tau}_2 = \boldsymbol{r}_2 \times (\boldsymbol{F}_2 + \boldsymbol{F}_{21}) = \boldsymbol{r}_2 \times \boldsymbol{F}_2 + \boldsymbol{r}_2 \times \boldsymbol{F}_{21}.$$

Then, since $\boldsymbol{F}_{12} = -\boldsymbol{F}_{21}$, the total torque on the particles is

$$\boldsymbol{\tau}_1 + \boldsymbol{\tau}_2 = \boldsymbol{r}_1 \times \boldsymbol{F}_1 + \boldsymbol{r}_2 \times \boldsymbol{F}_2 + (\boldsymbol{r}_2 - \boldsymbol{r}_1) \times \boldsymbol{F}_{21}.$$

Now the vector $\boldsymbol{r}_2 - \boldsymbol{r}_1 = \boldsymbol{r}_{21}$ has the direction of the line joining the two particles. If we make the *special assumption* that the internal forces $\boldsymbol{F}_{12}$ and $\boldsymbol{F}_{21}$ act along the line $\boldsymbol{r}_{21}$ joining the two particles, then the vectors $\boldsymbol{r}_2 - \boldsymbol{r}_1 = \boldsymbol{r}_{21}$ and $\boldsymbol{F}_{21}$ are parallel, and therefore $(\boldsymbol{r}_2 - \boldsymbol{r}_1) \times \boldsymbol{F}_{21} = 0$. The last term in the above equation thus disappears, leaving only the torques due to the *external* forces. That is, Eq. (9.20) becomes

$$\frac{d}{dt}(\boldsymbol{L}_1 + \boldsymbol{L}_2) = \boldsymbol{r}_1 \times \boldsymbol{F}_1 + \boldsymbol{r}_2 \times \boldsymbol{F}_2$$
$$= \boldsymbol{\tau}_{1,\text{ext}} + \boldsymbol{\tau}_{2,\text{ext}}.$$

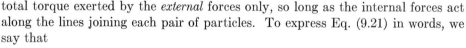

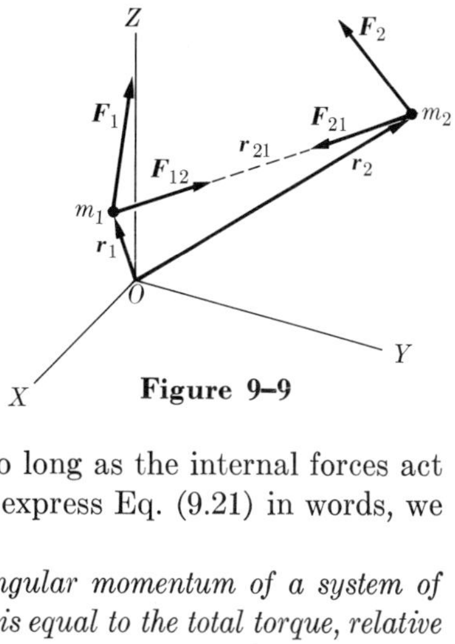

Figure 9–9

Generalizing this result to any number of particles, we obtain

$$\frac{d\boldsymbol{L}}{dt} = \boldsymbol{\tau}_{\text{ext}}. \tag{9.21}$$

In this equation $\boldsymbol{L} = \sum_i \boldsymbol{L}_i$ is the total angular momentum of the particles, and $\boldsymbol{\tau}_{\text{ext}}$ is the total torque exerted by the *external* forces only, so long as the internal forces act along the lines joining each pair of particles. To express Eq. (9.21) in words, we say that

> *the time rate of change of the total angular momentum of a system of particles relative to an arbitrary point is equal to the total torque, relative to the same point, of the external forces acting on the system.*

This statement may be considered as the fundamental law of the dynamics of rotation. In Chapter 10 we shall apply it to the motion of a rigid body.

If there are no external forces, or the sum of their torques is zero, $\boldsymbol{\tau}_{\text{ext}} = 0$; then

$$\frac{d\boldsymbol{L}}{dt} = \frac{d}{dt}(\textstyle\sum_i \boldsymbol{L}_i) = 0.$$

Integrating, we obtain

$$\boldsymbol{L} = \sum_i \boldsymbol{L}_i = \boldsymbol{L}_1 + \boldsymbol{L}_2 + \boldsymbol{L}_3 + \cdots = \text{const.} \tag{9.22}$$

Equation (9.22) constitutes the *law of conservation of angular momentum.* Expressed in words, it indicates that

> *the total angular momentum of an isolated system, or a system with zero external torque, is constant in magnitude and direction.*

This is the case, for example, of the electrons in an atom when one considers only the internal forces due to the electrostatic repulsion of the electrons and the electrostatic attraction of the nucleus, which are internal forces acting along the lines joining each pair of particles. Also, if we assume that the solar system is isolated and if we neglect the forces due to the rest of the galaxy, the total angular momentum of all the planets relative to the center of mass of the solar system remains constant. This conclusion holds with a great degree of accuracy. Similarly, the reason why the earth keeps rotating around its center of mass with an angular momentum that is essentially constant is that the external forces due to the sun and the other planets pass through the center of the earth and therefore have zero (or approximately zero) torque about the center of mass.

In spite of the special assumption involved in our derivation of the law of conservation of angular momentum (i.e., that the internal forces act along the lines joining each pair of particles), this law seems to be universally valid, applying to all processes so far observed, even when our special assumption does not seem to hold. The law of conservation of angular momentum implies that if, in an isolated system, the angular momentum of some part of it changes because of internal interactions, the rest of the system must experience an equal (but opposite) change of angular momentum, so that the total angular momentum is conserved.

For example, in a disintegrating nucleus the emitted particles, in many cases an electron and a neutrino, possess some angular momentum. Since only internal forces act in the disintegrating process, the angular momentum of the nucleus must change to exactly compensate for the angular momentum carried away by the emitted particles. Similarly, if an atom, molecule, or nucleus emits electromagnetic radiation, its angular momentum must change to exactly compensate for the angular momentum taken away by the radiation. Sometimes processes that would otherwise be possible in nature cannot occur because of some aspect, characteristic of the process, which makes it impossible for the process to satisfy the conservation of angular momentum.

EXAMPLE 9.5. Compute the angular momentum of two particles relative to their center of mass or frame of reference C.

Solution: Let $\boldsymbol{r}_{12} = \boldsymbol{r}_1 - \boldsymbol{r}_2$ be the position vector of particle 1 relative to particle 2. The position of the center of mass of the two particles (refer back to Fig. 9–6) relative to frame of reference L is

$$\boldsymbol{r}_{\text{CM}} = \frac{m_1\boldsymbol{r}_1 + m_2\boldsymbol{r}_2}{m_1 + m_2}.$$

Thus the position vector of each particle relative to the center of mass or frame of reference C is

$$\mathbf{r}_1' = \mathbf{r}_1 - \mathbf{r}_{\text{CM}} = \frac{m_2(\mathbf{r}_1 - \mathbf{r}_2)}{m_1 + m_2} = \frac{m_2\mathbf{r}_{12}}{m_1 + m_2},$$

$$\mathbf{r}_2' = \mathbf{r}_2 - \mathbf{r}_{\text{CM}} = \frac{m_2(\mathbf{r}_2 - \mathbf{r}_1)}{m_1 + m_2} = -\frac{m_1\mathbf{r}_{12}}{m_1 + m_2}.$$

Using the results of Example 9.4, we obtain the angular momentum relative to the center of mass,

$$\begin{aligned} \mathbf{L}_{\text{CM}} &= \mathbf{r}_1' \times \mathbf{p}_1' + \mathbf{r}_2' \times \mathbf{p}_2' \\ &= \left(\frac{m_2\mathbf{r}_{12}}{m_1 + m_2}\right) \times (\mu\mathbf{v}_{12}) + \left(-\frac{m_1\mathbf{r}_{12}}{m_1 + m_2}\right) \times (-\mu\mathbf{v}_{12}) \\ &= \mu\mathbf{r}_{12} \times \mathbf{v}_{12} = \mathbf{r}_{12} \times (\mu\mathbf{v}_{12}). \end{aligned}$$

Thus the angular momentum of the system relative to the center of mass is the same as that of a single particle of momentum $\mu\mathbf{v}_{12}$ and position vector $\mathbf{r}_{12}$. Note that in the final expression for $\mathbf{L}_{\text{CM}}$, the only quantities that appear are those that describe the *relative* position and motion of the two particles.

This result, for example, is important when we are computing the angular momentum of a hydrogen atom. We must use the distance and the velocity of the electron relative to the proton, but must replace the mass of the electron by the reduced mass of the electron-proton system, that is, $\mathbf{L}_{\text{CM}} = \mu_{\text{ep}}\mathbf{r}_{\text{ep}} \times \mathbf{v}_{\text{ep}}$, where the subscripts e and p refer to the electron and the proton, respectively.

When we are dealing with a many-particle system, it is customary to refer the total angular momentum to the center of mass, which is then called the *internal* angular momentum of the system. Internal angular momentum is thus a property of the system itself, and is independent of the observer. In the case of a rigid body or an elementary particle, the internal angular momentum is also called *spin*.

EXAMPLE 9.6. Establish a relationship between the angular momentum of a system of particles relative to the CM- or C-frame of reference (or internal angular momentum) and the angular momentum relative to the laboratory or L-frame.

Solution: For simplicity we shall consider a system composed of two particles. The angular momentum relative to the laboratory or L-frame is

$$\mathbf{L} = \mathbf{r}_1 \times \mathbf{p}_1 + \mathbf{r}_2 \times \mathbf{p}_2.$$

If $\mathbf{v}_1$ and $\mathbf{v}_2$ are the velocities relative to frame L and $\mathbf{v}_1'$ and $\mathbf{v}_2'$ the velocities relative to frame C, we have that $\mathbf{v}_1 = \mathbf{v}_1' + \mathbf{v}_{\text{CM}}$ and $\mathbf{v}_2 = \mathbf{v}_2' + \mathbf{v}_{\text{CM}}$. Then $\mathbf{p}_1 = m_1\mathbf{v}_1 = m_1(\mathbf{v}_1' + \mathbf{v}_{\text{CM}}) = \mathbf{p}_1' + m_1\mathbf{v}_{\text{CM}}$, and similarly $\mathbf{p}_2 = \mathbf{p}_2' + m_2\mathbf{v}_{\text{CM}}$. Thus, remembering that $\mathbf{r}_1 = \mathbf{r}_1' + \mathbf{r}_{\text{CM}}$ and $\mathbf{r}_2 = \mathbf{r}_2' + \mathbf{r}_{\text{CM}}$, we have

$$\begin{aligned} \mathbf{L} &= (\mathbf{r}_1' + \mathbf{r}_{\text{CM}}) \times (\mathbf{p}_1' + m_1\mathbf{v}_{\text{CM}}) + (\mathbf{r}_2' + \mathbf{r}_{\text{CM}}) \times (\mathbf{p}_2' + m_2\mathbf{v}_{\text{CM}}) \\ &= \mathbf{r}_1' \times \mathbf{p}_1' + \mathbf{r}_2' \times \mathbf{p}_2' + \mathbf{r}_{\text{CM}} \times (\mathbf{p}_1' + \mathbf{p}_2') + (m_1\mathbf{r}_1' + m_2\mathbf{r}_2') \times \mathbf{v}_{\text{CM}}. \end{aligned}$$

Remembering from Example 9.4 or Eq. (9.4) that $\mathbf{p}_1' + \mathbf{p}_2' = 0$ and the definitions of $\mathbf{L}_{\text{CM}}$ (Example 9.5) and $\mathbf{r}_{\text{CM}}$ (Eq. 9.2), we conclude that the angular momentum relative to the laboratory or L-frame is

$$\mathbf{L} = \mathbf{L}_{\text{CM}} + (m_1 + m_2)\mathbf{r}_{\text{CM}} \times \mathbf{v}_{\text{CM}} = \mathbf{L}_{\text{CM}} + M\mathbf{r}_{\text{CM}} \times \mathbf{v}_{\text{CM}}. \qquad (9.23)$$

The first term on the right gives the internal angular momentum relative to the CM- or C-frame, and the last term the *external* angular momentum relative to the L-frame, as if all the mass of the system were concentrated at the center of mass. For example, when a pitcher throws a spinning ball, the angular momentum due to the spinning is given by $\boldsymbol{L}_{\mathrm{CM}}$, while the angular momentum due to the translation of the ball is given by m_{ball} $\boldsymbol{r}_{\mathrm{CM}} \times \boldsymbol{v}_{\mathrm{CM}}$. A similar situation occurs for a spinning electron revolving around a proton in a hydrogen atom. This again indicates that we can separate the internal motion from the CM-motion insofar as the angular momentum is concerned. Although our proof is only for two particles, the result is valid for a system composed of any number of particles.

EXAMPLE 9.7. Relate the external torque about the center of mass with the internal angular momentum of a system of particles.

Solution: Considering again, for algebraic simplicity, a system composed of two particles m_1 and m_2 subject to external forces $\boldsymbol{F}_1$ and $\boldsymbol{F}_2$, we have that the total external torque relative to the origin of coordinates in the L-frame is

$$\begin{aligned}\boldsymbol{\tau}_{\mathrm{ext}} &= \boldsymbol{r}_1 \times \boldsymbol{F}_1 + \boldsymbol{r}_2 \times \boldsymbol{F}_2 = (\boldsymbol{r}_1' + \boldsymbol{r}_{\mathrm{CM}}) \times \boldsymbol{F}_1 + (\boldsymbol{r}_2' + \boldsymbol{r}_{\mathrm{CM}}) \times \boldsymbol{F}_2 \\ &= \boldsymbol{r}_1' \times \boldsymbol{F}_1 + \boldsymbol{r}_2' \times \boldsymbol{F}_2 + \boldsymbol{r}_{\mathrm{CM}} \times (\boldsymbol{F}_1 + \boldsymbol{F}_2).\end{aligned}$$

The first two terms in the preceding result give the external torque relative to the center of mass, and will be denoted by $\boldsymbol{\tau}_{\mathrm{CM}}$, while the last term gives the torque of the resultant external force $\boldsymbol{F}_{\mathrm{ext}} = \boldsymbol{F}_1 + \boldsymbol{F}_2$ as if it were applied at the center of mass. Thus

$$\boldsymbol{\tau}_{\mathrm{ext}} = \boldsymbol{\tau}_{\mathrm{CM}} + \boldsymbol{r}_{\mathrm{CM}} \times \boldsymbol{F}_{\mathrm{ext}}. \tag{9.24}$$

But, from the result of Example 9.6, we have $\boldsymbol{L} = \boldsymbol{L}_{\mathrm{CM}} + M\boldsymbol{r}_{\mathrm{CM}} \times \boldsymbol{v}_{\mathrm{CM}}$. Taking the time derivative of this expression, we obtain

$$\frac{d\boldsymbol{L}}{dt} = \frac{d\boldsymbol{L}_{\mathrm{CM}}}{dt} + M\boldsymbol{r}_{\mathrm{CM}} \times \frac{d\boldsymbol{v}_{\mathrm{CM}}}{dt} + M\frac{d\boldsymbol{r}_{\mathrm{CM}}}{dt} \times \boldsymbol{v}_{\mathrm{CM}}.$$

We recall that $d\boldsymbol{r}_{\mathrm{CM}}/dt = \boldsymbol{v}_{\mathrm{CM}}$, so that the last term is zero and, by using Eq. (9.9) (that is, $\boldsymbol{F}_{\mathrm{ext}} = M\,d\boldsymbol{v}_{\mathrm{CM}}/dt$), we obtain

$$\frac{d\boldsymbol{L}}{dt} = \frac{d\boldsymbol{L}_{\mathrm{CM}}}{dt} + \boldsymbol{r}_{\mathrm{CM}} \times \boldsymbol{F}_{\mathrm{ext}}.$$

Substituting the expressions for $d\boldsymbol{L}/dt$ and $\boldsymbol{\tau}_{\mathrm{ext}}$, which we have just obtained, into Eq. (9.21), we recognize that

$$\frac{d\boldsymbol{L}_{\mathrm{CM}}}{dt} = \boldsymbol{\tau}_{\mathrm{CM}}. \tag{9.25}$$

This relation is formally identical to Eq. (9.21), but there are some basic differences. Equation (9.21) is valid only when the angular momentum and torque are evaluated relative to a point fixed in an inertial frame of reference, usually the origin of coordinates. On the other hand, Eq. (9.25) is valid for the center of mass even if it is not at rest in an inertial frame of reference. Although this equation has been proved for two particles, it is valid for a system composed of any number of particles. It is especially useful in discussing the motion of a rigid body.

9.5 Kinetic Energy of a System of Particles

Let us consider a system composed of two particles of masses m_1 and m_2, subject to the external forces $\boldsymbol{F}_1$ and $\boldsymbol{F}_2$ and to the internal forces $\boldsymbol{F}_{12}$ and $\boldsymbol{F}_{21}$. At a particular instant they are at the positions indicated in Fig. 9–10, moving with velocities $\boldsymbol{v}_1$ and $\boldsymbol{v}_2$ along their paths C_1 and C_2. The equation of motion of each particle is

$$m_1\boldsymbol{a}_1 = \boldsymbol{F}_1 + \boldsymbol{F}_{12}, \qquad m_2\boldsymbol{a}_2 = \boldsymbol{F}_2 + \boldsymbol{F}_{21}. \tag{9.26}$$

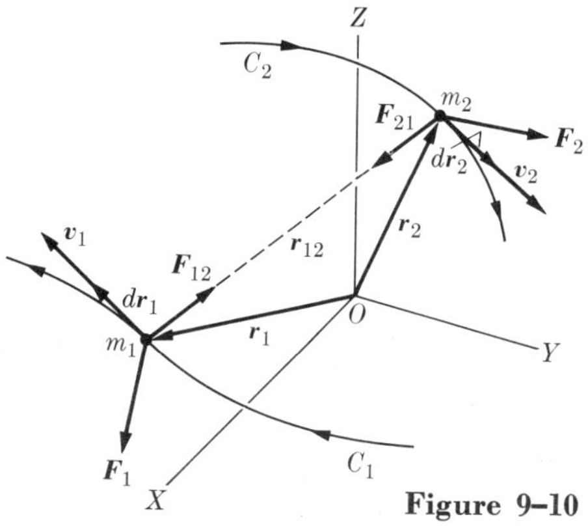

Figure 9–10

In a very small time interval dt, the particles experience displacements $d\boldsymbol{r}_1$ and $d\boldsymbol{r}_2$ tangent to their paths. When we take the scalar product of Eq. (9.26), the first with $d\boldsymbol{r}_1$ and the second with $d\boldsymbol{r}_2$, we have

$$m_1\boldsymbol{a}_1 \cdot d\boldsymbol{r}_1 = \boldsymbol{F}_1 \cdot d\boldsymbol{r}_1 + \boldsymbol{F}_{12} \cdot d\boldsymbol{r}_1,$$

and

$$m_2\boldsymbol{a}_2 \cdot d\boldsymbol{r}_2 = \boldsymbol{F}_2 \cdot d\boldsymbol{r}_2 + \boldsymbol{F}_{21} \cdot d\boldsymbol{r}_2.$$

Adding these two equations and remembering that $\boldsymbol{F}_{12} = -\boldsymbol{F}_{21}$, we obtain

$$m_1\boldsymbol{a}_1 \cdot d\boldsymbol{r}_1 + m_2\boldsymbol{a}_2 \cdot d\boldsymbol{r}_2 = \boldsymbol{F}_1 \cdot d\boldsymbol{r}_1 + \boldsymbol{F}_2 \cdot d\boldsymbol{r}_2 + \boldsymbol{F}_{12} \cdot (d\boldsymbol{r}_1 - d\boldsymbol{r}_2). \tag{9.27}$$

Now, since $d\boldsymbol{r}_1/dt = \boldsymbol{v}_1$ and $\boldsymbol{v}_1 \cdot d\boldsymbol{v}_1 = v_1\,dv_1$, we have that $\boldsymbol{a}_1 \cdot d\boldsymbol{r}_1 = (d\boldsymbol{v}_1/dt) \cdot d\boldsymbol{r}_1 = d\boldsymbol{v}_1 \cdot (d\boldsymbol{r}_1/dt) = v_1\,dv_1$. Similarly, $\boldsymbol{a}_2 \cdot d\boldsymbol{r}_2 = v_2\,dv_2$. Also $d\boldsymbol{r}_1 - d\boldsymbol{r}_2 = d(\boldsymbol{r}_1 - \boldsymbol{r}_2) = d\boldsymbol{r}_{12}$. Therefore Eq. (9.27) becomes

$$m_1v_1\,dv_1 + m_2v_2\,dv_2 = \boldsymbol{F}_1 \cdot d\boldsymbol{r}_1 + \boldsymbol{F}_2 \cdot d\boldsymbol{r}_2 + \boldsymbol{F}_{12} \cdot d\boldsymbol{r}_{12}.$$

Integrating from an initial time t_0 to any arbitrary time t, we obtain

$$m_1\int_{v_{10}}^{v_1} v_1\,dv_1 + m_2\int_{v_{20}}^{v_2} v_2\,dv_2 = \int_A^B (\boldsymbol{F}_1 \cdot d\boldsymbol{r}_1 + \boldsymbol{F}_2 \cdot d\boldsymbol{r}_2) + \int_A^B \boldsymbol{F}_{12} \cdot d\boldsymbol{r}_{12}, \tag{9.28}$$

where A and B are symbols used to designate the positions of *both* particles at times t_0 and t. Since $\int_{v_0}^{v} v\,dv = \frac{1}{2}v^2 - \frac{1}{2}v_0^2$, we have, for the left-hand side of Eq. (9.28),

$$\begin{aligned}(\tfrac{1}{2}m_1v_1^2 - \tfrac{1}{2}m_1v_{10}^2) + (\tfrac{1}{2}m_2v_2^2 - \tfrac{1}{2}m_2v_{20}^2)\\ = (\tfrac{1}{2}m_1v_1^2 + \tfrac{1}{2}m_2v_2^2) - (\tfrac{1}{2}m_1v_{10}^2 + \tfrac{1}{2}m_2v_{20}^2)\\ = E_k - E_{k,0},\end{aligned}$$

where

$$E_k = \tfrac{1}{2}m_1v_1^2 + \tfrac{1}{2}m_2v_2^2 \tag{9.29}$$

is the *total* kinetic energy of the system of two particles at time t, and $E_{k,0}$ the total kinetic energy at time t_0 relative to the frame of reference of the observer. The first term on the right-hand side of Eq. (9.28) gives the *total* work W_{ext} done by the *external* forces during the same interval of time. That is,

$$W_{\text{ext}} = \int_A^B (\boldsymbol{F}_1 \cdot d\boldsymbol{r}_1 + \boldsymbol{F}_2 \cdot d\boldsymbol{r}_2).$$

Finally the last term in Eq. (9.28) gives the work W_{int} done by the *internal* forces. That is,

$$W_{\text{int}} = \int_A^B \boldsymbol{F}_{12} \cdot d\boldsymbol{r}_{12}.$$

Substituting these notations into Eq. (9.28) gives

$$E_k - E_{k,0} = W_{\text{ext}} + W_{\text{int}}, \tag{9.30}$$

which we may express in words by saying that

> *the change in kinetic energy of a system of particles is equal to the work done on the system by the external and the internal forces.*

This is the natural extension of our previous result for one particle given in Eq. (8.13), and is valid for a system composed of any number of particles.

9.6 Conservation of Energy of a System of Particles

Let us now assume that the internal forces are conservative, and that therefore there exists a function $E_{p,12}$ depending on the coordinates of m_1 and m_2 such that

$$W_{\text{int}} = \int_A^B \boldsymbol{F}_{12} \cdot d\boldsymbol{r}_{12} = E_{p,12,0} - E_{p,12} \tag{9.31}$$

where $E_{p,12}$ is the value at time t and $E_{p,12,0}$ the value at time t_0. We shall call $E_{p,12}$ the *internal potential energy* of the system. If the internal forces act along the line $\boldsymbol{r}_{12}$ joining the two particles, then the internal potential energy depends only on the distance r_{12}, for the same reason that the potential energy due to a central force depends only on the distance r (Section 8.10). In this case the internal potential energy is independent of the frame of reference because it contains only the distance between the two particles, a situation which fairly well represents most of the interactions found in nature. Substituting Eq. (9.31) in Eq. (9.30), we obtain $E_k - E_{k,0} = W_{\text{ext}} + E_{p,12,0} - E_{p,12}$, or

$$(E_k + E_{p,12}) - (E_k + E_{p,12})_0 = W_{\text{ext}}. \tag{9.32}$$

The quantity

$$U = E_k + E_{p,12} = \tfrac{1}{2}m_1v_1^2 + \tfrac{1}{2}m_2v_2^2 + E_{p,12} \tag{9.33}$$

will henceforth be called the *proper energy* of the system. It is equal to the sum of the kinetic energies of the particles relative to the inertial observer and their internal potential energy which, as we showed before, is (under our assumptions) independent of the frame of reference.

If instead of two particles we have several, the proper energy is

$$U = E_k + E_{p,\,\text{int}} = \sum_{\substack{\text{All}\\\text{particles}}} \tfrac{1}{2}m_i v_i^2 + \sum_{\substack{\text{All}\\\text{pairs}}} E_{p,ij}, \tag{9.34}$$

where

$$E_k = \sum_{\substack{\text{All}\\\text{particles}}} \tfrac{1}{2}m_i v_i^2 = \tfrac{1}{2}m_1 v_1^2 + \tfrac{1}{2}m_2 v_2^2 + \tfrac{1}{2}m_3 v_3^2 + \cdots$$

and

$$E_{p,\,\text{int}} = \sum_{\substack{\text{All}\\\text{pairs}}} E_{p,ij} = E_{p,12} + E_{p,13} + \cdots + E_{p,23} + \cdots.$$

Note that the first sum, corresponding to the kinetic energy, has one term for *each* particle. Note also that the second sum, corresponding to the internal potential energy, has one term for *each pair* of particles because it refers to two-particle interactions only. If there are no internal forces, all the proper energy is kinetic.

Substituting the definition (9.33) of proper energy into Eq. (9.32), we have

$$U - U_0 = W_{\text{ext}}, \tag{9.35}$$

which states that

> *the change in proper energy of a system of particles is equal to the work done on the system by the external forces.*

This important statement is called the *law of conservation of energy.* So far this law has appeared as a consequence of the principle of conservation of momentum and the assumption that the internal forces are conservative. However, this law seems to be true in all the processes we observe in our universe, and therefore is considered of general validity, beyond the special assumptions under which we have stated it. Equation (9.8) expresses a system's interaction with the outside world by means of its change in momentum. Equation (9.35) expresses the same interaction by means of the system's change in energy.

Let us now consider an isolated system in which $W_{\text{ext}} = 0$, since there are no external forces. Then $U - U_0 = 0$ or $U = U_0$. That is,

> *the proper energy of an isolated system of particles remains constant,*

under the assumption that the internal forces are conservative. Thus if the kinetic energy of an isolated system increases, its internal potential energy must decrease by the same amount so that their sum remains the same. For example, in an isolated hydrogen molecule, the sum of the kinetic energy relative to some inertial frame of reference and the internal potential energy of the two protons and the two electrons remains constant.

The principle of conservation of momentum, together with the laws of conservation of energy and of angular momentum, are fundamental rules which seem to govern all the processes that may possibly occur in nature.

It may happen that the external forces acting on a system are also conservative, so that W_{ext} can be written as $W_{ext} = E_{p,ext,0} - E_{p,ext}$, where $E_{p,ext,0}$ and $E_{p,ext}$ are the values of the potential energy associated with the external forces at the initial and final state. Then Eq. (9.35) becomes

$$U - U_0 = E_{p,\text{ext},0} - E_{p,\text{ext}}$$

or

$$U + E_{p,\text{ext}} = U_0 + E_{p,\text{ext},0}.$$

The quantity

$$E = U + E_{p,\text{ext}} = E_k + E_{p,\text{int}} + E_{p,\text{ext}} \tag{9.36}$$

is called the *total energy* of the system. It remains constant during the motion of the system under both internal and external conservative forces. This result is similar to Eq. (8.29) for a single particle.

For example, a hydrogen atom, composed of an electron and a proton, has a proper energy equal to the kinetic energies of the electron and the proton and the internal potential energy due to their electrical interaction. If the atom is isolated, the sum of these two energies is constant. But if the atom is placed in an external field, its total energy must include, in addition, the potential energy due to the external field, and this is the energy that remains constant.

As another example, consider two masses m_1 and m_2 attached by a spring that has an elastic constant k. If the system is thrown into the air, the kinetic energy is $\frac{1}{2}m_1v_1^2 + \frac{1}{2}m_2v_2^2$, the internal potential energy is due to the extension or compression of the spring and is equal to $\frac{1}{2}kx^2$, where x is the deformation of the spring, and the external potential energy (due to the earth's gravitational attraction) is $m_1gy_1 + m_2gy_2$, where y_1 and y_2 are the heights of the particles above the earth's surface. The proper energy of the system is then $U = \frac{1}{2}m_1v_1^2 + \frac{1}{2}m_2v_2^2 + \frac{1}{2}kx^2$ and, if no other forces act on the system, the total energy is

$$E = \tfrac{1}{2}m_1v_1^2 + \tfrac{1}{2}m_2v_1^2 + \tfrac{1}{2}kx^2 + m_1gy_1 + m_2gy_2,$$

and this energy must remain constant during the motion.

Since the kinetic energy depends on the velocity, the value of the kinetic energy depends on the frame of reference used to discuss the motion of the system. We shall call *internal kinetic energy* $E_{k,\text{CM}}$ the kinetic energy referred to the CM- or C-frame of reference. The internal potential energy, which depends only on the distance between the particles, has the same value in all frames of reference (as explained before). Thus we shall define the *internal energy* of a system as the sum of its internal kinetic and potential energies. That is,

$$U_{\text{int}} = E_{k,\text{CM}} + E_{p,\text{int}}. \tag{9.37}$$

In the future, when we are dealing with a system of particles, we shall in general refer only to the internal energy, even if we do not write the subscript CM.

The internal potential energy of some systems is, in special circumstances, negligible compared with the internal kinetic energy. This is true, for example, in the case of a gas at high temperature. In this circumstance the internal energy may be considered all kinetic, and the principle of conservation of energy reduces to the conservation of kinetic energy.

EXAMPLE 9.8. Obtain the relation between the kinetic energy of a system of particles relative to the laboratory or L-frame of reference and the internal kinetic energy relative to the CM- or C-frame of reference.

Solution: Consider for simplicity two particles of masses m_1 and m_2 with velocities $\boldsymbol{v}_1$ and $\boldsymbol{v}_2$ in frame L, and velocities $\boldsymbol{v}_1'$ and $\boldsymbol{v}_2'$ relative to frame C. The two sets of velocities are related by $\boldsymbol{v}_1 = \boldsymbol{v}_1' + \boldsymbol{v}_{\text{CM}}$ and $\boldsymbol{v}_2 = \boldsymbol{v}_2' + \boldsymbol{v}_{\text{CM}}$, where $\boldsymbol{v}_{\text{CM}}$ is the velocity of the CM- or C-frame relative to frame L. Then the kinetic energy relative to L is

$$E_k = \tfrac{1}{2}m_1v_1^2 + \tfrac{1}{2}m_2v_2^2 = \tfrac{1}{2}m_1(\boldsymbol{v}_1' + \boldsymbol{v}_{\text{CM}})^2 + \tfrac{1}{2}m_2(\boldsymbol{v}_2' + \boldsymbol{v}_{\text{CM}})^2.$$

We may rewrite this statement as

$$E_k = \tfrac{1}{2}m_1v_1'^2 + \tfrac{1}{2}m_2v_2'^2 + \tfrac{1}{2}(m_1 + m_2)v_{\text{CM}}^2 + (m_1\boldsymbol{v}_1' + m_2\boldsymbol{v}_2') \cdot \boldsymbol{v}_{\text{CM}}.$$

Now the quantity $m_1\boldsymbol{v}_1' + m_2\boldsymbol{v}_2'$ is the total momentum of the system referred to the center of mass, and by Eq. (9.4) it must be zero. (See also Example 9.4.) The internal kinetic energy $E_{k,\text{CM}}$ referred to frame C is $E_{k,\text{CM}} = \tfrac{1}{2}m_1v_1'^2 + \tfrac{1}{2}m_2v_2'^2$. Therefore the kinetic energy E_k of the system, when referred to the laboratory frame L, may be written as

$$E_k = E_{k,\text{CM}} + \tfrac{1}{2}(m_1 + m_2)v_{\text{CM}}^2 = E_{k,\text{CM}} + \tfrac{1}{2}Mv_{\text{CM}}^2. \tag{9.38}$$

The first term, $E_{k,\text{CM}}$, is the *internal kinetic energy*. The second term on the right-hand side is the kinetic energy of a particle of mass $M = m_1 + m_2$ moving *with* the center of mass. It is called the *translational kinetic energy* of the system. Although Eq. (9.38) has been proved for two particles, it holds for a system composed of an arbitrary number of particles.

We note once more that we may separate the motion of the system into two parts, each with a well-defined kinetic energy. One is translational motion with the velocity of the center of mass and the other is internal motion relative to the center of mass.

Let us again think of the case of a pitcher throwing a spinning ball. The ball's total kinetic energy relative to the ground is the sum of its internal kinetic energy relative to the center of mass, which corresponds to the kinetic energy of spinning, and to its kinetic energy of translation relative to the ground, which is $\tfrac{1}{2}m_{\text{ball}}v_{\text{CM}}^2$. A similar situation is found in the case of a molecule. In general, it is the internal motion that we are interested in, and for that reason the C-frame is preferred for describing many processes.

As we have said before, the internal potential energy $E_{p,12}$ depends only on the distance between m_1 and m_2, and it is the same in frames C and L. Adding $E_{p,12}$ to both sides of Eq. (9.38) and using Eq. (9.33), we can write

$$U = U_{\text{int}} + \tfrac{1}{2}Mv_{\text{CM}}^2,$$

where $U_{\text{int}} = E_{k,\text{CM}} + E_{p,12}$. This equation relates the internal energy U_{int} and the proper energy U as measured in the C- and L-frames. Note that for an isolated system $\boldsymbol{v}_{\text{CM}}$ is constant and therefore, if U is constant, U_{int} is also. That is, when energy is conserved in an inertial frame L, it is also conserved in the center-of-mass frame C, and conversely.

EXAMPLE 9.9. Express the internal kinetic energy of two particles in terms of their reduced mass and their relative velocity.

Solution: The internal kinetic energy is $E_{k,\mathrm{CM}} = \frac{1}{2}m_1v_1'^2 + \frac{1}{2}m_2v_2'^2$. Using the results of Example 9.4, that is,

$$\boldsymbol{v}_1' = \frac{m_2\boldsymbol{v}_{12}}{m_1 + m_2}, \qquad \boldsymbol{v}_2' = -\frac{m_1\boldsymbol{v}_{12}}{m_1 + m_2},$$

we get

$$E_{k,\mathrm{CM}} = \tfrac{1}{2}m_1\left(\frac{m_2v_{12}}{m_1 + m_2}\right)^2 + \tfrac{1}{2}m_2\left(\frac{m_1v_{12}}{m_1 + m_2}\right)^2 = \tfrac{1}{2}\mu v_{12}^2.$$

Thus we find, as we did before for the angular momentum in Example 9.5, that the internal kinetic energy of a system of two particles is equivalent to that of one particle of mass equal to the reduced mass moving with the relative velocity $\boldsymbol{v}_{12}$. For example, the internal energy of a hydrogen atom is $U_{\mathrm{int}} = \frac{1}{2}\mu_{\mathrm{ep}}v_{\mathrm{ep}}^2 + E_p(r_{\mathrm{ep}})$, where the subscripts refer to the electron and the proton. The results we have derived in this and previous examples are of great importance because of their numerous applications, especially in atomic and nuclear physics.

Table 9–1 lists the more important relations that have been derived so far in this chapter, relations which are widely used in many applications.

TABLE 9–1

Relation	Equation number
Kinematic relations	
$\boldsymbol{P} = M\boldsymbol{v}_{\mathrm{CM}}$ $\quad(\boldsymbol{P}_{\mathrm{CM}} = 0)$	(9.3)
$\boldsymbol{L} = \boldsymbol{L}_{\mathrm{CM}} + M\boldsymbol{r}_{\mathrm{CM}} \times \boldsymbol{v}_{\mathrm{CM}}$	(9.23)
$\boldsymbol{\tau}_{\mathrm{ext}} = \boldsymbol{\tau}_{\mathrm{CM}} + \boldsymbol{r}_{\mathrm{CM}} \times \boldsymbol{F}_{\mathrm{ext}}$	(9.24)
$E_k = E_{k,\mathrm{CM}} + \frac{1}{2}Mv_{\mathrm{CM}}^2$	(9.38)
Dynamic relations	
$d\boldsymbol{P}/dt = \boldsymbol{F}_{\mathrm{ext}}$	(9.8)
or $M\boldsymbol{a}_{\mathrm{CM}} = \boldsymbol{F}_{\mathrm{ext}}$	(9.9)
$d\boldsymbol{L}/dt = \boldsymbol{\tau}_{\mathrm{ext}}$	(9.21)
or $d\boldsymbol{L}_{\mathrm{CM}}/dt = \boldsymbol{\tau}_{\mathrm{CM}}$	(9.25)
$E_k - E_{k,0} = W_{\mathrm{ext}} + W_{\mathrm{int}}$	(9.30)
$U - U_0 = W_{\mathrm{ext}}$	(9.35)
Energy definitions	
Proper energy, $U = E_k + E_{p,\mathrm{int}}$	(9.33)
Internal energy, $U_{\mathrm{int}} = E_{k,\mathrm{CM}} + E_{p,\mathrm{int}}$	(9.37)
Total energy $E = E_k + E_{p,\mathrm{int}} + E_{p,\mathrm{ext}}$	(9.36)

9.7 Collisions

When two particles approach each other, their mutual interaction changes their motion, thereby producing an exchange of momentum and of energy. We say that there has been a collision (we may say the same thing when we have two systems instead of two particles). This does not necessarily mean that the two particles (or systems) have been physically in contact, in a microscopic sense, as happens in the case of the macroscopic collision between two billiard balls or two cars. It means, in general, that an interaction entered into play when the two particles were close, as in the shaded region of Fig. 9–11, producing a measurable change in their motions in a relatively small time. For example, if an electron or a proton approaches an atom, electrical forces come into effect, producing a pronounced perturbation in the motions of the particles. The bending of the path of a comet when it approaches the solar system is also a collision. Sometimes the term *scattering* is used to refer to collisions in which the final particles (or systems) are the same as the initial ones.

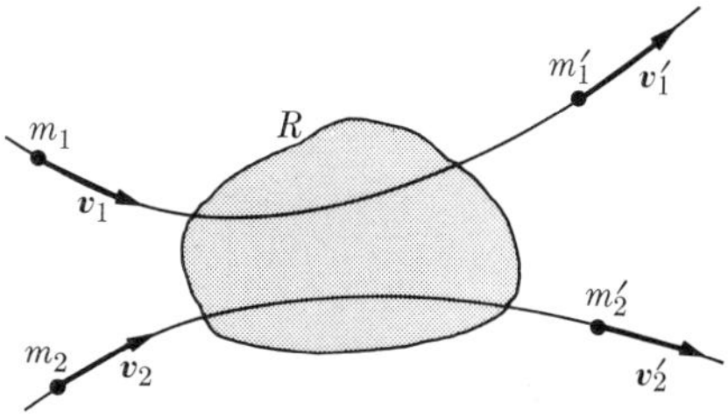

Fig. 9–11. Conservation of energy and momentum in a collision.

In some collisions, however, the final particles (or systems) are not necessarily identical to the initial ones. For example, in a collision between an atom A and a molecule BC, the end result may be the molecule AB and the atom C. In fact, this is the way in which many chemical reactions take place.

In a laboratory experiment on collision, one usually knows precisely the motion of the particles before the collision, since such motion depends on how the experiment has been prepared. For example, one particle may have been a proton or an electron accelerated in an electrostatic accelerator and the other particle may be an atom practically at rest in the laboratory. Then one observes the final state; i.e., the motion of the two particles far away from the region where they collided. If we know the forces between the particles, we may compute the final state, so long as we know the initial state. The analyis of such experiments thus provides valuable information about the interaction between the colliding particles. This is one of the reasons why collision experiments are so interesting to the physicist.

Since only internal forces enter into play in the collision, both the momentum and the total energy are conserved. Let $\boldsymbol{p}_1$ and $\boldsymbol{p}_2$ be the momenta of the particles before the collision and $\boldsymbol{p}_1'$ and $\boldsymbol{p}_2'$ be the momenta after the collision. The conservation of momentum requires that

$$\boldsymbol{p}_1 + \boldsymbol{p}_2 = \boldsymbol{p}_1' + \boldsymbol{p}_2'. \tag{9.39}$$

The internal potential energy before the collision is $E_{p,12}$. After the collision, because there may be internal rearrangements, it may be different, let us say $E'_{p,12}$. Similarly, the masses do not have to be the same. For example, a deuteron is a nucleus composed of a neutron and a proton; in passing near another nucleus, the neutron may be captured by the second nucleus, so that the proton will continue separately and the final particles will consist of the proton and a nucleus having an extra neutron.

The conservation of energy, according to Eq. (9.35), is then

$$E_k + E_{p,12} = E'_k + E'_{p,12},$$

where, remembering Eq. (8.12), we have

$$E_k = \tfrac{1}{2}m_1v_1^2 + \tfrac{1}{2}m_2v_2^2 = \frac{p_1^2}{2m_1} + \frac{p_2^2}{2m_2},$$

$$E'_k = \tfrac{1}{2}m'_1v_1'^2 + \tfrac{1}{2}m'_2v_2'^2 = \frac{p_1'^2}{2m'_1} + \frac{p_2'^2}{2m'_2}. \tag{9.40}$$

Let us introduce a quantity Q, defined by

$$Q = E'_k - E_k = E_{p,12} - E'_{p,12}, \tag{9.41}$$

and therefore equal to the difference between the final and the initial kinetic energies or between the initial and the final internal potential energies. When $Q = 0$, there is no change in kinetic energy and the collision is called *elastic*. Otherwise it is *inelastic*. When $Q < 0$, there is a decrease in kinetic energy with a corresponding increase in internal potential energy, and we say that there is an *inelastic collision of the first kind* (or *endoergic*). When $Q > 0$, there is an increase of kinetic energy at the expense of the internal potential energy, and we have an *inelastic collision of the second kind* (or *exoergic*).

Using Eq. (9.40) in Eq. (9.41), we may write

$$\frac{p_1'^2}{2m'_1} + \frac{p_2'^2}{2m'_2} = \frac{p_1^2}{2m_1} + \frac{p_2^2}{2m_2} + Q. \tag{9.42}$$

Equations (9.39) and (9.42) are enough to solve the collision problem completely.

If we refer the collision to the center of mass, the total momentum is zero according to Eq. (9.4), so that $\boldsymbol{p}_1 = -\boldsymbol{p}_2$ and $\boldsymbol{p}'_1 = -\boldsymbol{p}'_2$. We may then simplify Eq. (9.42) to read

$$\frac{1}{2}\left(\frac{1}{m'_1} + \frac{1}{m'_2}\right)p_1'^2 = \frac{1}{2}\left(\frac{1}{m_1} + \frac{1}{m_2}\right)p_1^2 + Q$$

or, using Eq. (9.15), which defines reduced mass, we obtain

$$\frac{p_1'^2}{2\mu'} = \frac{p_1^2}{2\mu} + Q \qquad \text{(in CM-frame of reference).} \tag{9.43}$$

Note that we use the same Q because, in view of its definition (9.41), it is independent of the frame of reference. In a collision, there is always an exchange of momentum between the two particles, but not necessarily always an exchange of kinetic energy between them. For example, if the collision is elastic ($Q = 0$) and the final particles are the same as the initial ones ($\mu = \mu'$), Eq. (9.43) gives $p'_1 = p_1$

and of course also $p_2' = p_2$. Thus in the CM-frame, the momenta after the elastic collision have the same magnitude as before and the particles retain their kinetic energies, so that no kinetic energy has been exchanged between them relative to the CM-frame. However there has been an exchange of momentum because the direction of their motions has been changed.

EXAMPLE 9.10. Obtain the Q value for a capture reaction.

Solution: An interesting example of inelastic collision occurs when, after the collision, the two particles continue moving together. In nuclear physics this process is called a *capture reaction*. It occurs, for example, when a neutron colliding with the proton of a hydrogen atom is captured to form a deuterium nucleus. Another collision which may be of this type is the collision between two plastic bodies. In this case the two particles, after the collision, move with the velocity of the center of mass; that is, from Example 9.4,

$$\boldsymbol{v}_{\mathrm{CM}} = \frac{m_1\boldsymbol{v}_1 + m_2\boldsymbol{v}_2}{m_1 + m_2}.$$

The Q of the reaction is thus

$$\begin{aligned} Q &= \tfrac{1}{2}(m_1 + m_2)v_{\mathrm{CM}}^2 - \tfrac{1}{2}m_1v_1^2 - \tfrac{1}{2}m_2v_2^2 \\ &= \frac{1}{2}\frac{m_1m_2}{m_1 + m_2}(\boldsymbol{v}_1 - \boldsymbol{v}_2)^2 = \tfrac{1}{2}\mu v_{12}^2, \end{aligned}$$

and hence Q depends entirely on the relative velocities of the particles before the collision. Can the student attach any meaning to the value obtained for Q, in view of the result of Example 9.9?

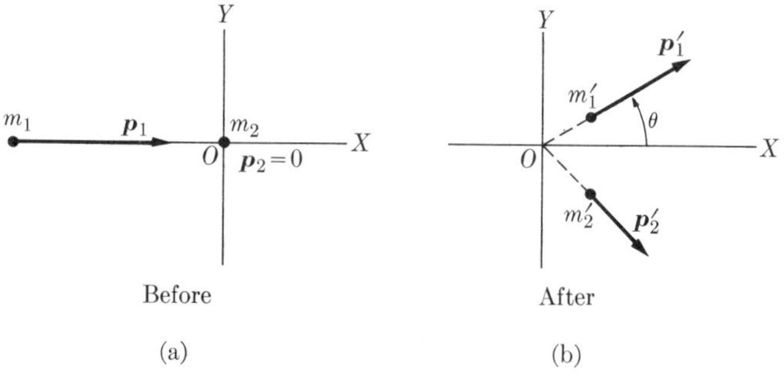

Fig. 9–12. Relation between momenta relative to the L-frame before and after a collision.

EXAMPLE 9.11. Obtain Q in terms of the kinetic energy of the particles before and after they collide, assuming that initially m_1 has a momentum $\boldsymbol{p}_1$ and that m_2 is at rest ($\boldsymbol{p}_2 = 0$) (see Fig. 9–12). Also assume that the masses of the particles after the collision are m_1' and m_2'.

Solution: The conservation of momentum gives $\boldsymbol{p}_1' + \boldsymbol{p}_2' = \boldsymbol{p}_1$ or $\boldsymbol{p}_2' = \boldsymbol{p}_1 - \boldsymbol{p}_1'$. Therefore

$$p_2'^2 = (\boldsymbol{p}_1 - \boldsymbol{p}_1')^2 = p_1^2 + p_1'^2 - 2p_1p_1'\cos\theta.$$

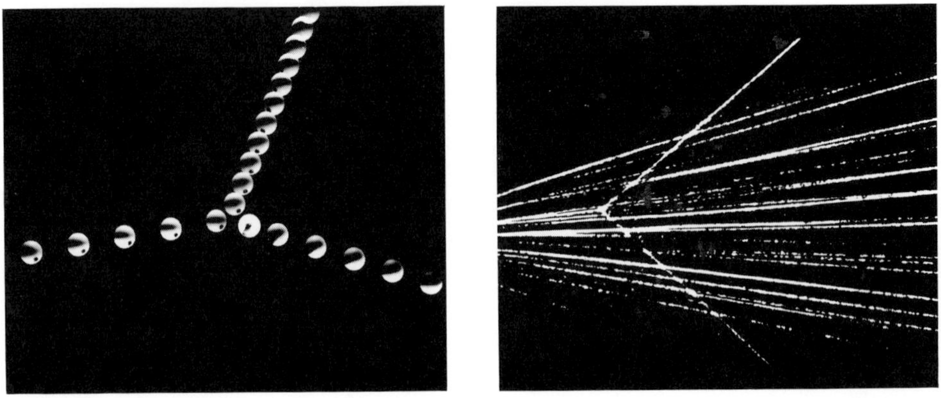

(a) (b)

Fig. 9–13. (a) Collision of two equal billiard balls. (b) Collision between two α-particles (helium nuclei). In both cases, one of the particles was initially at rest in the L-frame and their momenta make angles of 90° in the L-frame after the collision. [Part (a) courtesy of Educational Services, Inc.]

Using definition (9.41) for Q, we have

$$Q = \frac{p_1'^2}{2m_1'} + \frac{p_2'^2}{2m_2'} - \frac{p_1^2}{2m_1} = \frac{p_1'^2}{2m_1'} - \frac{p_1^2}{2m_1} + \frac{1}{2m_2'}(p_1^2 + p_1'^2 - 2p_1p_1' \cos\theta)$$

or

$$Q = \frac{1}{2}\left(\frac{1}{m_1'} + \frac{1}{m_2'}\right)p_1'^2 + \frac{1}{2}\left(\frac{1}{m_2'} - \frac{1}{m_1}\right)p_1^2 - \frac{p_1p_1'}{m_2'}\cos\theta.$$

Remembering that $E_k = p^2/2m$, we can express the above result as

$$Q = E_{k,1}'\left(1 + \frac{m_1'}{m_2'}\right) - E_{k,1}\left(1 - \frac{m_1}{m_2'}\right) - \frac{2\sqrt{m_1m_1'E_{k,1}E_{k,1}'}}{m_2'}\cos\theta.$$

This result, known as the *Q-equation*, is of great application in nuclear physics.

When the collision is elastic ($Q = 0$) and all the particles are identical ($m_1 = m_1' = m_2 = m_2'$), the conservation of energy gives $p_1'^2 + p_2'^2 = p_1^2$, while from the conservation of momentum, $\boldsymbol{p}_1 = \boldsymbol{p}_1' + \boldsymbol{p}_2'$, we have $p_1'^2 + p_2'^2 + 2\boldsymbol{p}_1' \cdot \boldsymbol{p}_2' = p_1^2$. Combining these results, we find that $\boldsymbol{p}_1' \cdot \boldsymbol{p}_2' = 0$ or $\boldsymbol{p}_1'$ is perpendicular to $\boldsymbol{p}_2'$. Thus, in the L-frame, the two particles move at right angles after the collision. This may be seen in the photograph of Fig. 9–13(a), which illustrates the collision of two billiard balls, one initially at rest. Figure 9–13(b) shows the collision of two He nuclei in a cloud chamber; the incoming He nucleus is an α-particle from a radioactive substance and the target He nucleus is from the gas in the chamber. In both cases, the two particles move at right angles after the collision.

EXAMPLE 9.12. A grenade at rest in the L-frame explodes into two fragments. Find the energies of the fragments in terms of Q.

Solution: Since the grenade is initially at rest, the total momentum is zero. After the explosion the two fragments separate in opposite directions with momenta $\boldsymbol{p}_1$ and $\boldsymbol{p}_2$ such that $\boldsymbol{p}_1 + \boldsymbol{p}_2 = 0$, or in magnitude $p_1 = p_2$. Then, from Eq. (9.41), with $E_k' = p_1^2/2m + p_2^2/2m$ and $E_k = 0$, we have

$$\frac{1}{2}\left(\frac{1}{m_1} + \frac{1}{m_2}\right) p_1^2 = Q \qquad \text{or} \qquad p_1 = p_2 = (2\mu Q)^{1/2}.$$

The kinetic energies of the fragments are

$$E_{k,1} = \frac{p_1^2}{2m_1} = \frac{m_2 Q}{m_1 + m_2}, \qquad E_{k,2} = \frac{p_2^2}{2m_2} = \frac{m_1 Q}{m_1 + m_2},$$

and are inversely proportional to their masses. This analysis applies equally well to the recoil of a firearm (remember Example 7.1), to the fission of a nucleus into two fragments illustrated in Fig. 9–14, or to the dissociation of a diatomic molecule.

If there are three fragments instead of two, several solutions are possible, since there are three momenta involved, but only two physical conditions: conservation of energy and of momentum. For example, if only two particles are observed in a particle reaction

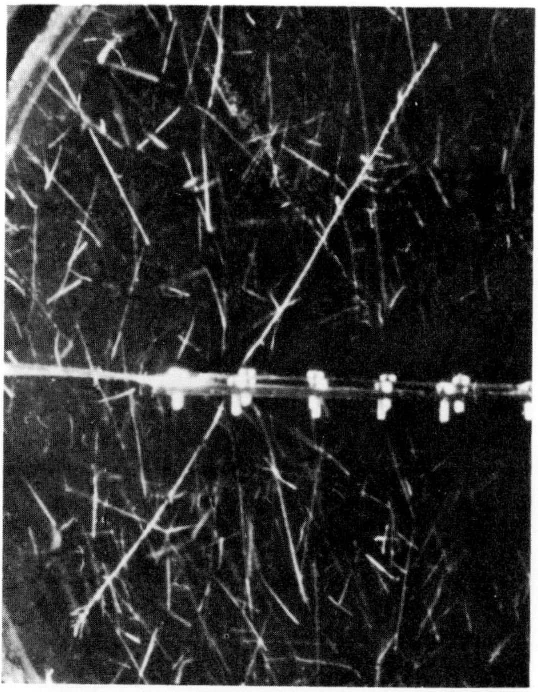

Fig. 9–14. Cloud-chamber photograph of the tracks of the two fragments resulting from the fission of a uranium nucleus [Bøggild, Brostrøm, and Lauritsen, *Phys. Rev.* **59**, 275 (1941)]. Initially the uranium nucleus was at rest in the thin horizontal metal plate at the center of the photograph. The two fragments move in opposite directions. From the analysis of the paths, we can estimate the energies of the fragments, which in turn (using the relation derived in Example 9.12) allow us to obtain the ratio of their masses. The effect of the neutrons released is neglected.

and the energy and the momentum of these two are not conserved, the physicist suspects the presence of a third particle that is not observed (either because it has no electric charge, or for some other reason). There are also certain theoretical considerations which enable him to recognize a case in which three particles are involved in the process (see Problem 9.70). The physicist then assigns a given momentum and energy to this hypothetical particle, thus conforming to the conservation laws. This procedure has so far always given results that are consistent with both theory and experiment.

EXAMPLE 9.13. Discuss the slowing down (or *moderation*) of neutrons undergoing elastic collisions while moving through a material whose atoms may be considered at rest. (The material is called the *moderator*.) In nuclear reactors, fast neutrons produced by uranium fission are slowed down by moving through a moderator.

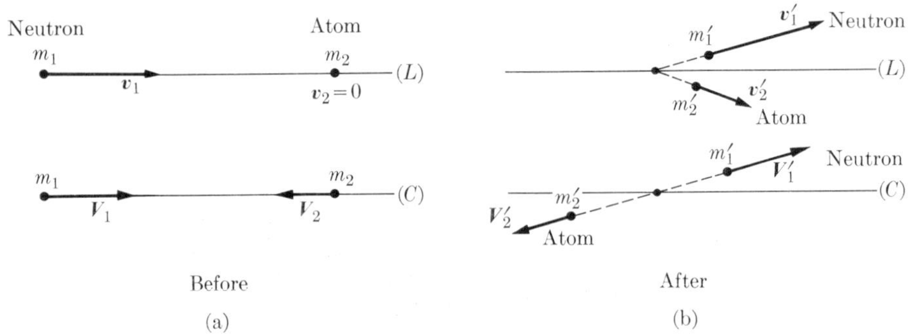

Fig. 9–15. Comparison of data relative to the L- and C-frames in a collision.

Solution: In this case the particles are the same before and after the collision and $m_1 = m_1'$, $m_2 = m_2'$. Also $\boldsymbol{p}_2 = 0$ and $Q = 0$. The calculation is easier if we work in the C-frame (Fig. 9–15). We shall call $A = m_2/m_1$ the ratio of the mass of the moderator atoms to that of the neutron, $\boldsymbol{v}_1$ the velocity of the neutron, and $\boldsymbol{v}_2$ $(= 0)$ the velocity of the atom. Before the collision the velocity of the center of mass according to Eq. (9.1) is therefore

$$\boldsymbol{v}_{\text{CM}} = \frac{m_1\boldsymbol{v}_1}{m_1 + m_2} = \frac{\boldsymbol{v}_1}{1 + A}.$$

The velocity of each particle in the CM-frame before the collision is

$$\boldsymbol{V}_1 = \boldsymbol{v}_1 - \boldsymbol{v}_{\text{CM}} = \frac{A\boldsymbol{v}_1}{1 + A}, \qquad \boldsymbol{V}_2 = 0 - \boldsymbol{v}_{\text{CM}} = -\frac{\boldsymbol{v}_1}{1 + A}. \tag{9.44}$$

Since we are dealing with an elastic collision in which the particles retain their identity, we have, according to the explanation following Eq. (9.42), that $p_1 = p_1'$ in the CM-frame, and therefore also $V_1 = V_1'$; that is, the velocity of m_1 has the same *magnitude* in the CM-frame before and after the collision. Similarly $V_2 = V_2'$. However, the directions of motion after the collision may be different in the center-of-mass frame (see Fig. 9–15). The velocity $\boldsymbol{v}_1$ of the neutron after the collision, relative to the L-system, is then

$$\boldsymbol{v}_1' = \boldsymbol{V}_1' + \boldsymbol{v}_{\text{CM}},$$

so that, according to Fig. 9–16,

$$v_1'^2 = V_1'^2 + v_{CM}^2 + 2\boldsymbol{V}_1' \cdot \boldsymbol{v}_{CM}$$
$$= V_1'^2 + v_{CM}^2 + 2V_1' v_{CM} \cos\phi.$$

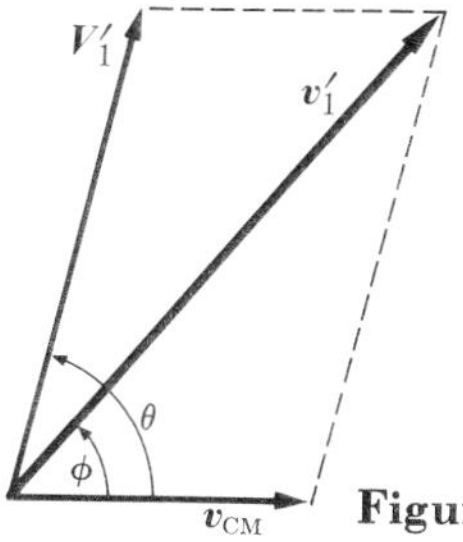

Figure 9–16

Using Eqs. (9.44) and remembering that $V_1' = V_1$, we obtain

$$v_1'^2 = v_1^2 \frac{A^2 + 2A\cos\phi + 1}{(A+1)^2}.$$

The relation between the kinetic energy of m_1 after and before the collision in the L-system is then

$$\frac{E'_{k,1}}{E_{k,1}} = \frac{v_1'^2}{v_1^2} = \frac{A^2 + 2A\cos\phi + 1}{(A+1)^2}.$$

For $\phi = 0$ (that is, collision without change in direction) $E'_{k,1} = E_{k,1}$ and there is no loss of kinetic energy. For $\phi = \pi$, or a head-on collision, there is maximum energy loss resulting in

$$\frac{E'_k}{E_k} = \frac{A^2 - 2A + 1}{(A+1)^2} = \left(\frac{A-1}{A+1}\right)^2.$$

The loss of energy per unit energy in this case is

$$\frac{E_k - E'_k}{E_k} = \frac{4A}{(A+1)^2}.$$

The energy loss is larger the closer A is to unity. This result is important when it comes to choosing the moderating material for quickly slowing down neutrons, as must be done in nuclear reactors. Atoms with the smallest value of A relative to the neutron are those of hydrogen ($A \cong 1$), and for that reason one would expect pure hydrogen to be the best moderator. However, even at room temperature, pure hydrogen is a gas, so that the number of hydrogen atoms per unit volume is relatively small. Therefore water is used instead. Water not only has the advantage of being abundant and inexpensive, but in addition it contains about 10^3 times more hydrogen atoms than hydrogen gas does, per unit volume. Unfortunately, hydrogen atoms tend to capture neutrons to form *deuterium*. On the other hand, since deuterium atoms have a relatively small tendency to capture neutrons, some nuclear reactors use *heavy* water, whose molecules are formed of deuterium (instead of hydrogen) and oxygen. (In this case $A = 2$.) Another common moderator is carbon ($A = 12$), which is used in the form of graphite.

II. SYSTEMS WITH A LARGE NUMBER OF PARTICLES

9.8 Many-Particle Systems: Temperature

The result expressed in Eq. (9.35) or its equivalent, the law of conservation of energy, when applied to a system composed of a small number of particles, such as our planetary system or an atom with few electrons, can be handled by computing the individual terms that make up the internal energy, according to Eq. (9.34). However, when the number of particles is very large, such as in a many-electron atom or a gas composed of billions of molecules, the problem becomes mathematically unmanageable. We must then use certain statistical methods for computing average values for the dynamical quantities instead of accurate individual values for each member of the system. In addition, in these complex systems we are not interested in the behavior of each individual component (since that behavior in general is not observable) but in the behavior of the system as a whole. The mathematical technique for dealing with these systems constitutes what is called *statistical mechanics.* If we forget about the internal structure of the system and simply apply Eq. (9.35), using *experimentally measured* values for U and W, we employ another branch of physics, called *thermodynamics.* In the present chapter we shall limit ourselves to an adaptation of Eq. (9.35) to systems composed of many particles without entering into a discussion of the methods of either statistical mechanics or thermodynamics. We shall also, unless otherwise stated, express all dynamical quantities relative to the CM-frame of reference for the system considered.

First let us define the *temperature* T of the system as a quantity related to the *average* kinetic energy of the particles in the CM-frame of reference. Thus temperature is defined independently of the motion of the system relative to the observer. The average kinetic energy of a particle is

$$E_{k,\,\text{ave}} = \frac{1}{N}\left(\sum_i \tfrac{1}{2}m_i v_i^2\right), \tag{9.45}$$

where N is the total number of particles and v_i is the velocity of the particle in the CM-frame of reference. If all the particles have the same mass, then

$$E_{k,\,\text{ave}} = \frac{1}{N}\sum_i \tfrac{1}{2}mv_i^2 = \tfrac{1}{2}m\left(\frac{1}{N}\sum_i v_i^2\right) = \tfrac{1}{2}m(v^2)_{\text{ave}} = \tfrac{1}{2}mv_{\text{rms}}^2,$$

where v_{rms} is called the "root-mean-square velocity of the particles," defined as

$$v_{\text{rms}}^2 = (v^2)_{\text{ave}} = \frac{1}{N}(v_1^2 + v_2^2 + v_3^2 + \cdots) = \frac{1}{N}\left(\sum_i v_i^2\right).$$

We do not need to indicate here the precise relation between temperature and average kinetic energy. It is sufficient at this time to assume that, given the average kinetic energy of a particle in a system, we can compute the temperature of the system, and conversely. In this sense we may speak of the temperature of a solid, of a gas, and even of a complex nucleus.

The fact that we are referring the motions to the center of mass in order to define temperature is important. Suppose we have a "hot" metal ball at rest in our laboratory and a "cold" metal ball moving very fast relative to our laboratory. The "hot" ball has a high temperature, which in turn means a large kinetic energy relative to its center of mass, which in this case happens to be at rest in the laboratory. On the other hand, the "cold" ball has a low temperature, which in turn means a small kinetic energy relative to its center of mass, which in our case is in motion relative to the observer. The fast-moving "cold" ball may have a larger total kinetic energy relative to the laboratory than the slow "hot" ball, but most of it is translational kinetic energy and this does not account for the temperature.

A system that has the same temperature throughout, so that the average kinetic energy of the molecules in any region of the system is the same, is said to be in *thermal equilibrium*. In an isolated system, whose total internal energy is constant, the temperature may change if the internal kinetic energy changes, because of a change of internal potential energy. For example, a mass of gas in interstellar space may be condensing because of strong attractive forces, resulting in a decrease of internal potential energy and a corresponding increase in kinetic energy. As a result, its temperature should increase. If, on the other hand, the system is expanding, its internal potential energy increases (if the forces are attractive), producing a decrease in kinetic energy and therefore a drop in temperature. But if the internal potential energy of an isolated system remains constant, which is the case for a gas contained in a rigid box, then the system's average kinetic energy will also remain constant; i.e., its temperature will not change. But if the system is not isolated, it may exchange energy with the rest of the universe, which may result in a change of its internal kinetic energy and then of its temperature.

Temperature should be expressed in joules/particle. However, it is customary to express it in *degrees*. The scale of temperature used in physics is the *absolute* scale. Its units are called *degrees Kelvin*, denoted by °K. In this scale, the melting temperature of ice at normal atmospheric pressure is 273.15°K and the boiling temperature of water at normal atmospheric pressure is 373.15°K. Thus the difference between these two temperatures is 100°K. The *centigrade* or Celsius temperature is defined according to $\theta_C = T - 273.15°\text{K}$. One degree Kelvin corresponds to about 1.38×10^{-23} J (or 8.61×10^{-4} eV) per particle.

9.9 Many-Particle Systems: Work

The exchange of energy of a system with the outside world is represented by the external work W_{ext} in Eq. (9.35). That is,

$$U - U_0 = W_{\text{ext}}.$$

If work is done *on* the system (W_{ext} positive), its internal energy increases, but if work is done *by* the system (W_{ext} negative), its internal energy decreases. This external work is the sum of the individual external works done on each of the particles of the system, but sometimes it can be easily computed on a statistical basis.

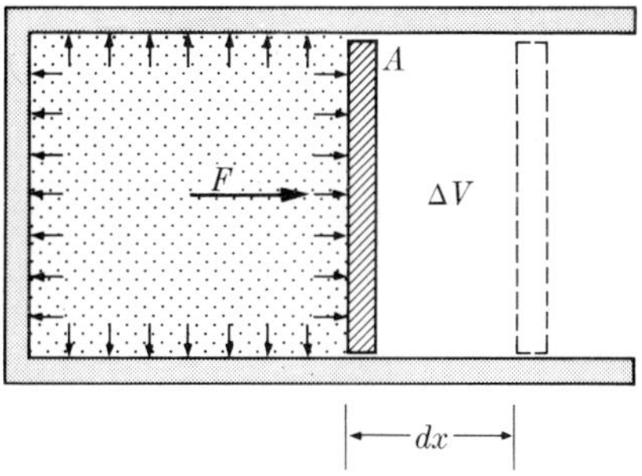

Fig. 9–17. Work done in a gas expansion.

Consider, for example, a gas inside a cylinder of which one wall is a movable piston (Fig. 9–17). The gas can exchange energy and momentum with the surroundings through the collisions and interactions of its molecules with the molecules of the walls. The exchange of momentum is represented by a force exerted by each molecule at the point of collision with the wall. These individual forces fluctuate at each point, but because there are a large number of collisions over a large area, the overall effect can be represented by an average force F acting on the whole area. If A is the area and p the *pressure* of the gas, defined as the average force per unit area (remember Example 9.2), then

$$p = F/A \qquad \text{or} \qquad F = pA. \tag{9.46}$$

If one wall of the container is movable, such as the piston of Fig. 9–17, the force exerted by the gas may produce a displacement dx of the wall. The exchange of energy of the system with the outside world may then be expressed by the work done by this force during the displacement. Since this is external work done *by* the system and not work done *on* the system, we must consider it negative. Therefore

$$dW_{\text{ext}} = -F\,dx = -pA\,dx = -p\,dV, \tag{9.47}$$

where $dV = A\,dx$ is the change in volume of the gas. Then if the volume changes from V_0 to V, the external work done on the system will be

$$W_{\text{ext}} = -\int_{V_0}^{V} p\,dV. \tag{9.48}$$

To compute this integral, we must know the relation between p and V. This relation has been studied for gases and other substances in great detail.

Very often, especially when we are dealing with thermal engines, it is preferable to compute the external work done *by* the system, denoted by W_{syst}, instead of the external work done *on* the system, W_{ext}. Since both works correspond to the same displacement but to forces equal and opposite, the two works are equal in magnitude but have opposite signs; that is, $W_{\text{syst}} = -W_{\text{ext}}$. Then, for example, the expansion work done by a gas, using Eq. (9.48), is

$$W_{\text{syst}} = \int_{V_0}^{V} p\,dV. \tag{9.49}$$

Let us now state some of the more common units in which pressure is expressed. Note first that pressure must be expressed as a unit of force divided by a unit of area. Thus in the MKSC system pressure is measured in *newtons per square meter*, or N m^{-2}. Other units frequently used are *dynes per square centimeter*, or dyn cm^{-2}, and *pounds-force per square inch*, or lbf in^{-2}. Another useful unit, used mainly for expressing the pressure of gases, is the *atmosphere*, abbreviated atm, and defined according to the equivalences

$$1 \text{ atm} = 1.013 \times 10^5 \text{ N m}^{-2} = 14.7 \text{ lbf in}^{-2}.$$

One atmosphere is, approximately, the normal pressure exerted by the earth's atmosphere on bodies at sea level.

EXAMPLE 9.14. A gas occupies a volume of 0.30 m^3, exerting a pressure of 2×10^5 N m^{-2}. At constant pressure, the volume expands to 0.45 m^3. Find the work done by the gas.

Solution: We use Eq. (9.49) and, when the pressure p remains constant,

$$W_{\text{syst}} = \int_{V_0}^{V} p\,dV = p\int_{V_0}^{V} dV = p(V - V_0). \tag{9.50}$$

This result is completely general and applies to any system whose volume changes under a constant pressure. Then, inserting the numerical values, we obtain $W_{\text{syst}} = 3 \times 10^4$ J.

EXAMPLE 9.15. A gas expands in such a way that the relation $pV = C$ (constant) holds. This relation [see Eq. (9.62) and Problem 9.67] requires that the temperature of the gas remain constant, and constitutes *Boyle's law.* Find the work done when the volume expands from V_1 to V_2.

Solution: Using Eq. (9.49), we obtain

$$W_{\text{syst}} = \int_{V_1}^{V_2} p\,dV = \int_{V_1}^{V_2} \frac{C\,dV}{V} = C \ln \frac{V_2}{V_1}. \tag{9.51}$$

Therefore the work done depends on the ratio V_2/V_1 between the two volumes (called the *expansion ratio*). In the design of internal combustion engines the compression (or expansion) ratio is one of the factors that determine the power of the engine.

9.10 Many-Particle Systems: Heat

It is important to bear in mind that Eq. (9.48) expresses a *macroscopic average* that sums all the individual exchanges of energy between the molecules of the gas and the molecules in the piston. But how does one compute the exchange of energy that occurs due to the interaction of the gas molecules with the walls that remain fixed? In this case the method used to evaluate W for the piston does not apply because, although we may still define an average force on the wall, we may not define an average displacement of the wall. At each individual interaction between the molecules of the gas and the wall, a small force is exerted and a small displacement of the molecules in the wall is produced. If we could compute each one of these infinitesimal amounts of work and add all of them, we would have the corresponding external work done by the system. However, this technique is obviously almost impossible because of the large number of factors involved. Accordingly, we shall define a new macroscopic or statistical concept called *heat.*

The average value of the external work or energy exchanged between a system and its surroundings due to the individual exchanges of energy which occur as a result of collisions between the molecules of the system and the molecules of the surroundings is called *heat, Q,* whenever it cannot be expressed macroscopically as force times distance. Therefore Q is composed of a sum of a very large number of very small individual external works, which are such that they cannot be expressed collectively as an average force times an average distance.

The heat Q is considered positive when it corresponds to a net external work done *on* the system and negative when it is equivalent to a net external work done *by* the system. In the first case we say that heat is *absorbed* by the system and in the second case we say that heat is *given off* by the system.

Since heat corresponds to work, it must be expressed in joules. However, heat is sometimes expressed in a unit called the *calorie*, whose definition was adopted in 1948 as 1 calorie = 4.1840 J. The calorie was first introduced as a unit of heat measurement when the nature of heat was unknown. But the calorie is simply another unit for measuring work and energy, and not heat alone.

At this point we must warn the student not to consider heat as a new or different form of energy. It is just a name given to a special form of work or energy transfer in which a very large number of particles participate. Before the concepts of interactions and of the atomic structure of matter were clearly understood, physicists had classified energy into two groups: *mechanical* energy, corresponding to kinetic and gravitational potential energy, and *nonmechanical* energy, divided into heat, chemical energy, electrical energy, radiation, etc. This division is no longer justified. Nowadays physicists recognize only kinetic and potential energy, with potential energy being denoted by a different expression depending on the nature of the corresponding physical interaction, and with heat and radiation being expressions of two mechanisms of energy transfer. "Chemical energy" is just a macroscopic term used to describe energy associated with electrical interactions in atoms and molecules, energy which manifests itself in chemical processes; that is, as atomic rearrangements in molecules.

When there is no exchange of energy (in the form of heat) between two systems, we say that they are in *thermal equilibrium*. This is a statistical concept, because individual molecules may exchange energy but, on the average, the same amount of energy is exchanged in one direction as in the other. *For thermal equilibrium to exist between two systems, the average molecular kinetic energies of the two interacting systems must be the same, so that no net exchange of kinetic energy by molecular collision is possible.* Therefore, in view of our preliminary definition of temperature as given in Section 9.8, we may say that

two systems in thermal equilibrium must be at the same temperature.

We may also conclude that energy is exchanged as heat only when the temperature of the two systems is different.

9.11 Reformulation of the Principle of Conservation of Energy for Many-Particle Systems

In the previous two sections we have seen that, when we are dealing with systems composed of a very large number of particles, we should express the *total external work* as the sum of two parts: $Q + W_{\text{ext}}$. Here W_{ext} expresses the external work when it can be computed as an average force times a distance, as discussed in Section 9.9, and Q represents the external work when it must be expressed as heat, as discussed in Section 9.10. Equation (9.35) for the principle of conservation of

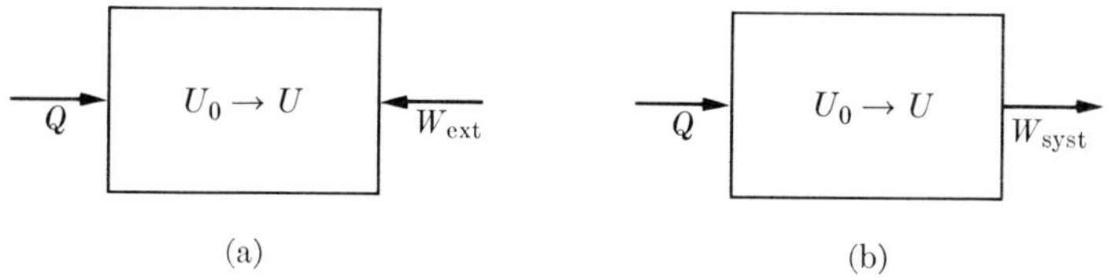

Fig. 9–18. Relation between heat, work, and internal energy.

energy must then be written in the form

$$U - U_0 = Q + W_{\text{ext}}, \tag{9.52}$$

which may be expressed in words by saying that

> *the change of internal energy of a system is equal to the heat absorbed plus the external work done on the system.*

Equation (9.52) can be seen pictorially in Fig. 9–18(a): Heat Q is *absorbed by* the system and work W_{ext} is *done on* the system. Their sum $Q + W_{\text{ext}}$ is *stored* as internal energy $U - U_0$ of the system. Sometimes, especially in engineering applications, instead of writing the external work W_{ext} done *on* the system, one writes the external work W_{syst} done *by* the system which, as explained before, is the negative of the work done *on* the system. Making $W_{\text{ext}} = -W_{\text{syst}}$, we have, instead of Eq. (9.52),

$$U - U_0 = Q - W_{\text{syst}}. \tag{9.53}$$

Equation (9.53) is illustrated in Fig. 9–18(b): heat Q is *absorbed by* the system, work W_{syst} is *done by* the system, and the difference $Q - W_{\text{syst}}$ is *stored* as internal energy $U - U_0$ of the system.

The statements related to Eqs. (9.52) and (9.53) constitute what is called the *first law of thermodynamics*, and is simply the law of conservation of energy applied to systems having a very large number of particles, with the external work conveniently split into two statistical terms, one still called work and the other called heat. Since enough has been said here to enable the student to understand the meaning of the concepts of heat and temperature as they will be used occasionally in succeeding chapters, we shall not pursue the subject of thermodynamics any further at this time.

9.12 The Virial Theorem for Many Particles

In this section we shall extend the virial theorem, introduced in Section 8.13 for the case of a single particle, to a many-particle system. In its new form it is applicable to the discussion of statistical or average properties of systems composed of many particles, especially the gases.*

---

* For an elementary application of the virial theorem to problems in chemistry, see B. H. Mahan, *University Chemistry*, Reading, Mass.: Addison-Wesley, 1965, page 412.

Let us first consider, for simplicity, a system composed of two particles, m_1 and m_2. We define the scalar quantity

$$A = m_1 \boldsymbol{v}_1 \cdot \boldsymbol{r}_1 + m_2 \boldsymbol{v}_2 \cdot \boldsymbol{r}_2 = \textstyle\sum_i m_i \boldsymbol{v}_i \cdot \boldsymbol{r}_i, \tag{9.54}$$

which is simply an extension of the quantity A defined for a single particle. Taking the time derivative of A, we have

$$\frac{dA}{dt} = m_1 \frac{d\boldsymbol{v}_1}{dt} \cdot \boldsymbol{r}_1 + m_1 \boldsymbol{v}_1 \cdot \frac{d\boldsymbol{r}_1}{dt} + m_2 \frac{d\boldsymbol{v}_2}{dt} \cdot \boldsymbol{r}_2 + m_2 \boldsymbol{v}_2 \cdot \frac{d\boldsymbol{r}_2}{dt},$$

or, since $\boldsymbol{v}_1 = d\boldsymbol{r}_1/dt$, $\boldsymbol{v}_2 = d\boldsymbol{r}_2/dt$, $\boldsymbol{a}_1 = d\boldsymbol{v}_1/dt$, and $\boldsymbol{a}_2 = d\boldsymbol{v}_2/dt$, then

$$\frac{dA}{dt} = (m_1 \boldsymbol{a}_1 \cdot \boldsymbol{r}_1 + m_2 \boldsymbol{a}_2 \cdot \boldsymbol{r}_2) + (m_1 v_1^2 + m_2 v_2^2).$$

The last term on the right, according to Eq. (9.29), is twice the kinetic energy, E_k, of the system. Then we may write

$$\frac{dA}{dt} = 2E_k + (m_1 \boldsymbol{a}_1 \cdot \boldsymbol{r}_1 + m_2 \boldsymbol{a}_2 \cdot \boldsymbol{r}_2).$$

Using Eq. (9.26) and remembering that $\boldsymbol{F}_{12} = -\boldsymbol{F}_{21}$ and $\boldsymbol{r}_1 - \boldsymbol{r}_2 = \boldsymbol{r}_{12}$, we see that

$$\begin{aligned} m_1 \boldsymbol{a}_1 \cdot \boldsymbol{r}_1 + m_2 \boldsymbol{a}_2 \cdot \boldsymbol{r}_2 &= (\boldsymbol{F}_1 + \boldsymbol{F}_{12}) \cdot \boldsymbol{r}_1 + (\boldsymbol{F}_2 + \boldsymbol{F}_{21}) \cdot \boldsymbol{r}_2 \\ &= \boldsymbol{F}_1 \cdot \boldsymbol{r}_1 + \boldsymbol{F}_2 \cdot \boldsymbol{r}_2 + \boldsymbol{F}_{12} \cdot (\boldsymbol{r}_1 - \boldsymbol{r}_2) \\ &= \boldsymbol{F}_1 \cdot \boldsymbol{r}_1 + \boldsymbol{F}_2 \cdot \boldsymbol{r}_2 + \boldsymbol{F}_{12} \cdot \boldsymbol{r}_{12}. \end{aligned}$$

Therefore our equation now reads

$$\frac{dA}{dt} = 2E_k + (\boldsymbol{F}_1 \cdot \boldsymbol{r}_1 + \boldsymbol{F}_2 \cdot \boldsymbol{r}_2 + \boldsymbol{F}_{12} \cdot \boldsymbol{r}_{12}) = 2E_k + B,$$

where, to simplify the writing, we have called B the expression inside the parentheses. Taking the time average of this equation, we have

$$\left[\frac{dA}{dt}\right]_{\text{ave}} = 2E_{k,\text{ave}} + B_{\text{ave}}. \tag{9.55}$$

Remembering the definition of time average given in Section 8.13 and the result given in Eq. (8.46), we again have

$$\left[\frac{dA}{dt}\right]_{\text{ave}} = \frac{A - A_0}{\tau}.$$

Again if the time τ is very large and A does not increase indefinitely with time, the quantity $(A - A_0)/\tau$ can be made so small that it can be considered as zero. This occurs if the system is bounded, such as in the case of a gas in a container, because then $\boldsymbol{r}_1$ and $\boldsymbol{r}_2$, and also $\boldsymbol{v}_1$ and $\boldsymbol{v}_2$, in Eq. (9.54) cannot increase indefinitely.

Therefore, making $(dA/dt)_{\text{ave}} = 0$ in Eq. (9.55), we find

$$2E_{k,\,\text{ave}} = -B_{\text{ave}} = -(\boldsymbol{F}_1 \cdot \boldsymbol{r}_1 + \boldsymbol{F}_2 \cdot \boldsymbol{r}_2 + \boldsymbol{F}_{12} \cdot \boldsymbol{r}_{12})_{\text{ave}}.$$

If instead of two particles we have many, the equation may be generalized to read

$$E_{k,\,\text{ave}} = -\frac{1}{2}\left(\sum_{\substack{\text{All} \\ \text{particles}}} \boldsymbol{F}_i \cdot \boldsymbol{r}_i + \sum_{\substack{\text{All pairs} \\ \text{of particles}}} \boldsymbol{F}_{ij} \cdot \boldsymbol{r}_{ij}\right)_{\text{ave}}, \qquad (9.56)$$

where the first summation on the right-hand side refers to the external forces acting on *each* particle and the second summation refers to the internal forces between *pairs* of particles. Equation (9.56) is called the *virial theorem* for a system of particles, the quantity on the right-hand side being called the *virial of the system.*

9.13 Equation of State of a Gas

One of the most interesting applications of the virial theorem is the derivation of the equation of state of a gas. By equation of state we mean an equation which describes the relation between the macroscopic quantities such as pressure, volume, and temperature, describing the state of a system. Of course, these macroscopic or statistical quantities are the direct result of the internal structure of the system and, under proper assumptions, we should be able to establish the correlation between internal structure and macroscopic behavior.

Let us *assume* a gas to be composed of molecules and subject to their mutual interactions and to the interactions with the walls of the container. We shall also *assume* for simplicity that the container is a cube of side a (a more general proof does not require this limitation) as shown in Fig. 9–19.

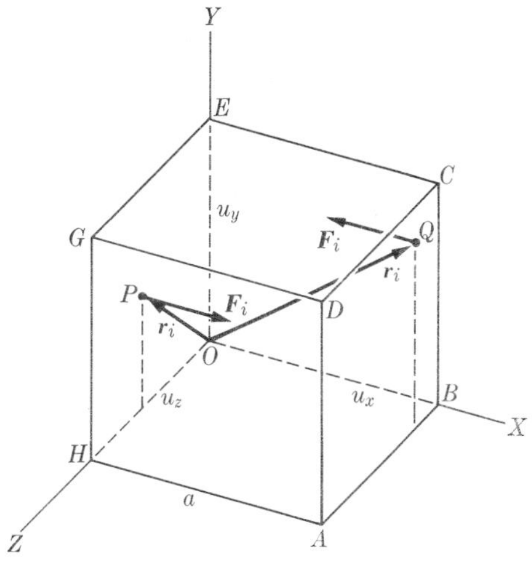

Figure 9–19

Let us evaluate Eq. (9.56) by starting with the first summation, corresponding to the external forces. A molecule experiences an external force only when it hits the walls and bounces back. We may *assume* that the force it experiences is perpendicular to the wall, an assumption that is only statistically correct. At the wall $OEGH$, having $x = 0$ at all points of its surface, a molecule hitting at point P, for example, experiences a force $\boldsymbol{F}_i = \boldsymbol{u}_x F_i$. Then $\boldsymbol{F}_i \cdot \boldsymbol{r}_i = F_i x_i = 0$, and wall $OEGH$ does not contribute to the virial because our choice of origin makes $x_i = 0$. The same result is obtained at walls $OBCE$ and $OHAB$.

At wall $ABCD$ a particle hitting at Q, for example, suffers a force parallel but opposite to OX; that is, $\boldsymbol{F}_i = -\boldsymbol{u}_x F_i$, and all particles impinging on that wall have $x_i = a$. Therefore $\boldsymbol{F}_i \cdot \boldsymbol{r}_i = -F_i a$. The sum $\sum_i \boldsymbol{F}_i \cdot \boldsymbol{r}_i$ for the wall we have considered is just $-\sum_i F_i a = -(\sum_i F_i)a = -Fa = -pa^3$, where, using Eq. (9.46), $F = pa^2$ is the total force exerted by the gas on the wall of area $A = a^2$, and p is the pressure of the gas. A similar result is obtained for the walls $CDGE$ and $ADGH$, resulting in a total contribution to the virial for the six walls of

$$\textstyle\sum_i \boldsymbol{F}_i \cdot \boldsymbol{r}_i = -3pa^3 = -3pV,$$

where $V = a^3$ is the volume occupied by the gas. Equation (9.56) then becomes

$$E_{k,\,\text{ave}} = \tfrac{3}{2}pV - \tfrac{1}{2}(\textstyle\sum_{ij} \boldsymbol{F}_{ij} \cdot \boldsymbol{r}_{ij})_{\text{ave}}$$

or

$$pV = \tfrac{2}{3}E_{k,\,\text{ave}} + \tfrac{1}{3}(\textstyle\sum_{ij} \boldsymbol{F}_{ij} \cdot \boldsymbol{r}_{ij})_{\text{ave}}. \tag{9.57}$$

The average kinetic energy of a molecule is $\frac{1}{2}mv_{\text{rms}}^2$, and the average energy of all the molecules in the gas is $E_{k,\text{ave}} = N(\frac{1}{2}mv_{\text{rms}}^2)$, where N is the total number of molecules. Making the substitution into Eq. (9.57), we have

$$pV = \tfrac{1}{3}Nmv_{\text{rms}}^2 + \frac{1}{3}\left(\sum_{\substack{\text{All}\\\text{pairs}}} \boldsymbol{F}_{ij} \cdot \boldsymbol{r}_{ij}\right)_{\text{ave}}, \tag{9.58}$$

which relates the pressure p and the volume V to molecular properties such as m, v_{rms}, and $\boldsymbol{F}_{ij}$. We define the *absolute temperature* T of the gas as directly proportional to the average kinetic energy of a molecule, expressing it by the relation

$$\tfrac{3}{2}kT = \tfrac{1}{2}mv_{\text{rms}}^2 \qquad \text{or} \qquad kT = \tfrac{1}{3}mv_{\text{rms}}^2, \tag{9.59}$$

where k is a universal constant called the *Boltzmann constant*, whose experimentally determined value (see note on the measurement of temperature on page 270) is

$$k = 1.38044 \times 10^{-23}\ \text{J}\ {}^\circ\text{K}^{-1}. \tag{9.60}$$

Then Eq. (9.58) becomes

$$pV = NkT + \frac{1}{3}\left(\sum_{\substack{\text{All}\\\text{pairs}}} \boldsymbol{F}_{ij} \cdot \boldsymbol{r}_{ij}\right)_{\text{ave}}. \tag{9.61}$$

We have now arrived at the equation of state of a gas. It is not yet in a final form because we have not evaluated the last term, which depends on the intermolecular forces. To evaluate it we must make some assumptions about the nature of intermolecular forces.

For the present, then, let us postulate an "ideal" gas; i.e., one which exists only as a model. An *ideal gas* is one in which the intermolecular forces are considered zero. Thus the last term in Eq. (9.61) disappears, and the equation of state for an ideal gas is

$$pV = NkT. \tag{9.62}$$

This equation is obeyed with surprisingly good approximation by many gases, and thus is an indication that intermolecular forces in gases are negligible except when the molecules are closely packed or the temperature is very low.

The interesting feature of Eq. (9.61) is that it clearly expresses the effect of the molecular forces on the pressure of the gas. For example, we see that if the intermolecular forces are attractive, the products $\boldsymbol{F}_{ij} \cdot \boldsymbol{r}_{ij}$ are all negative, so that the right-hand side of Eq. (9.61) will be less than for an ideal gas, resulting in a lower pressure, a result in agreement with our physical intuition.

EXAMPLE 9.16. Obtain the equation of state of an ideal gas by directly computing the pressure exerted by the gas on the walls of the container.

Solution: The student may recall that the pressure that the stream of gas of Example 9.2 exerts on the area A of the wall is

$$p = \frac{F}{A} = \frac{2Anmv^2\cos^2\theta}{A} = 2nmv^2\cos^2\theta,$$

where $v\cos\theta$ is the component of the molecular velocity along the normal to the wall. This gives the pressure due to the molecules moving in a direction making an angle θ with the normal to the wall. Thus in this case n is not the total number of molecules per unit volume but only those moving in the said direction. Therefore we should start by finding what fraction of the molecules are moving at an angle θ with the normal and add (actually integrate) their contributions for all directions. Instead we shall proceed in a simpler and more intuitive form that essentially gives the same result.

We may safely assume that statistically, at a particular instant, one-half the molecules have a component of their velocity which points toward the wall and the other half away from the wall. Thus we must replace n by $\frac{1}{2}n$, since only $\frac{1}{2}n$ are going to hit the wall. Also, if the wall is $ABCD$ of Fig. 9–19, then $v\cos\theta$ is the component v_x of the velocity along the X-axis which is the normal to the wall we have chosen. Making these changes in the above expression for p, we obtain

$$p = 2(\tfrac{1}{2}n)mv_x^2.$$

The magnitude of the velocity is $v^2 = v_x^2 + v_y^2 + v_z^2$. Actually we must use the average value $v_{x,\text{rms}}^2$ and therefore $v_{\text{rms}}^2 = v_{x,\text{rms}}^2 + v_{y,\text{rms}}^2 + v_{z,\text{rms}}^2$. But we may assume that if the gas is homogeneous the directions of the molecular velocities are distributed isotropically. Thus $v_{x,\text{rms}}^2 = v_{y,\text{rms}}^2 = v_{z,\text{rms}}^2$ and therefore $v_{x,\text{rms}}^2 = \frac{1}{3}v_{\text{rms}}^2$. Making these substitutions in the expression for p, we have then

$$p = 2(\tfrac{1}{2}n)m(\tfrac{1}{3}v_{\text{rms}}^2) = \tfrac{1}{3}nmv_{\text{rms}}^2 = \frac{1}{3}\frac{N}{V}mv_{\text{rms}}^2,$$

since $n = N/V$, N being the total number of molecules and V the volume. Therefore

$$pV = \tfrac{1}{3}Nmv_{\text{rms}}^2.$$

This result coincides with Eq. (9.58), except that the term corresponding to the internal forces is not present and therefore the equation corresponds to an ideal gas. The advantage of the virial method is that it clearly shows how to take into account the intermolecular forces. Can the student think of a way of incorporating the intermolecular forces into the logic we have used in this example?

Note on the measurement of temperature. In Section 9.8 we associated the temperature of a system of particles with the average kinetic energy of a particle in the CM-frame of reference. In Eq. (9.59), which is $\frac{3}{2}kT = \frac{1}{2}mv_{\text{rms}}^2$, we were more specific about the relation between the temperature of a gas and the average kinetic energy of the gas molecules. However, two important aspects must now be considered. First, in the defining equation (9.59) we introduced two new quantities, T (the absolute temperature) and k (Boltzmann's constant), and we must decide how they can be measured independently. Second, the student has an intuitive concept of temperature based on sensorial experience, as reflected by his feelings of hot and cold. He is accustomed to measuring temperature in terms of a number given by a device called a *thermometer*. Therefore it is necessary to correlate our definition of temperature with this intuitive notion.

Let us consider a mass M of a gas containing N molecules. If we neglect the effect of the intermolecular forces, the equation of state is given by Eq. (9.62); that is, $pV = NkT$. Suppose that we bring the gas into thermal equilibrium with some other physical system which we assume may be kept at a fixed temperature. This system may be a mixture of water and ice at its freezing point and at the standard pressure of one atm. We measure the pressure and the volume of the gas at this fixed temperature, obtaining the values p_0 and V_0, respectively. Next we decide to assign a convenient (but arbitrary) value T_0 to the fixed temperature, which is also the temperature of the gas. Therefore we may write $p_0V_0 = NkT_0$. This automatically fixes the value of the Boltzmann constant, $k = p_0V_0/NT_0$, where N can be obtained if we know the mass of each molecule.

To determine the temperature of the gas when its pressure is p and its volume is V, so that $pV = NkT$, we simply eliminate the factor Nk, using the standard values, and obtain

$$T = T_0(pV/p_0V_0),$$

which gives T in terms of our standard reference temperature T_0 and other measurable quantities. In this way our mass of gas has become a *gas thermometer*. Instead of a gas we may use other substances as thermometers, such as a liquid, or a metal rod whose dimensions (volume or length) change with the temperature. Since the equation of state of these substances is more complicated, in practice we calibrate these thermometers against a gas thermometer. In this case the thermometer agrees with the gas thermometer only at the calibration points. Since the property chosen may not vary linearly with the temperature, there may be slight discrepancies at intermediate temperatures.

We may choose the value of T_0 on the basis of several points of view. For example, we may choose another process that conceivably occurs at a fixed temperature, such as the process of water boiling at a certain temperature at the standard pressure of one atm. Then we may decide that the temperature of this second reference point is 100 units or *degrees* above T_0. If p_1 and V_1 are the pressure and volume of the gas at this new temperature, we have that $p_1V_1 = Nk(T_0 + 100)$. Solving for Nk from the equation $p_0V_0 = NkT_0$, and substituting this value in the above equation, we find that

$$T_0 = 100p_0V_0/(p_1V_1 - p_0V_0),$$

from which we can obtain a numerical value for T_0. The value obtained for T_0 as a result of this type of experiment (and many other experiments using different techniques) is $T_0 = 273.15$. Each of the units is called a *degree Kelvin*, designated by °K.

It is important to realize that our technique for measuring temperature is based on the ideal gas approximation. If we use different gases, the results obtained will be different because the effect of the intermolecular forces, as it appears in Eq. (9.61), is different for each gas. Usually hydrogen or helium is used. It is most desirable to be able to obtain a temperature scale independent of the substance being used as a measuring medium, a subject that is discussed in thermodynamics and will not be pursued here.

9.14 Fluid Motion

The general principles we have discussed in this chapter for many-particle systems can easily be applied to a discussion of fluid motion. Let us consider, for simplicity, a fluid (i.e., a liquid or a gas) moving along a cylindrical pipe of variable cross section A (Fig. 9–20). The pipe can be oriented in any direction, and therefore the X-axis is made coincident with its axis. We shall concentrate on a volume element of thickness dx and volume $A\,dx$. Although this volume is small, it still contains a very large number of molecules. We can discuss its motion by using Eq. (9.9) with the mass M replaced by $\rho(A\,dx)$, where ρ is the density of the fluid. The center of mass may be assumed to coincide with the center of the volume element, if the fluid is homogeneous, and v_{CM} is called the velocity of the fluid at that point. In our case, it is parallel to the X-axis.

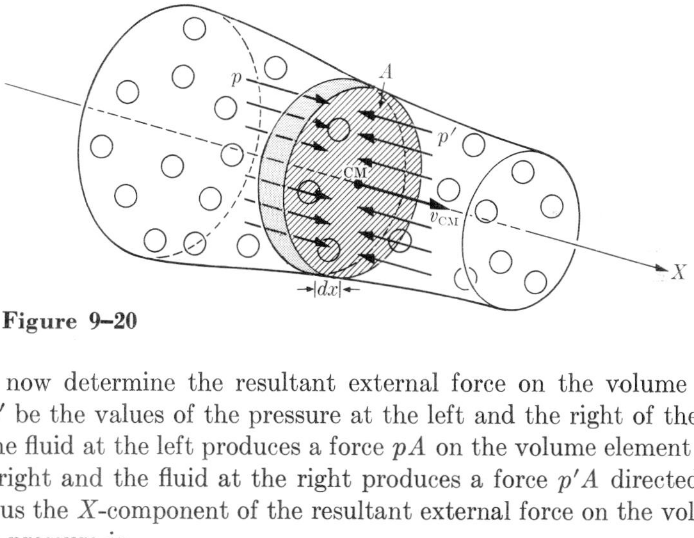

Figure 9–20

We must now determine the resultant external force on the volume of fluid. Let p and p' be the values of the pressure at the left and the right of the volume element. The fluid at the left produces a force pA on the volume element directed toward the right and the fluid at the right produces a force $p'A$ directed toward the left. Thus the X-component of the resultant external force on the volume element due to pressure is

$$dF_x = -p'A + pA = -(p' - p)A.$$

But $p' - p$ is the pressure difference between two points separated a distance dx; therefore $p' - p = dp$. Thus

$$dF_x = -(dp)A = -\frac{dp}{dx}(A\,dx).$$

Since $A\,dx$ is the volume, we conclude that *the force per unit volume* along the X-

axis due to pressure is

$$f_p = -\frac{dp}{dx}. \tag{9.63}$$

This result, when we compare it with Eq. (8.23), suggests that we may consider pressure as potential energy per unit volume. We may see that this is dimensionally correct, since p is expressed in N m^{-2}, which is the same as (N m)m^{-3} or J m^{-3}.

In addition to the pressure, there may be other external forces (such as gravity or an external electric or magnetic field) acting on the fluid inside the volume element. Let us say that f_e is any such force per unit volume (such as weight per unit volume); the resultant external force on the fluid inside the volume element is $(f_p + f_e)A\,dx = (-dp/dx + f_e)A\,dx$. (The forces between molecules within the volume element are internal forces, and must not be taken into account.) Thus the equation of motion according to Eq. (9.9), (and here we drop the subscript CM for the velocity), is

$$(\rho A\,dx)\frac{dv}{dt} = \left(-\frac{dp}{dx} + f_e\right)A\,dx$$

or, canceling the common factor $A\,dx$, we have

$$\rho\frac{dv}{dt} = -\frac{dp}{dx} + f_e. \tag{9.64}$$

If the force f_e is conservative, we have that $f_e = -dE_p/dx$, where E_p is the corresponding potential energy per unit volume. Then

$$\rho\frac{dv}{dt} = -\frac{dp}{dx} - \frac{dE_p}{dx} = -\frac{d}{dx}(p + E_p). \tag{9.65}$$

Before we go any further, we must be more specific about the nature of the fluid motion. The motion of a fluid is said to be *stationary* when the motion pattern does not change with time. This means that, although the velocity of a fluid element may change when the fluid element changes position, the velocity of the fluid at each point of space remains the same. To be more precise, if we follow a particular fluid element along its path of motion (Fig. 9–21), we may find that when it is at A its velocity is v and when it is at A' its velocity is v'. But if the motion is stationary, *all* fluid elements have velocity v when they pass through A, and velocity v' when they pass through A'. Thus the velocity of the fluid may be considered as a function of position instead of a function of time. When the motion is not stationary, the velocities at each position may change with time. For example, if at a certain time

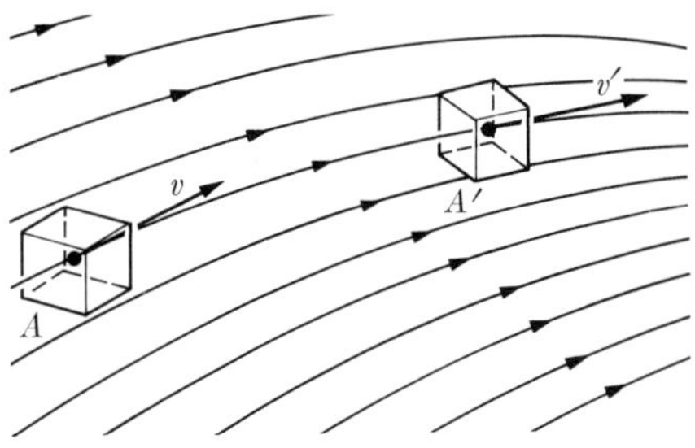

Fig. 9–21. Stationary flow. The lines shown are called *streamlines.*

the velocity of the fluid at A is v, at a later time the velocity, in general, will be different. In what follows we shall consider only stationary fluid motion.

In the case of stationary motion, when dt is the time required by the fluid element to move through the distance dx, we may write that

$$\frac{dv}{dt} = \frac{dv}{dx}\frac{dx}{dt} = v\frac{dv}{dx} = \frac{d}{dx}\left(\tfrac{1}{2}v^2\right).$$

Substituting this in Eq. (9.65), we have

$$\rho\frac{d}{dx}\left(\tfrac{1}{2}v^2\right) = -\frac{d}{dx}\left(p + E_p\right).$$

We assume that the fluid is incompressible (that is, that its density is constant); hence the left-hand side of the equation becomes $d(\frac{1}{2}\rho v^2)/dx$, and we may write the equation in the form

$$\frac{d}{dx}\left(\tfrac{1}{2}\rho v^2 + p + E_p\right) = 0$$

or

$$\tfrac{1}{2}\rho v^2 + p + E_p = \text{const.} \tag{9.66}$$

This result, known as *Bernoulli's theorem,* expresses the conservation of energy in the fluid. The first term is its kinetic energy per unit volume, the second is interpreted as its potential energy per unit volume associated with the pressure, and the third term is its potential energy per unit volume due to all other external forces. Therefore if all the forces acting on the fluid are conservative, and we follow the motion of a small volume of the fluid, we find that the total energy per unit volume remains constant.

In the particular case that the external force acting on the fluid is gravity, $E_p = \rho g z$ and Eq. (9.66) becomes

$$\tfrac{1}{2}\rho v^2 + p + \rho g z = \text{const.} \tag{9.67}$$

Let us consider two important cases. When the fluid moves in the horizontal direction only, the term $\rho g z$ remains constant and Eq. (9.67) reduces to

$$\tfrac{1}{2}\rho v^2 + p = \text{const.} \tag{9.68}$$

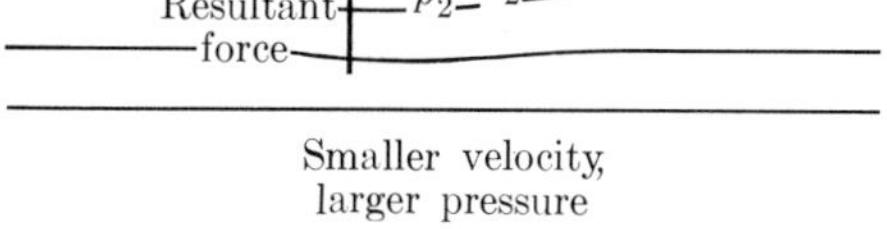

Fig. 9–22. Air lift on an airplane wing.

Thus, in a horizontal pipe, the greater the velocity, the lower the pressure, and conversely. This effect is used to produce the lift of an airplane (Fig. 9–22). The profile of the wing is so designed that the air has a greater velocity above the wing surface than below it, which produces a larger pressure below than above. This results in a net resultant upward force. If A is the area of the wing, the upward force is $F = A(p_1 - p_2) = \frac{1}{2}A\rho(v_2^2 - v_1^2)$ where the subscripts 1 and 2 refer to the conditions below and above the wing. As a good approximation, since

$$\tfrac{1}{2}(v_2^2 - v_1^2) = \tfrac{1}{2}(v_2 - v_1)(v_2 + v_1),$$

we may say that $\frac{1}{2}(v_2 + v_1)$ is equal to the plane's velocity, v, relative to the air. Then the resultant upward force, or *lift*, is

$$F = A\rho v(v_2 - v_1).$$

As our second example, consider a fluid at rest or moving with a constant velocity in a pipe. Under such circumstances, the term $\frac{1}{2}\rho v^2$ may be dropped from Eq. (9.67), which then reduces to $p + \rho gz =$ const. Designating the constant by p_0, we then have that the pressure in an incompressible fluid in equilibrium is given by

$$p = p_0 - \rho gz. \tag{9.69}$$

Obviously, p_0 is the value of the pressure at $z = 0$.

Our discussion could be extended to cases in which the fluid is compressible or the forces are not conservative. (This latter situation arises, for example, when a fluid does *shaft work* in driving some mechanism such as a turbine in a hydroelectric installation, or when heat is exchanged with the surroundings, as in an industrial chemical plant.) We shall omit these considerations here, however, since they belong to more specialized courses.

One last principle that is very important in discussing fluid motion is the *equation of continuity*, which expresses the conservation of mass of the fluid. Let us consider a fluid moving inside the pipe shown in Fig. 9–23 under steady conditions, so that mass is not being added or lost at any point. Let A_1 and A_2 be two sections of the pipe. The volume of fluid that passes through A_1 per unit time corresponds to a cylinder of base A_1 and length v_1, having a volume A_1v_1, and thus the mass of fluid that has passed through A_1 in a unit time is $\rho_1A_1v_1$. Similarly we have that $\rho_2A_2v_2$ is the amount of fluid that passes through A_2 per unit time. The conservation of mass, under the conditions stated, requires that the two masses be the same, or

$$\rho_1A_1v_1 = \rho_2A_2v_2, \tag{9.70}$$

which is the equation of continuity. If the fluid is incompressible, the density remains the same and Eq. (9.70) reduces to

$$A_1v_1 = A_2v_2, \tag{9.71}$$

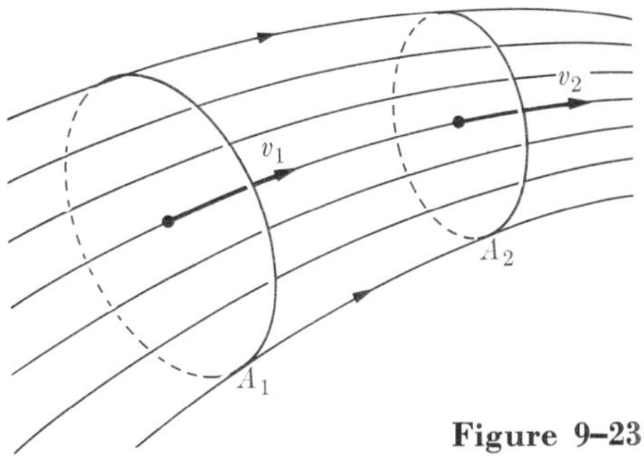

Figure 9–23

indicating that the velocity of the fluid is inversely proportional to the cross section of the tube, a result in agreement with our physical intuition.

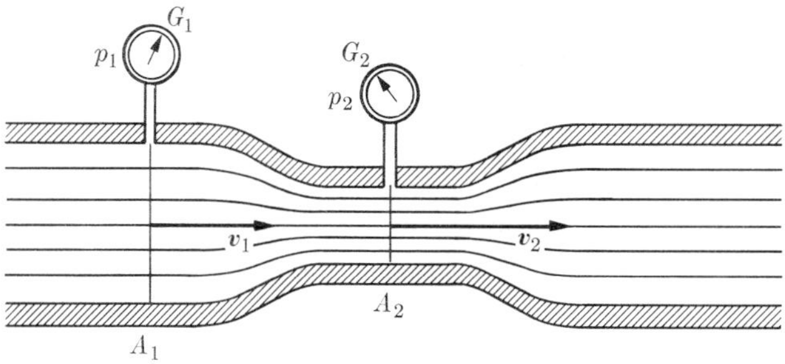

Figure 9–24

EXAMPLE 9.17. A method for determining the velocity of a fluid in a pipe is the *Venturi meter*, illustrated in Fig. 9–24. Two pressure gauges G_1 and G_2 measure the pressure in the pipe and at a contraction inserted in it. Obtain the velocity v_1 in terms of the pressure difference $p_1 - p_2$.

Solution: To obtain the expression for the velocity, we note that if v_1 and v_2 are the velocities at both sections, of areas A_1 and A_2, respectively, the equation of continuity (9.71) gives $A_1v_1 = A_2v_2$ or $v_2 = (A_1/A_2)v_1$. Also if the pipe is horizontal, Bernoulli's theorem, in the form of Eq. (9.68), gives us

$$\tfrac{1}{2}\rho v_1^2 + p_1 = \tfrac{1}{2}\rho v_2^2 + p_2.$$

Inserting the value of v_2 obtained previously and solving for v_1, we finally obtain

$$v_1 = \sqrt{\frac{2(p_1 - p_2)}{\rho[(A_1/A_2)^2 - 1]}}.$$

The amount of fluid passing through any section of the pipe per unit time is

$$V = A_1v_1 = A_1A_2\sqrt{\frac{2(p_1 - p_2)}{\rho(A_1^2 - A_2^2)}} = K\sqrt{p_1 - p_2},$$

where K is a constant depending on the pipe and on the nature of the fluid.

References

1. "A Sketch for a History of the Kinetic Theory of Gases," E. Mendoza, *Physics Today*, March 1961, page 36
2. "Development of the Kinetic Theory of Gases, V: The Equation of State," S. Brush, *Am. J. Phys.* **29**, 593 (1961)
3. *Mechanics* (second edition), by K. Symon. Reading, Mass.: Addison-Wesley, 1964, Chapter 4, Sections 5–11, 8–6 through 8–9
4. *Physical Mechanics* (third edition), by R. B. Lindsay. Princeton, N.J.: Van Nostrand, 1963, Chapter 6, Sections 11–1 through 11–5

5. *Introduction to Engineering Mechanics*, by J. Huddleston. Reading, Mass.: Addison-Wesley, 1961, Sections 13–1, 19–3, 19–5, 21–1
6. *Vector Mechanics*, by D. Christie. New York: McGraw-Hill, 1964, Sections 6.6, 7.3, 7.8, 7.14, 22.1 through 22.6
7. *The Feynman Lectures on Physics*, Volume I, by R. Feynman, R. Leighton, and M. Sands. Reading, Mass.: Addison-Wesley, 1963, Chapter 39
8. *Source Book in Physics*, by W. F. Magie. Cambridge, Mass.: Harvard University Press, 1963, page 73, Pascal; page 196, Mayer; page 212, Helmholtz; page 247, Bernoulli; page 255, Joule; page 257, Maxwell
9. *Foundations of Modern Physical Science*, by G. Holton and D. H. D. Roller. Reading, Mass.: Addison-Wesley, 1958, Chapter 25
10. *Thermodynamics, the Kinetic Theory of Gases, and Statistical Mechanics* (second edition), by Francis W. Sears. Reading, Mass.: Addison-Wesley, 1953, Chapter 1

Problems

9.1 A system is composed of three particles with masses 3 kg, 2 kg, and 5 kg. The first particle has a velocity of $\boldsymbol{u}_y(6)$ m s^{-1}. The second is moving with a velocity of 8 m s^{-1} in a direction making an angle of $-30°$ with the X-axis. Find the velocity of the third particle so that the CM appears at rest relative to the observer.

9.2 At a particular instant, three particles are moving as shown in Fig. 9–25. They are subject only to their mutual interactions, so that no external forces act. After a certain time, they are observed again and it is found that m_1 is moving as shown, while m_2 is at rest. Find the velocity of m_3. Assume that $m_1 = 2$ kg, $m_2 = 0.5$ kg, $m_3 = 1$ kg, $v_1 = 1$ m s^{-1}, $v_2 = 2$ m s^{-1}, $v_3 = 4$ m s^{-1} and $v_1' = 3$ m s^{-1}. Find the velocity of the CM of the system at the two times mentioned in the problem. At a given time the positions of the masses are $m_1(-0.8$ m, -1.1 m$)$, $m_2(0.8$ m, -1.1 m$)$, $m_3(1.4$ m, 0.8 m$)$. Draw a line showing the path of the CM of the system.

9.3 The masses $m_1 = 10$ kg and $m_2 = 6$ kg are joined by a rigid bar of negligible mass (Fig. 9–26). Being initially at rest, they are subject to forces $\boldsymbol{F}_1 = \boldsymbol{u}_x(8)$ N and $\boldsymbol{F}_2 = \boldsymbol{u}_y(6)$ N, as shown. (a) Find the coordinates of their CM as a function of time. (b) Express the total momentum as a function of time.

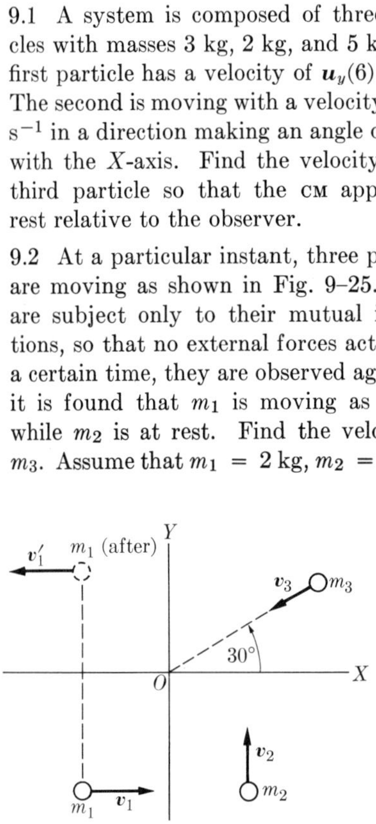

Figure 9–25

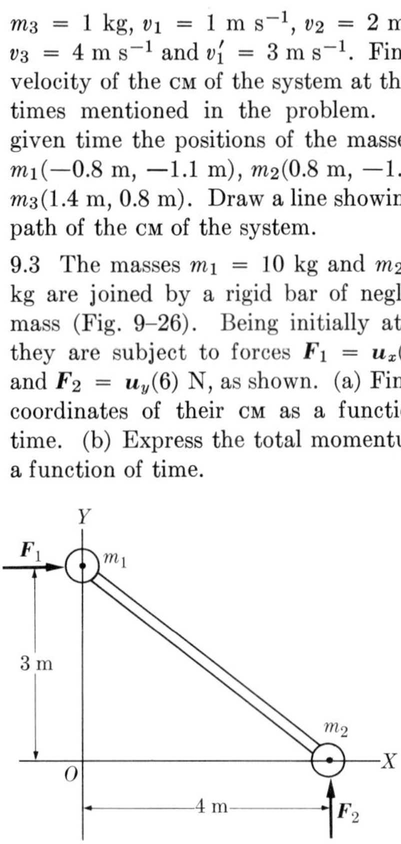

Figure 9–26

9.4 The two masses in Fig. 9–27 are initially at rest. Assuming that $m_1 > m_2$, find the velocity and acceleration of their CM at time t.

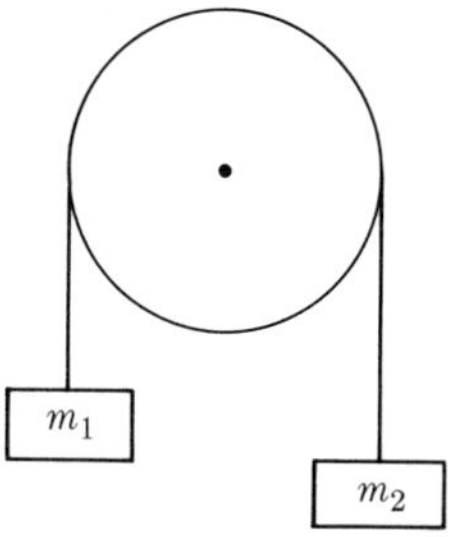

Figure 9–27

9.5 A stream of liquid, set at an angle θ, is directed against a plane surface (Fig. 9–28). The liquid, after hitting the surface, spreads over it. Find the pressure on the surface. The density of the liquid is ρ and its velocity is v.

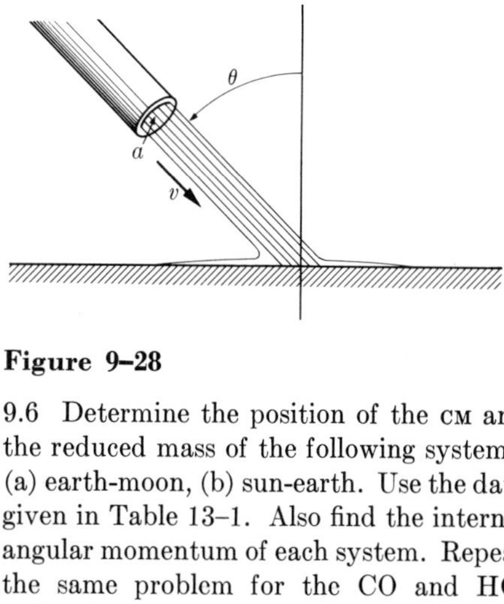

Figure 9–28

9.6 Determine the position of the CM and the reduced mass of the following systems: (a) earth-moon, (b) sun-earth. Use the data given in Table 13–1. Also find the internal angular momentum of each system. Repeat the same problem for the CO and HCl molecules. The bond length of the CO molecule is 1.13×10^{-10} m and of the HCl molecule is 1.27×10^{-10} m.

9.7 Two particles with masses 2 kg and 3 kg are moving, relative to an observer, with velocities of 10 m s^{-1} along the X-axis and 8 m s^{-1} at an angle of 120° with the X-axis, respectively. (a) Express each velocity in vector form. (b) Find the velocity of their CM. (c) Express the velocity of each particle relative to its CM. (d) Find the momentum of each particle in the CM-frame. (e) Find the relative velocity of the particles. (f) Calculate the reduced mass of the system. (g) Verify the relations given in Example 9.4.

9.8 Determine the total kinetic energy of the particles of Problem 9.7, relative to the laboratory and relative to their CM. Use two different methods for the second calculation. Verify the relations given in Example 9.8.

9.9 Assume that the particles of Problem 9.7 are at the points (0, 1, 1) and (—1, 0, 2), respectively. (a) Find the position of the CM. (b) Determine the angular momentum of the system relative to their CM. (c) Obtain the angular momentum relative to the origin. Use two different methods for (b) and (c).

9.10 A ^{236}U uranium nucleus at rest splits into two fragments, having masses of 140 amu and 90 amu. The Q of the reaction is 190 MeV. Find the energies and the velocities of the two fragments.

9.11 A ^{238}U nucleus at rest disintegrates, emitting an alpha particle (m = 4 amu) and leaving a residual nucleus of ^{234}Th ($M \approx 234$ amu). The total energy available is 4.18 MeV. Find (a) the kinetic energy of the alpha particle and of the residual nucleus, (b) their momenta, and (c) their velocities.

9.12 A nucleus, originally at rest, decays radioactively by emitting an electron of momentum 9.22×10^{-21} m kg s^{-1}, and, at right angles to the direction of the electron, a neutrino with momentum 5.33×10^{-21} m kg s^{-1}. (a) In what direction does the residual nucleus recoil? (b) What is its momentum? (c) Given that the mass of the residual nucleus is 3.90×10^{-25} kg, what are its velocity and kinetic energy?

9.13 A shell of mass m explodes into several fragments. The explosion has a positive Q-value. (a) Show that if the shell explodes into two fragments, they move in opposite directions in the C-frame of reference. (b) Show that if the shell explodes into three fragments, their momenta and velocities, all relative to the C-frame of reference, lie in one plane. (c) If the number of fragments is greater than three, is there any special requirement on their momenta relative to the C-frame of reference? (d) Show that if the shell divides into two equal fragments, their momenta and velocities in the C-frame of reference are equal to $(mQ/2)^{1/2}$ and $(2Q/m)^{1/2}$, respectively. (e) Show that if the shell divides into three equal fragments emitted symmetrically in the C-frame, their momenta and velocities in this frame are $\frac{1}{3}(2mQ)^{1/2}$ and $(2Q/m)^{1/2}$, respectively. (f) Repeat (e), assuming that two fragments are emitted with the same velocity relative to the C-frame but in directions making an angle of 90°. (g) How would the results of (d) and (e) appear to an observer in the L-frame if, at the time of the explosion, the shell were moving with a velocity $\frac{1}{4}(2Q/m)^{1/2}$ relative to the L-frame, and in the same direction of motion as one of the resulting fragments?

9.14 A projectile is fired at an angle of 60° with the horizontal and a muzzle velocity of 400 m s^{-1}. At the highest point of its trajectory it explodes into two fragments of equal mass, one of which falls vertically. (a) How far from the point of firing does the other fragment strike the ground if the terrain is level? (b) What was the energy released in the explosion?

9.15 A grenade of mass M is falling with a velocity v_0, at height h, when it explodes into two equal fragments that initially move horizontally in the C-frame. The explosion has a Q value of Mv_0^2. Determine the positions where the fragments will fall on the ground relative to the point directly below the grenade at the time of the explosion.

9.16 Repeat Problem 9.15 for a grenade moving horizontally at the time of the explosion.

9.17 A ball, having a mass of 4 kg and a velocity of 1.2 m s^{-1}, collides head-on with another ball of mass 5 kg moving at 0.6 m s^{-1} in the same direction. Find (a) the velocities of the balls after the collision (assuming that it is elastic), (b) the change in momentum of each ball.

9.18 Repeat the previous problem, assuming that the second ball is moving in the opposite direction.

9.19 Repeat the two previous problems if the two balls continue moving together.

9.20 A particle having a mass of 0.2 kg while moving at 0.40 m s^{-1} collides with another particle of mass 0.3 kg, which is at rest. After the collision the first particle moves at 0.20 m s^{-1} in a direction making an angle of 40° with its initial direction. Find the velocity of the second particle and the Q of the process.

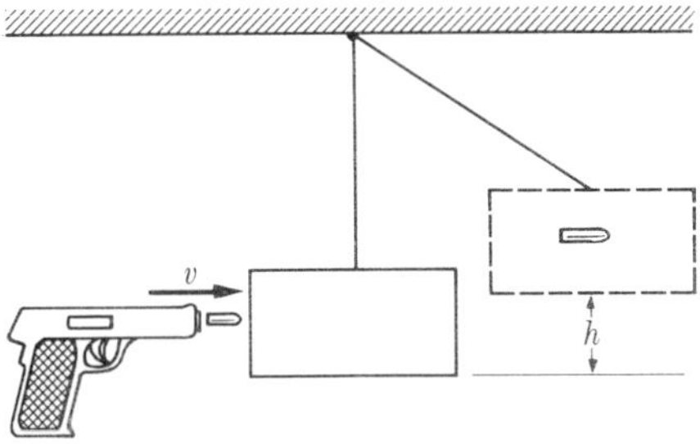

Figure 9–29

9.21 The arrangement in Fig. 9–29 is called a *ballistic pendulum*. It is used to determine the velocity of a bullet by measuring the height h the block rises after the bullet is embedded in it. Prove that the velocity of the bullet is given by

$$\sqrt{2gh}\,(m_1 + m_2)/m_1,$$

where m_1 is the mass of the bullet and m_2 the mass of the block.

9.22 A bullet of mass m and velocity v passes through a pendulum bob of mass M and emerges with velocity $v/2$ (Fig. 9–30). The pendulum bob is at the end of a string

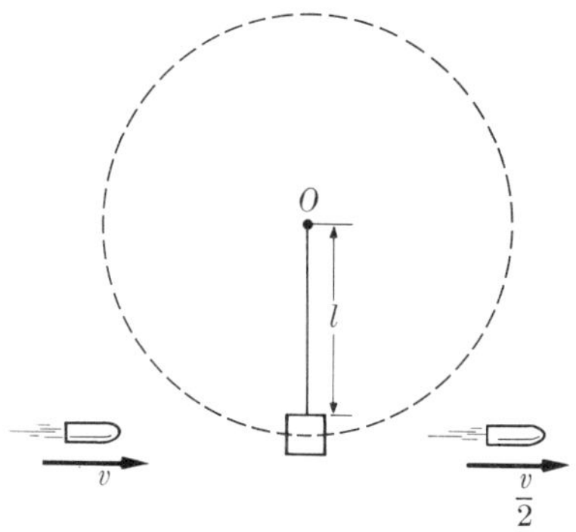

Figure 9–30

of length l. What is the minimum value of v such that the pendulum bob will swing through a complete circle?

9.23 A particle of mass 5 kg, moving at 2 m s^{-1}, collides with a particle of mass 8 kg initially at rest. If the collision is elastic, find the velocity of each particle after the collision (a) if the collision is head-on, (b) if the first particle is deflected 50° from its original direction of motion. Express all directions relative to the direction of the incoming particle.

9.24 A particle of mass m, moving with a velocity v, collides elastically and head-on with another particle of mass M (larger than m) having (a) an equal but opposite momentum, (b) the same kinetic energy, but moving in the opposite direction. Compute in each case the velocity of the first particle after the collision. (c) Show that if M is at rest and much larger than m, the change in kinetic energy of m is

$$\Delta E_k / E_k \approx -4(m/M).$$

9.25 It is found experimentally that in the head-on collision of two solid spheres, such as two billiard balls, the velocities after the collision are related to those before by the expression $v_1' - v_2' = -e(v_1 - v_2)$ where e is between zero and one, and is called the *coefficient of restitution.* This result was discovered by Newton and has only approximate validity. In addition, momentum is conserved in the collision. Prove the following: (a) The velocities after the collision are given by

$$v_1' = \frac{v_1(m_1 - m_2 e) + v_2 m_2(1 + e)}{m_1 + m_2}$$

and

$$v_2' = \frac{v_1 m_1(1 + e) + v_2(m_2 - m_1 e)}{m_1 + m_2}.$$

(b) The Q of the collision is

$$-\tfrac{1}{2}(1 - e^2)\frac{m_1 m_2}{m_1 + m_2}(v_1 - v_2)^2.$$

(c) What should be the value of e for the collision to be elastic?

9.26 In a *plastic collision* the two bodies move as one after the collision. (a) What is the value of the coefficient of restitution e? (b) Compute the Q of the reaction directly, and also by using the results of Problem 9.25 with the appropriate value of e.

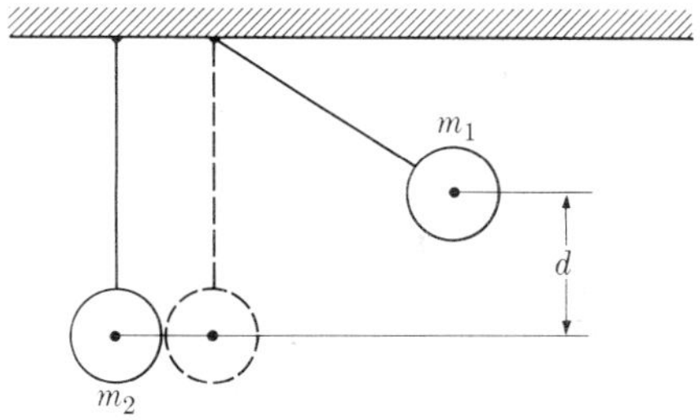

Figure 9–31

9.27 If the masses of balls m_1 and m_2 in Fig. 9–31 are 0.1 kg and 0.2 kg, respectively, and if m_1 is released when $d = 0.2$ m, find the heights to which they will return after colliding if the collision is (a) elastic, (b) inelastic with a coefficient of restitution equal to 0.9, (c) plastic ($e = 0$). Solve the problem also for a case in which mass m_2 is raised and released against a stationary m_1.

9.28 Discuss the physical results of a collision in which the value of e is (a) negative, (b) larger than one. Do you conclude then that these values of e are permissible for a collision between two solid spheres?

9.29 Assuming that the second body in Problem 9.25 is at rest and that its mass is very large compared with that of the first, find the velocity of each body after the collision, and also find the value of Q. Apply this result to determine how high a body, dropped from a height h, rebounds after hitting the floor. Do the experiment yourself with a marble and estimate from it the corresponding value of e.

9.30 Prove that the time required by the ball of Problem 9.29 to stop rebounding is $t = \sqrt{2h/g}\,(1 + e)/(1 - e)$.

9.31 Prove that if the ball of Problem 9.29 strikes the ground at an angle α with the vertical, it rebounds at an angle β, given by $\tan\beta = (1/e)\tan\alpha$, with a velocity $v' = v\sqrt{e^2\cos^2\alpha + \sin^2\alpha}$. Use these results to discuss the motion of a ball dropped from a table with an initial horizontal velocity v_0. Make a sketch of its trajectory, assuming that it makes several collisions with the floor.

9.32 Prove directly that if energy and momentum are conserved in an elastic collision, then

$$\boldsymbol{u} \cdot (\boldsymbol{v}_1' - \boldsymbol{v}_2') = -\boldsymbol{u} \cdot (\boldsymbol{v}_1 - \boldsymbol{v}_2),$$

where $\boldsymbol{u}$ is a unit vector in the direction in which the momentum of either of the particles has changed. This result means that in the collision the component of the relative velocity along the direction of momentum exchange is reversed. Apply this to the case of a head-on collision. Compare this with the results of Problem 9.25 with $e = 1$. [*Hint:* Write the two conservation laws, with all terms for each particle on each side of each equation.]

9.33 A neutron, having an energy of 1 MeV, moves through (a) deuterium and (b) carbon. Estimate for each material how many head-on collisions are required to reduce the neutron's energy to a thermal value of about 0.025 eV. The relative probability of neutron capture by these materials is 1:10. In which of these materials is there a larger probability of the neutron being captured before slowing down?

9.34 Prove that in a collision of a particle of mass m_1, moving with velocity v_1 in the L-frame, with a particle of mass m_2 at rest in the L-frame, the angles at which the first particle moves after the collision relative to its initial velocity are given by $\tan\theta = \sin\phi/(\cos\phi + 1/A)$, where $A = m_2/m_1$ and angles θ and ϕ refer to the L- and C-frames, respectively.

9.35 Verify, for the particles of the previous problem, that if $m_1 = m_2$ then $\theta = \frac{1}{2}\phi$. What is then the maximum value of θ?

9.36 Referring to Problem 9.34, show that the maximum value of θ for arbitrary A is given by $\tan\theta = A/\sqrt{1 - A^2}$. Discuss the situation when A is larger than one and when it is smaller than one.

9.37 In analyzing the deflection of alpha particles moving through hydrogen, physicists have found experimentally that the maximum deflection of an alpha particle in the L-frame is about 16°. Using the results of Problem 9.36, estimate the mass of the alpha particle relative to hydrogen. Check your answer with the actual value obtained by other techniques.

9.38 Prove that if the internal kinetic energy of a system of two particles is $E_{k,\,\text{CM}}$, the magnitudes of the velocities of the particles relative to the CM are:

$$v_1 = [2m_2E_{k,\,\text{CM}}/m_1(m_1 + m_2)]^{1/2}$$

and

$$v_2 = [2m_1E_{k,\,\text{CM}}/m_2(m_1 + m_2)]^{1/2}.$$

9.39 For the two particles in Fig. 9–32, we are given that $m_1 = 4$ kg, $m_2 = 6$ kg, $\boldsymbol{v}_1 = \boldsymbol{u}_x(2)$ m s^{-1} and $\boldsymbol{v}_2 = \boldsymbol{u}_y(3)$ m s^{-1}. (a) Determine the total angular momentum of the system relative to O and relative to the CM and verify the relation between them. (b) Determine the total kinetic energy relative to O and relative to the CM and verify the relation between them.

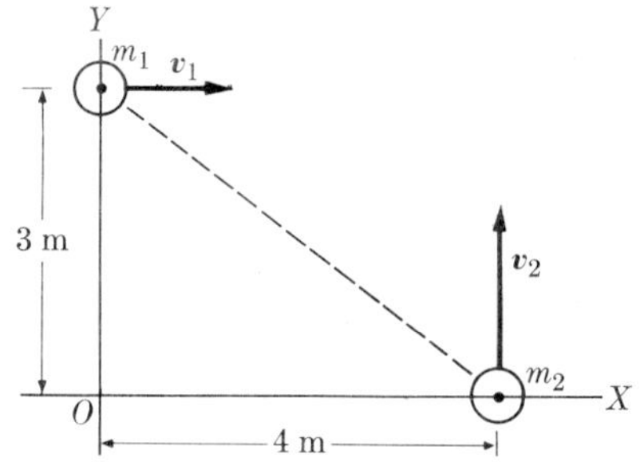

Figure 9–32

9.40 Assume that the two particles of the preceding problem are joined by an elastic spring, of constant 2×10^{-3} N m^{-1}, which is initially unstretched. (a) How will this affect the motion of the CM of the system? (b) What is the total internal energy of the system? Will it remain constant? (c) After a certain time, the spring is compressed by 4 cm. Find the internal kinetic and potential energies of the particles. (d) Determine the magnitudes of the velocities relative to the CM (can you also determine their directions?). Also determine (e) the magnitude of their relative velocity, (f) the angular momentum of the system relative to O and to the CM.

9.41 Two masses connected by a light rod, as shown in Fig. 9–33, are at rest on a horizontal frictionless surface. A third particle of mass 0.5 kg approaches the system with velocity $\boldsymbol{v}_0$ and strikes the 2-kg mass. What is the resulting motion of the CM of the two particles if the 0.5-kg mass bounces off with velocity $\boldsymbol{v}_f$ as shown?

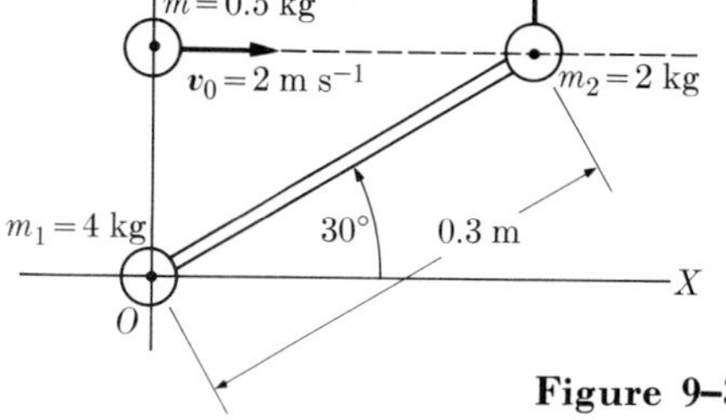

Figure 9–33

9.42 The potential energy due to the interaction between a proton and a deuterium atom is $E_{p,\text{int}} = 2.3 \times 10^{-28}/r$ J, where r is the separation between the two, expressed in meters. At a particular instant, a proton of energy 0.5 MeV is at a distance 2×10^{-12} m from a deuterium atom at rest, all referred to the L-frame. (a) Find the kinetic energy of the system in the L- and C-frames, as well as their internal potential energy [$m_{\text{proton}} = 1.0076$ amu, $m_{\text{deuteron}} = 2.0147$ amu]. (b) After a certain time the proton is at 10^{-13} m from the deuterium atom. Find the kinetic energy of the system in the L- and C-frames, as well as their potential energy. (c) Find the magnitude of the velocity of the CM in both cases.

9.43 Designating the earth, the moon, and the sun by the subscripts E, M, and S, respectively, write in full Eq. (9.34) for systems consisting of (a) the earth and the moon, (b) the earth, the moon, and the sun.

9.44 A gas is maintained at a constant pressure of 20 atm while it expands from a volume of 5×10^{-3} m^3 to a volume of 9×10^{-3} m^3. What amount of energy in the form of heat must be supplied to it (a) to maintain its internal energy constant? (b) to increase its internal energy by the same amount as the external work done? Express your result in calories and in joules.

9.45 A gas expands in such a way that at each instant the relation between its pressure and its volume is $pV^\gamma = C$, where γ is an appropriate constant. Prove that the work done in expanding from the volume V_1 to the volume V_2 is

$$W = (p_1V_1 - p_2V_2)/(\gamma - 1).$$

9.46 We recall (Problem 2.8) that one mole of a substance is an amount (expressed in *grams*) equal to its molecular (or atomic) mass expressed in amu. In one mole of any substance there is always the same number of molecules, called *Avogadro's number*, given by $N_A = 6.0225 \times 10^{23}$ mol^{-1}. Show that if N is the number of moles,

Eq. (9.62) can be written in the form

$$pV = \text{N}RT,$$

where $R = kN_A$, and is called the *gas constant*. Show also that $R = 8.3143$ J °K^{-1} mol^{-1}.

9.47 Prove that the result of Problem 9.46 can also be written in the form $p = \rho(RT/M)$, where ρ is the density of the gas and M is its molecular mass (expressed in kg).

9.48 Find the volume of one mole of any gas at STP; that is, at a temperature of 0°C and a pressure of one atmosphere. Also show that the number of molecules of any gas per cubic centimeter at STP is 2.687×10^{19}. This is called the *Loschmidt number*.

9.49 What is the average kinetic energy of a gas molecule at a temperature of 25°C? Express it in joules and in eV. What is the corresponding rms velocity if the gas is (a) hydrogen, (b) oxygen, (c) nitrogen? Note that the molecules of these gases are diatomic. Do the same for helium (monatomic) and carbon dioxide.

9.50 Find the internal energy of one mole of an ideal gas at 0°C (273°K). Does it depend on the nature of the gas? Why?

9.51 Find the change in internal energy of one mole of an ideal gas when its temperature changes from 0°C to 100°C. Do we also have to specify how the pressure and volume changed?

9.52 The process referred to in the preceding problem occurs at constant volume. (a) What was the work done by the gas? (b) What was the heat absorbed?

9.53 Repeat the previous problem when the process mentioned in Problem 9.51 occurs at constant pressure.

9.54 Identify the constant C that appears in Eq. (9.51) for the expansion work of a gas at constant temperature. (a) Compute the work done by one mole of an ideal gas when doubling its volume at a constant temperature equal to 0°C. (b) Compute the change in its internal energy and the heat absorbed.

9.55 Prove that if the potential energy for the interaction between two particles is $E_p = -Cr_{12}^{-n}$, then $\boldsymbol{r}_{12} \cdot \boldsymbol{F}_{12} = nE_p$. [*Hint:* Choose particle 1 as the origin of coordinates, and remember Section 8.13.]

9.56 Use the result of the preceding problem to rewrite the virial theorem, Eq. (9.56), in the form

$$E_{k,\text{ave}} = -\tfrac{1}{2}\left[\textstyle\sum_i \boldsymbol{F}_i \cdot \boldsymbol{r}_i + nE_p\right]_{\text{ave}},$$

where E_p corresponds to the total *internal* potential energy of the system. Note that if the system is isolated (i.e., no external forces act) then $E_{k,\text{ave}} = -\frac{1}{2}nE_{p,\text{ave}}$. Compare this last result with Eq. (8.49).

9.57 Assume that gravitational forces are attractive and follow the inverse-square law (Chapter 13) so that the total potential energy is negative and $n = 1$. Using the result of Problem 9.56, prove (a) that the total energy of an isolated mass system is negative, (b) that if energy is lost by the system (usually by radiation), the potential energy must decrease, (c) that this requires that the kinetic energy of the system increase, resulting in a corresponding increase in the temperature of the system. (These results are of great importance in astrophysics.)

9.58 Discuss the applicability of the virial theorem to a system in which the internal forces are repulsive. Assume that the potential energy between the two particles is $E_p = +Cr_{12}^{-n}$.

9.59 A body whose mass is 10 kg and which has a velocity of 3 m s^{-1} slides on a horizontal surface until friction causes it to stop. Determine the amount of energy transferred to internal molecular motion in both the body and the surface. Express it in joules and in calories. Would you say that this energy has been transferred as heat?

9.60 The masses of blocks A and B in Fig. 9–34 are m_1 and m_2. Between A and

B there is a frictional force of magnitude F, but B can slide frictionlessly on the horizontal surface. Initially A is moving with velocity v_0 while B is at rest. If no other forces act on the system, A will slow down and B will speed up until the two blocks move with the same velocity v. (a) What is the distance moved by A and B before this happens, measured relative to the horizontal surface? (b) What is the change in kinetic energy of the system in terms of the distance moved by A relative to B? (c) What has happened to the total momentum?

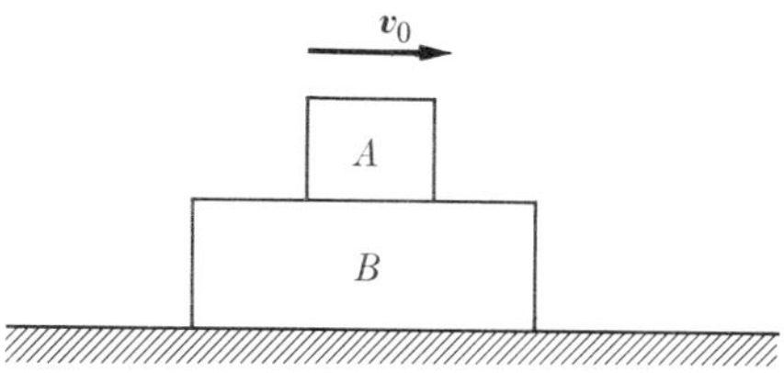

Figure 9–34

9.61 A horizontal pipe has a cross section of 10 cm^2 in one region and of 5 cm^2 in another. The water velocity at the first is 5 m s^{-1} and the pressure in the second is 2×10^5 N m^{-2}. Find (a) the velocity of the water in the second region and the pressure of the water in the first region, (b) the amount of water crossing a section in one minute, (c) the total energy per kilogram of water.

9.62 Repeat the previous problem for a case in which the pipe is tilted and the second section is 2 m higher than the first.

9.63 Verify that the equation of motion of a fluid in vector form is $\rho\, d\boldsymbol{v}/dt = -\text{grad}\, p + \boldsymbol{f}_e$.

9.64 Show that if there is a hole in the wall of a vessel and if the surface of the liquid inside the vessel is at a height h above the hole, the velocity of the liquid flowing through the hole is $v = \sqrt{2gh}$. Consider a cylindrical vessel having a diameter of 0.10 m and a height of 0.20 m. A hole 1 cm^2 in cross section is opened at its base. Water is flowing into the vessel at the rate of 1.4×10^{-4} m^3 s^{-1}. (a) Determine how high the water level will rise in the vessel. (b) After reaching that height the flow of water into the vessel is stopped. Find the time required for the vessel to empty.

9.65 Using the equation of motion derived in Problem 9.63, prove that, for a compressible fluid, Bernoulli's theorem adopts the form $(\frac{1}{2}v_2^2 + gz_2) - (\frac{1}{2}v_1^2 + gz_1) + \int_1^2 dp/\rho = W$, where W is the work per unit mass done *on* the fluid by other forces in addition to gravitation. [*Hint:* Separate the external force per unit volume $\boldsymbol{f}_{\text{ext}}$ into the weight $-\rho g \boldsymbol{u}_z$ and any other force that may act on the fluid, then divide the resulting equation of motion by ρ and multiply scalarly by $\boldsymbol{v}\, dt = d\boldsymbol{r}$, noting that $(\text{grad}\, p) \cdot d\boldsymbol{r} = dp$.]

9.66 A cylinder of height h and cross section A stands vertically in a fluid of density ρ_f. The fluid pressure is given by $p = p_0 - \rho_f g z$, according to Eq. (9.69). Prove that the total upward force on the cylinder due to the fluid pressure is $V\rho_f g$, where V is the cylinder's volume. Extend the result to a body of arbitrary shape by dividing it into thin vertical cylinders. (This result constitutes *Archimedes' principle*, and the force is known as the *buoyancy*.)

9.67 From Eq. (9.62), show that if the temperature of an ideal gas is constant, then pV = const or $p_1V_1 = p_2V_2$, a result known as *Boyle's law*. Show also that if the pressure is constant, then V/T = const or $V_1/T_1 = V_2/T_2$, a result known as *Charles' law*. Finally, show that if the volume is constant, then p/T = const or $p_1/T_1 = p_2/T_2$, a result known as *Gay-Lussac's law*. These laws were known experimentally long before they were synthesized in Eq. (9.62).

9.68 Consider a system composed of N identical particles, each of mass m (such as occurs in a gas). Show that the average kinetic energy of a particle relative to an observer who sees the center of mass moving with velocity v_{CM} is equal to the average kinetic energy of the particles relative to the C-frame of reference plus $\frac{1}{2}mv_{CM}^2$. [*Hint:* Use the relation given by Eq. (9.38).]

9.69 The pressure of a gas is related to its density by the equation $p = \rho(RT/M)$, where M is the molecular mass on the atomic scale (see Problem 9.47). (a) Using the result of Section 9.13, prove that if a gas is in equilibrium its pressure must change with the height according to

$$p = p_0 e^{-(Mg/RT)z}.$$

This is sometimes called the *barometric equation,* and may be used to estimate the variation of atmospheric pressure with height. (b) Prove that for small heights it reduces to the value given at the end of Section 9.14 for an incompressible fluid.

9.70 A bomb explodes into three fragments of equal mass m. The explosion releases an energy Q. In this case the laws of energy and momentum conservation do not uniquely determine the energy and momentum of each fragment. Referring the process to the C-frame of reference, show that (a) the kinetic energies of the fragments can be represented by the distances from a point P to the sides of an equilateral triangle of altitude Q. (b) Also show that the conservation of momentum requires that the point P be inside the circle (with radius $\frac{1}{3}Q$) inscribed in the triangle. This representation is called a *Dalitz diagram* (Fig. 9–35) and is widely used to describe the decay of a fundamental particle into three equal fragments. [*Hint:* For the proof of (b), note that in the C-frame the total momentum is zero, and thus $p_1 + p_2 \geq p_3$. Also the three energies can be expressed as $E_{k,1} = PN = \frac{1}{3}Q + r\cos(\phi - 2\pi/3)$, $E_{k,2} = PM = \frac{1}{3}Q + r\cos(\phi + 2\pi/3)$, and $E_{k,3} = PL = \frac{1}{3}Q + r\cos\phi$.]

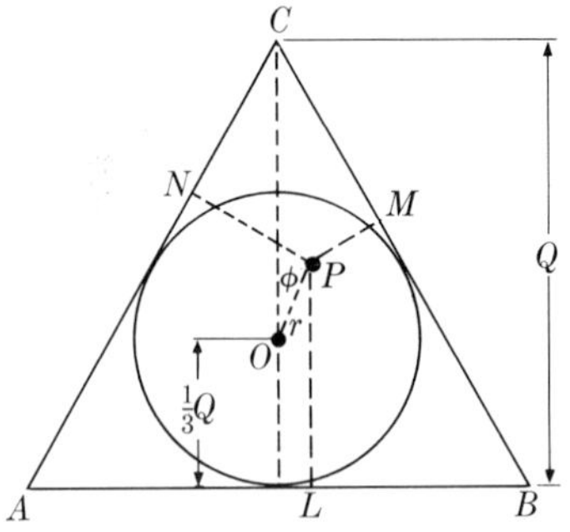

Figure 9–35

10
DYNAMICS OF A RIGID BODY

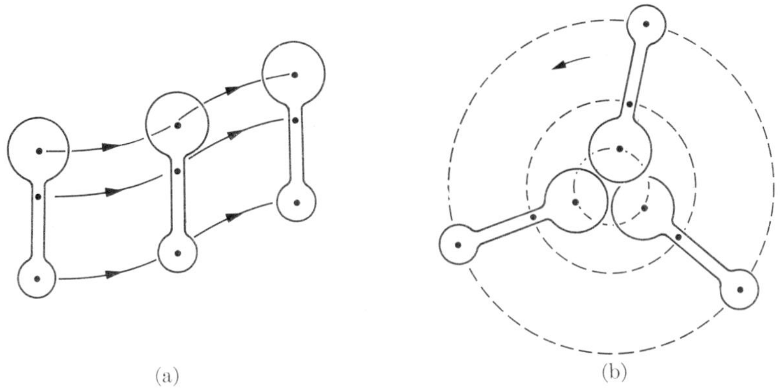

Fig. 10–1. (a) Motion of translation of a rigid body. (b) Motion of rotation of a rigid body.

10.1 Introduction

A special and important case of systems composed of many particles is a *rigid body*; that is, a body in which the distances between all its component particles remain fixed under the application of a force or torque. A rigid body therefore conserves its shape during its motion.

We may distinguish two types of motion of a rigid body. The motion is a *translation* when all the particles describe parallel paths so that the lines joining any two points in the body always remain parallel to its initial position (Fig. 10–1a). The motion is a *rotation* around an axis when all the particles describe circular paths around a line called the axis of rotation (Fig. 10–1b). The axis may be fixed or it may be changing its direction relative to the body during the motion.

The most general motion of a rigid body can always be considered as a combination of a rotation and a translation. That is, it is always possible to find a translating, nonrotating frame of reference in which the body's motion appears to be rotation only. For example, the motion of the body in Fig. 10–2 which passes from position 1 to position 2 can be considered as a translation represented by the displacement CC', joining the two positions of the center of mass, and a rotation around an axis through the center of mass C'.

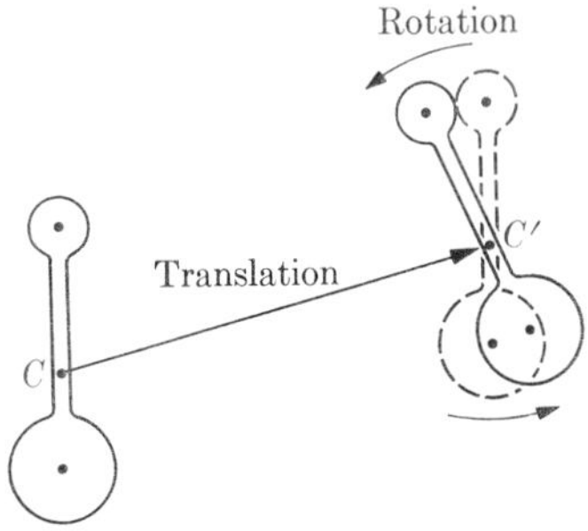

Fig. 10–2. General motion of a rigid body.

According to Eq. (9.9), $M\, d\boldsymbol{v}_{\text{CM}}/dt = \boldsymbol{F}_{\text{ext}}$, the motion of the center of mass is identical to the motion of a single particle whose mass is equal to the mass of the body and which is acted on by a force equal to the sum of all external forces applied to the body. This motion can be analyzed according to the methods explained in Chapter 7 for the dynamics of a particle, and therefore does not involve special techniques. In this chapter we shall ex-

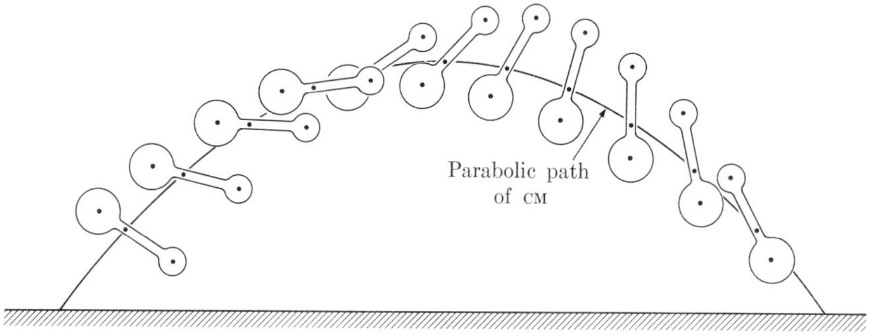

Fig. 10–3. Motion of a rigid body under the action of gravity. The CM describes the parabolic path corresponding to a particle of mass M under a force $M\boldsymbol{g}$, while the body rotates around the CM. Since the weight is applied at the CM, its torque around that point is zero and the angular momentum of the body relative to the CM remains constant during the motion.

amine the rotational motion of a rigid body around an axis which passes either through a point fixed in an inertial system or through the center of mass of the body. In the first case, Eq. (9.19), $d\boldsymbol{L}/dt = \boldsymbol{\tau}$ (where $\boldsymbol{L}$ and $\boldsymbol{\tau}$ are both computed relative to the fixed point) is used for discussing the motion, while in the second case, Eq. (9.25), $d\boldsymbol{L}_{\text{CM}}/dt = \boldsymbol{\tau}_{\text{CM}}$ must be used (Fig. 10–3).

10.2 Angular Momentum of a Rigid Body

Let us consider a rigid body rotating around an axis Z with angular velocity $\boldsymbol{\omega}$ (Fig. 10–4). Each of its particles describes a circular orbit with its center on the Z-axis. For example, particle A_i describes a circle of radius $R_i = A_iB_i$ with a velocity $\boldsymbol{v}_i = \boldsymbol{\omega} \times \boldsymbol{r}_i$, where $\boldsymbol{r}_i$ is the position vector relative to the origin O (this will be chosen as a point fixed in an inertial frame or at the center of mass of the body). The magnitude of the velocity is $v_i = \omega r_i \sin\theta_i = \omega R_i$, according to Eq. (5.48). Note that we write ω and not ω_i, because the angular velocity is the same for all particles in a rigid body. The angular momentum of particle A_i relative to the origin O is

$$\boldsymbol{L}_i = m_i \boldsymbol{r}_i \times \boldsymbol{v}_i.$$

Its direction is perpendicular to the plane determined by the vectors $\boldsymbol{r}_i$ and $\boldsymbol{v}_i$ and lies in the plane determined by $\boldsymbol{r}_i$ and the Z-axis. It therefore makes an angle $\pi/2 - \theta_i$ with the axis of rotation Z. The magnitude of $\boldsymbol{L}_i$ is $m_i r_i v_i$, and its component parallel to the Z-axis is

$$\begin{aligned} L_{iz} &= (m_i r_i v_i) \cos(\pi/2 - \theta_i) \\ &= m_i (r_i \sin\theta_i)(\omega R_i) = m_i R_i^2 \omega, \end{aligned}$$

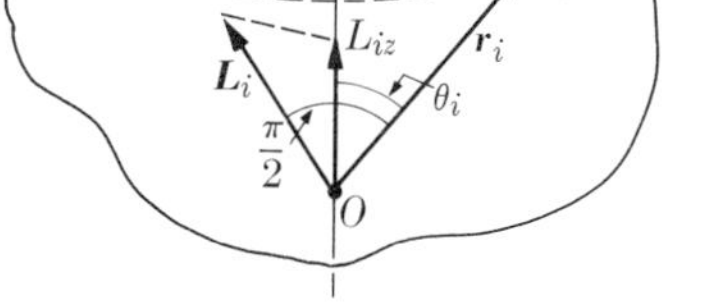

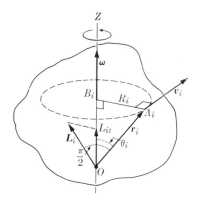

Fig. 10–4. Angular momentum of a rotating rigid body.

a result equivalent to Eq. (7.33) for a particle moving in a circle. The component of the total angular momentum of the rotating body along the rotation axis Z is

$$L_z = L_{1z} + L_{2z} + L_{3z} + \cdots = \sum_i L_{iz}$$
$$= (m_1 R_1^2 + m_2 R_2^2 + m_3 R_3^2 + \cdots)\omega = (\sum_i m_i R_i^2)\omega. \quad (10.1)$$

The quantity

$$I = m_1 R_1^2 + m_2 R_2^2 + m_3 R_3^2 + \cdots = \sum_i m_i R_i^2 \quad (10.2)$$

is called the *moment of inertia* of the body relative to the axis of rotation Z. It is obtained by adding, for each particle, the product of its mass times the square of its distance to the axis. The moment of inertia is a very important quantity that appears in many expressions related to the rotation of a rigid body. We may thus write Eq. (10.1) in the form

$$L_z = I\omega. \quad (10.3)$$

The total angular momentum of the body is

$$\boldsymbol{L} = \boldsymbol{L}_1 + \boldsymbol{L}_2 + \boldsymbol{L}_3 + \cdots = \sum_i \boldsymbol{L}_i,$$

and in general is *not* parallel to the axis of rotation, since we have indicated that the individual angular momenta $\boldsymbol{L}_i$ appearing in the sum are not parallel to the axis.

The student at this moment may wonder whether, for each body, there is some axis of rotation for which the total angular momentum is parallel to the axis. The answer is yes. It can be proved that for each body, no matter what its shape, there are (at least) three mutually perpendicular directions for which the angular momentum is parallel to the axis of rotation. These are called the *principal axes of inertia*, and the corresponding moments of inertia are called the *principal moments of inertia*, designated by I_1, I_2, and I_3. Let us designate the principal axes by $X_0Y_0Z_0$; they constitute a frame of reference attached to the body, and therefore in general rotate relative to the observer. When the body has some kind of symmetry, the principal axes coincide with some of the symmetry axes. For example, in a sphere, any axis passing through its center is a principal axis. For a

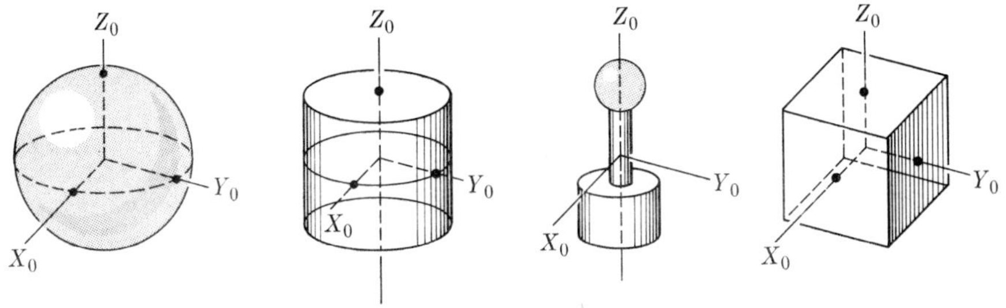

Fig. 10–5. Principal axis of symmetrical bodies.

cylinder, and in general for any body with cylindrical symmetry, the axis of symmetry, as well as any axis perpendicular to it, are principal axes. For a rectangular block the three principal axes are perpendicular to the surfaces and pass through the center of the block. These axes are illustrated in Fig. 10–5.

When the body rotates around a principal axis of inertia, the total angular momentum $\boldsymbol{L}$ is parallel to the angular velocity $\boldsymbol{\omega}$, which is always along the rotation axis, and instead of the scalar Eq. (10.3), which is valid for the Z-component along the rotation axis, we may write the vector relation

$$\boldsymbol{L} = I\boldsymbol{\omega}, \tag{10.4}$$

where I is the corresponding principal moment of inertia. We must insist that this vector relation is valid only for rotation about a principal axis of inertia.

In the more general case of rotation of a rigid body around an arbitrary axis, the angular momentum $\boldsymbol{L}$ can be expressed relative to the moving principal axes of inertia $X_0Y_0Z_0$ (Fig. 10–6) in the form

$$\boldsymbol{L} = \boldsymbol{u}_{x0}I_1\omega_{x0} + \boldsymbol{u}_{y0}I_2\omega_{y0} + \boldsymbol{u}_{z0}I_3\omega_{z0}, \tag{10.5}$$

where $\boldsymbol{u}_{x0}$, $\boldsymbol{u}_{y0}$, and $\boldsymbol{u}_{z0}$ are the unit vectors along X_0, Y_0, and Z_0 and ω_{x0}, ω_{y0}, and ω_{z0} are the components of $\boldsymbol{\omega}$ relative to the same axes. In this case, $\boldsymbol{L}$ and $\boldsymbol{\omega}$ have different directions, as we have stated before. The advantage of using this expression for $\boldsymbol{L}$ is that I_1, I_2, and I_3 are fixed quantities that can be evaluated for each body. However, since the unit vectors $\boldsymbol{u}_{x0}$, $\boldsymbol{u}_{y0}$, and $\boldsymbol{u}_{z0}$ rotate with the body, they are not necessarily constant in direction. The student can verify that Eq. (10.5) reduces to Eq. (10.4) for rotation around a principal axis (two of the components of $\boldsymbol{\omega}$ are zero).

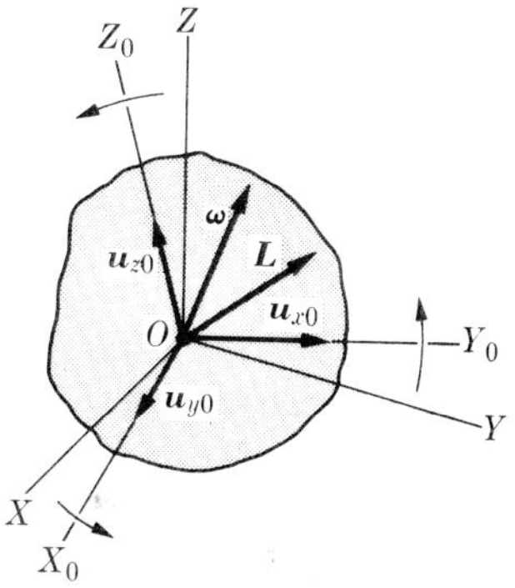

Fig. 10–6. Axes attached to the body and axes fixed in the laboratory.

EXAMPLE 10.1. Compute the angular momentum of the system illustrated in Fig. 10–7, which consists of two equal spheres of mass m mounted on arms connected to a bearing and rotating around the Z-axis. Neglect the masses of the arms.

Solution: In Fig. 10–7(a) we have a case in which the two arms are perpendicular to the axis of rotation Z. Each sphere describes a circle of radius R with velocity $v = \omega R$. The angular momentum of each sphere relative to O is then $mR^2\omega$, and is directed along the Z-axis. (Remember Fig. 7–22.) Thus the total angular momentum of the system is $L = 2mR^2\omega$ along the Z-axis, so that we can write in vector form $\boldsymbol{L} = 2mR^2\boldsymbol{\omega}$, indicating that the system is rotating about a principal axis. In fact, the principal axes $X_0Y_0Z_0$ are as shown in the figure, Z_0 coinciding with Z.* Note that $I = 2mR^2$ is the principal moment of inertia around the Z_0-axis, and thus the relation $\boldsymbol{L} = I\boldsymbol{\omega}$ holds for this case.

---

* Due to the symmetry of the system under consideration, any axis perpendicular to X_0 is a principal axis.

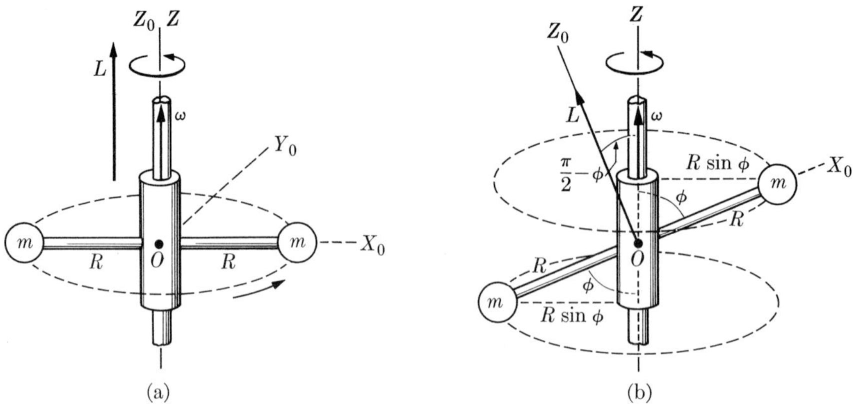

Figure 10–7

In Fig. 10–7(b) we have a case in which the two arms make an angle ϕ with the axis of rotation Z, so that $\boldsymbol{\omega}$ is not parallel to a principal axis. The radius of the circle described by each sphere is $R \sin\phi$, so that their velocities are, in magnitude, $(R \sin\phi)\omega$. The angular momentum of each sphere relative to O is then $mR(R\omega \sin\phi)$ and is directed perpendicular to the line joining the two spheres and in the plane determined by the Z- and X_0-axes. The total angular momentum is the sum of the two results, that is, $L = (2mR^2 \sin\phi)\omega$, and makes an angle $\pi/2 - \phi$ with the rotation axis. Thus in this case the system is not rotating about a principal axis, as we may also see from the geometry of the system. Note that the vector $\boldsymbol{L}$ is rotating (or, as it is sometimes called, *precessing*) around the Z-axis at the same rate as the system.

The component of $\boldsymbol{L}$ along the rotation axis is

$$L_z = L\cos(\pi/2 - \phi) = (2mR^2 \sin^2\phi)\omega,$$

in agreement with Eq. (10.3), since $I = 2m(R\sin\phi)^2$ is the moment of inertia of the system relative to the Z-axis.

10.3 Calculation of the Moment of Inertia

We shall now discuss the computational techniques for obtaining the moment of inertia, since this quantity will be used very often in this chapter. First we note that a rigid body is composed of a very large number of particles, so that the sum in Eq. (10.2) must be replaced by an integral, $I = \sum_i m_i R_i^2 = \int R^2\, dm$; or, if ρ is the density of the body, $dm = \rho\, dV$ according to Eq. (2.2), and

$$I = \int \rho R^2\, dV. \tag{10.6}$$

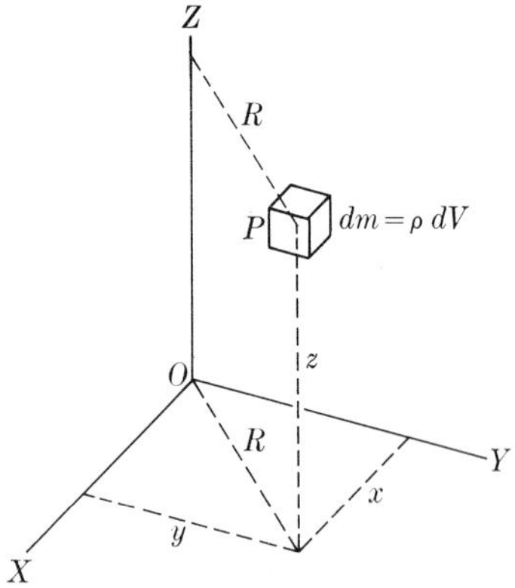

Figure 10–8

If the body is homogeneous, its density is constant, and instead of Eq. (10.6) we may write

$I = \rho \int R^2 \, dV$. The integral thus reduces to a geometrical factor, the same for all bodies with the same shape and size. We note from Fig. 10–8 that $R^2 = x^2 + y^2$, and therefore the moment of inertia around the Z-axis is

$$I_Z = \int \rho(x^2 + y^2) \, dV. \tag{10.7}$$

(We suggest that the student write the corresponding relations for I_x and I_y.)

If the body is a thin plate, as indicated in Fig. 10–9, we note that the moments of inertia relative to the X- and Y-axes may be written as $I_x = \int \rho y^2 \, dV$ and $I_y = \int \rho x^2 \, dV$ because the Z-coordinate is essentially zero. Comparison with Eq. (10.7) shows that in this case

$$I_z = I_x + I_y,$$

a result that is valid only for thin plates.

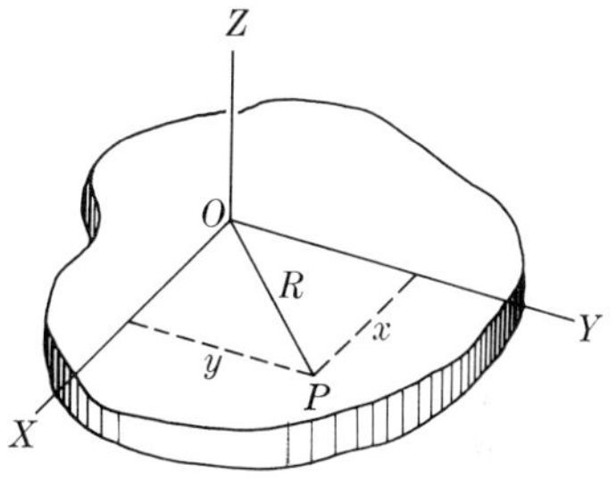

Figure 10–9

The moments of inertia relative to parallel axes are related by a very simple formula. Let Z be an arbitrary axis and Z_C a parallel axis passing through the center of mass of the body (Fig. 10–10). If a is the separation between the two axes, the following relation, called *Steiner's theorem*, holds,

$$I = I_C + Ma^2, \tag{10.8}$$

where I and I_C are the moments of inertia of the body relative to Z and Z_C, respectively, and M is the mass of the body. To prove this relation, let us choose the axes $X_C Y_C Z_C$ so that their origin is at the center of mass C and the Y_C axis is in the plane determined by Z and Z_C. The axes XYZ are chosen so that Y coincides with Y_C. The point P is any arbitrary point in the body M. Then, noting from Fig. 10–10 that $P'A$ is perpendicular to Y_C and $P'A = x$, $CA = y$, and $OC = a$, we have

$$\begin{aligned} R_C^2 &= x^2 + y^2, \\ R^2 &= x^2 + (y + a)^2 \\ &= x^2 + y^2 + 2ya + a^2 \\ &= R_C^2 + 2ya + a^2. \end{aligned}$$

Now the moment of inertia relative to the Z-axis is

$$\begin{aligned} I &= \sum mR^2 = \sum m(R_C^2 + 2ya + a^2) \\ &= \sum mR_C^2 + 2a\left(\sum my\right) + a^2 \sum m. \end{aligned}$$

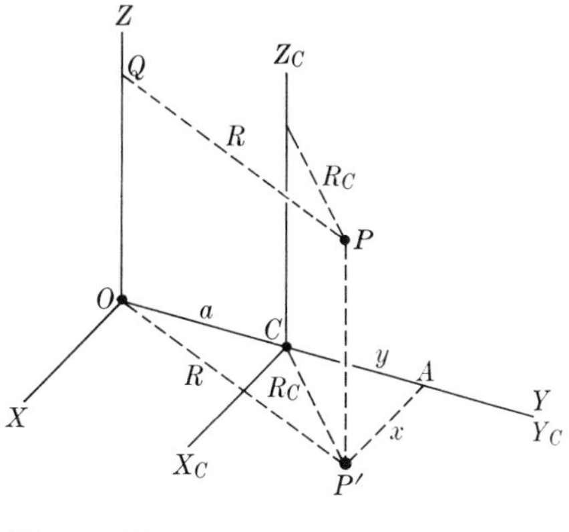

Figure 10–10

The first term is just the moment of

inertia I_C relative to the Z_C-axis, and in the last term $\sum m = M$, the total mass of the body. Therefore

$$I = I_C + 2a\sum my + Ma^2. \tag{10.9}$$

To evaluate the middle term, we recall from Eq. (4.21) that the position of the center of mass is given by $y_{CM} = \sum my/\sum m$. But in our case $y_{CM} = 0$ because the center of mass coincides with the origin C of the frame $X_CY_CZ_C$. Then $\sum my = 0$, and Eq. (10.9) reduces to Eq. (10.8), which is thus proved.

The moment of inertia must be expressed as the product of a unit of mass and the square of a unit of distance. Thus in the MKSC system the moment of inertia is expressed in m^2 kg.

TABLE 10–1 Radii of Gyration of Some Simple Bodies

K^2	Axis	K^2	Axis
	Cylinder		Thin rod
$\frac{R^2}{2}$	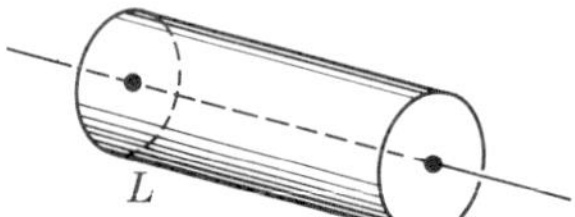	$\frac{L^2}{12}$	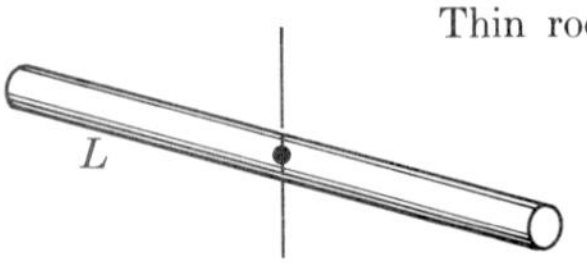
$\frac{R^2}{4} + \frac{L^2}{12}$	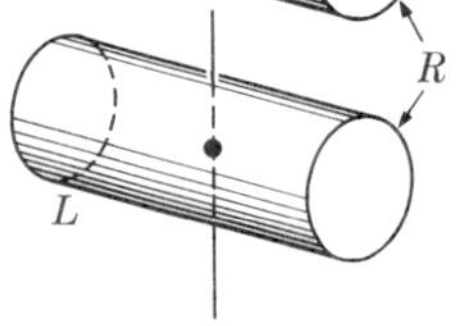		Disk
		$\frac{R^2}{2}$	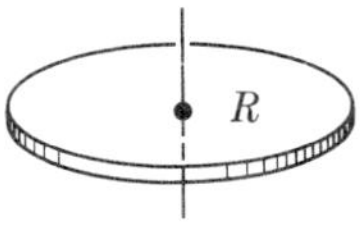
	Parallelepiped	$\frac{R^2}{4}$	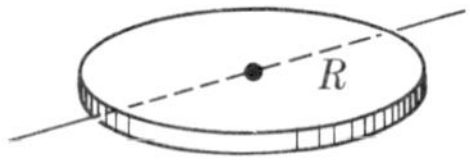
$\frac{a^2+b^2}{12}$	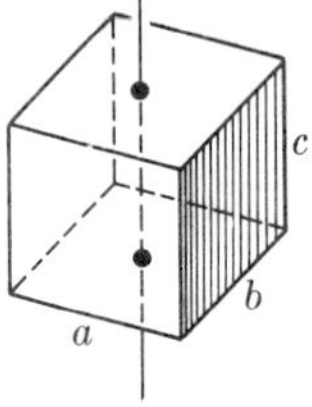		Ring
	Rectangular plate	R^2	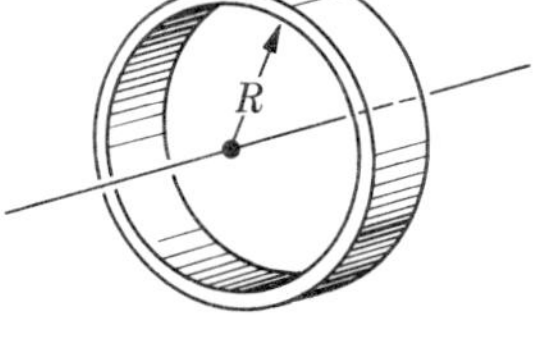
$\frac{a^2+b^2}{12}$	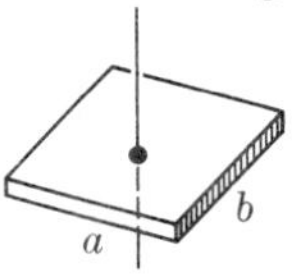		Sphere
$\frac{b^2}{12}$	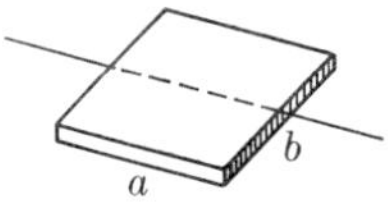	$\frac{2R^2}{5}$	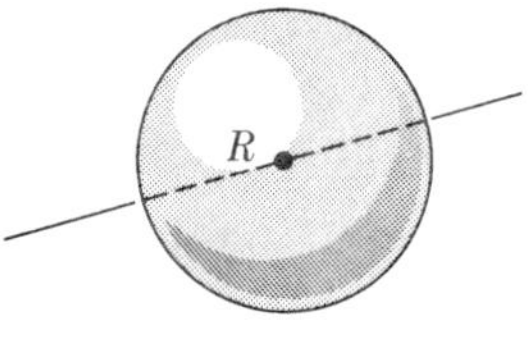

The *radius of gyration* of a body is a quantity K defined such that the following relation holds,

$$I = MK^2 \qquad \text{or} \qquad K = \sqrt{I/M}, \tag{10.10}$$

where I is the moment of inertia and M the mass of the body. It represents the distance from the axis at which all the mass could be concentrated without changing the moment of inertia. It is a useful quantity because it can be determined, for homogeneous bodies, entirely by their geometry. It can thus be easily tabulated, and helps us to compute the moments of inertia.* Table 10–1 gives the squares of the radii of gyration of several geometric figures.

EXAMPLE 10.2. Compute the moment of inertia of a homogeneous thin rod relative to an axis perpendicular to the rod and passing through (a) one end, and (b) the center.

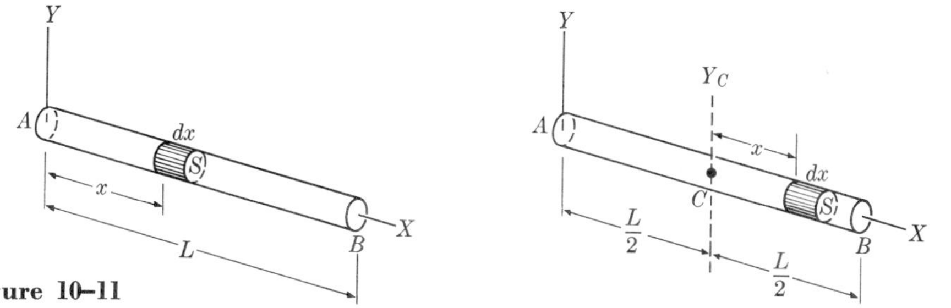

Figure 10–11

Solution: (a) Let us call L the length of the rod AB (Fig. 10–11) and S its cross section, which we assume is very small. Dividing the rod into small segments of length dx, we find that the volume of each segment is $dV = S\,dx$ and the distance from each element to the axis Y is $R = x$. Thus, using Eq. (10.6) with the density ρ constant, we have

$$I_A = \int_0^L \rho x^2 (S\,dx) = \rho S \int_0^L x^2\,dx = \tfrac{1}{3}\rho S L^3.$$

But SL is the volume of the rod and ρSL is the mass. Therefore

$$I_A = \tfrac{1}{3}ML^2.$$

Comparison with Eq. (10.10) gives the radius of gyration as $K^2 = \frac{1}{3}L^2$.

(b) To compute the moment of inertia relative to the axis Y_C passing through the center of mass C, we may proceed in three different ways. A very simple one is to assume the rod divided into two, each of mass $\frac{1}{2}M$ and length $\frac{1}{2}L$, with their ends touching at C, and use the previous result for each rod. Then

$$I_C = 2(\tfrac{1}{3})(\tfrac{1}{2}M)(\tfrac{1}{2}L)^2 = \tfrac{1}{12}ML^2.$$

Another method would be to proceed as before for the end A, but integrate from $-\frac{1}{2}L$ to

* For the technique of computing moments of inertia, see any calculus text; for example, *Calculus and Analytic Geometry*, third edition, by G. B. Thomas. Reading, Mass.: Addison-Wesley, 1962, Section 15.3.

$+\frac{1}{2}L$, since the origin is now at the center of the rod. We leave this solution to the student. A third method is to apply Steiner's theorem, Eq. (10.8), which in this case reads $I_A = I_C + M(\frac{1}{2}L)^2$, since $a = \frac{1}{2}L$. Thus

$$I_C = I_A - \tfrac{1}{4}ML^2 = \tfrac{1}{12}ML^2.$$

EXAMPLE 10.3. Compute the moment of inertia of a homogeneous disk relative to (a) an axis perpendicular to the disk passing through its center, and (b) an axis coincident with one diameter.

Solution: (a) From Fig. 10–12 we see that the symmetry of the problem suggests that we use, as the volume element, a ring of radius r and width dr. Thus if we call h the thickness of the disk, the volume of the ring is $dV = (2\pi r)(dr)h = 2\pi hr\,dr$. All the points of the ring are at distance r from the axis Z. Therefore, using Eq. (10.6), we obtain

$$I = \int_0^R \rho r^2 (2\pi hr\,dr)$$

$$= 2\pi\rho h \int_0^R r^3\,dr = \tfrac{1}{2}\pi\rho h R^4.$$

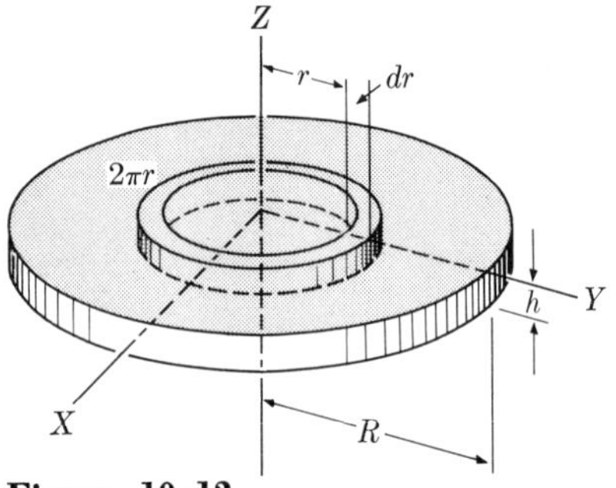

Figure 10–12

But $\pi R^2 h$ is the volume of the disk and $M = \rho(\pi R^2 h)$ is the total mass of the disk. Thus

$$I = \tfrac{1}{2}MR^2,$$

so that the radius of gyration is $K^2 = \frac{1}{2}R^2$.

(b) To obtain the moments of inertia with respect to the X- and Y-axes, we may proceed by direct integration (it is suggested that strips parallel or perpendicular to the corresponding axis be used as volume elements), but the symmetry of the problem allows a simpler procedure. Obviously $I_x = I_y$ in this case, and therefore, from the thin-plate formula, we have $I_z = I_x + I_y = 2I_x$ and

$$I_x = \tfrac{1}{2}I_z = \tfrac{1}{4}MR^2.$$

10.4 Equation of Motion for Rotation of a Rigid Body

In Eq. (9.21) we established a relation between the total angular momentum of a system of particles and the total torque of the forces applied to the particles when both torque and angular momentum are referred to a point at rest in an inertial system. That is,

$$\frac{d\mathbf{L}}{dt} = \boldsymbol{\tau}, \tag{10.11}$$

where $\mathbf{L} = \sum_i \mathbf{L}_i$ is the total angular momentum and $\boldsymbol{\tau} = \sum_i \boldsymbol{\tau}_i$ is the total torque due to the external forces. Obviously this equation also holds for a rigid body, which is a special case of a system of particles. Equation (10.11) thus constitutes the basic equation for discussing the rotational motion of a rigid body. We shall apply it first to the case of a rigid body rotating around a principal axis having a point fixed in an inertial system. Then, according to Eq. (10.4), $\boldsymbol{L} = I\boldsymbol{\omega}$. The external torque $\boldsymbol{\tau}$ must be the torque around the fixed point on the principal axis. Hence Eq. (10.11) becomes

$$\frac{d(I\boldsymbol{\omega})}{dt} = \boldsymbol{\tau}. \qquad (10.12)$$

If the axis remains fixed relative to the rigid body, the moment of inertia remains constant. Then

$$I\frac{d\boldsymbol{\omega}}{dt} = \boldsymbol{\tau} \qquad \text{or} \qquad I\boldsymbol{\alpha} = \boldsymbol{\tau}, \qquad (10.13)$$

where $\boldsymbol{\alpha} = d\boldsymbol{\omega}/dt$ is the angular acceleration of the rigid body. Comparison of Eqs. (10.12) and (10.13) with Eqs. (7.14) and (7.15) suggests a great similarity between the rotation of a rigid body about a principal axis and the motion of a particle. The mass m is replaced by the moment of inertia I, the velocity $\boldsymbol{v}$ by the angular velocity $\boldsymbol{\omega}$, the acceleration $\boldsymbol{a}$ by the angular acceleration $\boldsymbol{\alpha}$, and the force $\boldsymbol{F}$ by the torque $\boldsymbol{\tau}$.

For example, if $\boldsymbol{\tau} = 0$, then Eq. (10.12) indicates that $I\boldsymbol{\omega} = \text{const}$; and if the moment of inertia is constant then $\boldsymbol{\omega}$ is also constant. That is, *a rigid body rotating around a principal axis moves with constant angular velocity when no external torques are applied.* This could be considered as the law of inertia for rotational motion. [When the moment of inertia is variable, which may happen if the body is not rigid, the condition $I\boldsymbol{\omega} = \text{const}$ requires that if I increases (decreases) then $\boldsymbol{\omega}$ decreases (increases), a fact that has several applications.]

In the case of a body which is *not* rotating around a principal axis, we still have from Eq. (10.3) that $dL_z/dt = \tau_z$ or, if the orientation of the axis is fixed relative to the body so that I is constant,

$$I\frac{d\omega}{dt} = \tau_z, \qquad (10.14)$$

a result that differs from Eq. (10.13) in that τ_z refers to the component of the total external torque around the rotation axis and not to the total torque. In addition to the τ_z-component of the torque, there may be other torques required to maintain the body in a fixed position relative to the axis of rotation (see Example 10.7).

When the axis of rotation does not have a point fixed in an inertial system, we cannot use Eq. (10.11), and we must compute the angular momentum and the torque relative to the center of mass of the body. Thus we must use Eq. (9.25), which is

$$\frac{d\boldsymbol{L}_{\text{CM}}}{dt} = \boldsymbol{\tau}_{\text{CM}}. \qquad (10.15)$$

If the rotation is around a principal axis, this equation becomes $I\ (d\boldsymbol{\omega}/dt) = \boldsymbol{\tau}_{\text{CM}}$. If $\boldsymbol{\tau}_{\text{CM}} = 0$, which is the case when the only external force applied to the body is its weight, it then follows that $\boldsymbol{\omega}$ is constant (see Fig. 10–3).

EXAMPLE 10.4. A disk of radius 0.5 m and mass 20 kg can rotate freely around a fixed horizontal axis passing through its center. A force of 9.8 N is applied by pulling a string wound around the edge of the disk. Find the angular acceleration of the disk and its angular velocity after 2 s.

Solution: From Fig. 10–13 we see that the only external forces on the disk are its weight Mg, the downward pull F, and the forces F' at the pivots. The axis ZZ' is a principal axis. Taking torques with respect to the center of mass C, we find that the torque of the weight is zero. The combined torque of the F' forces is also zero. Thus $\tau = FR$. Applying Eq. (10.14) with $I = \frac{1}{2}MR^2$, we have $FR = (\frac{1}{2}MR^2)\alpha$ or $F = \frac{1}{2}MR\alpha$, giving an angular acceleration of

$$\alpha = \frac{2F}{MR} = \frac{2(9.8 \text{ N})}{(20 \text{ kg})(0.5 \text{ m})} = 1.96 \text{ rad s}^{-2}.$$

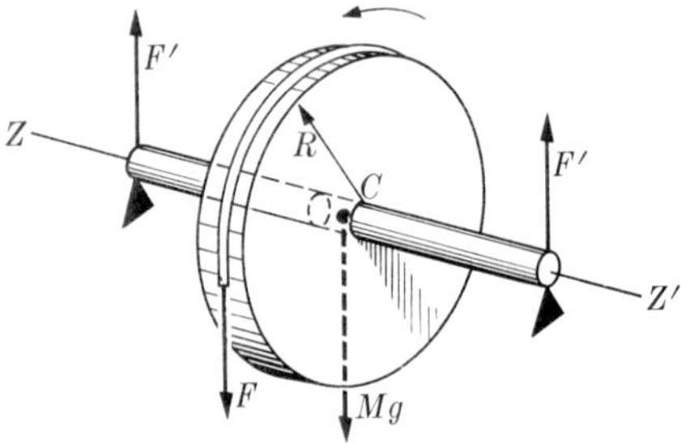

Figure 10–13

According to Eq. (5.54), the angular velocity after 2 s if the disk started from rest is

$$\omega = \alpha t = (1.96 \text{ rad s}^{-2})(2 \text{ s}) = 3.92 \text{ rad s}^{-1}.$$

Since the center of mass C is fixed, its acceleration is zero and we must have

$$2F' - Mg - F = 0 \qquad \text{or} \qquad F' = 205.8 \text{ N}.$$

EXAMPLE 10.5. Find the angular acceleration of the system illustrated in Fig. 10–14 for a body whose mass is 1 kg. The data for the disk are the same as in Example 10.4. The axis ZZ' is fixed and is a principal axis.

Solution: Since the mass of the body is 1 kg, its weight is $mg = 9.8$ N, which has the same value as the force F of Fig. 10–13. Therefore one would be tempted to consider this case as identical to the previous one and assume the results are the same. This is not, however, the case! The mass m, when falling, exerts a downward pull F on the disk, and by the law of action and reaction the disk exerts an equal but upward pull F on the mass m. Since the mass m is falling with accelerated motion, the net force on it cannot be zero. Thus F is not the same as mg, but smaller. Therefore the disk is subject also to a smaller torque.

The equation of motion of the mass m is

$$mg - F = ma = mR\alpha,$$

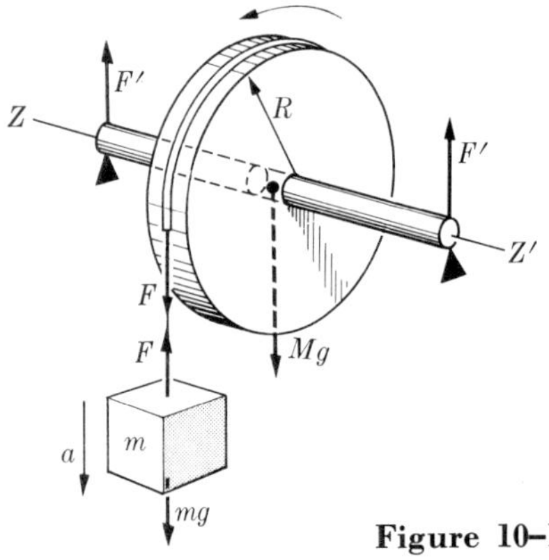

Figure 10–14

where the relation $a = R\alpha$ has been used. The equation of motion of the disk is $I\alpha = FR$ or (since $I = \frac{1}{2}MR^2$) $F = \frac{1}{2}MR\alpha$. Eliminating F between these two equations, we find that the angular acceleration is

$$\alpha = \frac{mg}{(m + \frac{1}{2}M)R} = 1.80 \text{ rad s}^{-2},$$

which is smaller than our previous result. The

downward acceleration of m is

$$a = R\alpha = \frac{mg}{m + \frac{1}{2}M} = 0.90 \text{ m s}^{-2},$$

which is smaller than $g = 9.80$ m s^{-2}, the value for free fall. The force F' at the pivot can be found as in the previous example.

EXAMPLE 10.6. Determine the angular acceleration of the disk of Fig. 10–15, as well as the downward acceleration of its center of mass. Assume the same data as for the disk of Example 10.4.

Solution: The axis of rotation is the principal axis Z_0Z_0'. This problem differs from the previous examples, however, in that the center of mass of the disk is not fixed, since the motion of the disk is similar to that of a yo-yo, and thus Eq. (10.15) must now be used. The rotation of the disk about axis Z_0Z_0' is given by the equation $I\alpha = FR$, since the torque of the weight Mg relative to C is zero. Thus, with $I = \frac{1}{2}MR^2$, we may write (after canceling a common factor R), $F = \frac{1}{2}MR\alpha$.

The downward motion of the center of mass has the acceleration $a = R\alpha$, and if we take into account the fact that the resultant external force is $Mg - F$, we have, using Eq. (9.9),

$$Mg - F = Ma = MR\alpha.$$

Eliminating the force F between this equation and the preceding one, and noting that the mass M cancels, we obtain from the resulting equation $\alpha = 2g/3R = 13.16$ rad s^{-2}. The downward acceleration of its center of mass is $a = R\alpha = \frac{2}{3}g = 6.53$ m s^{-2}, which is much less than the acceleration of free fall, and is independent of the size and mass of the disk.

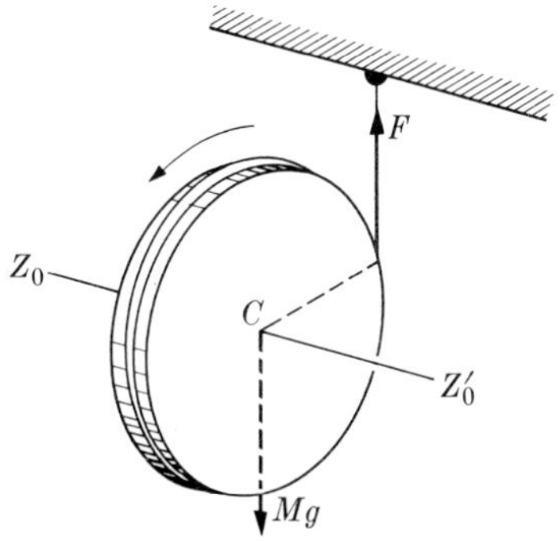

Figure 10–15

EXAMPLE 10.7. Compute the torque required to rotate the system of Fig. 10–7(b) with constant angular velocity.

Solution: In this case the angular velocity ω around the fixed axis Z does not change, and therefore $d\omega/dt = 0$. Two conclusions are immediately derived. First, we know that the total angular momentum $L = (2mR^2 \sin\phi)\omega$ remains constant in magnitude, and that the component along the Z-axis, $L_z = (2mR^2 \sin^2\phi)\omega$ is also constant. Second, the torque along the Z-axis, given by $\tau_z = I\, d\omega/dt$, is zero. At first sight we would be tempted to say, then, that no torque is required to maintain the system in motion. This is not, however, the case. The angular momentum $\boldsymbol{L}$ rotates with the system about the Z-axis (this is called *precession*, as mentioned at the end of Example 10.1), and a torque is required to produce this change in the direction of $\boldsymbol{L}$. The situation is entirely analogous to that found in uniform circular motion: The velocity remains constant in magnitude but a force is required to change its direction.

The torque $\boldsymbol{\tau}$ must be in the XY-plane, since $\tau_z = 0$. It must also be perpendicular to the Z_0Z-plane, determined by the direction of $\boldsymbol{L}$ (or the Z_0-axis) and the Z-axis (Figs. 10–16 and 10–17), and it must have the direction of the Y_0-axis. This can be seen as follows. Equation (10.11), $d\boldsymbol{L} = \boldsymbol{\tau}\, dt$, indicates that $d\boldsymbol{L}$ and $\boldsymbol{\tau}$ are parallel vectors (in

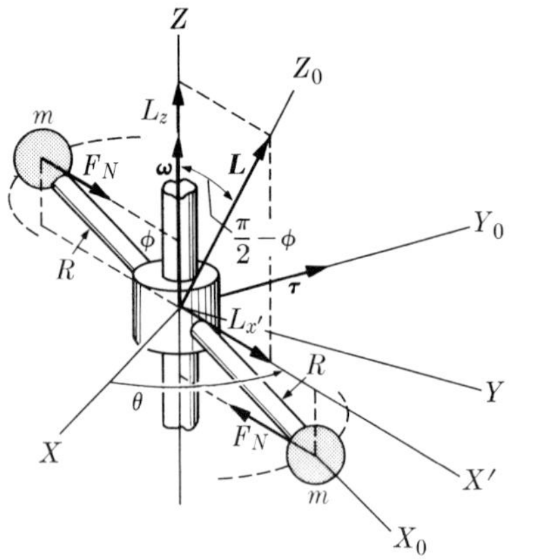

Fig. 10–16. Rotation of a body around an arbitrary axis.

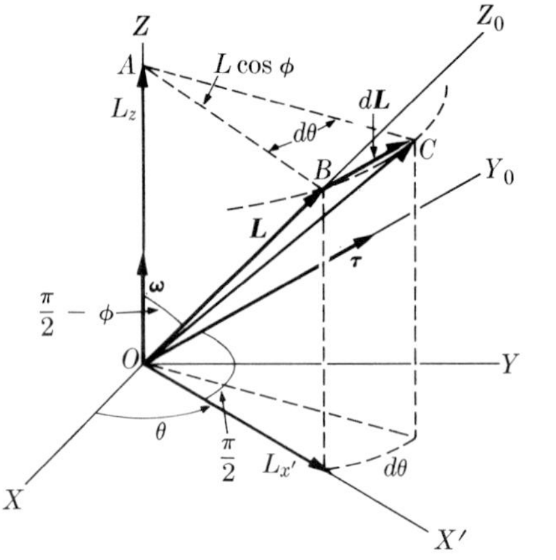

Fig. 10–17. Precession of the angular momentum of the body illustrated in Fig. 10–16.

the same sense that $d\boldsymbol{v}$ and $\boldsymbol{F}$ are parallel in the case of one particle). But, since $\boldsymbol{L}$ is constant in magnitude, $d\boldsymbol{L}$ is perpendicular to it, and so is $\boldsymbol{\tau}$. Since the vector $\boldsymbol{L}$ maintains a constant angle $\pi/2 - \phi$ with the Z-axis, its end point moves over a circle of radius $AB = L \sin(\pi/2 - \phi) = L \cos\phi$, and $d\boldsymbol{L}$ is tangent to the circle. This in turn implies that $d\boldsymbol{L}$ is perpendicular to the Z_0Z-plane (or parallel to Y_0), which means that $\boldsymbol{\tau}$ is also. To find the magnitude of $d\boldsymbol{L}$ we note from Fig. 10–17 that

$$|d\boldsymbol{L}| = AB\, d\theta = (L\cos\phi)\omega\, dt,$$

since $\omega = d\theta/dt$. Equating this to $\tau\, dt$ and introducing the value of L, we find that

$$\tau = (2mR^2 \sin\phi \cos\phi)\omega^2.$$

It is instructive to see the physical need for this torque. From Fig. 10–16 we note that the spheres, each of mass m, have uniform circular motion and each requires a centripetal force $F_N = m\omega^2 R \sin\phi$ to describe the circle of radius $R \sin\phi$. These two forces form a couple, whose lever arm is $2R\cos\phi$. Thus the torque of the couple is $\tau = (mR\omega^2 \sin\phi)(2R\cos\phi)$, which coincides with our previous result. Thus the torque is required to maintain the spheres at their fixed positions relative to the rotation axis.

We leave it up to the student to verify that, in the case depicted in Fig. 10–7(a) where the rotation is about a principal axis and at a constant angular velocity, this torque is not required. For this reason, and to avoid transverse torques such as those in the above example, the rotating parts of any mechanism should be mounted on a principal axis.

An alternative method of solution of the problem would be to find the components of $\boldsymbol{L}$ parallel to the fixed axes XYZ and obtain the components of $\boldsymbol{\tau}$ by straightforward application of Eq. (10.11). This is left as an exercise for the student (Problem 10.50).

EXAMPLE 10.8. Analyze the general motion of a rigid body under no external torques.

Solution: In this example we shall examine the general motion of a rigid body when no external torques are applied to it; that is, $\boldsymbol{\tau} = 0$. Then Eq. (10.11) gives $d\boldsymbol{L}/dt = 0$ or

$\boldsymbol{L}$ = const. Therefore the angular momentum remains constant in magnitude and direction relative to the inertial frame XYZ used by the observer.

Since torques and angular momenta are always computed with respect to a point, we must discover relative to which point the torque is zero. There are two possibilities: One exists when the point is fixed in an inertial frame of reference; then the angular momentum is computed about this point. The other case occurs when the torque about the center of mass is zero. This is, for example, the case for a ball which has been kicked by a football player. Once the ball is in the air, the only external force on it is its weight acting at the center of mass, and therefore there is no torque with respect to the center of mass. In this situation it is the angular momentum relative to the center of mass that remains constant. The motion of the center of mass is of no concern to us, since it is due to the resultant external force and the motion proceeds according to Eq. (9.9). It is the rotation about the center of mass that interests us.

In this example we shall use $\boldsymbol{L}$ to designate the angular momentum either about the fixed point or about the center of mass, and the discussion applies therefore to both cases. Let us suppose first that the body is rotating about a principal axis. Then Eq. (10.4) applies and $\boldsymbol{L} = I\boldsymbol{\omega}$. Thus if $\boldsymbol{L}$ = const, then $\boldsymbol{\omega}$ = const also. This means that the body rotates with a constant angular velocity about an axis fixed relative to both the body and the observer.

Next let us suppose that the body is not rotating about a principal axis. Then Eq. (10.5) applies, and the fact that $\boldsymbol{L}$ = const does not imply that $\boldsymbol{\omega}$ is constant. Thus the angular velocity of the body is changing and the axis of rotation does not remain fixed relative to the observer who sees $\boldsymbol{\omega}$ precessing around $\boldsymbol{L}$. The axis of rotation relative to the body is not fixed either. Equation (10.5), which refers $\boldsymbol{L}$ to the principal axes $X_0Y_0Z_0$, yields

$$L^2 = I_1^2\omega_{x0}^2 + I_2^2\omega_{y0}^2 + I_3^2\omega_{z0}^2 = \text{const}$$

when $\boldsymbol{L}$ = const. This expresses the condition which the components of $\boldsymbol{\omega}$ relative to the principal axes $X_0Y_0Z_0$ must fulfill. Since the coefficients I_1^2, I_2^2, and I_3^2 are positive and constant, this is the equation of an ellipsoid, if ω_{x0}, ω_{y0}, and ω_{z0} are considered as the coordinates of a point. Thus the end of the vector $\boldsymbol{\omega}$ must lie on this ellipsoid (Fig. 10–18). During the motion, the vector $\boldsymbol{\omega}$ also changes in magnitude and direction relative to the body and thus the tip of the vector describes a path on the ellipsoid that is called the *polhode* (from the Greek: *pole*, pole; *hodos*, path).

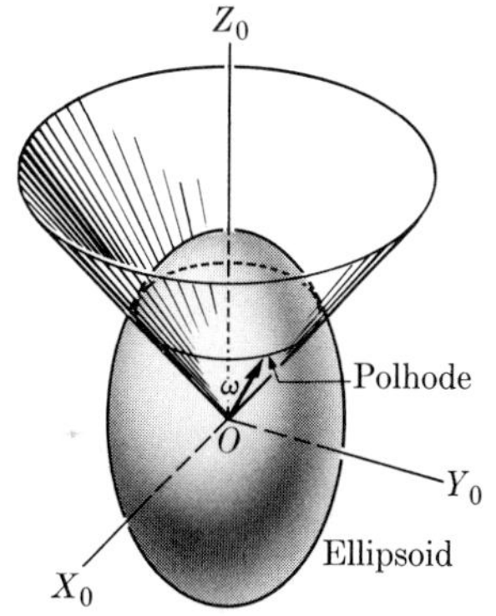

Fig. 10–18. Description of rigid body motion. The path described by the tip of the angular velocity vector, relative to axes attached to the body, is the polhode.

The motion we have just described is found in many important situations. For example, the forces exerted by the sun, the moon, and the planets on the earth are, practically, applied at the center of mass, and thus the torque about the center of mass is essentially zero (actually there is a small torque; see Example 10.10). The earth is not exactly a sphere, but is slightly pear-shaped, and it is not at present rotating about a principal axis. Therefore its axis of rotation is not fixed relative to itself.

The polhode of the earth's axis of rotation is illustrated in Fig. 10–19, which shows the path followed by the northern intersection of the axis of rotation during the period between 1931 and 1935. Because there are other factors involved, the shape of the curve

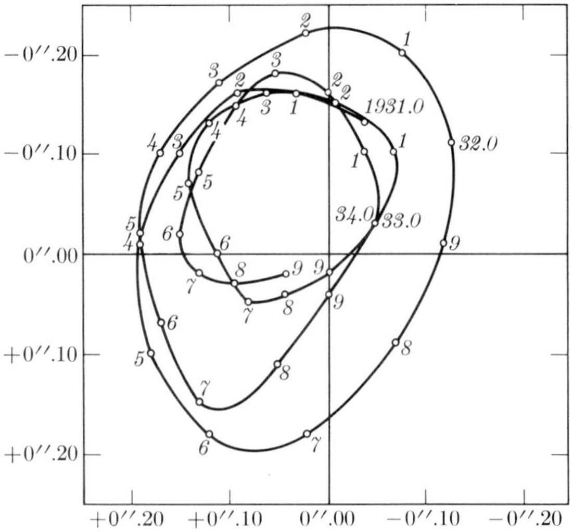

Fig. 10–19. Polhode of the earth's axis of rotation in the period 1931–1935.

is somewhat irregular, but the diameter of the curve never exceeds 15 m and the period of revolution of the axis is about 427 days.

The wobbling of a football after it has been kicked is another example of the change in the axis of rotation of a torque-free rigid body, since, in most cases, the angular momentum of the ball is not along one of its principal axes.

10.5 Kinetic Energy of Rotation

In Section 9.5 we defined the kinetic energy of a system of particles as

$$E_k = \sum_i \tfrac{1}{2} m_i v_i^2.$$

We have seen in Section 10.2 that, in the case of a rigid body rotating around an axis with angular velocity $\boldsymbol{\omega}$, the velocity of each particle is $v_i = \omega R_i$, where R_i is the distance of the particle to the axis of rotation. Then

$$E_k = \sum_i \tfrac{1}{2} m_i v_i^2 = \sum_i \tfrac{1}{2} m_i R_i^2 \omega^2 = \tfrac{1}{2}\left(\sum_i m_i R_i^2\right)\omega^2$$

or, recalling definition (10.2) of moment of inertia,

$$E_k = \tfrac{1}{2} I \omega^2. \tag{10.16}$$

Expression (10.16) is correct for any axis, even if it is not a principal axis, because the magnitude of the velocity is always $v_i = \omega R_i$, as may be inferred from the discussion in Section 10.2. When the rotation is about a principal axis, we can utilize Eq. (10.4) and write

$$E_k = \frac{L^2}{2I} \cdot \tag{10.17}$$

We can obtain an alternative and more general expression for the kinetic energy by using the components of $\boldsymbol{\omega}$ along the principal axes $X_0Y_0Z_0$. The result, which we shall not derive here, is

$$E_k = \tfrac{1}{2}(I_1\omega_{x0}^2 + I_2\omega_{y0}^2 + I_3\omega_{z0}^2).$$

Using the components of $\boldsymbol{L}$ along $X_0Y_0Z_0$ according to Eq. (10.5), we may write

$$E_k = \frac{1}{2}\left(\frac{L_{x0}^2}{I_1} + \frac{L_{y0}^2}{I_2} + \frac{L_{z0}^2}{I_3}\right),$$

which reduces to Eq. (10.17) for rotation about a principal axis. Of special interest, particularly in the discussion of molecular rotations, is the case when the body has symmetry of revolution, say about Z_0, so that $I_1 = I_2$. Then

$$E_k = \frac{1}{2}\left[\frac{1}{I_1}(L_{x0}^2 + L_{y0}^2) + \frac{1}{I_3}L_{z0}^2\right],$$

which may be written in the alternative form

$$E_k = \frac{L^2}{2I_1} + \frac{1}{2}\left(\frac{1}{I_3} - \frac{1}{I_1}\right)L_{z0}^2.$$

Let us now consider the general case in which the rigid body rotates about an axis passing through its center of mass and at the same time has translational motion relative to the observer. As we proved in Example 9.8, the kinetic energy of a body in an inertial frame of reference is $E_k = \frac{1}{2}Mv_{\text{CM}}^2 + E_{k,\text{CM}}$, where M is the total mass, $\boldsymbol{v}_{\text{CM}}$ is the velocity of the center of mass, and $E_{k,\text{CM}}$ is the internal kinetic energy relative to the center of mass. In the case of a rigid body, $\frac{1}{2}Mv_{\text{CM}}^2$ is just the translational kinetic energy, and therefore $E_{k,\text{CM}}$ must be the rotational kinetic energy relative to the center of mass, computed with the aid of Eq. (10.16). This is true because, in a rigid body, the center of mass is fixed relative to the body, and the only motion the body can have relative to the center of mass is rotation. Therefore we may write

$$E_k = \tfrac{1}{2}Mv_{\text{CM}}^2 + \tfrac{1}{2}I_C\omega^2, \tag{10.18}$$

where I_C is the moment of inertia relative to the axis of rotation passing through the center of mass.

Since the distance between the particles in a rigid body does not change during the motion, we may assume that its internal potential energy $E_{p,\text{int}}$ remains constant, and therefore we do not have to consider it when we are discussing the body's exchange of energy with its surroundings. Accordingly, the conservation of energy as expressed by Eq. (9.35) for a system of particles reduces, in the case of a rigid body, simply to

$$E_k - E_{k,0} = W_{\text{ext}}, \tag{10.19}$$

where W_{ext} is the work of the external forces. If the external forces are conservative,

$$W_{\text{ext}} = (E_{p,0} - E_p)_{\text{ext}}, \tag{10.20}$$

where $E_{p,\text{ext}}$ is the potential energy associated with the external forces, and Eq. (10.19) becomes (dropping the subscript "ext" for the potential energy),

$$E_k + E_p = (E_k + E_p)_0. \tag{10.21}$$

This result is similar to that for one particle as expressed in Eq. (8.29), and is a particularization of Eq. (9.36) for the case in which the internal potential energy does not change. (Recall that we said that this lack of change holds true when we are dealing with a rigid body.) Thus we call $E = E_k + E_p$ the total energy of a rigid body. When we use Eq. (10.18) for E_k, Eq. (10.21) for the total energy of the body becomes

$$E = \tfrac{1}{2}Mv_{\text{CM}}^2 + \tfrac{1}{2}I_C\omega^2 + E_p = \text{const.}$$

For example, if the body is falling under the action of gravity, $E_p = Mgy$, where y refers to the height of the CM of the body relative to a horizontal reference plane, and the total energy is

$$E = \tfrac{1}{2}Mv_{\text{CM}}^2 + \tfrac{1}{2}I_C\omega^2 + Mgy = \text{const.} \tag{10.22}$$

If some of the forces are not conservative (in the sense discussed in Section 8.12), we must write, instead of Eq. (10.20),

$$W_{\text{ext}} = E_{p,0} - E_p + W',$$

where W' is the work of the external nonconservative force. Equation (10.21) is now

$$(E_k + E_p) - (E_k + E_p)_0 = W'. \tag{10.23}$$

This expression has to be used, for example, when frictional forces in addition to gravitational forces are operating.

EXAMPLE 10.9. A sphere, a cylinder, and a ring, all with the same radius, roll down along an inclined plane starting at a height y_0. Find in each case the velocity when they arrive at the base of the plane.

Solution: Figure 10–20 shows the forces acting on the rolling body. They are the weight Mg, the reaction N of the plane, and the frictional force F at the point of contact with the plane. We could apply the same method used in Example 10.5 (and we recommend that the student try it). Instead we shall illustrate the solution by applying the principle of conservation of energy, as expressed by Eq. (10.22).

At the starting point B, when the body is at rest at an altitude y_0, its total energy is $E = Mgy_0$. At any intermediate position, the center of mass is moving with a translational velocity v and the body is rotating about the center of mass with angular velocity ω, the two being related in this case by $v = R\omega$. The total energy is thus

$$E = \tfrac{1}{2}Mv^2 + \tfrac{1}{2}I_C\omega^2 + Mgy = \tfrac{1}{2}Mv^2 + \tfrac{1}{2}(I_C/R^2)v^2 + Mgy.$$

Writing the moment of inertia as $I_C = MK^2$, where K is the radius of gyration according to definition (10.10), we may express the total energy as

$$E = \tfrac{1}{2}M\left(1 + \frac{K^2}{R^2}\right)v^2 + Mgy.$$

Equating this expression for the energy to the initial energy $E = Mgy_0$, we solve for the velocity

$$v^2 = \frac{2g(y_0 - y)}{1 + (K^2/R^2)}.$$

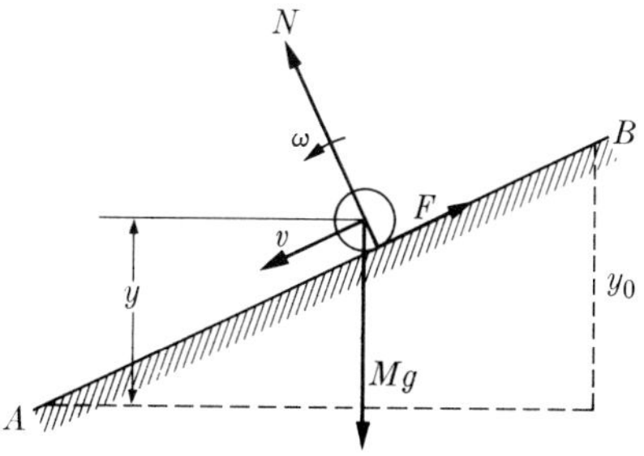

Fig. 10–20. Rolling of a body along an inclined plane.

If, instead of a rolling rigid body, we had a body which slid down the plane, we would not have to include rotational energy, and the result would be $v^2 = 2g(y_0 - y)$, as for a falling single particle. Thus we see that rotational motion results in a slowing down of translational motion. We can comprehend this if we realize that in a rolling body the initial potential energy must be used to produce both rotational and translational kinetic energy. But when the body slides down the plane, all the initial potential energy goes into translational kinetic energy.

Referring back to Table 10–1, we see that K^2/R^2 is equal to $\frac{2}{5}$ for the sphere, $\frac{1}{2}$ for the disk and 1 for the ring. Therefore we find that v^2 is equal to $\frac{10}{7}g(y - y_0)$ for the sphere, $\frac{4}{3}g(y - y_0)$ for the cylinder, and $g(y - y_0)$ for the ring. In other words, the sphere translates fastest, then the cylinder, and finally the ring. Could the student have guessed this result just from the geometry of the bodies?

An interesting result derived from the expression for v^2 is that the speed of a body going down a slope does not depend on the mass or the actual dimensions of the body, but only on the shape.

10.6 Gyroscopic Motion

As indicated in Section 10.4, the equation $d\mathbf{L}/dt = \boldsymbol{\tau}$ implies that in the absence of an external torque $\boldsymbol{\tau}$, the angular momentum $\mathbf{L}$ of the body remains constant. If the body is rotating about a principal axis, $\mathbf{L} = I\boldsymbol{\omega}$ and, as explained before, the body will keep on rotating about that axis with constant angular velocity.

This fact is best illustrated by the *gyroscope* (Fig. 10–21), which is a device for mounting a rotating wheel so that the axis can freely change its direction. The wheel G is mounted on the horizontal rod AB and counterbalanced by a weight W so that the total torque around O on the system is zero. The rod AB can move freely around both the X_0- and Z_0-axes, and the wheel is rotating (or spinning) rapidly around the Y_0-axis; these are the

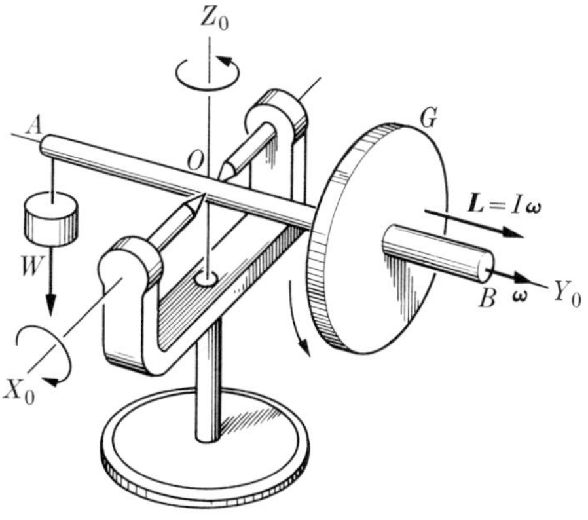

Fig. 10–21. Gyroscope under no torque.

principal axes of the gyroscope. Therefore the angular momentum of the system is parallel to the Y_0-axis when this axis is fixed in space. If we move the gyroscope around the room we note that AB always points in the same direction. Placing the gyro axis so that AB is horizontal and points in the east-west direction (position 1 of Fig. 10–22, where N represents the north pole of the earth and the arrow indicates the wheel's angular velocity), we shall observe that AB gradually tilts so that after six hours it is in a vertical position (position 4 of Fig. 10–22). This apparent rotation of AB is in fact due to the rotation of the earth, and while our laboratory moves from 1 to 4, the orientation of AB remains fixed in space.

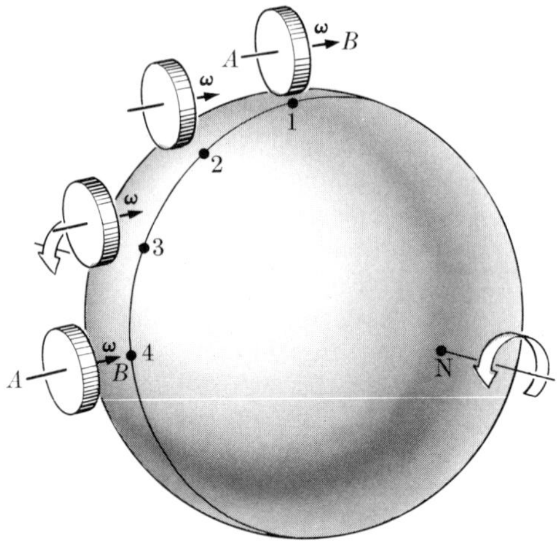

Fig. 10–22. The axis of rotation of a gyroscope under no torque remains fixed in space, and therefore rotates relative to the earth.

If the torque on the gyroscope is not zero, the angular momentum experiences a change in the time dt given by

$$d\boldsymbol{L} = \boldsymbol{\tau}\, dt. \tag{10.24}$$

In other words, the change in angular momentum is always in the direction of the torque (in the same way that the change of momentum of a particle is in the direction of the force), a situation we have already encountered in Example 10.7. In fact, the discussion that follows bears a great resemblance to that of Example 10.7, but there is a fundamental difference: Here the angular momentum arises mainly from the spin of the gyroscope, while in the system of Fig. 10–16 the angular momentum arose from rotation around the Z-axis, with no spin at all.

If the torque $\boldsymbol{\tau}$ is *perpendicular* to the angular momentum $\boldsymbol{L}$, the change $d\boldsymbol{L}$ is also perpendicular to $\boldsymbol{L}$ and the angular momentum changes in direction but not in magnitude. That is, the axis of rotation changes in direction but the magnitude of the angular momentum remains constant. As we said in Example 10.7, this situation is similar to the case of circular motion under a centripetal force, in which the force is perpendicular to the velocity and the velocity changes in direction but

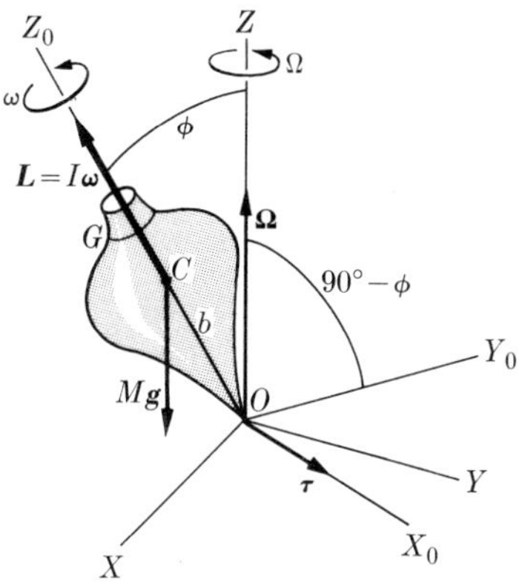

Fig. 10–23. Gyroscope subject to an external torque.

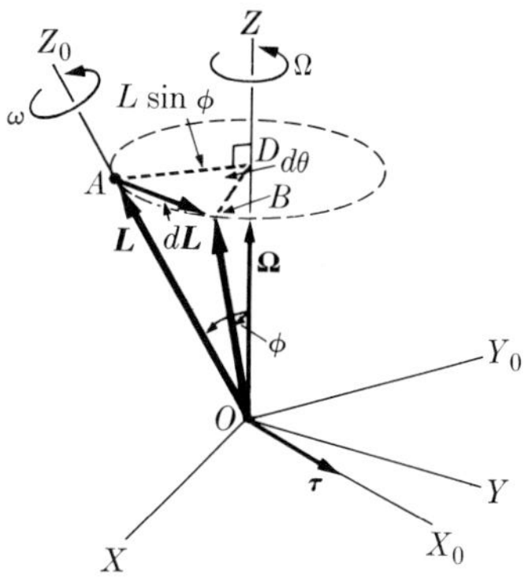

Fig. 10–24. Precession of gyroscope axis.

not in magnitude. The motion of the axis of rotation around a fixed axis due to an external torque is called *precession*, as indicated previously in Example 10.7.

This situation is found, for example, in the common top, a toy which is a species of gyroscope (Fig. 10–23). Note that for the top the principal axis X_0 has been chosen in the XY-plane, and thus Y_0 lies in the plane determined by Z and Z_0. Because of the cylindrical symmetry of the top, the principal axes $X_0Y_0Z_0$ are not spinning with angular velocity ω. The origin of both sets of axes has been chosen at point O, which is fixed in an inertial frame of reference. Thus both $\boldsymbol{L}$ and $\boldsymbol{\tau}$ must be computed relative to O. When the top rotates around its symmetry axis OZ_0 with angular velocity $\boldsymbol{\omega}$, its angular momentum $\boldsymbol{L}$ is also parallel to OZ_0. The external torque $\boldsymbol{\tau}$ is due to the weight $M\boldsymbol{g}$ acting at the center of mass C and is equal to the vector product $(\overrightarrow{OC}) \times (M\boldsymbol{g})$. The torque $\boldsymbol{\tau}$ is therefore perpendicular to the plane Z_0OZ, and thus also perpendicular to $\boldsymbol{L}$. In magnitude,

$$\tau = Mgb \sin \phi, \tag{10.25}$$

where ϕ is the angle between the symmetry axis Z_0 and the vertical axis Z, and $b = OC$ gives the position of the center of mass.

As indicated in Fig. 10–24, in a small time dt the vector $\boldsymbol{L}$ changes from position OA to position OB, its change being $\overrightarrow{AB} = d\boldsymbol{L}$, parallel to $\boldsymbol{\tau}$. The end of vector $\boldsymbol{L}$ describes a circle around Z of radius $AD = OA \sin \phi = L \sin \phi$, and in time dt the radius AD moves through an angle $d\theta$ to the position BD. The angular velocity of precession Ω is defined as the rate at which the axis OZ_0 of the body rotates around the axis OZ fixed in the laboratory; that is,

$$\Omega = \frac{d\theta}{dt}, \tag{10.26}$$

and is represented by a vector parallel to OZ. The magnitude of $d\boldsymbol{L}$ is

$$|d\boldsymbol{L}| = AD\, d\theta = (L \sin \phi)(\Omega\, dt).$$

But from Eq. (10.24), we have that $|d\boldsymbol{L}| = \tau\, dt$. Then, equating both results, we may write

$$\Omega L \sin \phi = \tau \tag{10.27}$$

or, using Eq. (10.25) for the torque, we obtain

$$\Omega = \frac{\tau}{L \sin \phi} = \frac{Mgb}{I\omega}. \tag{10.28}$$

Noting the relative orientation of the vectors $\boldsymbol{\Omega}$, $\boldsymbol{L}$, and $\boldsymbol{\tau}$ in Fig. 10–24, we see that Eq. (10.27) can be written in vector form as

$$\boldsymbol{\Omega} \times \boldsymbol{L} = \boldsymbol{\tau}, \tag{10.29}$$

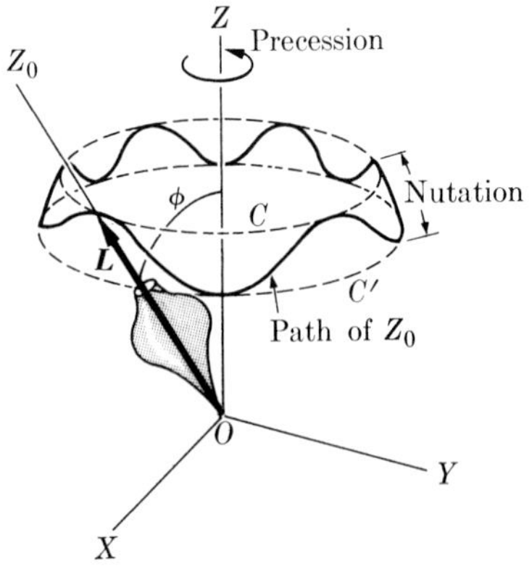

Fig. 10–25. Precession and nutation of gyroscope axis.

which is a very useful expression. [It should be compared with the similar expression $\boldsymbol{\omega} \times \boldsymbol{p} = \boldsymbol{F}$ for uniform circular motion, given by Eq. (7.30), since both represent the same mathematical relation among the vectors involved.]

Results (10.27) or (10.28) are approximate. They are valid only if ω is very large compared with Ω, a situation compatible with Eq. (10.28). The reason is that if the body is precessing around *OZ* it also has an angular momentum around that axis, and therefore its total angular momentum is not $I\boldsymbol{\omega}$, as we have assumed, since the resultant angular velocity is $\boldsymbol{\omega} + \boldsymbol{\Omega}$. However, if the precession is very slow (that is, if Ω is very small compared with ω), the angular momentum around *OZ* can be neglected, as we implicitly did in our calculation. Our derivation is then applicable.

A more detailed discussion indicates that in general the angle ϕ does not remain constant, but oscillates between two fixed values, so that the end of $\boldsymbol{L}$, at the same time that it precesses around Z, oscillates between the two circles C and C' (Fig. 10–25), describing the path indicated. This oscillatory motion of the axis Z' is called *nutation.* Nutation, like precession, contributes to the total angular momentum, but in general its contribution is even smaller than that of precession.

Gyroscopic phenomena are of wide application. The tendency of a gyroscope to maintain the axis of rotation fixed in space is a principle which is used in the stabilizers aboard ships and in automatic pilots of airplanes. Another interesting example of gyroscopic motion is the *precession of the equinoxes,* as discussed in Section 2.3. The plane of the equator makes an angle of 23° 27′ with the plane of the earth's orbit or *ecliptic.* The intersection of the two planes is the *line of equinoxes.* The earth is a giant gyroscope whose axis of rotation is essentially the line passing through the north and south poles. This axis is precessing around the normal to the plane of the ecliptic in the east-west direction, as indicated in Fig. 10–26, with a period of 27,725 years or with a precessional angular velocity of about 50.27″ of arc per year, or 7.19×10^{-11} rad s^{-1}. This precession of the earth's axis results in an equal change in direction of the line of equinoxes, an effect discovered about 135 B.C. by Hipparchus.

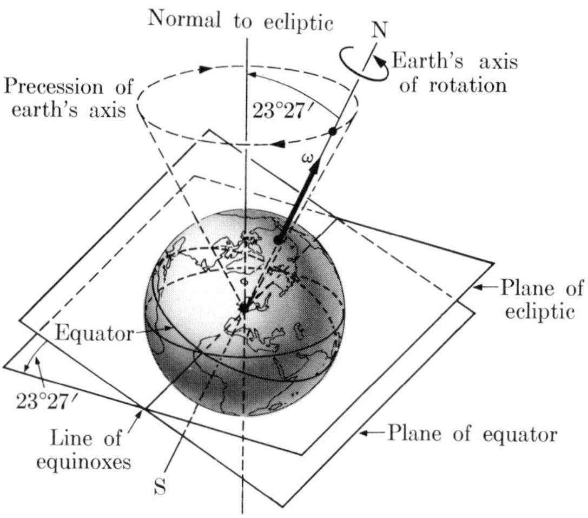

Fig. 10–26. Precession of earth's axis of rotation.

The precession of the equinoxes is due to the torque exerted on the earth by the sun and the moon. The earth is not a sphere but approximates an ellipsoid, with the larger diameter in the equatorial plane (actually the earth is pear-shaped). Detailed calculations have shown that this geometrical shape, combined with the inclination of the earth's axis relative to the ecliptic, has the result that the forces exerted by the sun and the moon on the earth have a resultant torque relative to the center of mass of the earth. The direction of the torque is perpendicular to the earth's axis. The axis of rotation of the earth must then precess under the action of this torque. In Chapter 15 we shall see that a similar effect is present (although the physical reasons for it are different) when a charged particle, such as an electron or a proton, moves in a magnetic field. The earth's axis also experiences a nutation with an amplitude of 9.2″ and an oscillation period of 19 years.

Another application of gyroscopic motion, also associated with the rotation of the earth, is the *gyroscopic compass.* Suppose that we have a gyroscope in position G of Fig. 10–27, where arrow 1 indicates the sense of rotation of the earth. The gyroscope is arranged so that its axis must be kept in a horizontal plane. This can be done, for example, by floating the gyroscope in a liquid. Let us assume that initially the gyroscope axis points in the E–W direction. When the earth rotates,

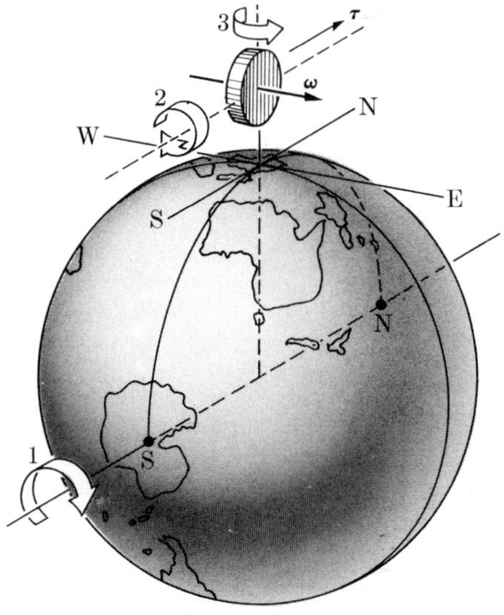

Fig. 10–27. Gyroscopic compass.

the horizontal plane and the E–W direction rotate in the same way. Therefore, if the axis of the gyroscope were maintained in the E–W direction, the axis would have to rotate as indicated by arrow 2. But that is equivalent to applying a torque in the south–north direction. Therefore the axis of the gyroscope, under the action of this torque, will turn around the vertical until it points north, as indicated by arrow 3. The gyroscopic compass has the special advantage of pointing toward the true north, since it is not subject to any local magnetic anomalies.

EXAMPLE 10.10. Estimate the magnitude of the torque which must be exerted on the earth in order to produce the observed rate of precession of the equinoxes.

Solution: Using Eq. (10.27), we have that $\tau = \Omega L \sin\phi$, where

$$\phi = 23^\circ\, 27' \qquad \text{and} \qquad \Omega = 7.19 \times 10^{-11}\ \text{rad s}^{-1}$$

is the precessional angular velocity of the earth. We must thus first compute the angular momentum of the earth. Since the earth's axis of rotation deviates only slightly from a principal axis, we may use the relation $L = I\omega$. The value of ω was given in Example 5.11 as 7.29×10^{-5} rad s^{-1}. The moment of inertia of the earth, from Table 10–1, assuming that the earth is spherical, is

$$\begin{aligned} I = \tfrac{2}{5}MR^2 &= \tfrac{2}{5}(5.98 \times 10^{24}\ \text{kg})(6.38 \times 10^6\ \text{m})^2 \\ &= 9.72 \times 10^{37}\ \text{m}^2\ \text{kg}. \end{aligned}$$

Therefore $\tau = 2.76 \times 10^{27}$ N m.

TABLE 10–2 Comparison Between the Dynamics of Translation and Rotation

Translation		Rotation	
Linear momentum	$\boldsymbol{p} = m\boldsymbol{v}$	Angular momentum	$\boldsymbol{L} = I\boldsymbol{\omega}$*
Force	$\boldsymbol{F} = d\boldsymbol{p}/dt$	Torque	$\boldsymbol{\tau} = d\boldsymbol{L}/dt$
Body of constant mass	$\boldsymbol{F} = m\boldsymbol{a}$	Body of constant moment of inertia	$\boldsymbol{\tau} = I\boldsymbol{\alpha}$*
Force perpendicular to momentum	$\boldsymbol{F} = \boldsymbol{\omega} \times \boldsymbol{p}$	Torque perpendicular to angular momentum	$\boldsymbol{\tau} = \boldsymbol{\Omega} \times \boldsymbol{L}$
Kinetic energy	$E_k = \frac{1}{2}mv^2$	Kinetic energy	$E_k = \frac{1}{2}I\omega^2$
Power	$P = \boldsymbol{F} \cdot \boldsymbol{v}$	Power	$P = \boldsymbol{\tau} \cdot \boldsymbol{\omega}$

* Formulas marked with an asterisk are valid only for rotation around a principal axis.

References

1. "Moments of Inertia of Solid Rectangular Parallelepipeds, Cubes, and Twin Cubes, and Two Other Regular Polyhedra," J. Satterly, *Am. J. Phys.* **25,** 70 (1957)
2. "Moments of Inertia of Plane Triangles," J. Satterly, *Am. J. Phys.* **26,** 452 (1958)
3. "Elementary Analysis of the Gyroscope," E. Barker, *Am. J. Phys.* **28,** 808 (1960)
4. "Resource Letter *CM*-1 on the Teaching of Angular Momentum and Rigid Body Motion," John I. Shonle, *Am. J. Phys.* **33,** 879 (1965)
5. *Mechanics* (second edition), by K. Symon. Reading, Mass.: Addison-Wesley, 1964, Chapters 5 and 11
6. *Physical Mechanics* (third edition), by R. B. Lindsay. Princeton, N.J.: Van Nostrand, 1963, Chapter 7
7. *Introduction to Engineering Mechanics,* by J. Huddleston. Reading, Mass.: Addison-Wesley, 1961, Sections 10–1, 10–2, 10–3, Chapters 12 and 13
8. *Vector Mechanics,* by D. Christie. New York: McGraw-Hill, 1964, Chapters 13, 15, and 16
9. *A Source Book of Physics,* by W. F. Magie. Cambridge, Mass.: Harvard University Press, 1963; page 65, Poinsot
10. *The Feynman Lectures on Physics,* Volume I, by R. Feynman, R. Leighton, and M. Sands. Reading, Mass.: Addison-Wesley, 1963, Chapters 18, 19, and 20

Problems

10.1 A thin rod 1 m long has a negligible mass. There are 5 bodies placed along it, each having a mass of 1.00 kg, and situated at 0 cm, 25 cm, 50 cm, 75 cm, and 100 cm from one end. Calculate the moment of inertia of the entire system with respect to an axis perpendicular to the rod that passes through (a) one end, (b) the second mass, and (c) the center of mass. Calculate the radius of gyration in each case. Verify Steiner's theorem.

10.2 Solve the previous problem again, this time for a rod whose mass is 0.20 kg.

10.3 Three masses, each of 2 kg, are situated at the vertices of an equilateral triangle whose sides measure 10 cm each. Calculate the moment of inertia of the system and its radius of gyration with respect to an axis perpendicular to the plane determined by the triangle and passing through (a) a vertex, (b) the middle point of one side, and (c) the center of mass.

10.4 Prove that the moment of inertia of a system composed of two masses m_1 and m_2, separated a distance r relative to an axis passing through their centers of mass and perpendicular to the line joining the two masses, is μr^2, where μ is the reduced mass of the system. Apply it to the CO molecule ($r = 1.13 \times 10^{-10}$ m) and the HCl molecule ($r = 1.27 \times 10^{-10}$ m).

10.5 Find the moment of inertia of the CO_2 molecule relative to an axis passing through the center of mass and perpendicular to the axis. The molecule is linear, with the C atom in the center. The C—O distance is 1.13×10^{-10} m.

10.6 In the H_2O molecule, the distance H—O is 0.91×10^{-10} m and the angle between the two H—O bonds is 105°. Determine the moments of inertia of the molecule relative to the three principal axes shown in Fig. 10–28, and passing through the center of mass. Express the angular momen-

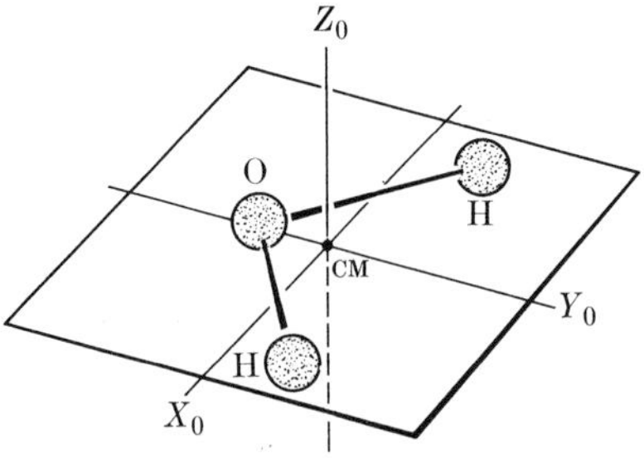

Figure 10–28

tum and kinetic energy of the molecule relative to the principal axes when the molecule is rotating about an arbitrary axis.

10.7 The NH_3 molecule (Fig. 10–29) is a pyramid with the N atom at the vertex and the three H atoms at the base. The length of the N—H bonds is 1.01×10^{-10} m and the angle between two such bonds is 108°. Find the three principal moments of inertia relative to axes passing through the center of mass. (The three axes are oriented as follows: Z_0 is perpendicular to the base, X_0 is in the plane determined by one N—H bond and the Z_0-axis, and Y_0 is thus parallel to the line joining the other two H atoms.)

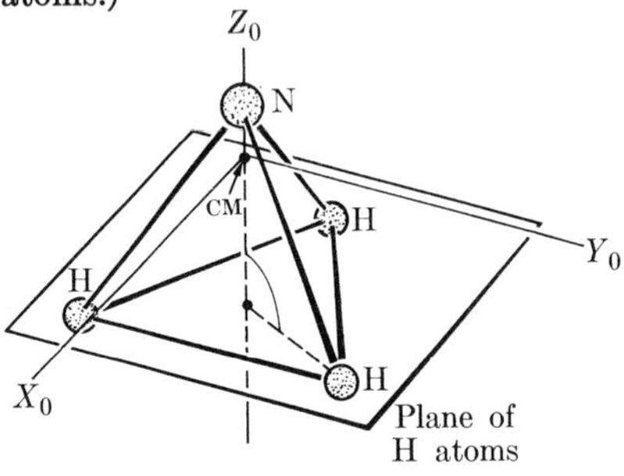

Figure 10–29

10.8 Two boys, each with a mass of 25 kg, are sitting on the opposite ends of a horizontal plank which is 2.6 m long and has a mass of 10 kg. The beam is rotating at 5 rpm about a vertical axis passing through its center. What will be the angular velocity if each boy moves 60 cm toward the center of the beam without touching the floor? What is the change in the kinetic energy of rotation of the entire system?

10.9 Referring to the previous problem, assume that, when the boys are in the initial position, a horizontal force of 120 N perpendicular to the plank is applied at one meter from the axis. Find the angular acceleration of the system.

10.10 The moment of inertia of a wheel is 1000 lb ft^2. At a given instant its angular velocity is 10 rad s^{-1}. After it rotates through an angle of 100 radians, its angular velocity is 100 rad s^{-1}. Calculate the torque applied to the wheel and the increase in kinetic energy.

10.11 A rotating wheel is subject to a torque of 10 N m due to the friction on the axis. The radius of the wheel is 0.6 m, its mass is 100 kg, and it is rotating at 175 rad s^{-1}. How long will the wheel take to stop? How many revolutions will it make before stopping?

10.12 A cylinder of 20 kg mass and 0.25 m radius is rotating at 1200 rpm about an axis that passes through its center. What is the constant tangential force necessary to stop it after 1800 revolutions?

10.13 A disk with a mass of 50 kg and a radius of 1.80 m can spin about its axis. A constant force of 19.6 N is exerted on the edge of the disk. Calculate (a) its angular acceleration, (b) the angle it describes, (c) its angular momentum, and (d) its kinetic energy after 5 s.

10.14 The velocity of an automobile increases from 5 km hr^{-1} to 50 km hr^{-1} in 8 s. The radius of its wheels is 45 cm. What is their angular acceleration? The mass of each wheel is 30 kg and its radius of gyration is 0.3 m. What is the initial and final angular momentum of each wheel?

10.15 The flywheel of a steam engine has a mass of 200 kg and a radius of gyration of 2 m. When it is rotating at 120 rpm the steam inlet is closed. Supposing that the flywheel stops in 5 min, what is the torque due to friction on the axis of the flywheel?

What is the work done by the torque during this time?

10.16 A cart with a mass of 2000 g has four wheels, each of 6 cm radius and 150 g mass. Calculate the linear acceleration of the cart when a force of 0.6 N is exerted upon it.

10.17 The rotating parts of an engine have a mass of 15 kg and a radius of gyration of 15 cm. Calculate the angular momentum and kinetic energy when they are rotating at 1800 rpm. What torque and power are necessary in order to reach this angular velocity in 5 s?

10.18 The radius of a five-cent piece is 1 cm and its mass is 5 g. It is rolling on an inclined plane at 6 rps. Find (a) its kinetic energy of rotation, (b) its kinetic energy of translation, and (c) its total kinetic energy. What is the vertical distance it would have to fall in order to reach this amount of kinetic energy?

10.19 Repeat Example 8.9, assuming that the ball has a radius r and that it rolls along the track instead of sliding.

10.20 The automobile of Problem 10.14 has a mass of 1600 kg, and its velocity increases in 8 s as described. Calculate (a) the initial and final rotational kinetic energy of each wheel, (b) the initial and final total kinetic energy of each wheel, and (c) the total final kinetic energy of the automobile.

10.21 A truck with a mass of 10 tons is moving with a velocity of 6.6 m s^{-1}. The radius of each wheel is 0.45 m, its mass is 100 kg, and its radius of gyration is 30 cm. Calculate the total kinetic energy of the truck.

10.22 An iron ring whose radii are 0.60 m and 0.50 m has a mass of 18 kg. It rolls down an inclined plane, reaching the bottom with a velocity of 3.6 m s^{-1}. Calculate the total kinetic energy and the vertical height through which it falls.

10.23 The rod in Fig. 10–30, whose length is L and whose mass is m, can rotate freely in a vertical plane around its end A. It is initially held in a horizontal position and then released. At the time it makes an angle α with the vertical, compute (a) its angular acceleration, (b) its angular velocity, and (c) the forces at the pivot.

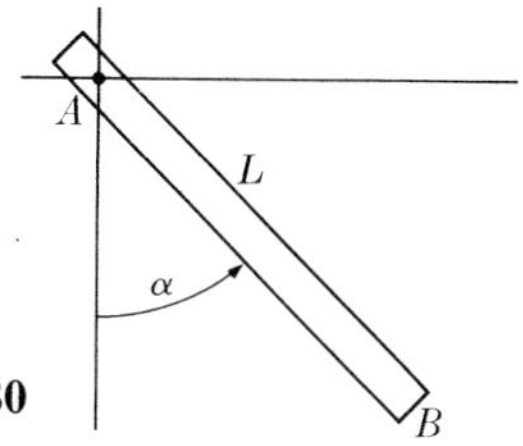

Figure 10–30

10.24 A uniform rod, hanging straight down, of length 1.0 m and mass 2.5 kg, is pivoted at its upper end. It is struck at the base by a horizontal force of 100 N that lasts only $\frac{1}{50}$ s. (a) Find the angular momentum acquired by the rod. (b) Will the rod reach a vertically upright position?

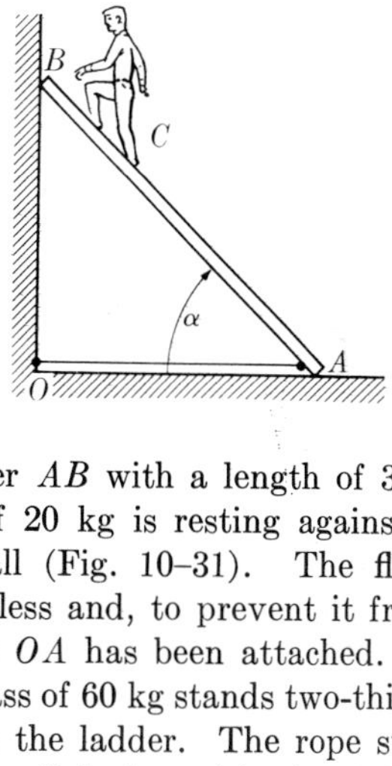

Figure 10–31

10.25 A ladder AB with a length of 3 m and a mass of 20 kg is resting against a frictionless wall (Fig. 10–31). The floor is also frictionless and, to prevent it from sliding, a rope OA has been attached. A man with a mass of 60 kg stands two-thirds of the way up the ladder. The rope suddenly breaks. Calculate (a) the initial acceleration of the center of mass of the system of ladder plus man, and (b) the initial angular acceleration around the center of mass. [*Hint:* Note that the initial angular velocity of the ladder is zero.]

10.26 The horizontal rod AB in Fig. 10–32, which is held by frictionless bearings at its ends, can rotate freely around its horizontal

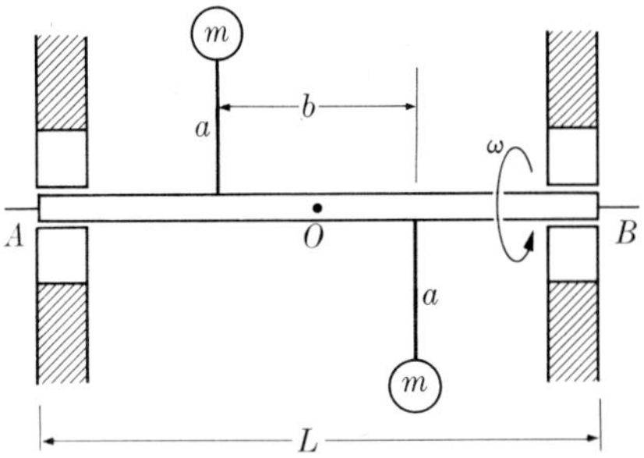

Figure 10–32

axis. Two equal masses held in position, as shown, by rigid rods of negligible mass are symmetrically located relative to the center of the rod. Find (a) the angular momentum of the system relative to the center of mass when the system is rotating with angular velocity ω, and (b) the forces exerted at the bearings.

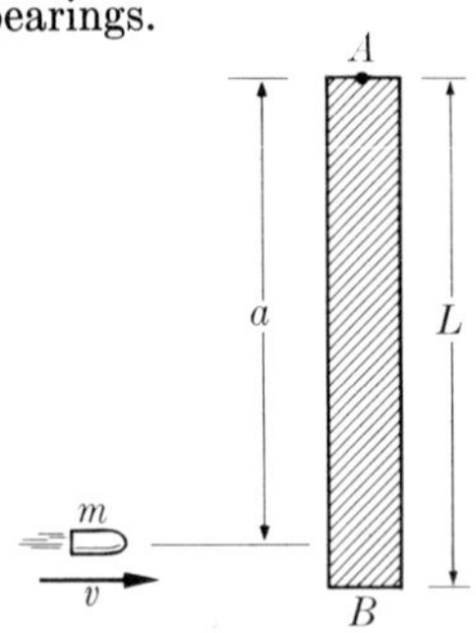

Figure 10–33

10.27 A rod of length L and mass M (Fig. 10–33) can rotate freely around a pivot at A. A bullet of mass m and velocity v hits the rod at a distance a from A and becomes imbedded in it. (a) Find the angular momentum of the system around A immediately before and after the bullet hits the rod. (b) Determine the momentum of the system immediately before and after the collision. Explain your answer carefully. (c) Under what conditions will the momentum be conserved? (d) What is the Q of the collision?

10.28 A rod of length L and mass m lies on a frictionless horizontal plane (Fig. 10–34). During a very short interval Δt it is struck by a force F that produces an

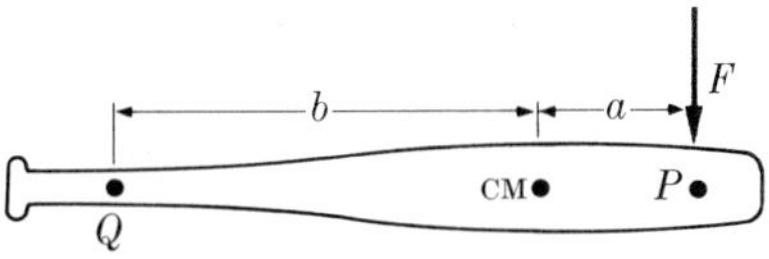

Figure 10–34

impulse I. The force acts at a point P which is a distance a from the center of mass. Find (a) the velocity of the center of mass, and (b) the angular velocity around the center of mass. (c) Determine the point Q that initially remains at rest in the L-frame, showing that $b = K^2/a$, where K is the radius of gyration about the center of mass. The point Q is called the *center of percussion*. (For example, a baseball player must hold the bat at the center of percussion in order to avoid feeling a stinging sensation when he hits the ball.) Prove also that if the force strikes at Q, the center of percussion will be at P.

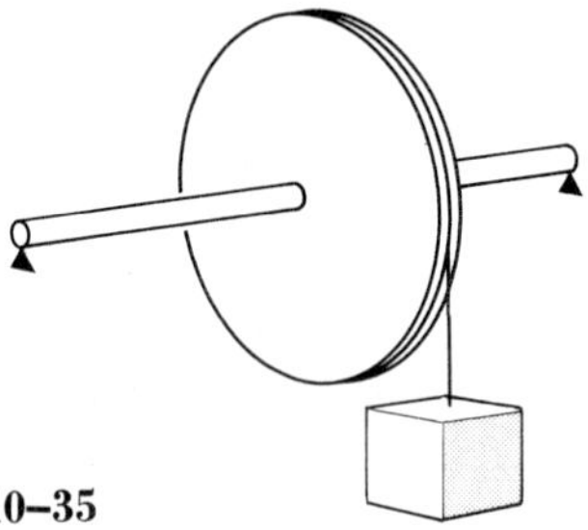

Figure 10–35

10.29 The wheel of Fig. 10–35, which has a radius of 0.5 m and a mass of 25 kg, can rotate about its horizontal axis. A rope wrapped around the wheel has a mass of 10 kg hanging from its free end. Calculate (a) the angular acceleration of the wheel, (b) the linear acceleration of the body, and (c) the tension in the rope.

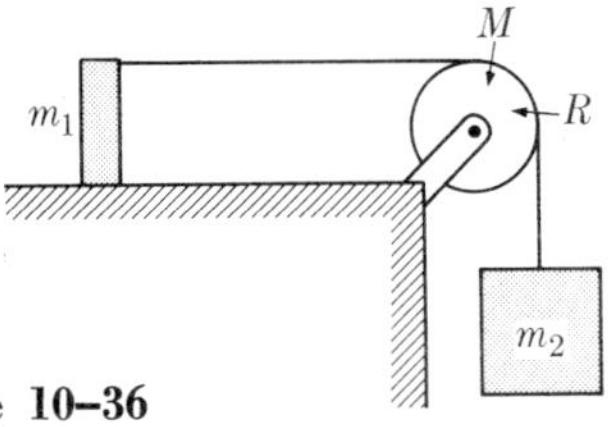

Figure 10–36

10.30 Calculate the acceleration of the system in Fig. 10–36 if the radius of the pulley is R, its mass is m, and it is rotating due to the friction on the rope. In this case $m_1 = 50$ kg, $m_2 = 200$ kg, $M = 15$ kg, and $R = 10$ cm.

10.31 A string is wrapped around the small cylinder in Fig. 10–37. Assuming that we pull with a force F, calculate the acceleration of the cylinder. Determine the sense of the motion. Here $r = 3$ cm, $R = 5$ cm, $F = 0.1$ kgf, and $m = 1$ kg.

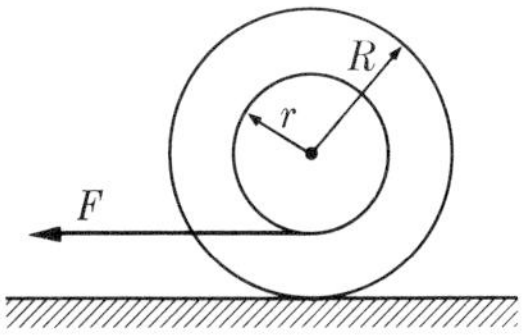

Figure 10–37

10.32 In the system represented in Fig. 10–38, $M = 1.0$ kg, $m = 0.2$ kg, $r = 0.2$ m. Calculate the linear acceleration of m, the angular acceleration of the cylinder M, and the tension in the rope. Neglect the effect of the small pulley.

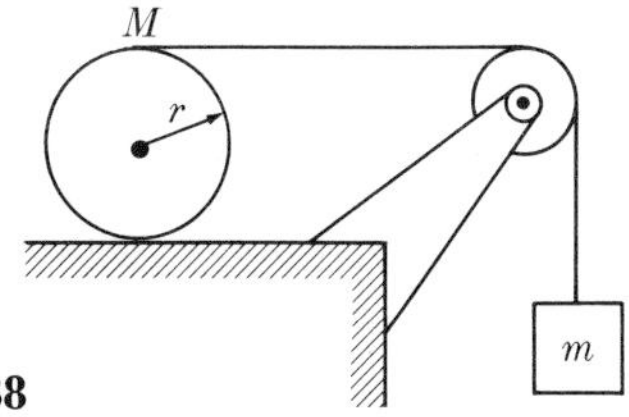

Figure 10–38

10.33 Determine, for the system in Fig. 10–39, the angular velocity of the disk and the linear velocity of m and m'. Calculate the tension in each rope. Assume that $m =$

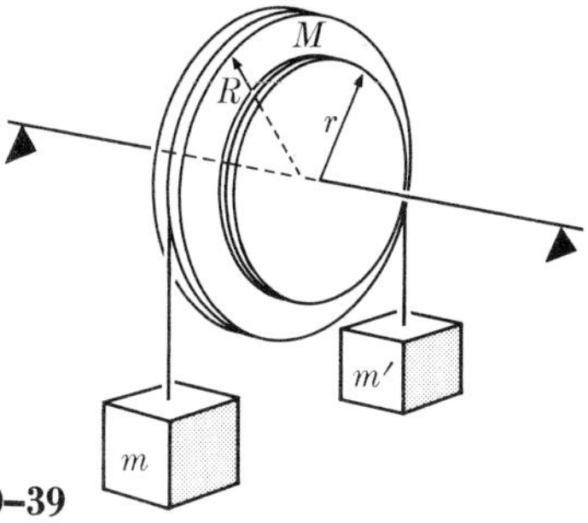

Figure 10–39

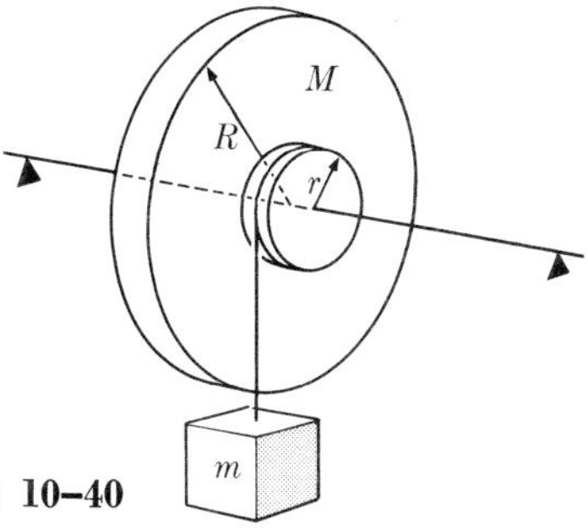

Figure 10–40

600 g, $m' = 500$ g, $M = 800$ g, $R = 8$ cm, and $r = 6$ cm.

10.34 For the system in Fig. 10–40, calculate the acceleration of m and the tension in the rope, assuming that the moment of inertia of the small disk of radius r is negligible. In this case $r = 4$ cm, $R = 12$ cm, $M = 4$ kg, and $m = 2$ kg.

10.35 In Fig. 10–41, $M = 6$ kg, $m = 4$ kg, $m' = 3$ kg, and $R = 0.40$ m. Compute (a) the total kinetic energy gained by the system after 5 s, and (b) the tension in the string.

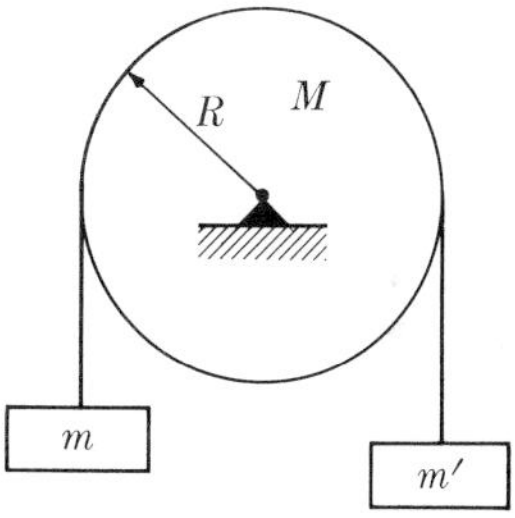

Figure 10–41

10.36 The two disks in Fig. 10–42 have equal masses m and radii R. The upper disk can rotate freely around a horizontal axis through its center. A rope is wrapped

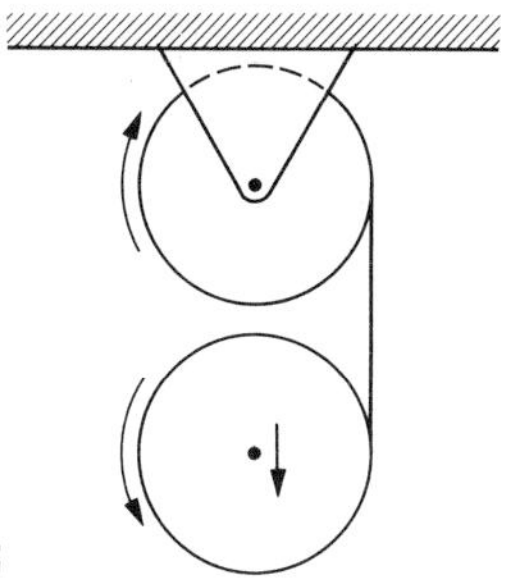

Figure 10–42

around both disks and the lower one is permitted to fall. Find (a) the acceleration of the center of mass of the lower disk, (b) the tension in the rope, and (c) the angular acceleration of each disk around its center of mass.

10.37 The mass of the gyroscope in Fig. 10–43 is 0.10 kg. The disk, which is located 10 cm from the ZZ'-axis, has a 5-cm radius. This disk is rotating about the YY'-axis with an angular velocity of 100 rad s^{-1}. What is the angular velocity of precession?

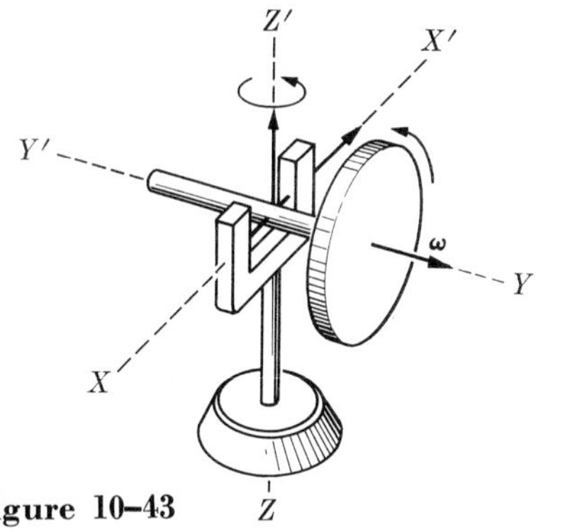

Figure 10–43

10.38 A classroom demonstration gyroscope consists of a metal ring whose radius is 0.35 m, whose mass is 5 kg, and which is attached by spokes to an axis projecting 20 cm on each side. The demonstrator holds the axis in a horizontal position while the ring rotates at 300 rpm. Find the magnitude and direction of the force exerted by each of the demonstrator's hands on the axis in the following cases: (a) the axis is moved parallel to itself; (b) the axis is rotated about its center in a horizontal plane at 2 rpm; (c) the axis is rotated about its center in a vertical plane at 2 rpm. Also calculate what the angular velocity of the ring would have to be in order for its axis to remain horizontal if the gyroscope were to be supported by only one hand.

10.39 Prove that, for a rigid body, $dE_k/dt = \boldsymbol{\omega} \cdot \boldsymbol{\tau}$. This equation shows that $\boldsymbol{\omega} \cdot \boldsymbol{\tau}$ is the rotational power. [*Hint:* Note that $\boldsymbol{v} = \boldsymbol{\omega} \times \boldsymbol{r}$ for a rotating body. First obtain the equation for a single particle, using Eq. (8.10), and then add the result to obtain the equation for all particles in the rigid body.]

10.40 Note that when a body moves under no torque, not only is the angular momentum constant, but also the kinetic energy of rotation is constant. Obtain the equation of the polhode (Example 10.8) by finding the intersection of the ellipsoids corresponding to L^2 and to E_k. Analyze the result obtained.

10.41 Prove that the moment of inertia of a rigid body about an axis making angles α, β, γ with the three principal axes is

$$I = I_1 \cos^2 \alpha + I_2 \cos^2 \beta + I_3 \cos^2 \gamma.$$

10.42 A solid block whose sides are 0.20 m, 0.30 m, and 0.40 m and which has a mass of 4 kg is rotating about an axis passing through the longest diagonal at 120 rpm. (a) Find the angular momentum with reference to the principal axes. (b) Determine the angle between the angular momentum and the axis of rotation. (c) Find the kinetic energy of rotation. [*Hint:* Use the result of Problem 10.41 to obtain the moment of inertia.]

10.43 For the block in the previous problem, assume that the angular velocity is constant. Determine (a) the torque applied to the block with reference to the principal axes, and (b) the angle between the torque and the axis of rotation.

10.44 A particle of mass m moves around an axis with an angular velocity $\boldsymbol{\omega}$ so that its velocity is $\boldsymbol{v} = \boldsymbol{\omega} \times \boldsymbol{r}$, according to Eq. (5.48). Prove that the components of its angular momentum are

$$L_x = m[\omega_x(y^2 + z^2) - \omega_y yz - \omega_z zx],$$
$$L_y = m[-\omega_x xy + \omega_y(z^2 + x^2) - \omega_z zy],$$
$$L_z = m[-\omega_x xz - \omega_y yz + \omega_z(x^2 + y^2)].$$

10.45 Extend the result of the preceding problem to the case of a rigid body, to obtain

$$L_x = I_x\omega_x - I_{xy}\omega_y - I_{zx}\omega_z,$$
$$L_y = -I_{xy}\omega_x + I_y\omega_y - I_{yz}\omega_z,$$
$$L_z = -I_{zx}\omega_x - I_{yz}\omega_y + I_z\omega_z,$$

where

$$I_x = \sum m(y^2 + z^2),$$
$$I_y = \sum m(z^2 + x^2),$$
$$I_z = \sum m(x^2 + y^2)$$

are the moments of inertia relative to the three coordinate axes, according to Eq. (10.7), and

$$I_{xy} = \sum mxy,$$
$$I_{yz} = \sum myz,$$
$$I_{zx} = \sum mzx$$

are called the *products of inertia*. By comparing these results with Eq. (10.5), the student may recognize that the principal axes are those for which the three products of inertia are zero. Note also that the rotational behavior of a rigid body is determined in general by six quantities: the three moments of inertia and the three products of inertia.

10.46 Determine the three moments of inertia and the three products of inertia of the body of Fig. 10–16 relative to (a) the X_0-, Y_0-, and Z_0-axes, (b) the X-, Y_0-, and Z-axes, and (c) the X'-, Y_0-, and Z-axes. Are these quantities always constant?

10.47 Compute the products of inertia of the H_2O and NH_3 molecules relative to the axes illustrated in Problems 10.6 and 10.7, and verify that the axes are principal.

10.48 Verify the vector relation

$$(\boldsymbol{A} \times \boldsymbol{B}) \cdot (\boldsymbol{C} \times \boldsymbol{D}) = (\boldsymbol{A} \cdot \boldsymbol{C})(\boldsymbol{B} \cdot \boldsymbol{D}) - (\boldsymbol{A} \cdot \boldsymbol{D})(\boldsymbol{B} \cdot \boldsymbol{C}).$$

Apply it to prove that, for the body of Problem 10.44, $v^2 = (\boldsymbol{\omega} \times \boldsymbol{r})^2 = \omega^2 r^2 - (\boldsymbol{\omega} \cdot \boldsymbol{r})^2$. Then write its kinetic energy in the form

$$E_k = \tfrac{1}{2}m[\omega_x^2(y^2 + z^2) + \omega_y^2(z^2 + x^2) + \omega_z^2(x^2 + y^2) - 2\omega_x\omega_y xy - 2\omega_y\omega_z yz - 2\omega_z\omega_x xz].$$

10.49 Extend the result of the previous problem to write the kinetic energy of a rotating rigid body in the form

$$E_k = \tfrac{1}{2}[I_x\omega_x^2 + I_y\omega_y^2 + I_z\omega_z^2 - 2I_{xy}\omega_x\omega_y - 2I_{yz}\omega_y\omega_z - 2I_{zx}\omega_z\omega_x].$$

Note that it reduces to the values given in Section 10.5 for the case of principal axes when the products of inertia are zero.

10.50 Solve Example 10.7 by first finding the components of $\boldsymbol{L}$ parallel to the fixed axes XYZ and then calculating the components of $\boldsymbol{\tau}$ by direct application of Eq. (10.11). Also consider the case of accelerated rotation ($d\omega/dt \neq 0$).

11
HIGH-ENERGY DYNAMICS

11.1 Introduction

In the preceding chapters we have developed a dynamical theory—called *classical* or *newtonian* mechanics—to describe the motion of the bodies we observe around us. The theory is based on several assumptions. For example, we have seen that momentum can be expressed as $\boldsymbol{p} = m\boldsymbol{v}$, where the mass m is a coefficient characteristic of the particle or system; we have consistently considered this mass m to be an invariant coefficient of each particle or system. So long as the range of velocities we observe is not very large, this assumption about the mass seems to be a valid one, compatible with our experience. But there is a possibility that if we experiment with very large velocities this assumption may not remain correct. In fact, discrepancies are found whenever we study the motion of very energetic particles, such as the inner electrons in atoms, or the particles found in cosmic rays or produced in high-energy accelerators. The purpose of this chapter is to develop a general theory of motion valid for low-energy as well as for high-energy particles. We shall base our development of this theory on the Lorentz transformation, already discussed in Section 6.6, and on the *principle of relativity.* For this reason the new theory is also called *relativistic mechanics.*

11.2 Classical Principle of Relativity

In Chapter 6 we discussed the relative nature of motion and derived expressions for the velocities and accelerations as measured by two observers in different kinds of relative motion. In particular, in Section 6.3, we derived the Galilean transformation for two observers in uniform relative translational motion.

In Chapter 7 we emphasized the fact that the laws of motion have to be considered as referred, or relative, to an inertial observer. We presently assume that two different inertial observers moving with a constant relative velocity will correlate their respective observations of the same phenomenon by Galileo's transformation. We must now look more critically into this matter, verifying that if the laws of dynamics hold for one inertial observer they hold for all inertial observers. It is necessary to verify this statement only for the *principle of conservation of momentum* and for the *definition of force*, since all the other dynamical laws are derived from these two. The hypothesis that *all laws of dynamics must be the same for all inertial observers moving with constant velocity relative to each other* is what constitutes the *classical principle of relativity.*

Let us consider two particles, of masses m_1 and m_2, and call $\boldsymbol{v}_1$ and $\boldsymbol{v}_2$ their velocities as measured by some inertial observer O. If no external forces act on the particles, the principle of conservation of momentum requires that

$$m_1\boldsymbol{v}_1 + m_2\boldsymbol{v}_2 = \text{const.} \tag{11.1}$$

For another inertial observer O', moving relative to O with the constant velocity $\boldsymbol{v}$, the velocities of m_1 and m_2 are $\boldsymbol{v}_1' = \boldsymbol{v}_1 - \boldsymbol{v}$ and $\boldsymbol{v}_2' = \boldsymbol{v}_2 - \boldsymbol{v}$, according to Eq. (6.9), which is derived from the Galilean transformation. Substituting these into Eq. (11.1), we have

$$m_1(\boldsymbol{v}_1' + \boldsymbol{v}) + m_2(\boldsymbol{v}_2' + \boldsymbol{v}) = \text{const},$$

or

$$m_1\boldsymbol{v}_1' + m_2\boldsymbol{v}_2' = \text{const} - (m_1 + m_2)\boldsymbol{v} = \text{const}. \tag{11.2}$$

Note that the new result is constant only if $\boldsymbol{v}$ is also constant; that is, if O' is another inertial observer. Equation (11.2) is entirely similar to Eq. (11.1), and therefore both inertial observers verify the same principle of conservation of momentum.

Let us next discuss the relation between the force measured by two inertial observers O and O' moving with a constant relative velocity $\boldsymbol{v}$. Suppose that O and O' both measure the same mass for a particle they observe in motion, an assumption substantiated by experience, at least so long as the relative velocity $\boldsymbol{v}$ is small compared with the velocity of light. If $\boldsymbol{V}$ and $\boldsymbol{V}'$ are the respective values of the particle's velocity relative to the two observers, they are related by Eq. (6.9), $\boldsymbol{V} = \boldsymbol{V}' + \boldsymbol{v}$. Since $\boldsymbol{v}$ is constant, $d\boldsymbol{v}/dt = 0$, and we have that

$$\frac{d\boldsymbol{V}}{dt} = \frac{d\boldsymbol{V}'}{dt} \quad \text{or} \quad \boldsymbol{a} = \boldsymbol{a}'. \tag{11.3}$$

That is, both observers measure the same acceleration (recall Eq. 6.13). According to the definition of force given in Eq. (7.12), we have that the force measured by each observer is

$$\boldsymbol{F} = \frac{d\boldsymbol{p}}{dt} = m\frac{d\boldsymbol{V}}{dt} = m\boldsymbol{a} \quad \text{and} \quad \boldsymbol{F}' = \frac{d\boldsymbol{p}'}{dt} = m\frac{d\boldsymbol{V}'}{dt} = m\boldsymbol{a}'.$$

In view of the fact that $\boldsymbol{a} = \boldsymbol{a}'$, we conclude that

$$\boldsymbol{F} = \boldsymbol{F}'. \tag{11.4}$$

Therefore *both inertial observers measure the same force on the particle* when the observers compare their measurements using the Galilean transformation.

We leave it to the student to verify that if the energy is conserved relative to the inertial observer O, that is, if

$$E = \tfrac{1}{2}m_1v_1^2 + \tfrac{1}{2}m_2v_2^2 + E_{p,12} = \text{const},$$

then it is also conserved relative to the inertial observer O', and

$$E' = \tfrac{1}{2}m_1v_1'^2 + \tfrac{1}{2}m_2v_2'^2 + E'_{p,12} = \text{const},$$

where $E'_{p,12} = E_{p,12}$ if the potential energy depends only on the distance between the particles. (For the relation between E' and E, see Problem 11.1.) Therefore, insofar as the fundamental laws of dynamics are concerned, the description of the motion is the same for both inertial observers.

EXAMPLE 11.1. Discuss the form of the equation of motion when it is used with reference to a noninertial observer.

Solution: If an observer O' is noninertial, this means that his velocity $\boldsymbol{v}$ relative to an inertial observer O is not constant in time. Thus $d\boldsymbol{v}/dt \neq 0$. Then, since $\boldsymbol{V} = \boldsymbol{V}' + \boldsymbol{v}$, we have that

$$\frac{d\boldsymbol{V}}{dt} = \frac{d\boldsymbol{V}'}{dt} + \frac{d\boldsymbol{v}}{dt} \qquad \text{or} \qquad \boldsymbol{a} = \boldsymbol{a}' + \frac{d\boldsymbol{v}}{dt}.$$

The force measured by the inertial observer O is $\boldsymbol{F} = m\boldsymbol{a}$. Then, if the noninertial observer O' uses the same definition of force, he writes $\boldsymbol{F}' = m\boldsymbol{a}'$. Therefore, in view of the relation between $\boldsymbol{a}$ and $\boldsymbol{a}'$,

$$\boldsymbol{F}' = \boldsymbol{F} - m\frac{d\boldsymbol{v}}{dt}. \tag{11.5}$$

Thus *the noninertial observer measures a force different from that of the inertial observer.* In other words, the noninertial observer considers that, in addition to the force $\boldsymbol{F}$ measured by the inertial observer (which includes all the interactions to which the particle is subject), there is another force $\boldsymbol{F}''$ acting on the particle, where

$$\boldsymbol{F}'' = -m\, d\boldsymbol{v}/dt, \tag{11.6}$$

so that the resultant force on the particle is $\boldsymbol{F} + \boldsymbol{F}''$. This fictitious force is called an *inertial force.*

When we want to describe the motion of a particle relative to the earth (which is not an inertial frame of reference) we sometimes use this kind of logic. In this case $d\boldsymbol{v}/dt$ is the centripetal acceleration $\boldsymbol{\omega} \times (\boldsymbol{\omega} \times \boldsymbol{r})$ (recall Eq. 6.25). Therefore the inertial force is $\boldsymbol{F}'' = -m\boldsymbol{\omega} \times (\boldsymbol{\omega} \times \boldsymbol{r})$, which corresponds to a centrifugal force acting on the particle in addition to its weight.

11.3 Special Principle of Relativity

In 1905, the German physicist Albert Einstein (1879–1955) went a step further and proposed a *special principle of relativity*, by stating that

> *all laws of nature (not only of dynamics) must be the same for all inertial observers moving with constant velocity relative to each other.*

This new, or special, principle of relativity has a great implication because, if we accept it, we must express all physical laws in a form that does not change when we transform from one inertial observer to another, a fact we have just verified for the laws of dynamics, using the Galilean transformation. The result of this requirement is that it restricts the mathematical expressions of these laws. Among the laws that must remain invariant for all inertial observers are those describing electromagnetic phenomena; these will be discussed in detail in later chapters.

But we may now state in advance that these laws, when expressed relative to an inertial observer, involve a velocity c; that is, the velocity of light. Therefore the special principle of relativity, as formulated by Einstein, requires that the velocity of light be the same for all inertial observers.

Einstein's assumption was motivated in part by the memorable series of experiments started around 1880 by Michelson and Morley, who measured the velocity of light in different directions, trying to see how the motion of the earth affects the velocity of light. We discussed their experiment in Chapter 6 (particularly in Example 6.7). The results, as indicated in Chapter 6, have always been negative, indicating that *the velocity of light is independent of the motion of the observer.*

Now, according to Eq. (6.9), the velocity of an object is never the same for two observers in relative motion if their observations are related by a Galilean transformation. On the other hand, the velocity of light is the same to all inertial observers if their measurements are related by the Lorentz transformation, as discussed in Section 6.6. Therefore it seems apparent that to satisfy the new principle of relativity we must use the Lorentz transformation instead of the Galilean transformation. Accordingly, we shall restate the principle of relativity in the following way:

> *Inertial observers must correlate their observations by means of the Lorentz transformation, and all physical quantities must transform from one inertial system to another in such a way that the expression of the physical laws is the same for all inertial observers.*

The rest of this chapter will be devoted to a discussion of how this new formulation of the principle of relativity affects the dynamical quantities defined previously. From the practical point of view, the theory we shall develop is important only for velocities comparable to that of light, and therefore must be used when the particles have a very high energy. For particles which have low velocities, the Galilean transformation is still a very good approximation for relating physical quantities in two inertial frames, and newtonian mechanics provides a satisfactory formalism for describing these phenomena. The theory to be developed is called the *special* theory of relativity because it applies only to inertial observers. When the observers are not inertial, we employ the *general* theory of relativity, which we shall discuss briefly at the end of Chapter 13.

Even if, from the practical point of view, we may ignore the special theory of relativity in many instances, from the conceptual point of view it has produced a profound modification in our theoretical approach to the analysis of physical phenomena.

11.4 Momentum

In Chapter 7 we defined the momentum of a particle as $\boldsymbol{p} = m\boldsymbol{v}$, and assumed that the mass m was independent of the velocity. However, as a result of many experiments with high-energy particles, such as fast electrons and protons produced by modern accelerators, or found in cosmic rays, it has been found that this assumption is no longer valid. Let us recall that the force applied to a particle has been defined as $\boldsymbol{F} = d\boldsymbol{p}/dt$, and by exerting known forces on fast particles we may determine experimentally the corresponding expression for $\boldsymbol{p}$. [We may, for example, observe the motion of electrons (or other charged particles) of different energies in known electric and magnetic fields.] The result of these experiments has been that the mass of a particle moving with a velocity $\boldsymbol{v}$ relative to the ob-

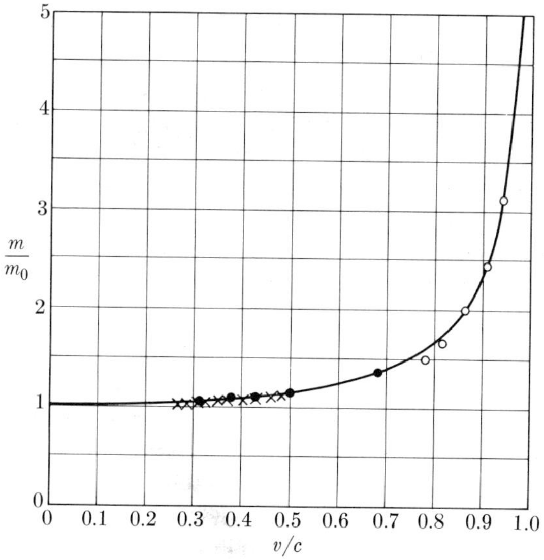

Fig. 11–1. Experimental confirmation of the variation of mass with velocity. The solid curve is a plot based on Eq. (11.7). The experimental data of W. Kaufmann (1901) is plotted as open circles, that of A. Bucherer (1909) as solid circles, and that of C. Guye and C. Lavanchy (1915) as crosses.

server appears to be given by

$$m = \frac{m_0}{\sqrt{1 - v^2/c^2}} = km_0. \tag{11.7}$$

Here k is as defined in Eq. (6.32) and m_0 is a constant, characteristic of each particle, called the *rest mass,* since it is the value of m when $v = 0$; that is, when the particle is at rest relative to the observer. The presence of the factor $\sqrt{1 - v^2/c^2}$, which we encountered before in Chapter 6 when we were dealing with the Lorentz transformation, is not surprising, since our new principle of relativity based on this transformation may require its use.

The variation of mass with velocity according to Eq. (11.7) is illustrated in Fig. 11–1. This figure is essentially identical to Fig. 6–15, since both give k in terms of v/c. It can be seen that only at very large velocities is there any noticeable increase in the mass of the particle. For example, even at $v = 0.5c$, $m/m_0 = 1.15$, or only a 15 percent increase in mass.

The momentum of a particle moving with velocity $\boldsymbol{v}$ relative to an observer must therefore be expressed as:

$$\boldsymbol{p} = m\boldsymbol{v} = \frac{m_0\boldsymbol{v}}{\sqrt{1 - v^2/c^2}} = km_0\boldsymbol{v}. \tag{11.8}$$

For small velocities ($v \ll c$), k can be equated to one, and this new expression becomes identical to that used in previous chapters.

We still have to verify that this expression for momentum meets the requirements of the principle of relativity. That is, we must verify that, if the motion of the particle is referred to a different inertial observer, relative to which the particle is moving with velocity $\boldsymbol{v}'$, the momentum $\boldsymbol{p}'$ is expressed by replacing $\boldsymbol{v}$ with $\boldsymbol{v}'$ in Eq. (11.8), and that the two expressions for the momentum are compatible with the Lorentz transformation which relates the two observers. We also have to verify that this new definition of momentum is compatible with the invariance of the principle of conservation of momentum for all inertial observers. This matter will be deferred until Sections 11.7 and 11.9.

EXAMPLE 11.2. Compare the relative increase in velocity with the relative increase in momentum.

Solution: The relative increase in momentum is defined as dp/p and the relative increase in velocity as dv/v. Momentum and velocity are related by Eq. (11.8), which in scalar form is

$$p = \frac{m_0 v}{(1 - v^2/c^2)^{1/2}}.$$

The definition of relative increase in velocity suggests that we first take the logarithm of this expression. That is,

$$\ln p = \ln m_0 + \ln v - \tfrac{1}{2}\ln\left(1 - \frac{v^2}{c^2}\right).$$

Differentiating, we obtain

$$\frac{dp}{p} = \frac{dv}{v} + \frac{(v/c^2)\,dv}{1 - v^2/c^2} = \frac{1}{1 - v^2/c^2}\,\frac{dv}{v} = k^2\,\frac{dv}{v}.$$

We see then that at low velocities, when v^2/c^2 is negligible, we have $dp/p = dv/v$, and the relative increases in momentum and velocity are equal, in agreement with our common experience. However, at large velocities, comparable with c, the factor multiplying dv/v is very large, and thus it is possible to produce a relatively large increase in momentum with a relatively small increase in velocity. For example, for $v = 0.7c$, we have that $dp/p \approx 2(dv/v)$, and for $v = 0.99c$, we obtain $dp/p \approx 50(dv/v)$.

11.5 Force

In Chapter 7 we defined the force on a particle by means of Eq. (7.12), which was derived from the principle of conservation of momentum. This definition will also be maintained in relativistic mechanics. Thus we restate force as

$$\boldsymbol{F} = \frac{d\boldsymbol{p}}{dt} = \frac{d}{dt}(m\boldsymbol{v}) = \frac{d}{dt}\left(\frac{m_0\boldsymbol{v}}{\sqrt{1 - v^2/c^2}}\right). \tag{11.9}$$

When we are dealing with *rectilinear motion* we consider only the magnitudes, and thus we may write

$$F = \frac{d}{dt}\left[\frac{m_0 v}{(1 - v^2/c^2)^{1/2}}\right] = \frac{m_0(dv/dt)}{(1 - v^2/c^2)^{3/2}} = \frac{m}{1 - v^2/c^2}\,\frac{dv}{dt}. \tag{11.10}$$

In Eq. (11.10), m has the value given by Eq. (11.7). Since dv/dt is the acceleration, we conclude that for a high-energy particle the equation $F = ma$ does not hold for rectilinear motion. On the other hand, in the case of *uniform circular motion*, the velocity remains constant in magnitude but not in direction, and Eq. (11.9) becomes

$$\boldsymbol{F} = \frac{m_0}{(1 - v^2/c^2)^{1/2}} \frac{d\boldsymbol{v}}{dt} = m \frac{d\boldsymbol{v}}{dt}.$$

But $d\boldsymbol{v}/dt$ is then the normal or centripetal acceleration whose magnitude is v^2/R, where R is the radius of the circle, according to Eq. (5.44). Therefore the magnitude of the normal or centripetal force becomes

$$F_N = \frac{m_0}{(1 - v^2/c^2)^{1/2}} \frac{v^2}{R} = m \frac{v^2}{R} = \frac{pv}{R}. \tag{11.11}$$

We observe that the relation $\boldsymbol{F} = m\boldsymbol{a}$ holds in the case of uniform circular motion if we use for the mass its relativistic expression (11.7). In the general case of *curvilinear motion*, noting that dv/dt is the tangential acceleration and v^2/R the normal acceleration (according to Eq. 5.44), we conclude from Eqs. (11.10) and (11.11) that the components of the force along the tangent and normal to the path are, using Eq. (11.7),

$$\begin{aligned} F_T &= \frac{m_0}{(1 - v^2/c^2)^{3/2}} a_T = \frac{m}{1 - v^2/c^2} a_T = k^2 m a_T, \\ F_N &= \frac{m_0}{(1 - v^2/c^2)^{1/2}} a_N = m a_N. \end{aligned} \tag{11.12}$$

An immediate conclusion is that the force is *not* parallel to the acceleration (Fig. 11–2) because the coefficients multiplying a_T and a_N are different. Thus a vector relation of the type $\boldsymbol{F} = m\boldsymbol{a}$ does not hold for particles which have high energy, unless the body moves with uniform circular motion. However, the more fundamental relation $\boldsymbol{F} = d\boldsymbol{p}/dt$ still remains valid, because it is our *definition* of force. Another interesting feature is that, proportionately, the tangential component F_T is larger than the normal component F_N. This is because the normal force changes only the direction of the velocity without changing its magnitude, and thus also without changing the mass. But the tangential force not only has to change the magnitude of the velocity but also, as a consequence, increases the mass of the particle.

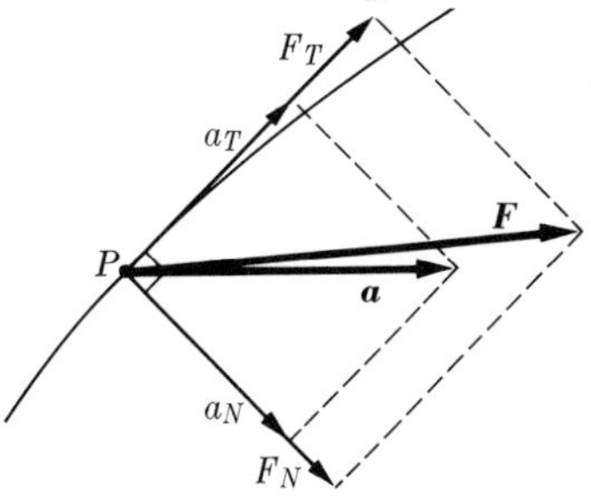

Fig. 11–2. At high velocity, the force is not parallel to the acceleration.

EXAMPLE 11.3. Rectilinear motion under a constant force in relativistic dynamics.

Solution: This motion, in nonrelativistic mechanics, corresponds to motion with constant acceleration. Thus if we measure time and displacement from the point where the particle started moving, we may use Eqs. (5.10) and (5.11) to find that $v = at$ and

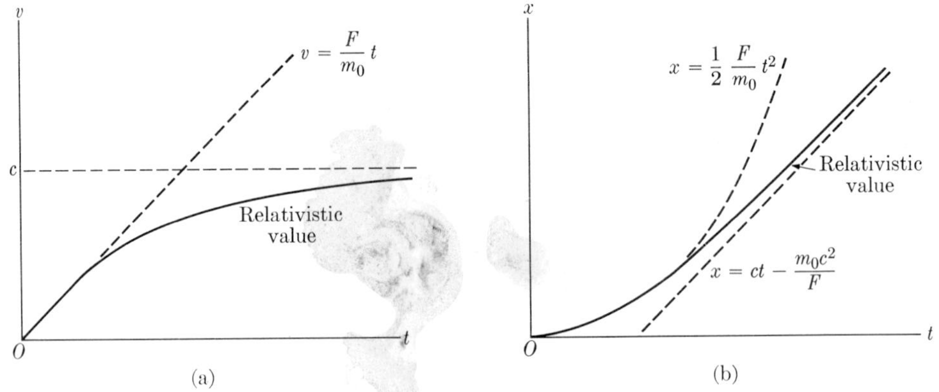

Fig. 11–3. Relativistic rectilinear motion under a constant force.

$x = \frac{1}{2}at^2$, where $a = F/m_0$ is the constant acceleration. In relativistic mechanics we start with Eq. (11.9) written in scalar form, since the motion is in a straight line and no changes in direction are involved. Thus

$$F = \frac{d}{dt}\left[\frac{m_0 v}{(1 - v^2/c^2)^{1/2}}\right].$$

Integrating this expression, while taking into account the fact that F is constant (and that for $t = 0$, $v = 0$), we have

$$\frac{m_0 v}{\sqrt{1 - v^2/c^2}} = Ft.$$

Solving for the velocity, we find that

$$v = c\,\frac{(F/m_0c)t}{\sqrt{1 + (F/m_0c)^2t^2}}.$$

For very small t (that is, when the measurement takes place at the beginning of the motion), the second term in the denominator can be neglected and $v \approx (F/m_0)t$, which is the nonrelativistic expression because in that case $a = F/m_0$. For very large t (that is, when the measurement is made after the particle has been accelerating for a long time), the 1 in the denominator can be neglected in comparison with the second term, and $v \approx c$. Thus, instead of increasing indefinitely, the velocity approaches the limiting value c, which is the speed of light. This variation of velocity with time is indicated by the solid line in Fig. 11–3(a). The momentum, however, is given as $p = Ft$, and increases indefinitely. To obtain the displacement of the particle we recall that $v = dx/dt$. Therefore

$$\frac{dx}{dt} = c\,\frac{(F/m_0c)t}{\sqrt{1 + (F/m_0c)^2t^2}}.$$

Integrating (letting $x = 0$ at $t = 0$), we have

$$x = \frac{m_0c^2}{F}\left[\sqrt{1 + \left(\frac{F}{m_0c}\right)^2 t^2} - 1\right].$$

Using the binomial expansion (M.28) with $n = \frac{1}{2}$, the above equation reduces to $x = \frac{1}{2}(F/m_0)t^2$ for small values of t; this is the nonrelativistic value. For large t, we have $x \approx ct - (m_0c^2/F)$, which corresponds to uniform motion with velocity c. Thus the distance is less than if the nonrelativistic expression were valid at all velocities. This is indicated by the solid line in Fig. 11–3(b). This problem is of interest in a number of contexts; for example, in the motion of a charged particle in a linear accelerator.

11.6 Energy

To compute the kinetic energy of a particle using the new definition of momentum, we use the same procedure as in Section 8.5 when we were talking about newtonian mechanics. That is, recalling that $v = ds/dt$, we obtain

$$E_k = \int_0^v F_T\,ds = \int_0^v \frac{d}{dt}(mv)\,ds = \int_0^v v\,d(mv).$$

Integrating by parts (see Eq. M.41) and using the relativistic expression (11.7) for mass, we have

$$\begin{aligned} E_k &= mv^2 - \int_0^v mv\,dv = \frac{m_0v^2}{\sqrt{1 - v^2/c^2}} - \int_0^v \frac{m_0v\,dv}{\sqrt{1 - v^2/c^2}} \\ &= \frac{m_0v^2}{\sqrt{1 - v^2/c^2}} + m_0c^2\sqrt{1 - v^2/c^2} - m_0c^2. \end{aligned}$$

Combining the first two terms of the right-hand side into one, we finally obtain the kinetic energy of a particle moving with velocity v relative to the observer as

$$E_k = \frac{m_0c^2}{\sqrt{1 - v^2/c^2}} - m_0c^2 = (m - m_0)c^2, \tag{11.13}$$

where Eq. (11.7) has been used in writing the last part. Result (11.13) is very suggestive. It indicates that the gain in kinetic energy can be considered as a gain in mass as a result of the dependence of the mass on the velocity, according to Eq. (11.7). This interpretation can be extended to associate a change in mass Δm to any change in energy ΔE of the system. Both changes are related by the expression

$$\Delta E = (\Delta m)c^2, \tag{11.14}$$

which is an extension of Eq. (11.13). For example, the conservation of energy of an isolated system requires that $(E_k + E_p)_2 = (E_k + E_p)_1 = \text{const}$, or $E_{k2} - E_{k1} = E_{p1} - E_{p2}$. But, according to Eq. (11.13), $E_{k2} - E_{k1} = (m_2 - m_1)c^2$. Therefore

$$(m_2 - m_1)c^2 = E_{p1} - E_{p2}. \tag{11.15}$$

Equation (11.15) means that any change in the internal potential energy of the system, due to an internal rearrangement, may be expressed as a change in the mass of the system as a result of the change in internal kinetic energy. This procedure is valid so long as the total energy is conserved. Because of the factor c^2, changes in mass are appreciable only if the changes in energy are very large. For that reason the change of mass resulting from energy transformations is appreciable only in nuclear interactions or in high-energy physics, and is practically negligible in chemical reactions.

The quantity m_0c^2 which appears in Eq. (11.13) is called the *rest energy* of the particle, and the quantity

$$E = E_k + m_0c^2 = \frac{m_0c^2}{\sqrt{1 - v^2/c^2}} = mc^2 \tag{11.16}$$

is the *total* energy of the particle. The total energy of the particle, as here defined, includes kinetic energy and rest energy, but not potential energy.

Combining Eq. (11.8) with Eq. (11.16), we see that $v = c^2p/E$. This expression gives the velocity in terms of momentum and energy. Since $\boldsymbol{v}$ and $\boldsymbol{p}$ have the same direction, this expression is also valid for the vectors themselves, and we may write

$$\boldsymbol{v} = \frac{c^2\boldsymbol{p}}{E}. \tag{11.17}$$

Equation (11.16) is equivalent to

$$E = c\sqrt{m_0^2c^2 + p^2}, \tag{11.18}$$

as we may see by replacing p by its expression (11.8) and verifying that Eq. (11.18) becomes Eq. (11.16).

At first sight, Eq. (11.13) for the relativistic kinetic energy may seem quite distinct from Eq. (8.12) for the newtonian kinetic energy (that is, $E_k = \frac{1}{2}mv^2$). However, it is not. When v is small compared with c, we may expand the denominator in Eq. (11.7), using the binomial theorem (M.22):

$$m = m_0\left(1 - \frac{v^2}{c^2}\right)^{-1/2} = m_0\left(1 + \frac{1}{2}\frac{v^2}{c^2} + \frac{3}{8}\frac{v^4}{c^4} + \cdots\right).$$

Substituting in Eq. (11.13), we find that

$$E_k = \tfrac{1}{2}m_0v^2 + \tfrac{3}{8}m_0\frac{v^4}{c^2} + \cdots \tag{11.19}$$

The first term is our familiar kinetic energy of Eq. (8.12). The second, and succeeding terms, are negligible if $v \ll c$. In this way we verify again that newtonian mechanics is only an approximation of relativistic mechanics, valid for small velocities or energies and using for the mass its rest value. On the other hand, at very large velocities we may replace v by c in the numerator of Eq. (11.8) for the momentum, writing $p = mc$. Then the kinetic energy given in Eq. (11.13) becomes

$$E_k = pc - m_0c^2 = c(p - m_0c). \tag{11.20}$$

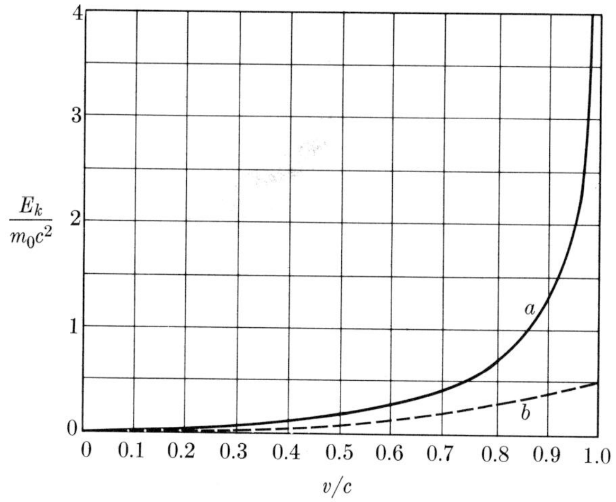

Fig. 11–4. Variation of kinetic energy with velocity; (a) relativistic, (b) newtonian.

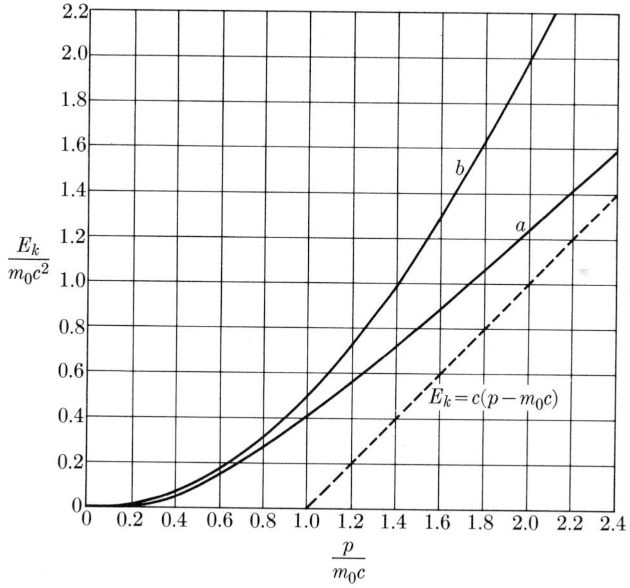

Fig. 11–5. Variation of kinetic energy with momentum; (a) relativistic, (b) newtonian.

In Fig. 11–4, the variation of the kinetic energy E_k as given by Eq. (11.13) has been indicated by curve a, and the newtonian kinetic energy $E_k = \frac{1}{2}m_0v^2$ by curve b. This figure clearly shows that, at equal velocities, the relativistic energy is larger than the newtonian value. In Fig. 11–5 kinetic energy has been represented in terms of momentum. It may be seen that, for equal momenta, the relativistic energy (curve a) is smaller than the newtonian energy (curve b). The relativistic curve tends asymptotically to the value given by Eq. (11.20).

We must note that the ratios m/m_0 and E_k/m_0c^2 are the same for all particles having the same velocity. Thus, since the mass of the proton is about 1850 times the mass of the electron, the relativistic effects in the motion of the protons are noticeable only at energies 1850 times larger. For that reason the motion of protons and neutrons in atomic nuclei can be treated in many instances without relativistic considerations, while the motion of electrons requires, in most instances, a relativistic approach.

An interesting special case occurs when there is a particle of zero rest mass ($m_0 = 0$). Then Eq. (11.18) becomes

$$E = cp \qquad \text{or} \qquad p = E/c. \tag{11.21}$$

And hence, from Eq. (11.17), we find that the velocity of the particle is $v = c$. Therefore, a particle with zero rest mass can move only with the velocity of light and can never be at rest in an inertial system. This is the case of the photon, and it seems to be true also for the neutrino, as we shall see in later chapters. Relation (11.21) also holds when a given particle, even if its mass m_0 is not zero, moves at a velocity comparable with that of light, so that its momentum p is very large compared with m_0c. We may see that this is the case because, when in Eq. (11.18) we neglect the term m_0c in comparison with p, the equation reduces to Eq. (11.21).

EXAMPLE 11.4. Compare the relative increase in velocity and in momentum with the relative increase in energy.

Solution: Solving Eq. (11.18) for v, we get

$$v = c\left(1 - \frac{m_0^2c^4}{E^2}\right)^{1/2}.$$

When the velocity of a particle increases by the amount dv and its energy by the amount dE, the relative increase in velocity is given by dv/v and the relative increase in energy by dE/E. This suggests, as in Example 11.2, that we must take the logarithm of the above expression before differentiating. That is,

$$\ln v = \ln c + \tfrac{1}{2}\ln\left(1 - \frac{m_0^2c^4}{E^2}\right).$$

Differentiating, we obtain

$$\frac{dv}{v} = \frac{m_0^2c^4}{E^2 - m_0^2c^4}\,\frac{dE}{E}.$$

If the energy of the particle is very high compared with its rest mass, so that $E \gg m_0c^2$, we may neglect $m_0^2c^4$ in the denominator, resulting in

$$\frac{dv}{v} = \frac{m_0^2c^4}{E^2}\,\frac{dE}{E}.$$

The coefficient multiplying the relative increase in energy is always smaller than unity because, at high energy, E is much larger than m_0c^2. Therefore at high energies dv/v is very small compared with dE/E. In other words, at high energies it is possible to increase the energy of the particle without appreciably increasing its velocity. This characteristic is of great importance in the design of high-energy accelerators, both linear and circular. We suggest that the student repeat the same calculation, using newtonian mechanics, and compare results.

On the other hand, insofar as momentum p is concerned, we have from Eq. (11.18) that

$$\ln E = \ln c + \tfrac{1}{2} \ln (m_0^2c^2 + p^2)$$

and, differentiating, we obtain

$$\frac{dE}{E} = \frac{p^2}{m_0^2c^2 + p^2} \frac{dp}{p}.$$

At high energies, when p is much larger than m_0c, we get $dE/E \approx dp/p$, and the momentum increases in the same proportion as the energy.

EXAMPLE 11.5. Curvilinear motion under a constant force in relativistic dynamics.

Solution: In nonrelativistic mechanics this motion corresponds to a parabolic path, as happens with a projectile (recall Section 5.7). To solve this problem in relativistic mechanics, it is easier to use the momentum and energy relations. Let us assume that at $t = 0$ the particle is at O (Fig. 11–6), moving along the X-axis with momentum p_0, while the force $\boldsymbol{F}$ is perpendicular to it (or along the Y-axis). The equation of motion $\boldsymbol{F} = d\boldsymbol{p}/dt$, expressed in terms of its components along the X- and Y-axes, becomes

$$\frac{dp_x}{dt} = 0, \qquad \frac{dp_y}{dt} = F.$$

Integrating each of these expressions gives $p_x = p_0$ (const), $p_y = Ft$. Thus the total momentum after time t, when the particle has reached point A, is

$$p = \sqrt{p_x^2 + p_y^2} = \sqrt{p_0^2 + F^2t^2},$$

and the total energy, using Eq. (11.18), is

$$E = c\sqrt{m_0^2c^2 + p_0^2 + F^2t^2} = \sqrt{E_0^2 + c^2F^2t^2},$$

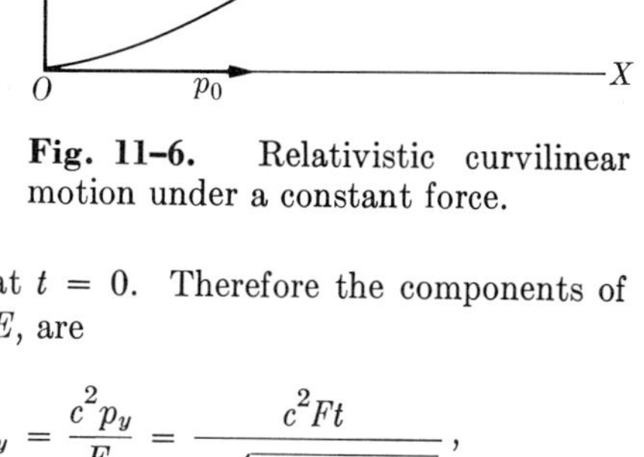

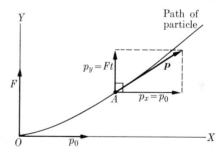

Fig. 11–6. Relativistic curvilinear motion under a constant force.

where $E_0 = c\sqrt{m_0^2c^2 + p_0^2}$ is the total energy at $t = 0$. Therefore the components of the velocity, using the vector relation $\boldsymbol{v} = c^2\boldsymbol{p}/E$, are

$$v_x = \frac{c^2p_x}{E} = \frac{c^2p_0}{\sqrt{E_0^2 + c^2F^2t^2}}, \qquad v_y = \frac{c^2p_y}{E} = \frac{c^2Ft}{\sqrt{E_0^2 + c^2F^2t^2}},$$

from which the magnitude of the velocity can easily be obtained. By integrating these expressions, the coordinates x and y of the particle may be expressed as functions of time. From these the equation of the path results. We leave the student to do these last steps, and to compare the path with the nonrelativistic parabola (see Problem 11.11).

11.7 Transformation of Energy and Momentum

According to the principle of relativity, Eq. (11.18) relating energy and momentum must be the same for all inertial observers. It is therefore important to compare these quantities as measured by two observers in relative motion. For observer O, Eq. (11.18) can be written in the form

$$p^2 - \frac{E^2}{c^2} = -m_0^2c^2. \tag{11.22}$$

We remember that $\boldsymbol{p}$ is a vector quantity with components p_x, p_y, and p_z. Then $p^2 = p_x^2 + p_y^2 + p_z^2$, and Eq. (11.22) becomes

$$p_x^2 + p_y^2 + p_z^2 - \frac{E^2}{c^2} = -m_0^2c^2. \tag{11.23}$$

In order to be consistent with the assumption of the principle of relativity, this expression must remain invariant for all inertial observers. That is, in another frame of reference (observer O') moving with velocity v relative to the original frame to which Eq. (11.23) is referred, we must have

$$p_{x'}'^2 + p_{y'}'^2 + p_{z'}'^2 - \frac{E'^2}{c^2} = -m_0^2c^2, \tag{11.24}$$

where m_0 remains the same because it corresponds to the rest mass. In other words, we must have

$$p_x^2 + p_y^2 + p_z^2 - \frac{E^2}{c^2} = p_{x'}'^2 + p_{y'}'^2 + p_{z'}'^2 - \frac{E'^2}{c^2}. \tag{11.25}$$

The structures of Eqs. (11.23), (11.24), and (11.25) are similar to those of Eqs. (6.30) and (6.31) if we make the correspondence

$$p_x \to x, \quad p_y \to y, \quad p_z \to z, \qquad \text{and} \qquad ct \to E/c.$$

Therefore the invariance of Eq. (11.23) requires a transformation among its elements such as the Lorentz transformation holding for x, y, z, and t. This leads to

$$\begin{aligned}
p_{x'}' &= \frac{p_x - vE/c^2}{\sqrt{1 - v^2/c^2}}, \\
p_{y'}' &= p_y, \\
p_{z'}' &= p_z, \\
E' &= \frac{E - vp_x}{\sqrt{1 - v^2/c^2}}.
\end{aligned} \tag{11.26}$$

This result, together with the corresponding expression for energy, shows how our definition of momentum given in Eq. (11.8) satisfies the first requirement of the special principle of relativity; namely, the momentum has a proper transformation under a Lorentz transformation.

Note that we have found two sets of associated quantities—that is, x, y, z, ct and p_x, p_y, p_z, E/c—that appear to transform among themselves following the rules of the Lorentz transformation. Undoubtedly we may also expect other physical quantities to transform in a similar fashion. A common characteristic of all these sets of quantities is that they have four "components"; i.e., they are expressed by four numbers. For that reason they are called *four-vectors*, and can supposedly be depicted in a four-dimensional representative space. One method of adapting the physical laws to the invariance requirements of the principle of relativity is by writing them as relations between scalars, four-vectors, and other related quantities (tensors). We shall not elaborate on this subject, since it belongs with a more extensive discussion of the theory of relativity, beyond the scope and purpose of this text.

EXAMPLE 11.6. Express the inverse relations between energy and momentum corresponding to Eqs. (11.26). That is, give the values measured by O expressed in terms of those measured by O'.

Solution: We refer the student to Example 6.4, corresponding to the equivalent problem for the coordinates x, y, z, and the time t. We can thus arrive at the result we want simply by reversing the sign of v and exchanging primed and unprimed quantities in Eqs. (11.26), obtaining

$$\begin{aligned} p_x &= \frac{p'_{x'} + vE'/c^2}{\sqrt{1 - v^2/c^2}}, \\ p_y &= p'_{y'}, \\ p_z &= p'_{z'}, \\ E &= \frac{E' + vp'_{x'}}{\sqrt{1 - v^2/c^2}}. \end{aligned} \tag{11.27}$$

EXAMPLE 11.7. Apply the results of the previous example to the case when the particle is at rest relative to O'.

Solution: In this case $p'_{x'} = p'_{y'} = p'_{z'} = 0$ and $E' = m_0c^2$. Therefore the transformation equations give

$$p_x = \frac{m_0 v}{\sqrt{1 - v^2/c^2}}, \qquad p_y = 0, \qquad p_z = 0, \qquad E = \frac{m_0 c^2}{\sqrt{1 - v^2/c^2}}.$$

The first three equations give the momentum and the last equation the energy as measured by O. Comparison with Eq. (11.8) for the momentum and Eq. (11.16) for the energy shows that they correspond exactly to the momentum and the energy of a particle moving along the X-axis with velocity v. This is just the case, since the particle, being at rest relative to O', must appear as moving with velocity v relative to O. The merit of this example is that the relations (11.26), and their inverse (11.27), which were derived in a somewhat intuitive way using the principle of relativistic invariance, are compatible with the previous expressions for energy and momentum derived using a different starting point. Thus this example shows the consistency of our logic.

EXAMPLE 11.8. Discuss the transformation of energy and momentum for a particle with zero rest mass. For simplicity suppose the motion of the particle to be along the direction of relative motion of the two observers.

Solution: Since $m_0 = 0$, we may assume that the relation $E = cp$, according to Eq. (11.21), holds for observer O. Then, using Eqs. (11.26), with $p'_{x'} = p'$ and $p_x = p$ because the motion is along the X-axis, and using $E = cp$, we have for observer O',

$$p' = \frac{p - v(cp)/c^2}{\sqrt{1 - v^2/c^2}} = p\,\frac{1 - v/c}{\sqrt{1 - v^2/c^2}}.$$

Using this result for p', we obtain for the energy

$$E' = \frac{cp - vp}{\sqrt{1 - v^2/c^2}} = cp\,\frac{1 - v/c}{\sqrt{1 - v^2/c^2}} = cp'.$$

Therefore the relation $E' = cp'$ also holds for observer O'. This example, as the preceding example does, increases the student's confidence in the consistency of the theory. It is suggested that the student repeat the problem, assuming that the particle moves in an arbitrary direction.

11.8 Transformation of Force

The force acting on a particle as measured by observers O and O' is, respectively,

$$\boldsymbol{F} = \frac{d\boldsymbol{p}}{dt} \quad \text{and} \quad \boldsymbol{F}' = \frac{d\boldsymbol{p}'}{dt'}, \tag{11.28}$$

as required by the principle of relativity, since both observers must use the same equations of motion. The relation between $\boldsymbol{F}$ and $\boldsymbol{F}'$ is in general rather complicated, since we cannot use as simple a reasoning as we used for the energy and the momentum relationships. Therefore we shall compute this relation only for the special case in which the particle is momentarily at rest in the system O'. Then $\boldsymbol{F}'$ is called the *proper force.*

Using Eqs. (11.26), we obtain

$$\begin{aligned} F'_{x'} &= \frac{dp'_{x'}}{dt'} = \frac{dt}{dt'}\frac{d}{dt}\left(\frac{p_x - vE/c^2}{\sqrt{1 - v^2/c^2}}\right) \\ &= \frac{dt}{dt'}\frac{1}{\sqrt{1 - v^2/c^2}}\left(\frac{dp_x}{dt} - \frac{v}{c^2}\frac{dE}{dt}\right). \end{aligned} \tag{11.29}$$

Now from the inverse Lorentz transformation (see the last equation in Example 6.4), we have that

$$t = \frac{t' + vx'/c^2}{\sqrt{1 - v^2/c^2}},$$

and since $dx'/dt = 0$ because the particle is at rest relative to O',

$$\frac{dt}{dt'} = \frac{1}{\sqrt{1 - v^2/c^2}}. \tag{11.30}$$

Also, according to the definition of force, $dp_x/dt = F_x$. From the definitions of energy E and kinetic energy $E_k = E - m_0c^2$, as well as the fact that the work $F_x\,dx$ must be equal to dE_k, we have that

$$\frac{dE}{dt} = \frac{dE_k}{dt} = \frac{F_x\,dx}{dt} = F_x v, \tag{11.31}$$

because in this case $dx/dt = v$. Making all these substitutions in Eq. (11.29), we finally obtain

$$F'_{x'} = F_x. \tag{11.32}$$

For the component parallel to the Y-axis, since $F_y = dp_y/dt$, we obtain

$$F'_{y'} = \frac{dp'_{y'}}{dt'} = \frac{dt}{dt'}\frac{dp_y}{dt} = \frac{F_y}{\sqrt{1 - v^2/c^2}} = kF_y. \tag{11.33}$$

Similarly for the Z-component, with $F_z = dp_z/dt$, we have

$$F'_{z'} = \frac{dp'_{z'}}{dt'} = \frac{F_z}{\sqrt{1 - v^2/c^2}} = kF_z, \tag{11.34}$$

where k is as defined in Eq. (6.32). Equations (11.32), (11.33), and (11.34) relate the force $\boldsymbol{F}$ measured by an observer in an arbitrary inertial frame of reference with the force $\boldsymbol{F}'$ measured by an observer in the inertial frame of reference in which the particle is momentarily at rest. The fact that the transformation law for force is different from that for the four-vector quantities momentum and energy places it in a different category from these two quantities, since force is not part of a four-vector. It also makes force a less useful concept, in the theory of relativity, than momentum and energy are. Consequently a somewhat different definition of force has been proposed. We shall not discuss this definition here, except to say that it has the advantage of transforming as a four-vector. However, even if force transforms in a way different from momentum and energy, its transformation guarantees that the equation of motion, $\boldsymbol{F} = d\boldsymbol{p}/dt$, will be invariant for all inertial observers, which was our fundamental requirement. The relation between forces $\boldsymbol{F}$ and $\boldsymbol{F}'$ has been indicated in Fig. 11–7.

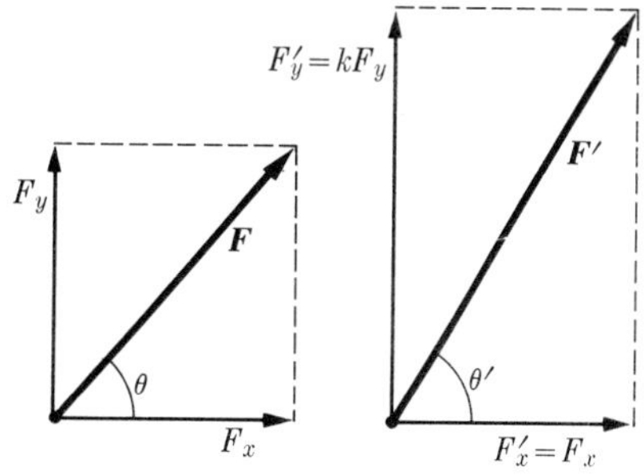

Fig. 11–7. Lorentz transformation of force components.

11.9 Systems of Particles

Let us consider a system of particles, each of momentum $\boldsymbol{p}_i$ and energy E_i. Neglecting their interactions, we may write the total momentum of the system as $\boldsymbol{P} = \sum_i \boldsymbol{p}_i$ and the total energy as

$$E = \textstyle\sum_i E_i = \sum_i m_i c^2 = Mc^2.$$

Thus, using Eq. (11.17), we may associate with the system a velocity defined by

$$\boldsymbol{v}_C = \frac{c^2\boldsymbol{P}}{E} = \frac{\boldsymbol{P}}{M}. \tag{11.35}$$

Recalling Section 9.2, we could say that this is the velocity of the center of mass of the system, and consider that the system appears as a body of mass M moving with velocity $\boldsymbol{v}_C$. We remind the student, however, that (for the reasons given in Section 9.2) when mass depends on velocity, we cannot define the center of mass. Therefore we shall call the velocity given by Eq. (11.35) the *system velocity*.

Suppose that we have two different inertial observers each examining the system of particles. Relative to observer O the total momentum and energy are $\boldsymbol{P} = \sum_i \boldsymbol{p}_i$ and $E = \sum_i E_i$. Relative to O' these quantities are $\boldsymbol{P}' = \sum_i \boldsymbol{p}_i'$ and $E' = \sum_i E_i'$. If the velocity of O' relative to O is v, along the X-axis, each E_i and $\boldsymbol{p}_i$ transform into E_i' and $\boldsymbol{p}_i'$, according to Eqs. (11.26). Thus their sums also transform in the same way, and we may write

$$\begin{aligned} P'_{x'} &= \frac{P_x - vE/c^2}{\sqrt{1 - v^2/c^2}}, \\ P'_{y'} &= P_y, \\ P'_{z'} &= P_z, \\ E' &= \frac{E + vP_x}{\sqrt{1 - v^2/c^2}}. \end{aligned} \tag{11.36}$$

Now if, relative to O, momentum and energy are conserved, $\boldsymbol{P} = \text{const}$ and $E = \text{const}$, then the above transformation equations imply that $\boldsymbol{P}' = \text{const}$ and $E' = \text{const}$, and the two conservation laws also hold for O'. We have therefore verified the second of the requirements imposed on our theory, as indicated at the end of Section 11.4. We also note that, because of the structure of the transformation equations, the two conservation laws must hold simultaneously; in other words they cannot be independent of each other. This situation is different from the nonrelativistic case.

Next consider the special case in which the relative velocity of the two observers is parallel to the total momentum $\boldsymbol{P}$. Then $P_x = P$, $P_y = P_z = 0$, and the first of Eqs. (11.36) reduces to

$$P' = \frac{P - vE/c^2}{\sqrt{1 - v^2/c^2}}.$$

By analogy with the L- and C-frames of reference introduced in Chapter 9,

we define the C-frame in relativistic mechanics as the frame of reference in which the total momentum of the system is zero.

Therefore, if observer O' is attached to the C-frame of reference, the momentum P' is zero. If we set $P' = 0$ in the preceding expression, the velocity of O' relative to O (who uses the L-frame of reference), is $v = c^2P/E$. Comparison with Eq. (11.35) shows that the C-frame moves with the system velocity $\boldsymbol{v}_C$ relative to the L-frame. This is the same result as obtained in the nonrelativistic situation of Chapter 9.

We indicated at the beginning of this section that we were neglecting interactions between particles of the system. Consideration of interactions that depend on the relative position of the particles poses serious difficulties in the theory of relativity. For example, we saw in Chapter 6 that the concept of simultaneity in the position of two particles, which is required in order to define an interaction, is not an invariant concept. Furthermore, the velocity of transmission of the interaction must be taken into account. For that reason, special techniques are required to discuss interactions in a manner consistent with the theory of relativity.

EXAMPLE 11.9. Discuss the C-frame of reference for two identical particles moving in the same direction.

Solution: The properties of the C-frame can easily be discussed for the case of two particles. Consider a system of two identical particles that appear, relative to observer O, as moving along the X-axis of the L-frame (used by O) with velocities v_1 and v_2. Their respective masses are m_1 and m_2, computed according to Eq. (11.7), with the same value of m_0 for both. The total momentum in the L-frame is

$$P = p_1 + p_2 = m_1v_1 + m_2v_2. \tag{11.37}$$

Relative to the C-frame the total momentum of the system is zero. Thus

$$P' = p_1' + p_2' = 0.$$

This requires that the momentum of the two particles in the C-frame be the same in magnitude, but that the particles move in opposite directions. Then Eq. (11.8) requires that the magnitudes of the velocities of the particles in the C-frame be the same. Thus the particles appear to be moving with velocities v' and $-v'$. Designating the velocity of the C-frame relative to the L-frame by v_C and using Eq. (6.38) for the transformation of velocities, with v replaced by v_C, we have

$$v_1 = \frac{v' + v_C}{1 + v'v_C/c^2}, \qquad v_2 = \frac{-v' + v_C}{1 - v'v_C/c^2}.$$

These may be written in the alternative forms:

$$v_1 = v_C + \frac{v'(1 - v_C^2/c^2)}{1 + v'v_C/c^2}, \qquad v_2 = v_C - \frac{v'(1 - v_C^2/c^2)}{1 - v'v_C/c^2}.$$

Thus we can obtain the total momentum in the L-frame by substituting these values into Eq. (11.37). This gives

$$P = (m_1 + m_2)v_C + v'(1 - v_C^2/c^2)\left(\frac{m_1}{1 + v'v_C/c^2} - \frac{m_2}{1 - v'v_C/c^2}\right). \tag{11.38}$$

Replacing m_1 and m_2 in the last term by their values according to Eq. (11.7), we obtain

$$m_0v'(1 - v_C^2/c^2)\left(\frac{1}{\sqrt{1 - v_1^2/c^2}\,(1 + v'v_C/c^2)} - \frac{1}{\sqrt{1 - v_2^2/c^2}\,(1 - v'v_C/c^2)}\right).$$

Using the identities of Problem 6.38, we may simplify each term inside the parentheses. It can be seen that both terms are equal to $1/\sqrt{(1 - v_C^2/c^2)(1 - v'^2/c^2}$, and thus their difference is zero. Therefore the last term in Eq. (11.38) disappears, and P reduces to

$$P = (m_1 + m_2)v_C \qquad \text{or} \qquad v_C = P/M.$$

This is just Eq. (11.35) adapted to our particular case of two particles moving in the same direction. Therefore we verify that, in relativity theory as well as in classical theory, the C-frame (relative to which the total momentum of the system is zero) is moving, relative to the L-frame, with the velocity v_C given by Eq. (11.35).

11.10 High-Energy Collisions

The principles of conservation of energy and momentum must be satisfied for any collision, irrespective of the energies of the particles. In Section 9.7 this subject was discussed for the low-energy (or nonrelativistic) region. However, at high energies, the concepts and techniques developed in this chapter must be used. Consider, for example, two particles, whose *rest* masses are m_1 and m_2, moving before the collision with momenta $\boldsymbol{p}_1$ and $\boldsymbol{p}_2$ relative to some inertial frame of reference. The interaction between the particles is appreciable only during the small time interval in which the particles are very close (this corresponds to the shaded region in Fig. 9–11). Recall from Section 9.7 that a collision was defined as having occurred if the interaction produced measurable changes in a relatively short time and over a relatively short distance. Suppose that after the collision, when the interaction is again negligible, the resulting particles now have rest masses m_3 and m_4 and move with momenta $\boldsymbol{p}_3$ and $\boldsymbol{p}_4$ relative to the original inertial frame of reference. The conservation of momentum and the conservation of energy are expressed by

$$\boldsymbol{p}_1 + \boldsymbol{p}_2 = \boldsymbol{p}_3 + \boldsymbol{p}_4 \qquad \text{and} \qquad E_1 + E_2 = E_3 + E_4, \tag{11.39}$$

or, using Eq. (11.18), we have

$$c\sqrt{m_1^2c^2 + p_1^2} + c\sqrt{m_2^2c^2 + p_2^2} = c\sqrt{m_3^2c^2 + p_3^2} + c\sqrt{m_4^2c^2 + p_4^2}. \tag{11.40}$$

The collision described by Eqs. (11.39) and (11.40) can be indicated schematically by $1 + 2 \rightarrow 3 + 4$. The application of Eqs. (11.39) and (11.40) in general is complicated algebraically because of the presence of the radicals in Eq. (11.40) and for that reason we shall illustrate their use in some simple but very important cases.

EXAMPLE 11.10. Discuss a relativistic collision when particle 1 (called the incident particle) has zero rest mass and is identical to particle 3, and particle 2 is at rest in our laboratory system and is identical to particle 4.

Solution: The process is shown schematically in Fig. 11–8. Using Eqs. (11.18) and (11.21), we obtain the value of the momentum and the energy relative to observer O as being

$$p_1 = E/c, \qquad p_2 = 0, \qquad p_3 = E^\dagger/c, \qquad p_4,$$
$$E_1 = E, \qquad E_2 = m_0c^2, \qquad E_3 = E^\dagger, \qquad E_4 = c\sqrt{m^2c^2 + p_4^2}.$$

The conservation of momentum is now

$$\boldsymbol{p}_1 = \boldsymbol{p}_3 + \boldsymbol{p}_4, \tag{11.41}$$

and the conservation of energy is

$$E + m_0c^2 = E^\dagger + c\sqrt{m_0^2c^2 + p_4^2}. \tag{11.42}$$

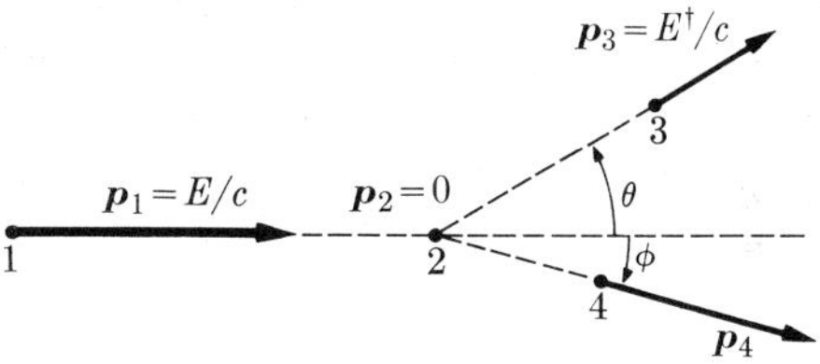

Fig. 11–8. High-energy collision.

Suppose we are interested in the energy $E^\dagger$ of the incident particle after the collision. We must then eliminate $\boldsymbol{p}_4$ from the above equations. Solving Eq. (11.41) for $\boldsymbol{p}_4$, we obtain $\boldsymbol{p}_4 = \boldsymbol{p}_1 - \boldsymbol{p}_3$. Squaring the result, we get

$$p_4^2 = p_1^2 + p_3^2 - 2\boldsymbol{p}_1 \cdot \boldsymbol{p}_3.$$

Using the corresponding values for the momenta, we have

$$p_4^2 = \frac{E^2}{c^2} + \frac{E^{\dagger 2}}{c^2} - \frac{2EE^\dagger}{c^2}\cos\theta.$$

Solving Eq. (11.42) for p_4^2 then gives us

$$p_4^2 = \frac{1}{c^2}(E + m_0c^2 - E^\dagger)^2 - m_0^2c^2$$
$$= \frac{E^2}{c^2} + \frac{E^{\dagger 2}}{c^2} + \frac{2(E - E^\dagger)m_0c^2}{c^2} - \frac{2EE^\dagger}{c^2}.$$

Equating both results for p_4^2, we have

$$\frac{2(E - E^\dagger)m_0c^2}{c^2} - \frac{2EE^\dagger}{c^2} = -\frac{2EE^\dagger}{c^2}\cos\theta$$

or

$$E - E^\dagger = \frac{EE^\dagger}{m_0c^2}(1 - \cos\theta).$$

Dividing both sides by $EE^\dagger$ yields

$$\frac{1}{E^\dagger} - \frac{1}{E} = \frac{1}{m_0c^2}(1 - \cos\theta). \qquad (11.43)$$

This expression gives $E^\dagger$ in terms of E and the scattering angle θ of particle 3. Note that $E > E^\dagger$ always, and the incident particle loses energy, as it should, since the other particle, initially at rest, is in motion after the collision.

Result (11.43) is very important in the discussion of the scattering of light (or photons) by free electrons—the so-called Compton effect—which will be discussed in great detail in Chapter 19. Note that Eq. (11.43) cannot be satisfied by $E^\dagger = 0$ for any scattering angle. Therefore, it is impossible that the incident particle be completely absorbed by an otherwise free particle.

EXAMPLE 11.11. In most high-energy experiments a very fast incident particle collides with another particle at rest in the laboratory system. We want to know the *threshold energy*; that is, the minimum kinetic energy of the particle in the laboratory or L-frame which is necessary to obtain a particular reaction. Obtain the equation for the threshold energy needed for the creation of a proton-antiproton pair in a proton-proton collision.

Solution: At this point it is enough to say that an antiproton is a particle whose mass is equal to that of a proton and whose electrical charge is equal, in absolute value, to that of a proton, but of negative sign. We designate the proton by p^+ and the antiproton by p^-. Part of the kinetic energy of a fast proton which collides with another proton at rest in the laboratory is used to produce a proton-antiproton, or p^+, p^- pair. We can represent the process schematically as

$$\mathrm{p}^+ + \mathrm{p}^+ \rightarrow \mathrm{p}^+ + \mathrm{p}^+ + \mathrm{p}^+ + \mathrm{p}^-.$$

The two protons on the left and the first two on the right side of the equation represent the incident and the target protons. The last two correspond to the result of the collision: the proton-antiproton pair. (Note that, although the number of particles has changed, the total charge remains the same. As we shall see later, this is an example of another conservation principle: the principle of conservation of charge.) Initially one of the protons is at rest (zero momentum) in the L-frame and the other is moving toward it with momentum $\boldsymbol{p}$.

Before the collision the total momentum relative to observer O in the L-frame is $\boldsymbol{p}$ and the total energy is $E = c\sqrt{m_0^2c^2 + p^2} + m_0c^2$. After the collision the total momentum must still be $\boldsymbol{p}$ and the total energy E. The minimum energy required for the incident particle is that which is needed when the final products are at rest relative to the C-frame moving with the system velocity relative to L (see Section 11.9). The products can never be at rest relative to the L-frame because of conservation of momentum. But in this case the total energy relative to the C-frame is $E' = 4m_0c^2$, and the total momentum is $\boldsymbol{p}' = 0$. That means that the four resulting particles appear in the L-frame to be moving together with the same velocity, and in order to guarantee the conservation of momentum each must have a momentum of $\frac{1}{4}\boldsymbol{p}$. Thus their total energy relative to O is $4c\sqrt{m_0^2c^2 + (p/4)^2}$ or $c\sqrt{16m_0^2c^2 + p^2}$. Equating the energies before and after the collision, we have

$$c\sqrt{m_0^2c^2 + p^2} + m_0c^2 = c\sqrt{16m_0^2c^2 + p^2}.$$

This is an algebraic equation in p whose solution is $p = 4\sqrt{3}\, m_0c$, which thus gives the minimum momentum which the incident proton must have relative to O so that the reaction can take place. (What is the velocity of this proton?) Accordingly, the total energy of the incident proton relative to O is $c\sqrt{m_0^2c^2 + p^2} = 7m_0c^2$ and its kinetic energy will be $6m_0c^2$.

Thus, in order for the reaction we are considering to occur in the laboratory, the incident proton must be accelerated until its kinetic energy in the L-frame is $6m_0c^2$. The rest mass of the proton has the value $m_0 = 1.67 \times 10^{-27}$ kg. Then the energy $6m_0c^2$ is equivalent to 9.0×10^{-10} J or about 5.6×10^9 eV.

One of the chief uses of high-energy accelerators is to produce fast particles above the threshold kinetic energy in the L-frame so that scientists can produce in the laboratory, under controlled conditions, some processes which they have observed in cosmic rays.

EXAMPLE 11.12. Obtain the threshold energy for the reaction $1 + 2 \to 3 + 4$, in which the four particles are different.

Solution: Since the particles have different masses, we cannot use the symmetry principles that we used implicitly in our previous example. Let us assume that particle 2 is at rest in the laboratory, so that $p_2 = 0$. The energy of each particle in the L-frame before the collision is then

$$E_1 = c\sqrt{m_1^2c^2 + p_1^2} \quad \text{and} \quad E_2 = m_2c^2. \tag{11.44}$$

The *total* energy and momentum of the system in the laboratory are

$$E = E_1 + m_2c^2, \qquad \boldsymbol{P} = \boldsymbol{p}_1. \tag{11.45}$$

Quantities E and $\boldsymbol{P}$ must transform from one inertial frame of reference to another according to Eqs. (11.26), which implies that the expression $P^2 - E^2/c^2$ must remain invariant. Then

$$P^2 - E^2/c^2 = P'^2 - E'^2/c^2.$$

If we transform to the C-frame, we must have $\boldsymbol{P}' = 0$, since the total momentum is zero in this frame of reference. Then $P^2 - E^2/c^2 = -E'^2/c^2$, or the total energy E' in the C-frame, according to Eq. (11.45), is

$$E' = \sqrt{E^2 - c^2P^2} = \sqrt{(E_1 + m_2c^2)^2 - c^2p_1^2}.$$

Using the value of E_1 from Eq. (11.44), we have

$$E' = c\sqrt{(m_1^2 + m_2^2)c^2 + 2E_1m_2}. \tag{11.46}$$

Remembering from Eq. (11.16) that $E_1 = E_{k1} + m_1c^2$, where E_{k1} is the kinetic energy of particle 1 in the laboratory, we have

$$\begin{aligned} E' &= c\sqrt{(m_1^2 + m_2^2)c^2 + 2(E_{k1} + m_1c^2)m_2} \\ &= c\sqrt{(m_1 + m_2)^2c^2 + 2E_{k1}m_2}. \end{aligned} \tag{11.47}$$

The minimum energy required to produce particles m_3 and m_4 after the reaction is that energy at which the resulting particles are at rest in the C-system. In the L-system it is impossible for both particles to be at rest at the same time because of the conservation of momentum. In this case $E'_3 = m_3c^2$ and $E'_4 = m_4c^2$, and the energy after the collision is $E' = (m_3 + m_4)c^2$. Equating this with Eq. (11.47), which gives the total energy in the C-frame before the collision, we have

$$c\sqrt{(m_1 + m_2)^2c^2 + 2E_{k1}m_2} = (m_3 + m_4)c^2$$

or, solving for E_{k1},

$$\begin{aligned} E_{k1} &= \frac{c^2}{2m_2}[(m_3 + m_4)^2 - (m_1 + m_2)^2] \\ &= \frac{c^2}{2m_2}[(m_3 + m_4) - (m_1 + m_2)][(m_3 + m_4) + (m_1 + m_2)]. \end{aligned}$$

The *Q-value* for this reaction [remember Eq. (9.41) for newtonian collisions] is defined by

$$Q = [(m_1 + m_2) - (m_3 + m_4)]c^2, \tag{11.48}$$

which is equal to the difference between initial and final rest energies. Then the expression for E_{k1} becomes

$$E_{k1} = -\frac{Q}{2m_2}(m_1 + m_2 + m_3 + m_4), \tag{11.49}$$

which gives the threshold kinetic energy for particle 1 (the incident particle) in the L-frame. If Q is positive, then E_{k1} is negative and the reaction can occur no matter what the kinetic energy of the incident particle is. This is due to the fact that the initial particles have a rest energy greater than that needed to produce final particles which are also at rest. But if Q is negative, E_{k1} is positive and the incident particle must then have a certain minimum kinetic energy, because the rest energy of the initial particles is not enough to produce the final particles.

References

1. "On the Origins of the Special Theory of Relativity," G. Holton. *Am. J. Phys.* **28,** 627 (1960)
2. "Henri Poincaré and the Principle of Relativity," C. Scribner. *Am. J. Phys.* **32,** 672 (1964)
3. "Speed and Kinetic Energy of Relativistic Electrons," W. Bertozzi. *Am. J. Phys.* **32,** 551 (1964)
4. "Massless Particles," R. Good. *Am. J. Phys.* **28,** 679 (1960)
5. *An Introduction to the Special Theory of Relativity*, R. Katz. Princeton, N.J.: Momentum Books, D. Van Nostrand Co., 1964
6. *The Special Theory of Relativity*, D. Bohm. New York: W. A. Benjamin, 1964
7. *Introductory Mechanics*, E. Taylor. New York: John Wiley & Sons, 1963, Chapters 11, 12, and 13
8. *The Feynman Lectures on Physics*, Volume I, R. Feynman, R. Leighton, and M. Sands. Reading, Mass.: Addison-Wesley, 1963, Chapters 15, 16, and 17

Problems

11.1 Assume that E and E' are the values of the total energy of a system of two interacting particles as measured by two inertial observers O and O' moving with relative velocity $\boldsymbol{v}$. Prove that

$$E = E' + (m_1 + m_2)(\boldsymbol{v}'_{CM} \cdot \boldsymbol{v} + \tfrac{1}{2}v^2).$$

Compare with results given in Chapter 9. Assume that the energies are low enough to use newtonian dynamics.

11.2 Compare the nonrelativistic equations of motion of a particle as determined by an inertial observer O and another observer O' rotating relative to the first with a constant angular velocity. Discuss the inertial forces that are observed by O'. [*Hint:* Review Section 6.4.]

11.3 At what velocity is the momentum of a particle equal to m_0c? What is the total energy and the kinetic energy in this case?

11.4 An electron moves in a circular path of radius 2×10^{-2} m in such a way that its velocity is $(0.5 + 0.01t)c$. Find the angle between the force and the acceleration when $t = 10$ s.

11.5 A particle of rest mass m_0 with a velocity of $0.8c$ is subject to a force which is (a) parallel to the velocity, (b) perpendicular to the velocity. Determine the ratio of the force to the acceleration in each case. Also, in the second case, find the radius of curvature and compare with the nonrelativistic values.

11.6 The rest mass of an electron is 9.109×10^{-31} kg and that of a proton is 1.675×10^{-27} kg. Compute their rest energies in joules and in eV.

11.7 Find the exit momentum and velocity of a proton in the Brookhaven accelerator, given that the proton kinetic energy is 3×10^{10} eV.

11.8 The radius of the proton path in the Brookhaven accelerator is 114 m. Find the centripetal force required to hold it in orbit when it has reached its final kinetic energy.

11.9 An electron has a velocity of $0.8c$. Find the velocity of a proton having (a) the same momentum, (b) the same kinetic energy.

11.10 Estimate the value of the corrective term $\frac{3}{8}m_0v^4/c^2$ relative to the first term in Eq. (11.19) for (a) an electron in a hydrogen atom whose velocity is 2.2×10^6 m s^{-1}, (b) a proton coming from a cyclotron with a kinetic energy of 30 MeV, (c) protons coming from the Brookhaven accelerator with a kinetic energy of 3×10^{10} eV.

11.11 Complete Example 11.5 by obtaining the coordinates of the particle as a function of time and compare with the nonrelativistic values. Show also that the equation of the path is

$$y = \frac{E_0}{F} \cosh \frac{Fx}{p_0c}.$$

11.12 An accelerator produces protons with a velocity of $0.9c$ at the rate of 3×10^{18} particles per second in bursts that last 10^{-5} s each. Find the total energy needed to accelerate all the particles in one burst. If there are 100 bursts per second, find the power required to accelerate the particles.

11.13 Calculate, in eV, the energy required to accelerate an electron and a proton from (a) rest up to $0.500c$, (b) $0.500c$ to $0.900c$, (c) $0.900c$ to $0.950c$, (d) $0.950c$ to $0.990c$. What general conclusion do you reach?

11.14 The kinetic energy of a certain particle can be written as pc with an error in the total energy not greater than 1%. What is its minimum velocity? What is the kinetic energy, in eV, of an electron and a proton moving at that velocity?

11.15 What maximum velocity must a particle have if its kinetic energy is to be written as $\frac{1}{2}m_0v^2$ with an error no greater than 1%? What is the kinetic energy, in eV, of an electron and a proton moving with that velocity?

11.16 Show that $v/c = [1 - (m_0c^2/E)^2]^{1/2}$. From this relation find the velocity of a particle when E is (a) equal to its rest energy, (b) twice its rest energy, (c) 10 times its rest energy and (d) one thousand times the rest energy. Compute the corresponding energies in eV for an electron and a proton. Make a plot of v/c against E/m_0c^2.

11.17 Prove that the momentum of a particle can be written as

$$p = (E_k^2 + 2m_0c^2E_k)^{1/2}/c.$$

Plot p/m_0c as a function of E_k/m_0c^2.

11.18 Electrons are accelerated up to a kinetic energy of 10^9 eV. Find (a) the ratio of their mass to the rest mass, (b) the ratio of their velocity to the velocity of light, (c) the ratio of their total energy to their rest-mass energy. Repeat the same problem for protons of the same energy.

11.19 Since energy/velocity has the same dimensions as momentum, the unit MeV/c has been introduced as a convenient unit for measuring the momentum of elementary particles. Express the value of this unit in m kg s^{-1}. Find, in terms of this unit, the momentum of an electron having a total energy of 5.0 MeV. Repeat for a proton having a total energy of 2×10^3 MeV.

11.20 Determine the total energy and the velocity of an electron having a momentum of 0.60 MeV/c. Repeat for a proton.

11.21 An electron is moving at a velocity $0.6c$ relative to an observer O. A force of 9.109×10^{-19} N as measured in the frame of reference attached to the electron is applied parallel to the relative velocity. Find the acceleration of the electron relative to both frames of reference.

11.22 Solve Problem 11.21 for a case in which the force is applied perpendicular to the relative velocity.

11.23 Solve Problems 11.21 and 11.22 for a case in which the value of the force is relative to the observer O.

11.24 Calculate the momentum, total energies, and kinetic energy of a proton moving with a velocity $v = 0.99c$ relative to the laboratory in the following cases: (a) in the L-frame, (b) in the frame defined by the proton, (c) in the C-frame defined by the proton and a helium atom at rest in the laboratory.

11.25 A proton with a kinetic energy of 10^{10} eV collides with a proton at rest. Find (a) the system velocity, (b) the total momentum and the total energy in the L-frame, (c) the kinetic energy of the two particles in the C-frame.

11.26 An electron having a total energy E_e makes a head-on collision with a proton at rest. If the electron energy is very large compared with its rest energy, the electron must be treated relativistically, but if, in addition, it is small compared with the rest energy of the proton, the proton can be treated nonrelativistically. Prove then that (a) the proton recoils with a velocity approximately equal to $(2E_e/m_0c^2)c$, (b) the energy transferred from the electron to the proton is $2E_e^2/m_0c^2$. Apply to a case in which the electrons have a kinetic energy of 100 MeV. [*Hint:* For the electron, $E = cp$, while for the proton $E_k = p^2/2m$. Also note that if the proton moves forward, the electron bounces back, so that the *direction* of its momentum is reversed.]

11.27 One method of obtaining the energy needed for a nuclear reaction is to send two particles against each other. When the particles are identical and their energies are the same, the C-frame coincides with the laboratory. This method is used at CERN where protons, accelerated to an energy of 28 Gev, are kept circulating in opposite directions in two "storage rings"; at a convenient time the two beams are made to collide. (a) What is the total energy available for a reaction? (b) What is the kinetic energy of one of the protons in the frame of reference in which the other proton is at rest? This is the energy to which a proton would have to be accelerated to produce the same reaction when colliding with a target at rest in the laboratory. Do you see any advantage in the idea of "storage rings"?

11.28 Obtain the relativistic law (11.26) for the transformation of momentum and energy by writing $\boldsymbol{p}' = m_0\boldsymbol{V}'/\sqrt{1 - V'^2/c^2}$ and $E' = m_0c^2/\sqrt{1 - V'^2/c^2}$, and expressing the velocity $\boldsymbol{V}'$ in terms of the velocity $\boldsymbol{V}$ measured by O and their relative velocity $\boldsymbol{v}$, using Eq. (6.36). [*Hint:* Use the relations obtained in Problem 6.38.]

11.29 Prove that the general law for the transformation of force when the particle is not at rest relative to O' is

$$F'_x = F_x - \left(\frac{vV_y/c^2}{1 - vV_x/c^2}\right)F_y - \left(\frac{vV_z/c^2}{1 - vV_x/c^2}\right)F_z,$$

$$F'_y = \frac{\sqrt{1 - v^2/c^2}}{1 - vV_x/c^2}F_y,$$

$$F'_z = \frac{\sqrt{1 - v^2/c^2}}{1 - vV_x/c^2}F_z,$$

where $\boldsymbol{V}$ refers to the velocity of the particle relative to O. Verify that they reduce to Eqs. (11.32), (11.33), and (11.34) if the particle is at rest relative to O'.

11.30 Prove that the transformation for energy and momentum can be written in the vector form

$$\boldsymbol{p}' = \boldsymbol{p} - \frac{(\boldsymbol{p}\cdot\boldsymbol{v})\boldsymbol{v}}{v^2} + k\left[\frac{(\boldsymbol{p}\cdot\boldsymbol{v})\boldsymbol{v}}{v^2} - \frac{\boldsymbol{v}E}{c^2}\right],$$

$$E' = k(E - \boldsymbol{v}\cdot\boldsymbol{p}).$$

11.31 A particle of rest mass m_1, moving with velocity $\boldsymbol{v}_1$ in the L-frame, collides with a particle of rest mass m_2, at rest in the L-frame. (a) Prove that the velocity of the C-frame of the system composed of the two particles is

$$\boldsymbol{v}_C = \frac{\boldsymbol{v}_1}{1 + A\sqrt{1 - v_1^2/c^2}},$$

where $A = m_2/m_1$. (b) Prove that in the C-frame the velocity of m_1 is

$$\boldsymbol{v}'_1 = \frac{\boldsymbol{v}_1 A\sqrt{1 - v_1^2/c^2}}{1 - v_C^2/c^2 + A\sqrt{1 - v_C^2/c^2}}$$

and that the velocity of m_2 *is* $-\boldsymbol{V}_C$. (c) Compute the values of the preceding quantities when v_1 is small compared with c, and compare your result with those of Example 9.13.

11.32 Using the Lorentz transformation laws for energy and momentum, prove that if $\boldsymbol{v}_C = c^2\boldsymbol{P}/E$ is the system velocity relative to an observer O while the system velocity to another observer O', in motion relative to O with velocity $\boldsymbol{V}$ along the X-axis, is $\boldsymbol{v}'_C = c^2\boldsymbol{P}'/E'$, then $\boldsymbol{v}_C$, $\boldsymbol{v}'_C$, and $\boldsymbol{V}$ are related by Eqs. (6.36) for the transformation of velocities. Also prove that if $\boldsymbol{v}'_C = 0$ (or $\boldsymbol{P}' = 0$), then $\boldsymbol{v}_C = \boldsymbol{V}$. This was one of our basic assumptions in Section 11.9 when we defined the system velocity. Hence we see that the theory developed is consistent with the Lorentz transformation.

11.33 A particle of rest mass m_1 and momentum p_1 collides inelastically with a particle of mass m_2 at rest in the laboratory. The two particles stick together without change in total rest mass. Find (a) the velocity of the resulting particle relative to the L-frame, (b) the Q of the collision.

11.34 Discuss Problem 11.33 for a case in which the resulting particle has a rest mass of m_3 that is different from the combined rest mass $m_1 + m_2$ of the two colliding particles.

11.35 A particle of rest mass m_1 and momentum p_1 collides inelastically with a particle of rest mass m_2 at rest in the laboratory. The resulting products are a particle of rest mass m_3 and a particle of zero rest mass. Find the energy of the last particle (a) in the C-frame, (b) in the L-frame.

11.36 Assume that the recoil angle of the particle of mass m_0 in Example 11.10 is ϕ. Prove that the kinetic energy of the particle after the collision is

$$E_k = \frac{2E(E/m_0c^2)\cos^2\phi}{1 + 2(E/m_0c^2) + (E/m_0c^2)^2\sin^2\phi}.$$

11.37 A particle of rest mass m_1 and momentum p_1 collides elastically with a particle of mass m_2 at the rest in the L-frame and is deviated an angle θ. Prove that the momentum and energy of m_1 after the collision are

$$p_3 = p_1 \frac{(m_1^2c^2 + m_2E_1)\cos\theta + (E_1 + m_2c^2)\sqrt{m_2^2 - m_1^2\sin^2\theta}}{(E_1/c + m_2c)^2 - p_1^2\cos^2\theta},$$

$$E_3 = \frac{(E_1 + m_2c^2)(m_1^2c^2 + m_2E_1) + c^2p_1^2\cos\theta\sqrt{m_2^2 - m_1^2\sin^2\theta}}{(E_1/c + m_2c)^2 - p_1^2\cos^2\theta}.$$

11.38 Referring to Problem 11.37, prove that if particle m_2 recoils at an angle ϕ relative to the direction of motion of the incident particle, then its momentum and energy are

$$p_4 = p_1 \frac{2m_2(E_1 + m_2c^2)\cos\phi}{(E_1/c + m_2c)^2 - p_1^2\cos^2\phi},$$

$$E_4 = m_2c^2 \times \left[1 + \frac{2p_1^2\cos^2\phi}{(E_1/c + m_2c)^2 - p_1^2\cos^2\phi}\right].$$

11.39 Refer again to Problems 11.37 and 11.38. Assume that the two particles have the same rest mass. After the collision the incoming particle moves in the C-frame at an angle ϕ relative to the initial direction and the other particle moves in the opposite direction. Prove that the angles θ and θ' which they move relative to the L-frame are

$$\tan\theta = \sqrt{1 - v^2/c^2}\tan\tfrac{1}{2}\phi$$

and

$$\tan\theta' = \sqrt{1 - v^2/c^2}\cot\tfrac{1}{2}\phi.$$

Conclude from this that $\theta + \theta' \leq \frac{1}{2}\pi$ and that the closer v is to c, the smaller the angle $\theta + \theta'$ between the two particles in the L-frame is. Compare with the results given in Example 9.11 for a nonrelativistic collision. [*Hint:* Note that before the collision the two particles move in the C-frame with velocities v and $-v$ and after the collision they continue moving in opposite directions with the same velocities.]

11.40 Referring to Problem 11.37, verify that if particle 1 has a zero rest mass, then the values of p_3 and E_3 reduce to those of Example 11.10.

11.41 Prove that the equation of motion of a rocket moving at relativistic velocities and subject to no external forces is $m\,dv/dm + v_e'(1 - v^2/c^2) = 0$, where m is the instantaneous rest mass of the rocket, v is its velocity relative to the observer and v_e' is the exhaust velocity relative to the rocket. Also prove, by integration, that the final velocity is given by

$$v = \frac{c[1 - (m/m_0)2v_e'/c]}{1 + (m/m_0)2v_e'/c}.$$

[*Hint:* Write the equations of conservation of momentum and energy relative to the observer, noting that the rest mass of the exhaust gases is not the same as the change in rest mass of the rocket.]

11.42 A particle of rest mass m_0 splits (or decays) into two particles of rest masses m_1 and m_2. Prove that in the C-frame the energies of the resulting particles are

$$E_1' = (m_0^2 + m_1^2 - m_2^2)c^2/2m_0$$

and

$$E_2' = (m_0^2 + m_2^2 - m_1^2)c^2/2m_0.$$

Also find their momenta.

11.43 Solve Problem 11.42 for the case of particles in the L-frame, given that the momentum of particle m_0 in this frame is p. Also prove that if p_1 and p_2 are the momenta of the resulting particles and θ the angle between them,

$$m_0^2c^4 = (m_1 + m_2)^2c^4 + 2E_1E_2 - 2m_1m_2c^4 - 2p_1p_2c^2 \cos \theta.$$

11.44 In a collision between particles m_1 and m_2, m_1 is moving with momentum p_1 and m_2 is at rest in the L-frame. After the collision, in addition to particles m_1 and m_2 there appear particles $m_3, m_4, \ldots$. Prove that the threshold kinetic energy in the L-frame for this process is

$$E_{k1} = (\Delta m)c^2[1 + m_1/m_2 + \Delta m/2m_2],$$

where $\Delta m = m_3 + m_4 + \cdots$. Apply this equation to the creation of a proton-antiproton pair, as discussed in Example 11.11.

11.45 A particle of rest mass m_1, moving with an extremely large total energy E_1 so that its velocity is approximately equal to c, collides with a particle of rest mass m_2 which is at rest. Show that the system velocity is $c(1 - m_2c^2/E_1)$ and that the energy available in the C-frame is

$$(2E_1m_2c^2)^{1/2}.$$

11.46 Consider a reaction in which a particle of zero rest mass and energy E_1 collides with a particle of rest mass m_2 which is at rest in the laboratory. The final products of the reaction are two particles: one of rest mass m_2 and another of rest mass m_3. Show that the threshold energy E_1 for the reaction is

$$E_1 = m_3(1 + m_3/2m_2)c^2.$$

11.47 Determine the Q-value and the threshold kinetic energy in the L-frame of reference of the incident (the π^-) particle for both the following reactions: (a) $\pi^- + p^+ \rightarrow n + \pi^0$; (b) $\pi^- + p^+ \rightarrow \Sigma^- + K^+$. The rest masses of these particles are:

Particle	Rest mass, kg
π^-	0.2489×10^{-27}
π^0	0.2407×10^{-27}
p^+	1.6752×10^{-27}
n	1.6748×10^{-27}
Σ^-	1.9702×10^{-27}
K^+	0.8805×10^{-27}

[*Hint:* Use the results of Example 11.12.]

11.48 An elementary particle of rest mass m_0 disintegrates, dividing into other elementary particles. The process has a nonzero Q-value. (a) Prove that if the particle divides into two equal fragments they must move in the C-frame in opposite directions with a momentum equal to

$$\tfrac{1}{2}(2m_0Q - Q^2/c^2)^{1/2}.$$

(b) Prove that if the particle disintegrates into three equal fragments, emitted symmetrically in the C-frame, the momentum of each particle is equal to

$$\tfrac{1}{3}(2m_0Q - Q^2/c^2)^{1/2}.$$

(c) Verify that results (a) and (b) reduce, respectively, to the nonrelativistic expressions given in parts (d) and (e) of Problem 9.13 when Q is much smaller than m_0c^2. (d) Apply the result of part (b) above to the elementary particle called a *tau-meson* ($m_0 = 8.8 \times 10^{-28}$ kg), which disintegrates into three fragments called *pi-mesons* ($m_0 = 2.5 \times 10^{-28}$ kg). Evaluate the Q of the process and find the magnitude of the velocities of the fragments in the C-frame. What percentage error is obtained if we use the nonrelativistic expressions of Problem 9.13?

12 OSCILLATORY MOTION

12.1 Introduction

One of the most important motions encountered in nature is the oscillatory (or vibrational) motion. A particle is oscillating when it moves periodically about an equilibrium position. The motion of a pendulum is oscillatory. A weight attached to a stretched spring, once it is released, starts oscillating. The atoms in a solid are vibrating. Similarly, the atoms in molecules are vibrating relative to each other. The electrons in a radiating or receiving antenna are in rapid oscillation. An understanding of vibrational motion is also essential for the discussion of wave phenomena, which we shall deal with in Part 3 of this text.

Of all the oscillatory motions, the most important is *simple harmonic motion* (SHM), because, besides being the simplest motion to describe mathematically, it constitutes a rather accurate description of many oscillations found in nature. Most of our discussion in this chapter will concentrate on this kind of motion.

12.2 Kinematics of Simple Harmonic Motion

By definition, we say that a particle moving along the X-axis has simple harmonic motion when its displacement x relative to the origin of the coordinate system is given as a function of time by the relation

$$x = A \sin (\omega t + \alpha). \tag{12.1}$$

The quantity $\omega t + \alpha$ is called the *phase*, and thus α is the initial phase; i.e., its value for $t = 0$. Although we have defined simple harmonic motion in terms of a sine function, it may just as well be expressed in terms of a cosine function, the only difference being an initial phase difference of $\pi/2$. Since the sine (or cosine) function varies between a value of -1 and $+1$, the displacement of the particle varies between $x = -A$ and $x = +A$. The maximum displacement from the origin, A, is defined as the *amplitude* of the simple harmonic motion. The sine function repeats itself every time the angle increases by 2π. Thus the displacement of the particle repeats itself after a time interval of $2\pi/\omega$. Therefore simple harmonic motion is periodic, and its period is $P = 2\pi/\omega$. The frequency ν of a simple harmonic motion is equal to the number of complete oscillations per unit time; thus $\nu = 1/P$. The quantity ω, called the *angular frequency* of the oscillating particle, is related to the frequency by a relation similar to Eq. (5.51) for circular motion, namely

$$\omega = \frac{2\pi}{P} = 2\pi\nu. \tag{12.2}$$

The velocity of the particle, determined by using Eq. (5.2), is

$$v = \frac{dx}{dt} = \omega A \cos (\omega t + \alpha). \tag{12.3}$$

Similarly, the acceleration is given by

$$a = \frac{dv}{dt} = -\omega^2 A \sin (\omega t + \alpha) = -\omega^2 x, \tag{12.4}$$

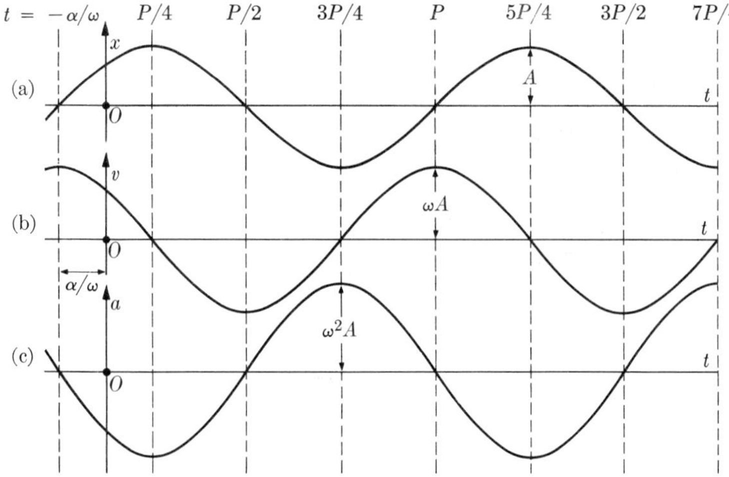

Fig. 12–1. Graphs of displacement, velocity, and acceleration versus time in SHM.

which indicates that in simple harmonic motion the acceleration is always proportional and opposite to the displacement. In Fig. 12–1, we have illustrated x, v, and a as functions of time.

The displacement of the particle moving with SHM can also be considered as the X-component of a vector $\overrightarrow{OP'}$, with $OP' = A$, rotating counterclockwise around O with angular velocity ω, and making (at each instant) an angle $\omega t + \alpha$ with the negative Y-axis, also measured counterclockwise. In Fig. 12–2 we have represented the vector $\overrightarrow{OP'}$ in several positions. The student may verify that at any time the X-component of $\overrightarrow{OP'}$ is given by $x = OP = OP' \sin(\omega t + \alpha)$, in accordance with Eq. (12.1).

The velocity and acceleration of the particle can also be represented by rotating vectors $\overrightarrow{OV'}$ and $\overrightarrow{OA'}$, whose lengths are ωA and $\omega^2 A$, respectively, and whose

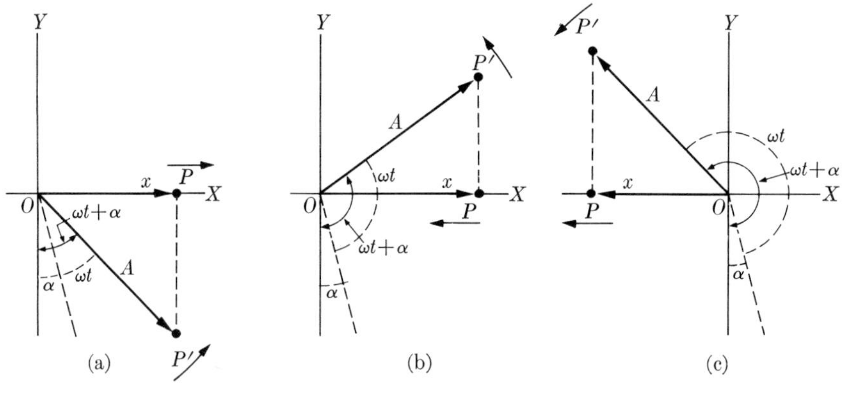

Fig. 12–2. Rotating vector for displacement in SHM.

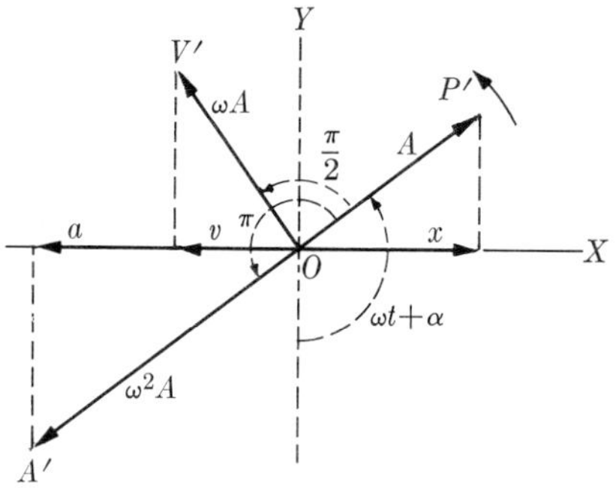

Fig. 12–3. Rotating vectors for displacement, velocity, and acceleration in SHM.

components along the X-axis give the velocity v and the acceleration a of the particle which is moving with SHM. The relative orientation of these rotating vectors is illustrated in Fig. 12–3. One can see that $\overrightarrow{OV'}$ is advanced $\pi/2$ and $\overrightarrow{OA'}$ is advanced π relative to the rotating vector OP'.

EXAMPLE 12.1. Determine whether P in the mechanism illustrated in Fig. 12–4 is moving with SHM. In this mechanism, QQ' is a rod on which the cylinder P can slide; it is connected by a rod L to the rim of a wheel of radius R rotating with constant angular velocity ω. (This is a mechanism found in many steam engines; it transforms the oscillatory motion of the piston into the rotational motion of the wheel.)

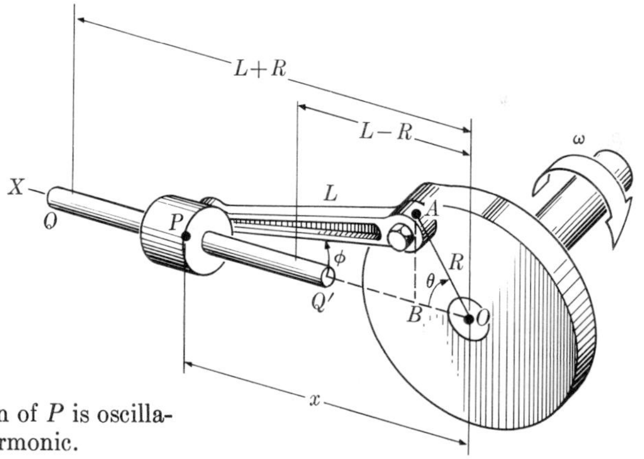

Fig. 12–4. The motion of P is oscillatory but not simple harmonic.

Solution: From the figure we can easily see that P oscillates between a position at a distance $L + R$ from O and a position at a distance $L - R$ from O. To determine whether the motion is simple harmonic, we must find out whether the displacement of P follows Eq. (12.1). From the geometry of the figure we have that $x = R\cos\theta + L\cos\phi$ and $L\sin\phi = R\sin\theta$, so that $\sin\phi = (R/L)\sin\theta$ and

$$\cos\phi = (1 - \sin^2\phi)^{1/2} = \frac{1}{L}(L^2 - R^2\sin^2\theta)^{1/2}.$$

Thus

$$x = R\cos\theta + (L^2 - R^2\sin^2\theta)^{1/2},$$

which, since $\theta = \omega t$, leads to

$$x = R\cos\omega t + (L^2 - R^2\sin^2\omega t)^{1/2}.$$

This gives the displacement of P in terms of time. When we compare this equation with Eq. (12.1), we see that the first term, $R\cos\omega t$, corresponds to simple harmonic motion with $\alpha = \pi/2$, but the second term does not. Thus, although the motion of P is oscillatory, it is not simple harmonic.

A mechanical engineer designing a mechanism such as that in Fig. 12–4 has to figure out how to apply the proper force at P so that the displacement x is given by the above equation, and so that the wheel moves with uniform circular motion. When P is attached to the piston of a steam engine this is done by regulating the admission of steam.

EXAMPLE 12.2. Discuss the motion of a particle of mass m on which an oscillating force $\boldsymbol{F} = \boldsymbol{F}_0 \sin\omega t$ is acting.

Solution: The equation of motion of the particle is $m\boldsymbol{a} = \boldsymbol{F}_0\sin\omega t$, or since $\boldsymbol{a} = d\boldsymbol{v}/dt$,

$$\frac{d\boldsymbol{v}}{dt} = \frac{\boldsymbol{F}_0}{m}\sin\omega t.$$

Integrating this equation yields

$$\boldsymbol{v} = -\frac{\boldsymbol{F}_0}{m\omega}\cos\omega t + \boldsymbol{v}_0,$$

where $\boldsymbol{v}_0$ is a constant of integration and not the initial velocity which is obtained by allowing $t = 0$. As may be seen, the initial velocity is $\boldsymbol{v}_0 - \boldsymbol{F}_0/m\omega$. When we recall that $\boldsymbol{v} = d\boldsymbol{r}/dt$ and integrate a second time, we obtain

$$\boldsymbol{r} = -\frac{\boldsymbol{F}_0}{m\omega^2}\sin\omega t + \boldsymbol{v}_0 t + \boldsymbol{r}_0,$$

which gives the position of the particle as a function of time. Here $\boldsymbol{r}_0$ is the initial position of the particle. If we assume that $\boldsymbol{r}_0 = 0$, the path of the particle is as illustrated in Fig. 12–5. As may be seen, the particle advances to the right, but oscillates around the axis in the direction given by $\boldsymbol{F}_0$. This figure must not be confused with Fig. 12–1(a), which gives the displacement as a function of time for a particle moving with SHM. The

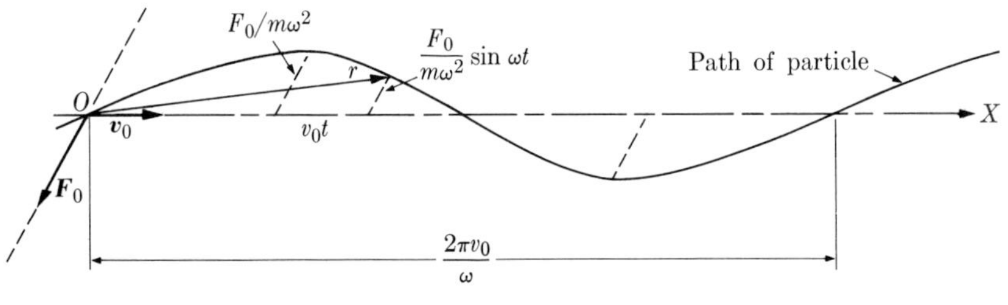

Fig. 12–5. Plane motion under a harmonic force.

physical situation we have illustrated occurs, for example, when an electron (or any charged particle) moves through an oscillating electric field.

We suggest that the student consider the particular case when $\boldsymbol{F}_0$ and $\boldsymbol{v}_0$ are parallel, and then plot the displacement as a function of time.

12.3 Force and Energy in Simple Harmonic Motion

From Eq. (12.4) we can compute the force which must act on a particle of mass m in order for it to oscillate with simple harmonic motion. Applying the equation of motion $F = ma$, and substituting the result of Eq. (12.4), which gives the acceleration, we have

$$F = -m\omega^2 x = -kx, \tag{12.5}$$

where we have set

$$k = m\omega^2 \qquad \text{or} \qquad \omega = \sqrt{k/m}. \tag{12.6}$$

This indicates that *in simple harmonic motion the force is proportional to the displacement, and opposed to it.* Thus the force is always pointing toward the origin O. This is the point of equilibrium, since at the origin $F = 0$ because $x = 0$. We may also say that the force F is attractive, the center of attraction being the point O. The force given by Eq. (12.5) is the type of force that appears when one deforms an elastic body such as a spring; we gave several examples of this force in Chapter 8. The constant $k = m\omega^2$, sometimes called the *elastic constant,* represents the force required to displace the particle one unit of distance. Combining Eqs. (12.2) and (12.6), we can write the equations

$$P = 2\pi\sqrt{\frac{m}{k}}, \qquad \nu = \frac{1}{2\pi}\sqrt{\frac{k}{m}}, \tag{12.7}$$

which express the period and the frequency of a simple harmonic motion in terms of the mass of the particle and the elastic constant of the applied force. The kinetic energy of the particle is

$$E_k = \tfrac{1}{2}mv^2 = \tfrac{1}{2}m\omega^2 A^2 \cos^2(\omega t + \alpha). \tag{12.8}$$

Or, since $\cos^2\theta = 1 - \sin^2\theta$, using Eq. (12.1) for the displacement, we can also express the kinetic energy as

$$E_k = \tfrac{1}{2}m\omega^2 A^2[1 - \sin^2(\omega t + \alpha)] = \tfrac{1}{2}m\omega^2(A^2 - x^2). \tag{12.9}$$

We note that *the kinetic energy is maximum at the center* ($x = 0$) *and zero at the extremes of oscillation* ($x = \pm A$).

To obtain the potential energy we remember Eq. (8.24), $F = -dE_p/dx$. Using Eq. (12.5) for the force, we can write

$$dE_p/dx = kx.$$

Integrating (choosing the zero of the potential energy at the origin or equilibrium position), we obtain

$$\int_0^{E_p} dE_p = \int_0^x kx\,dx \qquad \text{or} \qquad E_p = \tfrac{1}{2}kx^2 = \tfrac{1}{2}m\omega^2x^2. \tag{12.10}$$

Thus *the potential energy is a minimum (zero) at the center* ($x = 0$) *and increases as the particle approaches either extreme of the oscillation* ($x = \pm A$). Adding Eqs. (12.9) and (12.10), we obtain, for the total energy of the simple harmonic oscillator,

$$E = E_k + E_p = \tfrac{1}{2}m\omega^2A^2 = \tfrac{1}{2}kA^2, \tag{12.11}$$

which is a constant quantity. This was to be expected from Eq. (8.29), since the force is conservative. Therefore we may say that, during an oscillation, there is a continuous exchange of kinetic and potential energies. In moving away from the equilibrium position, potential energy increases at the expense of kinetic energy; the reverse happens when the particle moves toward the equilibrium position.

Figure 12–6 shows the potential energy

$$E_p = \tfrac{1}{2}kx^2$$

represented by a parabola. For a given total energy E, represented by the horizontal line, the limits of oscillation are determined by its intersections with the potential energy curve, as we explained in Section 8.11. Since the parabola E_p is symmetric, the limits of oscillation are at equal distances $\pm A$ from O. At any point x the kinetic energy E_k is given by the distance between the curve $E_p(x)$ and the line E.

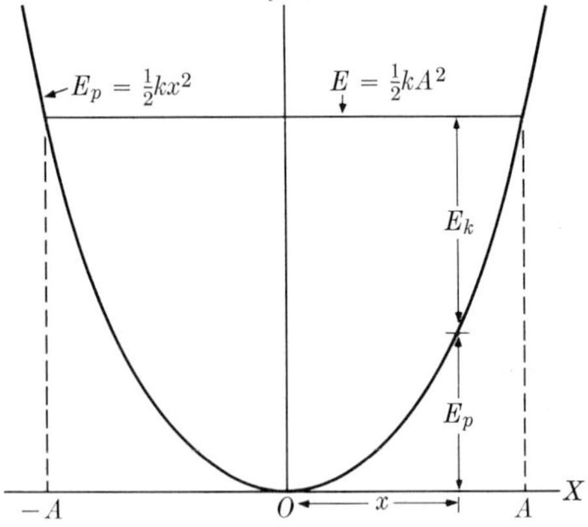

Fig. 12–6. Energy relations in SHM.

12.4 Dynamics of Simple Harmonic Motion

In Section 12.2 we defined simple harmonic motion by means of its kinematic properties, as expressed by Eq. (12.1). Only at a later stage did we discuss the kind of force required to produce such a motion (given by Eq. 12.5). However, it is important to discuss the inverse problem: We shall prove that, given an attractive force proportional to the displacement (that is, $F = -kx$), the resulting motion is simple harmonic.

One procedure is to start from the equation of motion, $F = ma$, with $F = -kx$, and, remembering that in rectilinear motion $a = d^2x/dt^2$, write the equation

$$m\frac{d^2x}{dt^2} = -kx \qquad \text{or} \qquad m\frac{d^2x}{dt^2} + kx = 0.$$

Setting $\omega^2 = k/m$, we may write

$$\frac{d^2x}{dt^2} + \omega^2 x = 0. \tag{12.12}$$

This is a differential equation whose solutions are known to be sine or cosine functions of ωt. Substituting for x the value $A \sin(\omega t + \alpha)$, we can verify directly that this expression for x, which corresponds to simple harmonic motion, satisfies Eq. (12.12). Thus we say that $x = A \sin(\omega t + \alpha)$ is the general solution of Eq. (12.12) because it has two arbitrary constants, the amplitude A and the initial phase α.* Therefore we verify the fact that *an attractive force proportional to the displacement produces simple harmonic motion.*

At this point we forewarn the student that this differential equation (12.12) appears in many different situations in physics. Whenever it is found, it indicates that the corresponding phenomenon is oscillatory according to the law $A \sin(\omega t + \alpha)$, whether it is describing a linear or an angular displacement of a particle, a current in an electric circuit or the ion concentration in a plasma, the temperature of a body, or any of a multitude of other physical situations.

EXAMPLE 12.3. Discuss the solution of Eq. (12.12) for simple harmonic motion in terms of the initial displacement x_0 and the initial velocity v_0.

Solution: We have indicated that the general solution of Eq. (12.12) is

$$x = A \sin(\omega t + \alpha).$$

Thus the velocity is $v = dx/dt = \omega A \cos(\omega t + \alpha)$. Therefore, setting $t = 0$, we have

$$x_0 = A \sin\alpha, \qquad v_0 = \omega A \cos\alpha.$$

From this we obtain

$$\tan\alpha = \omega x_0/v_0 \qquad \text{and} \qquad A = (x_0^2 + v_0^2/\omega^2)^{1/2}.$$

For example, if the particle is initially at the equilibrium position $x_0 = 0$ and receives a blow giving a velocity v_0, we have $\alpha = 0$ and $A = v_0/\omega$. The displacement is then given by $x = v_0/\omega \sin \omega t$. The total energy of the particle, according to Eq. (12.11), will be $E = \frac{1}{2}k(v_0/\omega)^2 = \frac{1}{2}mv_0^2$, which is equal to the initial kinetic energy.

On the other hand, if the particle is separated the distance x_0 from the equilibrium position and then released, $v_0 = 0$, and thus $\tan\alpha = \infty$ or $\alpha = \pi/2$ and $A = x_0$. The displacement is then given by $x = x_0 \cos \omega t$. Using Eq. (12.11), we obtain the total energy of the particle as $E = \frac{1}{2}kx_0^2$, which is equal to the initial potential energy.

EXAMPLE 12.4. Derive a general expression for the period of an oscillatory motion, using the principle of conservation of energy.

---

* The general solution of Eq. (12.12) may also be written in the alternative form $x = a \sin \omega t + b \cos \omega t$, where a and b are arbitrary constants. This solution is equivalent to $x = A \sin(\omega t + \alpha)$ if we make $a = A \cos\alpha$ and $b = A \sin\alpha$.

Solution: Referring to the discussion of Section 8.9 for rectilinear motion under conservative forces, we find that Eq. (8.34) applies; that is,

$$\int_{x_0}^{x} \frac{dx}{[(2/m)(E - E_p(x))]^{1/2}} = t,$$

where $E_p(x)$ is the potential energy of the motion and E the total energy. According to the discussion of Section 8.11, the particle oscillates between the positions given by the values x_1 and x_2 obtained by solving the equation $E_p(x) = E$ (recall Fig. 8–18). If, in the above equation, we make $x_0 = x_1$ and $x = x_2$, the time t corresponds to one-half an oscillation and therefore is equal to one-half the period: $t = \frac{1}{2}P$. Therefore the preceding equation yields

$$P = 2\int_{x_1}^{x_2} \frac{dx}{\sqrt{(2/m)(E - E_p)}}. \tag{12.13}$$

This is a general formula that gives the period of any oscillatory motion, whether it is SHM or not. Note that it allows us to compute the period if we know the potential energy $E_p(x)$, even if we have not solved the equation of motion to obtain x as a function of t. We suggest that the student insert the value $E_p = \frac{1}{2}kx^2$ (which corresponds to simple harmonic motion) and obtain $P = \pi A\sqrt{2m/E}$, by making $x_1 = -A$ and $x_2 = +A$, thus verifying that this result is identical to Eq. (12.11).

12.5 The Simple Pendulum

An example of simple harmonic motion is the motion of a pendulum. A simple pendulum is defined as a particle of mass m suspended from a point O by a string of length l and of negligible mass (Fig. 12–7). If the particle is pulled aside to position B so that the string makes an angle θ_0 with the vertical OC, and then released, the pendulum will oscillate between B and the symmetric position B'.

To determine the nature of the oscillations, we must write the equation of motion of the particle. The particle moves in an arc of a circle of radius $l = OA$. The forces acting on the particle are its weight $m\boldsymbol{g}$ and the tension $\boldsymbol{T}$ along the string. The tangential component of the resultant force is, from the figure,

$$F_T = -mg \sin \theta,$$

where the minus sign appears because it is opposed to the displacement $s = CA$. The equation for the tangential motion is $F_T = ma_T$ and, since the particle moves along a circle of radius l, we may use Eq. (5.56) (with R replaced by l) to express the tangential acceleration. That is, $a_T = l\, d^2\theta/dt^2$. The equation for the tangential motion is thus

$$ml\frac{d^2\theta}{dt^2} = -mg \sin \theta \qquad \text{or} \qquad \frac{d^2\theta}{dt^2} + \frac{g}{l}\sin \theta = 0. \tag{12.14}$$

This equation is not of the same type as Eq. (12.12) because of the presence of $\sin \theta$. However, if the angle θ is small, which is true if the amplitude of the oscilla-

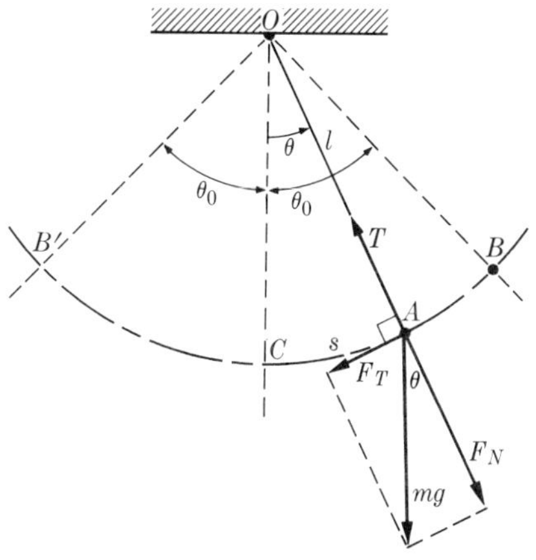

Fig. 12–7. Oscillatory motion of a pendulum.

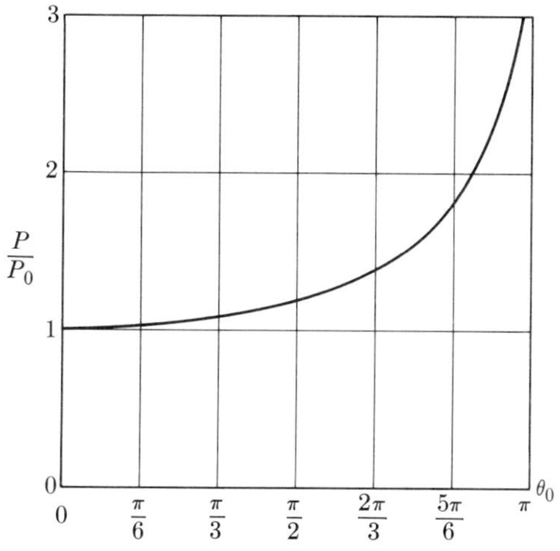

Fig. 12–8. Variation of the period of a pendulum with the amplitude.

tions is small, we may use Eq. (M.30) and write $\sin\theta \sim \theta$ in Eq. (12.14) for the motion of the pendulum, which becomes

$$\frac{d^2\theta}{dt^2} + \frac{g}{l}\,\theta = 0.$$

This is a differential equation identical to Eq. (12.12), with x replaced by θ, this time referring to angular rather than linear motion. Thus we may conclude that, within our approximation, the angular motion of the pendulum is simple harmonic, with $\omega^2 = g/l$. The angle θ can thus be expressed in the form $\theta = \theta_0 \sin(\omega t + \alpha)$. Then, using Eq. (12.2), $P = 2\pi/\omega$, we can express the period of oscillation as

$$P = 2\pi\sqrt{\frac{l}{g}}\cdot \tag{12.15}$$

Note that the period is independent of the mass of the pendulum. For larger amplitudes, the approximation $\sin\theta \sim \theta$ is not valid. In that case, the formula for the period depends on the amplitude θ_0. If we wish to obtain the general formula for the period, we first express the potential energy of the pendulum as a function of the angle (Example 8.7) and substitute this into the expression for P given by Eq. (12.13). We shall omit the mathematical details, but indicate that the result can be expressed as a series,

$$P = 2\pi\sqrt{l/g}\,\left(1 + \tfrac{1}{4}\sin^2 \tfrac{1}{2}\theta_0 + \tfrac{9}{64}\sin^4 \tfrac{1}{2}\theta_0 + \cdots\right).$$

The variation of P with the amplitude θ_0, expressed in terms of the period $P_0 = 2\pi\sqrt{l/g}$ corresponding to very small amplitudes, is illustrated in Fig. 12–8. Note that only for very large amplitudes does the period differ appreciably from P_0. For small amplitudes it is enough to take only the first corrective term, and even then substitute $\frac{1}{2}\theta_0$ for $\sin \frac{1}{2}\theta_0$, resulting in

$$P = 2\pi\sqrt{l/g}\,(1 + \tfrac{1}{16}\theta_0^2), \tag{12.16}$$

where θ_0 must be expressed in radians. This is a sufficient approximation for most practical situations. In fact, the corrective term $\theta_0^2/16$ amounts to less than 1% for amplitudes less than 23°.

There is, however, a special arrangement in which the period of a pendulum is independent of the amplitude. This is called the *cycloidal pendulum.* A cycloid is a curve generated by a point on the rim of a disk rolling on a plane, as shown in Fig. 12–9. If we build a path in a vertical plane with the shape of a cycloid, and let a mass m slide back and forth along it under the action of gravity, the amplitude of the motion will depend on the point from which the particle is released, but the period will always be $P = 4\pi\sqrt{a/g}$, where a is the radius of the circle generating the cycloid.

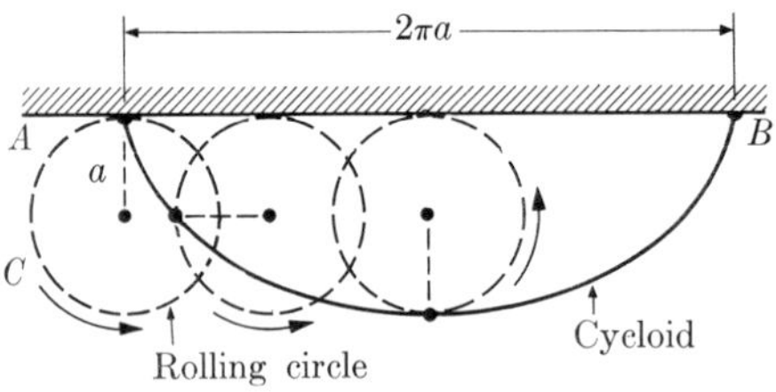

Fig. 12–9. Definition of cycloid.

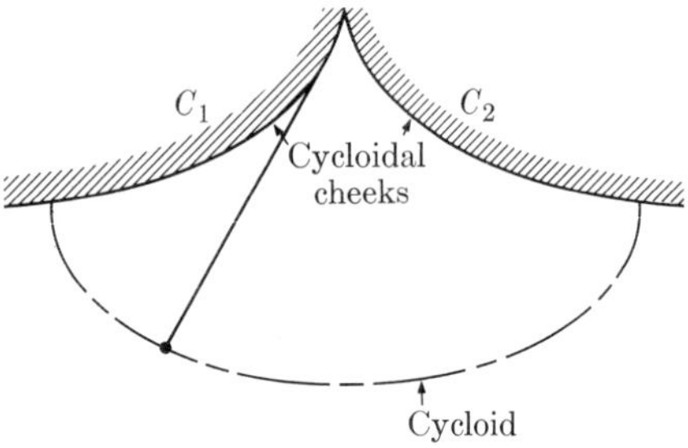

Fig. 12–10. Cycloidal pendulum.

A practical way of constructing a cycloidal pendulum is illustrated in Fig. 12–10, where C_1 and C_2 are two cycloid cheeks. Then, by geometrical reasoning, it can be proved that when the pendulum is suspended between them, its bob also describes a cycloid, and therefore the period of oscillation is independent of the amplitude.*

EXAMPLE 12.5. Compute the tension in the string of a pendulum as a function of the angle the string makes with the vertical.

Solution: To compute the tension T, we first obtain the centripetal force on the particle,

$$F_C = T - F_N = T - mg\cos\theta,$$

since, from Fig. 12–7, F_N is given by $mg\cos\theta$. We then equate it to the mass times the centripetal acceleration mv^2/l (note that l is the radius) according to Eq. (7.28), resulting in

$$T - mg\cos\theta = mv^2/l\cdot$$

---

* For more detail on the cycloid, see G. B. Thomas, *Calculus and Analytic Geometry*, third edition. Reading, Mass.: Addison-Wesley, 1962, Section 12.2.

We obtain the velocity by using the result of Example 8.7. That is,

$$v^2 = 2gl(\cos\theta - \cos\theta_0),$$

and therefore

$$T = mg(3\cos\theta - 2\cos\theta_0).$$

This expression is valid for any amplitude, since no approximation has been made regarding the angle θ.

12.6 Compound Pendulum

A compound (or physical) pendulum is any rigid body that can oscillate freely around a horizontal axis under the action of gravity. Let ZZ' (Fig. 12–11) be the horizontal axis and C the center of mass of the body. When the line OC makes an angle θ with the vertical, the Z-component of the torque acting on the body is $\tau_z = -mgb\sin\theta$, where b is the distance OC between the Z-axis and the center of mass C. If I is the moment of inertia of the body around the Z-axis, and $\alpha = d^2\theta/dt^2$ is the angular acceleration, Eq. (10.14), $I\alpha = \tau_z$, gives $I\, d^2\theta/dt^2 = -mgb\sin\theta$. Assuming that the oscillations are of small amplitude, we may approximate again, with $\sin\theta \sim \theta$, so that the equation of motion is

$$\frac{d^2\theta}{dt^2} = -\frac{mgb}{I}\theta$$

or

$$\frac{d^2\theta}{dt^2} + \frac{gb}{K^2}\theta = 0.$$

Here we have used $I = mK^2$, where K is the radius of gyration, defined in Eq. (10.10). We may compare this equation of motion with Eq. (12.12), showing that the oscillatory angular motion is simple harmonic, with $\omega^2 = gb/K^2$. Thus the period of the oscillations is

$$P = 2\pi\sqrt{K^2/gb}. \tag{12.17}$$

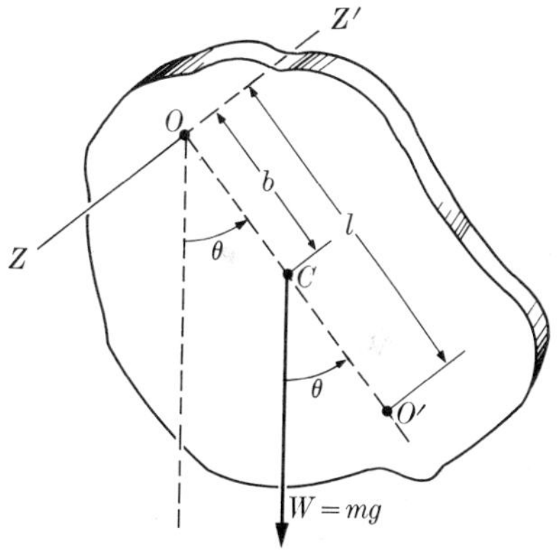

Fig. 12–11. Compound pendulum.

The quantity $l = K^2/b$ is called the length of the equivalent simple pendulum, since a simple pendulum of that length has the same period as the compound pendulum. We note that the period of the compound pendulum is independent of its mass, as well as of its geometrical shape, so long as the radius of gyration K and the position of the center of mass, given by b, remain the same.

EXAMPLE 12.6. A ring of radius 0.10 m is suspended from a peg, as illustrated in Fig. 12–12. Determine its period of oscillation.

Solution: We denote the radius of the ring by R. Its moment of inertia with respect to an axis passing through its center of mass C is $I_C = mR^2$ (see Table 10–1). Then, if we apply Steiner's theorem, Eq. (10.8), with $a = R$, the moment of inertia relative to an axis passing through the point of suspension O is

$$I = I_C + mR^2 = mR^2 + mR^2 = 2mR^2,$$

which yields a radius of gyration $K^2 = 2R^2$. Also in our case $b = R$. Therefore, using Eq. (12.17), we obtain

$$P = 2\pi\sqrt{\frac{2R^2}{gR}} = 2\pi\sqrt{\frac{2R}{g}},$$

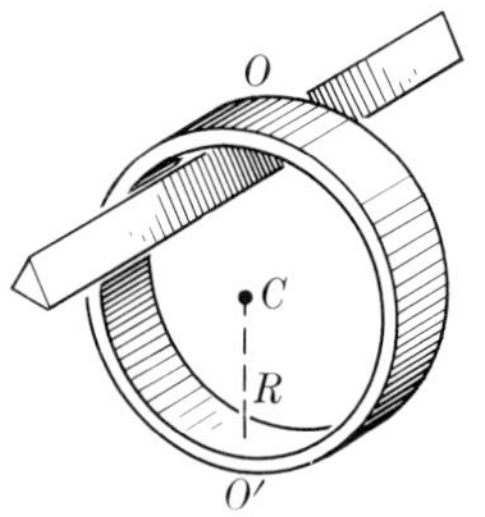

Figure 12–12

which indicates that the length of the equivalent simple pendulum is $OO' = 2R$, which is the same as the diameter of the ring. When we introduce the values $R = 0.10$ m and $g = 9.8$ m s^{-2}, we obtain $P = 0.88$ s.

EXAMPLE 12.7. A sphere of radius R is suspended by a string from a fixed point, so that the distance from the center of the sphere to the point of suspension is l. Find the period of the pendulum.

Solution: Unless the radius R is very small compared with the length l, we cannot consider the pendulum as simple, and must use the expressions which we have discussed in this section. From Table 10–1 we have that the moment of inertia of a sphere relative to an axis passing through its center is $\frac{2}{5}mR^2$. Thus, when we apply Steiner's theorem, the moment of inertia relative to the point of suspension is, with $a = l$,

$$I = \tfrac{2}{5}mR^2 + ml^2 = m(l^2 + \tfrac{2}{5}R^2).$$

This yields a radius of gyration $K^2 = l^2 + \frac{2}{5}R^2 = l^2(1 + 0.4R^2/l^2)$. Thus, applying Eq. (12.17) and noting that $b = l$ in this case, we have

$$P = 2\pi\sqrt{\frac{l(1 + 0.4R^2/l^2)}{g}} = 2\pi\sqrt{\frac{l}{g}}\left(1 + 0.4\frac{R^2}{l^2}\right)^{1/2}.$$

Since in general R is small compared with l, we may replace $(1 + 0.4R^2/l^2)^{1/2}$ by $1 + 0.2R^2/l^2$, using the binomial approximation (M.28). Therefore

$$P = 2\pi\sqrt{\frac{l}{g}}\left(1 + 0.2\frac{R^2}{l^2}\right).$$

The first term gives the period, if we neglect the size of the sphere. For example, if $l = 1$ m and $R = 0.01$ m, we have $R^2/l^2 = 10^{-4}$, and the correction term is 1.00002. Thus the finite size of the pendulum bob increases the period by 0.002%, an amount that is negligible in most cases.

EXAMPLE 12.8. Discuss the torsion pendulum.

Solution: Another example of simple harmonic motion is the torsion pendulum, consisting of a body suspended from a wire or fiber (Fig. 12–13) in such a way that line OC passes through the center of mass of the body. When the body is rotated an angle θ from its equilibrium position, the wire is twisted, exerting on the body a torque τ around OC

opposing the displacement θ and of magnitude proportional to it, $\tau = -\kappa\theta$, where κ is the torsion coefficient of the wire. If I is the moment of inertia of the body around the axis OC, the equation of motion, using Eq. (10.14) with $\alpha = d^2\theta/dt^2$, is

$$I\frac{d^2\theta}{dt^2} = -\kappa\theta \qquad \text{or} \qquad \frac{d^2\theta}{dt^2} + \frac{\kappa}{I}\theta = 0.$$

Again we find the differential equation (12.12), so that the angular motion is simple harmonic, with $\omega^2 = \kappa/I$; the period of oscillation is

$$P = 2\pi\sqrt{I/\kappa}. \tag{12.18}$$

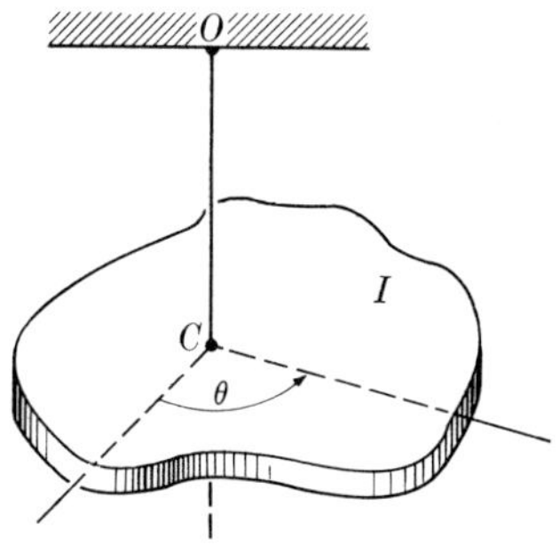

Fig. 12–13. Torsion pendulum. The center of mass is at C.

This result is interesting because we may use it to experimentally determine the moment of inertia of a body by suspending the body from a wire whose torsion coefficient κ is known, and then measuring the period P of the oscillation.

12.7 Superposition of Two SHM: Same Direction, Same Frequency

We shall now consider the superposition, or *interference*, of two simple harmonic motions which produce a displacement of the particle along the same line. Let us first discuss the case when both have the same frequency (Fig. 12–14). The displacement of the particle produced by each simple harmonic motion is given by

$$x_1 = OP_1 = A_1 \sin(\omega t + \alpha_1)$$

and

$$x_2 = OP_2 = A_2 \sin(\omega t + \alpha_2).$$

The resulting displacement of the particle is given by

$$x = OP = x_1 + x_2$$
$$= A_1 \sin(\omega t + \alpha_1) + A_2 \sin(\omega t + \alpha_2).$$

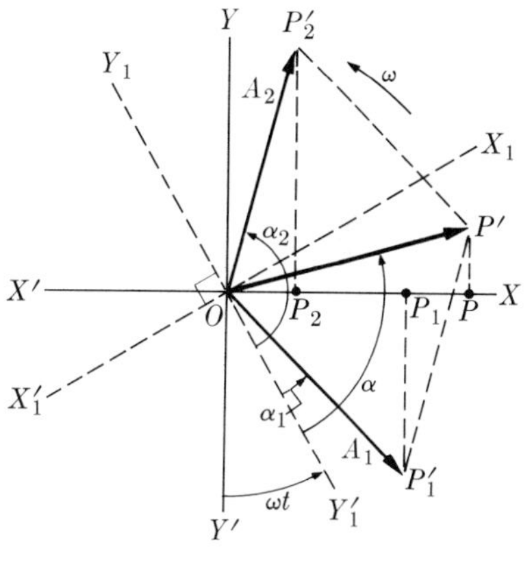

Fig. 12–14. Composition of two SHM of same frequency.

We shall now prove that x also corresponds to a simple harmonic motion of the same frequency. Finding the vector sum $\overrightarrow{OP'}$ of the rotating vectors $\overrightarrow{OP'_1}$ and $\overrightarrow{OP'_2}$, we note that its X-component is just the sum of the X-components of $\overrightarrow{OP'_1}$ and $\overrightarrow{OP'_2}$ (that is, $x_1 + x_2$), and therefore is equal to x. Also, since the angle between $\overrightarrow{OP'_1}$ and $\overrightarrow{OP'_2}$ has the fixed value $\delta = \alpha_2 - \alpha_1$, the vector $\overrightarrow{OP'}$ has a constant magnitude A, and also rotates around O with angular velocity ω. Therefore the rotating vector $\overrightarrow{OP'}$ generates a simple harmonic motion of angular frequency ω,

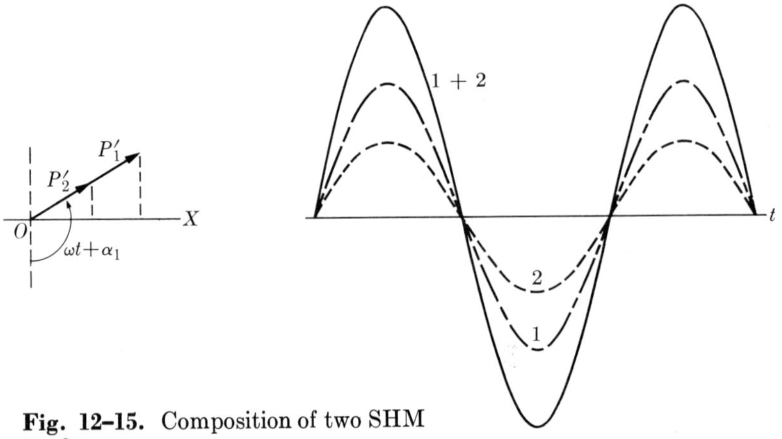

Fig. 12–15. Composition of two SHM in phase.

and we can write for $x = OP$,

$$x = A \sin (\omega t + \alpha). \tag{12.19}$$

We compute the amplitude A by applying Eq. (3.3) for the resultant of two vectors:

$$A = \sqrt{A_1^2 + A_2^2 + 2A_1A_2 \cos \delta}. \tag{12.20}$$

The initial phase α can be found by projecting the three vectors on axes OX_1 and OY_1 which rotate with angular velocity ω and which constitute a frame of reference in which vectors $\overrightarrow{OP_1'}$, $\overrightarrow{OP_2'}$, and $\overrightarrow{OP'}$ are at rest. Then, from the law of vector addition, we have

$$A \cos \alpha = A_1 \cos \alpha_1 + A_2 \cos \alpha_2$$

and

$$A \sin \alpha = A_1 \sin \alpha_1 + A_2 \sin \alpha_2.$$

Dividing, we obtain

$$\tan \alpha = \frac{A_1 \sin \alpha_1 + A_2 \sin \alpha_2}{A_1 \cos \alpha_1 + A_2 \cos \alpha_2}. \tag{12.21}$$

Let us consider some important special cases. If $\alpha_2 = \alpha_1$, then $\delta = 0$, and we say that the two motions are *in phase*. Their rotating vectors are parallel, and Eqs. (12.20) and (12.21) give

$$A = A_1 + A_2, \qquad \alpha = \alpha_1. \tag{12.22}$$

Hence the two simple harmonic motions interfere by reinforcement because their amplitudes add (Fig. 12–15). If $\alpha_2 = \alpha_1 + \pi$, then $\delta = \pi$, and we say that the two simple harmonic motions are in *opposition*. Their rotating vectors are antiparallel and Eqs. (12.20) and (12.21) give, if $A_1 > A_2$,

$$A = A_1 - A_2, \qquad \alpha = \alpha_1, \tag{12.23}$$

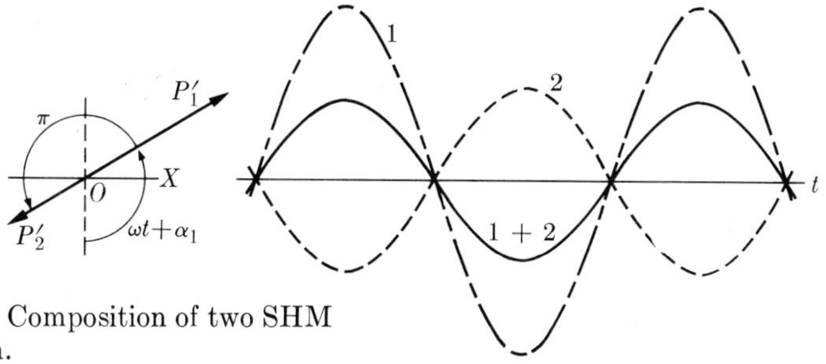

Fig. 12–16. Composition of two SHM in opposition.

and the two simple harmonic motions interfere by attenuation because their amplitudes subtract (Fig. 12–16). In particular, if $A_1 = A_2$, the two simple harmonic motions completely cancel each other. (What would happen if $A_1 < A_2$?) If $\alpha_2 = \alpha_1 + \pi/2$, then $\delta = \pi/2$, and it is said that two simple harmonic motions are *in quadrature*. Then, by application of Eq. (12.20), we obtain

$$A = \sqrt{A_1^2 + A_2^2}. \tag{12.24}$$

The student may verify from Eq. (12.21) that the expression for α is given by

$$\alpha = \alpha_1 + \arctan \frac{A_2}{A_1}. \tag{12.25}$$

The two rotating vectors are, in this case, perpendicular. In Fig. 12–17, the case when $A_1 = \sqrt{3}\, A_2$ has been represented so that $\alpha = \alpha_1 + \pi/6$ and $A = 2A_2$. The student should investigate the case in which $\alpha_2 = \alpha_1 + 3\pi/2$.

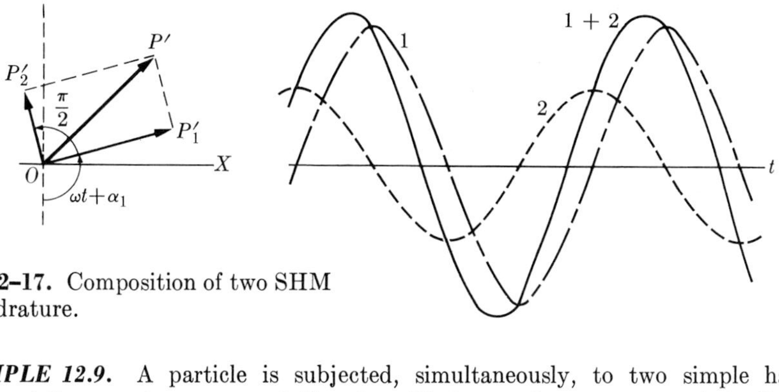

Fig. 12–17. Composition of two SHM in quadrature.

EXAMPLE 12.9. A particle is subjected, simultaneously, to two simple harmonic motions of the same frequency and direction. Their equations are $x_1 = 10 \sin (2t + \pi/4)$ and $x_2 = 6 \sin (2t + 2\pi/3)$. Find the resultant motion.

Solution: The phase difference is $\delta = \alpha_2 - \alpha_1 = 2\pi/3 - \pi/4 = 5\pi/12$. Therefore, since the amplitudes are $A_1 = 10$ and $A_2 = 6$, the resultant amplitude is

$$A = \sqrt{10^2 + 6^2 + 2(10)(6) \cos (5\pi/12)} = 12.92.$$

The initial phase is given by

$$\tan \alpha = \frac{10 \sin(\pi/4) + 6 \sin(2\pi/3)}{10 \cos(\pi/4) + 6 \cos(2\pi/3)} = 6.527,$$

so that $\alpha = 81.3° = 1.42$ rad. Therefore the resultant motion is described by the equation $x = 12.92 \sin(2t + 1.42)$.

12.8 Superposition of Two SHM: Same Direction, Different Frequency

The case in which two interfering simple harmonic motions in the same direction have different frequencies is also of importance. Consider, for simplicity, the case in which $\alpha_1 = 0$ and $\alpha_2 = 0$; then the motions are described by the equations $x_1 = A_1 \sin \omega_1 t$ and $x_2 = A_2 \sin \omega_2 t$.

The angle between the rotating vectors $\overrightarrow{OP'_2}$ and $\overrightarrow{OP'_1}$ (Fig. 12–18) is now $\omega_1 t - \omega_2 t = (\omega_1 - \omega_2)t$, and is not constant. Therefore, the resultant vector $\overrightarrow{OP'}$ does not have constant length and does not rotate with constant angular velocity. In consequence, the resultant motion, $x = x_1 + x_2$ is not simple harmonic. However, as we see from Fig. 12–18, the "amplitude" of the motion is

$$A = \sqrt{A_1^2 + A_2^2 + 2A_1A_2 \cos(\omega_1 - \omega_2)t}, \tag{12.26}$$

and it "oscillates" between the values $A = A_1 + A_2$ [when $(\omega_1 - \omega_2)t = 2n\pi$] and $A = |A_1 - A_2|$ [when $(\omega_1 - \omega_2)t = 2n\pi + \pi$]. It is then said that the amplitude is *modulated*. The frequency of the amplitude oscillation is expressed by

$$\nu = (\omega_1 - \omega_2)/2\pi = \nu_1 - \nu_2, \tag{12.27}$$

and thus is equal to the difference of the frequencies of the two interfering motions.

Figure 12–19 shows the variation of A with t. The situation described arises when, for example, two tuning forks of close but different frequencies are vibrating simultaneously at nearby places. One observes a fluctuation in the intensity of the

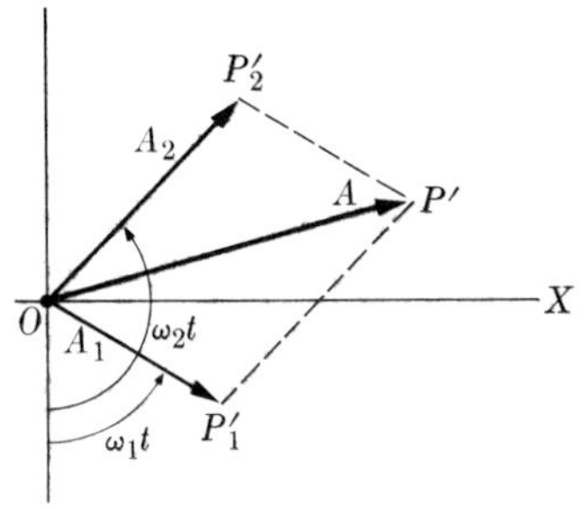

Fig. 12–18. Composition of two SHM of different frequencies.

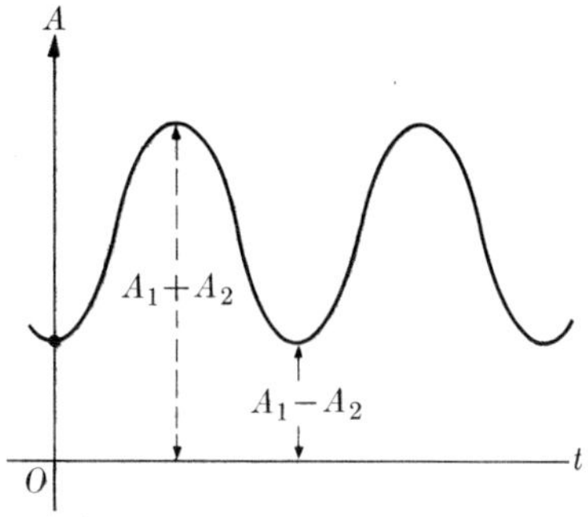

Fig. 12–19. Amplitude fluctuation or beats.

sound, called *beats*, which is due to the change in amplitude, as illustrated in Fig. 12–19.

An interesting situation occurs when $A_1 = A_2$; that is, when the two amplitudes are equal. Then, using Eq. (M.7), we obtain

$$\begin{aligned} x = x_1 + x_2 &= A_1(\sin \omega_1 t + \sin \omega_2 t) \\ &= 2A_1 \cos \tfrac{1}{2}(\omega_1 - \omega_2)t \sin \tfrac{1}{2}(\omega_1 + \omega_2)t, \end{aligned} \tag{12.28}$$

indicating that the motion is oscillatory with angular frequency $\frac{1}{2}(\omega_1 + \omega_2)$ and amplitude

$$A = 2A_1 \cos \tfrac{1}{2}(\omega_1 - \omega_2)t. \tag{12.29}$$

This result can be obtained directly from Eq. (12.26) by setting $A_2 = A_1$. The plot of x against t is illustrated in Fig. 12–20, in which the dashed line shows the modulation of the amplitude.

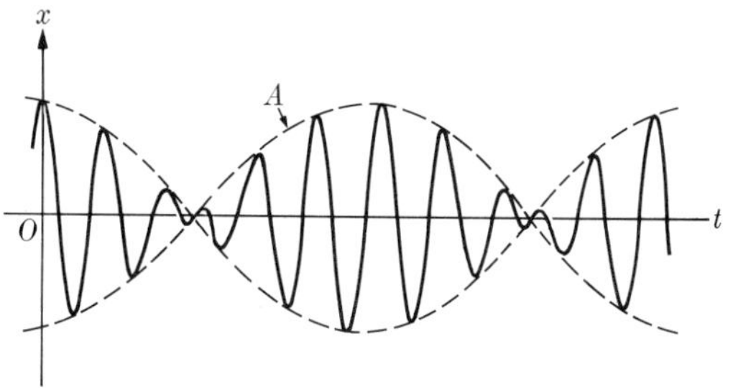

Fig. 12–20. Beats when the two amplitudes are the same.

12.9 Superposition of Two SHM: Perpendicular Directions

Let us now consider the case in which a particle moves in a plane in such a way that its two coordinates x and y oscillate with simple harmonic motion. We examine first a case in which the two motions have the same frequency. Choosing our origin of time so that the initial phase for the motion along the X-axis is zero, we have for the x-coordinate

$$x = A \sin \omega t. \tag{12.30}$$

The motion along the Y-axis is described by the equation

$$y = B \sin (\omega t + \delta), \tag{12.31}$$

where δ is now the phase difference between the x- and y-oscillations. We have also assumed that the amplitudes A and B are different. The path of the particle is obviously limited by the lines $x = \pm A$ and $y = \pm B$.

We shall now consider some special cases. If the two motions are in phase, $\delta = 0$ and $y = B \sin \omega t$, which may be combined with Eq. (12.30) to yield

$$y = (B/A)x.$$

This is the equation of the straight line PQ in Fig. 12–21, and the motion which results is simple harmonic, with amplitude $\sqrt{A^2 + B^2}$, because the displacement along the line PQ is

$$r = \sqrt{x^2 + y^2} = \sqrt{A^2 + B^2} \sin \omega t. \tag{12.32}$$

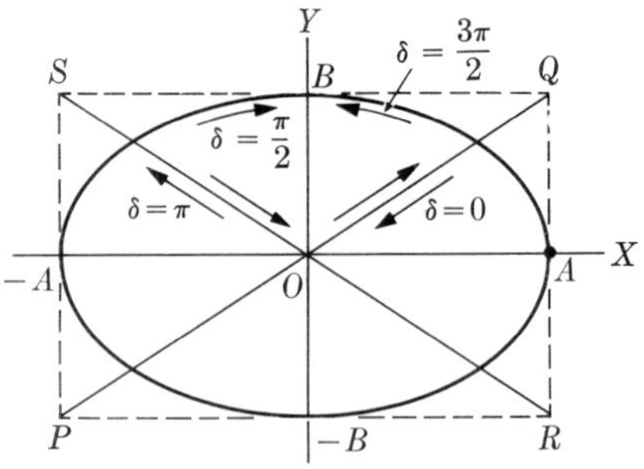

Fig. 12–21. Composition of two SHM of the same frequency but in perpendicular directions. The path depends on the phase difference.

If the two motions are in opposition, $\delta = \pi$ and $y = -B \sin \omega t$. Combined with Eq. (12.30), this gives

$$y = -\frac{B}{A} x,$$

which is the equation of the straight line RS. The motion is again simple harmonic, with amplitude $\sqrt{A^2 + B^2}$. Therefore we say that when $\delta = 0$ or π, the interference of two perpendicular simple harmonic motions of the same frequency results in *rectilinear polarization.*

When $\delta = \pi/2$, it is said that the motions along the X- and Y-axes are in *quadrature,* and

$$y = B \sin (\omega t + \pi/2) = B \cos \omega t.$$

Combined with Eq. (12.30), this gives

$$\frac{x^2}{A^2} + \frac{y^2}{B^2} = 1,$$

which is the equation of the ellipse illustrated in Fig. 12–21. The ellipse is traversed in a clockwise sense. This may be verified by finding the velocity of the particle at the point $x = +A$, at which the velocity is parallel to the Y-axis. At this point, from Eq. (12.30), we must have $\sin \omega t = 1$. The Y-component of the

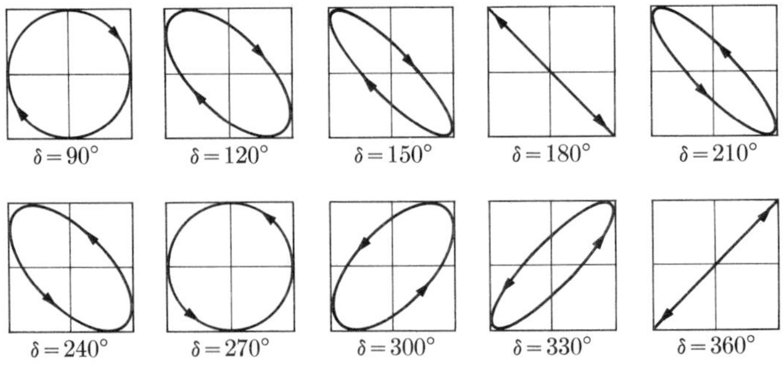

Fig. 12–22. Paths for selected phase differences.

velocity is $v_y = dy/dt = -\omega B \sin \omega t = -\omega B$. Since it is negative, the point passes through A moving downward, which corresponds to a clockwise sense of rotation. The same ellipse is obtained if $\delta = 3\pi/2$ or $-\pi/2$, but then the motion is counterclockwise (can the student verify this statement?). Thus we may say that when the phase difference δ is $\pm\pi/2$, the interference of two simple harmonic motions of the same frequency results in *elliptical polarization*, with the axes of the ellipse parallel to the directions of the two motions.

When $A = B$, the ellipse transforms into a circle and we have *circular polarization*. For an arbitrary value of the phase difference δ, the path is still an ellipse, but its axes are rotated relative to the coordinate axes. The paths for selected phase differences are shown in Fig. 12–22.

According to Section 12.3, the motions described by Eqs. (12.30) and (12.31) require forces along the X- and Y-axes equal to $F_x = -kx$ and $F_y = -ky$. The resultant force acting on the particle is therefore

$$\begin{aligned} \boldsymbol{F} &= \boldsymbol{u}_x F_x + \boldsymbol{u}_y F_y \\ &= -k(\boldsymbol{u}_x x + \boldsymbol{u}_y y) = -k\boldsymbol{r}, \end{aligned} \tag{12.33}$$

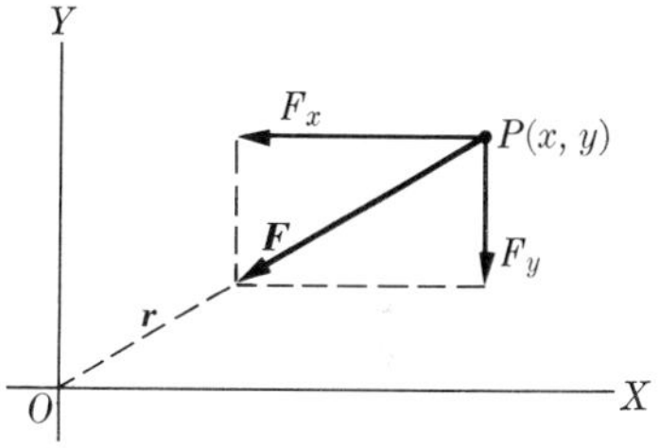

Fig. 12–23. Attractive force proportional to displacement.

where $\boldsymbol{r} = \overrightarrow{OP}$ (Fig. 12–23) is the position vector of the particle. Therefore the motion we have described kinematically in this section is produced by an attractive central force proportional to the displacement.

The force given by Eq. (12.33) always produces a plane motion even if the particle can move in space, because the force is central and therefore the most general path under such a force is an ellipse. The potential energy corresponding to the

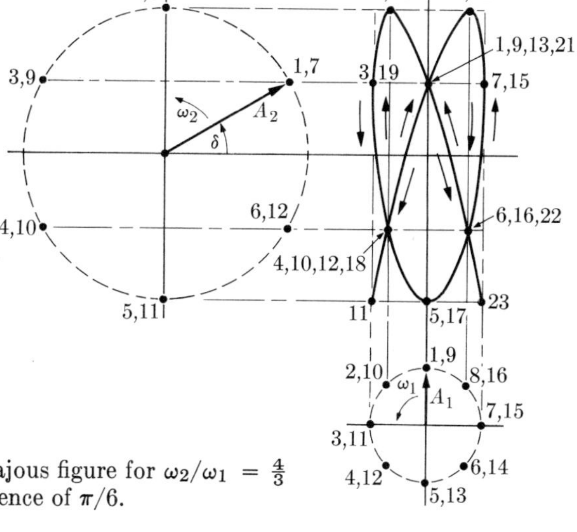

Fig. 12–24. Lissajous figure for $\omega_2/\omega_1 = \frac{4}{3}$ and a phase difference of $\pi/6$.

force of Eq. (12.33) is (remember Example 8.8):

$$E_p = \tfrac{1}{2}k(x^2 + y^2) = \tfrac{1}{2}kr^2. \tag{12.34}$$

Another interesting situation is the interference of two perpendicular oscillatory motions of different frequencies. That is,

$$x = A_1 \sin \omega_1 t, \qquad y = A_2 \sin (\omega_2 t + \delta). \tag{12.35}$$

Fig. 12–25. Lissajous figures. They depend on the ratio ω_2/ω_1 and on the phase difference.

Figure 12–24 illustrates the case in which $\omega_1 = \frac{3}{4}\omega_2$ and $\delta = \pi/6$. The resulting path is the solid line. Such a path depends on the ratio ω_2/ω_1 and on the phase difference δ. These paths are called *Lissajous figures*, and are illustrated in Fig. 12–25 for several values of the ratio ω_2/ω_1 and several phase differences in each case.

12.10 Coupled Oscillators

A situation very frequently encountered is that of two *coupled* oscillators. Three possible situations are illustrated in Fig. 12–26. In (a), we have two masses m_1 and m_2 attached to springs k_1 and k_2 and coupled by spring k, so that the motions of m_1 and m_2 are not independent. In (b), we have two pendulums coupled by string AB. In (c), the bodies I_1 and I_2 attached to rods k_1 and k_2 are coupled by rod k, forming two coupled torsional pendulums. We shall encounter a similar situation in Section 17.11 (Volume II) when we discuss coupled oscillating electric circuits. The net effect of the coupling of two oscillators can be described as an exchange of energy between them.

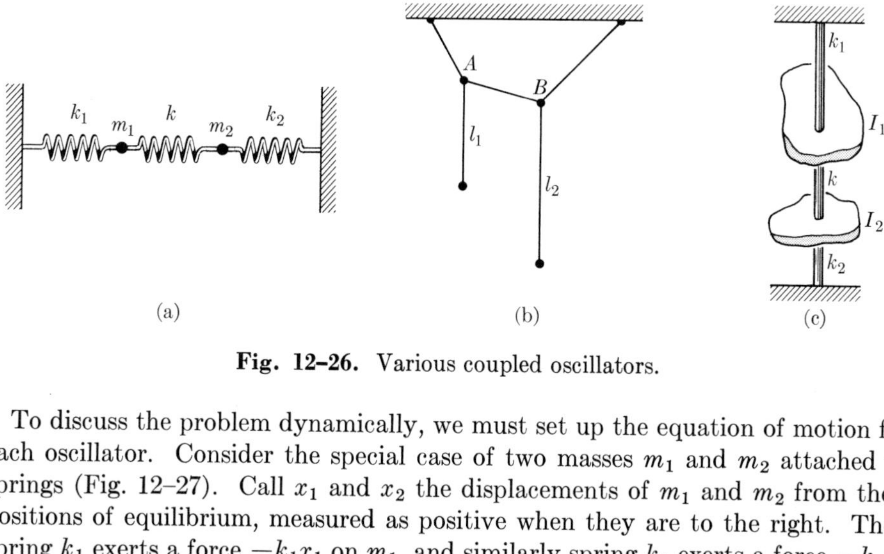

Fig. 12–26. Various coupled oscillators.

To discuss the problem dynamically, we must set up the equation of motion for each oscillator. Consider the special case of two masses m_1 and m_2 attached to springs (Fig. 12–27). Call x_1 and x_2 the displacements of m_1 and m_2 from their positions of equilibrium, measured as positive when they are to the right. Then spring k_1 exerts a force $-k_1x_1$ on m_1, and similarly spring k_2 exerts a force $-k_2x_2$

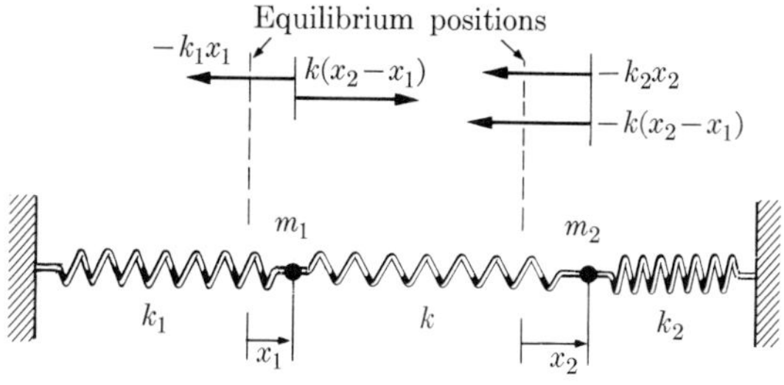

Fig. 12–27. Coupled oscillators.

on m_2. Spring k has suffered an elongation $x_2 - x_1$, and therefore the forces exerted on each particle when it tries to recover its original length are $k(x_2 - x_1)$ on m_1 and $-k(x_2 - x_1)$ on m_2. Therefore the equation of motion of each particle [using Eq. (7.15), which we recall is $m\,d^2x/dt^2 = F$] is

$$m_1 \frac{d^2x_1}{dt^2} = -k_1x_1 + k(x_2 - x_1)$$

and

$$m_2 \frac{d^2x_2}{dt^2} = -k_2x_2 - k(x_2 - x_1).$$

Combining similar terms, we may write

$$\frac{d^2x_1}{dt^2} + \frac{k_1 + k}{m_1} x_1 = \frac{k}{m_1} x_2$$

and (12.36)

$$\frac{d^2x_2}{dt^2} + \frac{k_2 + k}{m_2} x_2 = \frac{k}{m_2} x_1.$$

The left-hand sides of these equations are very similar to Eq. (12.12), except that the elastic constant for each particle has been replaced by $k_1 + k$ and $k_2 + k$. This, in view of Eq. (12.7), is equivalent to a change in the frequency of oscillation relative to their frequencies when uncoupled. Another difference in Eq. (12.36) relative to Eq. (12.12) is that, instead of zero on the right-hand side, we have a term referring to the other oscillator. This we may call the *coupling term.* Instead of attempting to obtain the general solution of Eq. (12.36), we shall indicate the main results, limiting ourselves to the special case of two identical oscillators, so that $m_1 = m_2$ and $k_1 = k_2$. This case, although simpler, has essentially all the features of the general case. Then Eqs. (12.36) become

$$\frac{d^2x_1}{dt^2} + \frac{k_1 + k}{m_1} x_1 = \frac{k}{m_1} x_2, \qquad \frac{d^2x_2}{dt^2} + \frac{k_1 + k}{m_1} x_2 = \frac{k}{m_1} x_1. \tag{12.37}$$

It can be proved that the general motion of the two coupled oscillators, described by Eqs. (12.37), may be considered as the superposition of two *normal modes* of oscillation. In one of the normal modes, the two oscillators move in phase with equal amplitudes. That is,

$$x_1 = A_1 \sin(\omega_1 t + \alpha_1), \qquad x_2 = A_1 \sin(\omega_1 t + \alpha_1), \tag{12.38}$$

where

$$\omega_1 = \sqrt{k_1/m_1}. \tag{12.39}$$

That is, the frequency of the coupled oscillators is the same as the frequency of oscillation which each mass would have if there were no coupling. This is easily understood because, since the two oscillators have the same amplitude and are in phase, the center spring does not suffer any stretching and therefore does not exert any force on the masses, which move as if they were not coupled.

In the second normal mode, the two oscillators move in opposition with equal amplitude. That is,

$$x_1 = A_2 \sin(\omega_2 t + \alpha_2), \qquad x_2 = -A_2 \sin(\omega_2 t + \alpha_2), \tag{12.40}$$

where

$$\omega_2 = \sqrt{(k_1 + 2k)/m_1}, \tag{12.41}$$

and therefore the frequency is higher than the frequency without coupling. This is also easily understood because now the center spring is stretched and compressed, and this amounts to increasing the elastic constant of each oscillator. These two normal modes of oscillation are represented schematically in Fig. 12–28. The normal modes (12.38) and (12.40) correspond to a situation in which the two masses move with a constant phase difference, which is zero in mode (12.38) and π in mode (12.40). The two masses simultaneously pass through their equilibrium positions and reach their maximum displacements simultaneously.

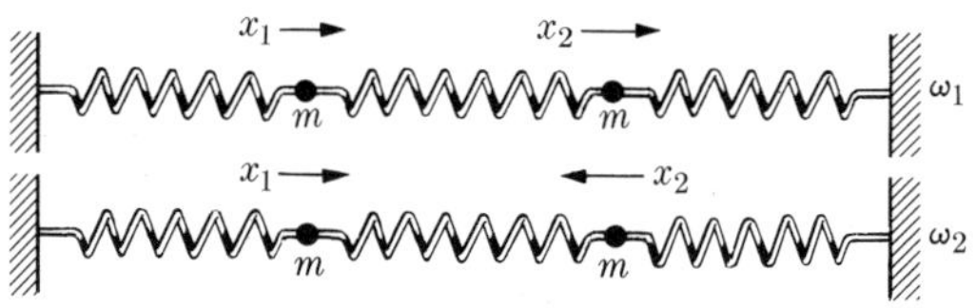

Fig. 12–28. Normal vibrations of two identical coupled oscillators.

The general solution of Eqs. (12.37) involves a linear combination of the normal modes of oscillation. That is,

$$x_1 = A_1 \sin(\omega_1 t + \alpha_1) + A_2 \sin(\omega_2 t + \alpha_2) \tag{12.42}$$

and

$$x_2 = A_1 \sin(\omega_1 t + \alpha_1) - A_2 \sin(\omega_2 t + \alpha_2). \tag{12.43}$$

We can see that these two equations express the general solution of Eq. (12.37) from the fact that they contain four arbitrary constants, A_1, α_1, A_2, and α_2, a situation which corresponds to a set of two second-order coupled differential equations. These two equations indicate that x_1 and x_2 are the resultants of the interference of two simple harmonic motions in the same direction but of different frequencies and phases, a situation already discussed in Section 12.8. Therefore what was explained there applies in this case.

To get a better understanding of the physics of the problem, let us consider the special case of equal amplitudes, $A_1 = A_2$, and assume that the initial phases are zero ($\alpha_1 = \alpha_2 = 0$). Then, using Eq. (M.7), we have

$$\begin{aligned} x_1 &= A_1 \sin \omega_1 t + A_1 \sin \omega_2 t = A_1(\sin \omega_1 t + \sin \omega_2 t) \\ &= [2A_1 \cos \tfrac{1}{2}(\omega_1 - \omega_2)t] \sin \tfrac{1}{2}(\omega_1 + \omega_2)t \end{aligned}$$

and

$$\begin{aligned} x_2 &= A_1 \sin \omega_1 t - A_1 \sin \omega_2 t = A_1(\sin \omega_1 t - \sin \omega_2 t) \\ &= [2A_1 \sin \tfrac{1}{2}(\omega_1 - \omega_2)t] \cos \tfrac{1}{2}(\omega_1 + \omega_2)t. \end{aligned}$$

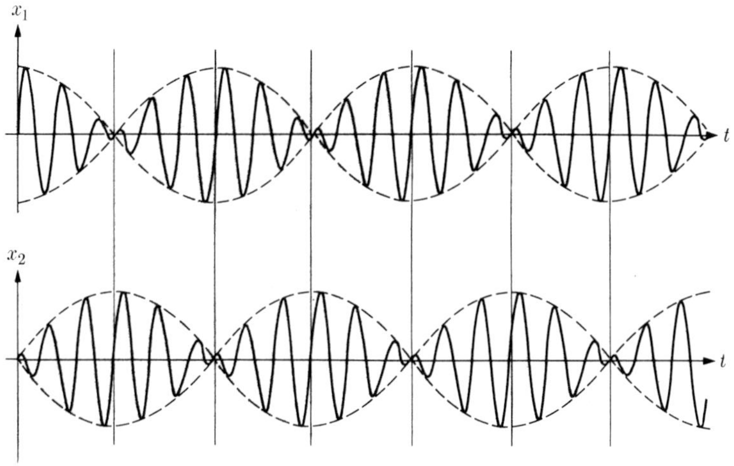

Fig. 12–29. Identical coupled oscillators with same amplitude.

Comparing these expressions with Eq. (12.29), we see that the modulating amplitude for x_1 is $2A \cos \frac{1}{2}(\omega_1 - \omega_2)t$, but the modulating amplitude for x_2 is $2A \sin \frac{1}{2}(\omega_1 - \omega_2)t = 2A \cos [\frac{1}{2}(\omega_1 - \omega_2)t - \pi/2]$. We see then that the two modulating amplitudes have a phase difference of $\pi/2$, or a quarter of the modulating period. The variations of x_1 and x_2 with t are illustrated in Fig. 12–29. Because of the phase difference between the two modulating amplitudes, there is an exchange of energy between the two oscillators. During one-quarter of the modulating period, the modulating amplitude of one oscillator decreases and that of the other increases, resulting in a transfer of energy from the first to the second. During the next quarter period, the situation reverses and energy flows in the opposite direction. The process repeats itself continuously. This can easily be observed experimentally by using two pendulums, arranged as in Fig. 12–26(b).

It is also interesting to consider the total energy of the system. The total kinetic energy is $E_k = \frac{1}{2}m_1^2v_1^2 + \frac{1}{2}m_2v_2^2$. To obtain the potential energy, we apply Eq. (12.10) to each spring, which yields $E_p = \frac{1}{2}k_1x_1^2 + \frac{1}{2}k_2x_2^2 + \frac{1}{2}k(x_1 - x_2)^2$, since x_1, x_2, and $x_1 - x_2$ are the elongations of each spring, or

$$E_p = \tfrac{1}{2}(k_1 + k)x_1^2 + \tfrac{1}{2}(k_2 + k)x_2^2 - kx_1x_2.$$

The total energy is then

$$E = E_k + E_p = [\tfrac{1}{2}m_1v_1^2 + \tfrac{1}{2}(k_1 + k)x_1^2] + [\tfrac{1}{2}m_2v_2^2 + \tfrac{1}{2}(k_2 + k)x_2^2] - kx_1x_2. \qquad (12.44)$$

The term in the first bracket depends on x_1 alone, and may be called the energy of m_1; the term in the second bracket corresponds to the energy of m_2. But the last term contains both x_1 and x_2, and is called the *coupling* or *interaction energy*. This term is the one which describes the exchange of energy between the two oscillators. In the absence of this term, the energy of each oscillator is constant. When there is a coupling, it is the total energy that is constant. This is a general result and, as we saw in Chapter 9, whenever two systems interact, resulting in an exchange of energy, the total energy of the system is of the form

$$E = (E_k + E_p)_1 + (E_k + E_p)_2 + (E_p)_{12}, \tag{12.45}$$

where the last term represents the interaction.

Coupled oscillators are found in many physical situations, as indicated above. An important case is the vibration of atoms in a molecule. A molecule is not a rigid structure; the atoms oscillate about their equilibrium positions. However, the oscillation of each atom affects its interaction with the others, and therefore they form a system of coupled oscillators.

Let us consider, for example, the case of a linear triatomic molecule such as CO_2. Geometrically this molecule has the array O=C=O, as indicated in Fig. 12–30, and is similar to the oscillators in Fig. 12–27. The relative motion of the three atoms can be described in terms of normal oscillations. In Fig. 12–30(a), the oxygen atoms oscillate in phase, with the carbon atom moving in the opposite direction to conserve the position of the center of mass. This mode corresponds to oscillation ω_1 of Fig. 12–28. In Fig. 12–30(b), the two oxygen atoms move in opposite directions, relative to the carbon atom, which remains fixed at the center of mass. This mode corresponds to oscillation ω_2 of Fig. 12–28. The situation of Fig. 12–30(c) has not been considered previously. It corresponds to a motion perpendicular to the line joining the atoms with an angular frequency ω_3, resulting in a bending of the molecule. For the CO_2 molecule, the values of the three angular frequencies are

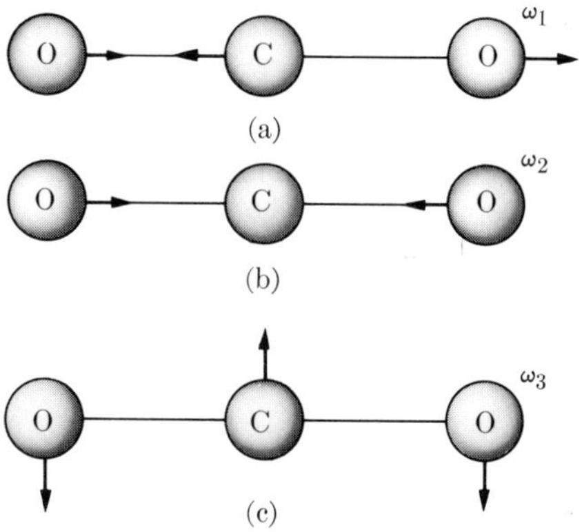

Fig. 12–30. Normal vibrations of the CO_2 molecule.

$$\omega_1 = 4.165 \times 10^{13}\ \mathrm{s}^{-1}, \qquad \omega_2 = 7.047 \times 10^{13}\ \mathrm{s}^{-1}, \qquad \omega_3 = 2.001 \times 10^{13}\ \mathrm{s}^{-1}.$$

If the molecule is not linear or if it has more than three atoms, the analysis of the normal oscillations becomes more complicated, but essentially remains the

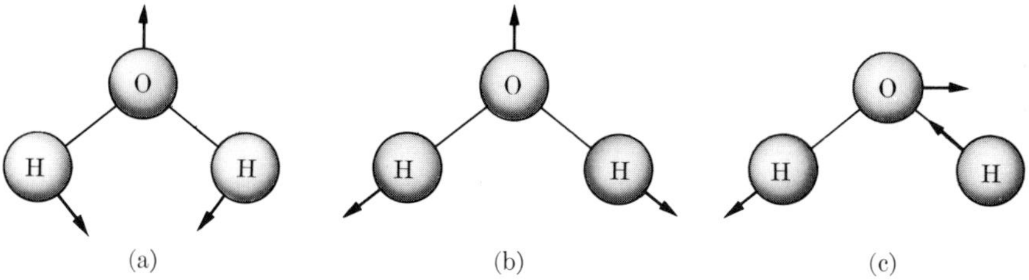

Fig. 12–31. Normal vibrations of the H_2O molecule.

same. For example, for the water molecule H_2O, in which the O atom is at the vertex of an angle of 105° and the H atoms are on each side, the normal vibrations are as illustrated in Fig. 12–31. Their frequencies are $10.96 \times 10^{13}\ \mathrm{s}^{-1}$, $11.27 \times 10^{13}\ \mathrm{s}^{-1}$ and $4.78 \times 10^{13}\ \mathrm{s}^{-1}$.

12.11 Anharmonic Oscillations

Simple harmonic motion is generated by a force $F = -kx$ corresponding to a potential energy $E_p = \frac{1}{2}kx^2$, when x is measured from the equilibrium position O. When the equilibrium position is at x_0 instead of the origin, as in Fig. 12–32, then we must write

$$E_p = \tfrac{1}{2}k(x - x_0)^2.$$

The graph of E_p is a parabola with its vertex at x_0. If the total energy is E, intersecting E_p at A and at B, the particle oscillates between positions x_1 and x_2, which are symmetrically located with respect to x_0. Noting that

$$dE_p/dx = k(x - x_0) \qquad \text{and} \qquad d^2E_p/dx^2 = k,$$

we may write for the angular frequency,

$$\omega = \sqrt{k/m} = \sqrt{(d^2E_p/dx^2)/m}. \tag{12.46}$$

Consider now a case in which the potential energy is not a parabola but has a well-defined minimum, as indicated in Fig. 12–33. This is the situation more often found in physical systems and results in *anharmonic oscillatory motion*. If the total energy is E, the particle will oscillate between positions x_1 and x_2, which in general are asymmetric with respect to the equilibrium position x_0. The frequency of the oscillations now depends on the energy. To obtain an estimate of the frequency, we proceed as follows.

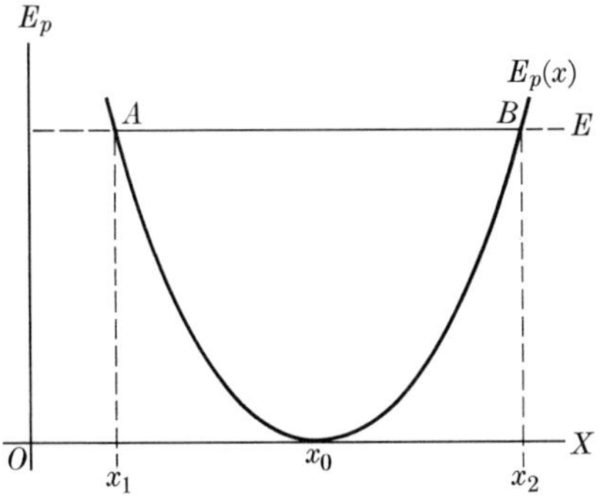

Fig. 12–32. Harmonic oscillator with equilibrium position at x_0.

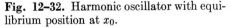

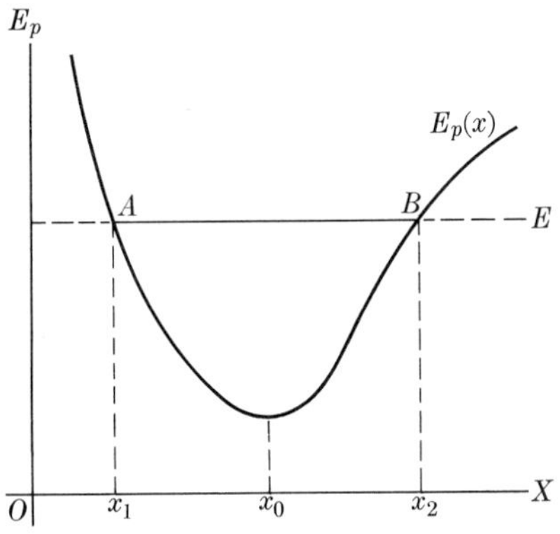

Fig. 12–33. Anharmonic oscillator with equilibrium position at x_0.

Given a function $f(x)$, Taylor's theorem* (see Eq. M.31) allows us to express it as a power series,

$$f(x) = f(x_0) + (df/dx)_0(x - x_0) + \tfrac{1}{2}(d^2f/dx^2)_0(x - x_0)^2 + \tfrac{1}{6}(d^3f/dx^3)_0(x - x_0)^3 + \cdots,$$

where the subscript zero means that the derivatives are evaluated at $x = x_0$. Applying this theorem to $E_p(x)$, and noting that at x_0 we have $(dE_p/dx)_0 = 0$ (because there is a minimum of E_p at x_0), we get

$$\begin{aligned} E_p(x) &= E_p(x_0) + \tfrac{1}{2}(d^2E_p/dx^2)_0(x - x_0)^2 + \tfrac{1}{6}(d^3E_p/dx^3)_0(x - x_0)^3 + \cdots \\ &= E_p(x_0) + \tfrac{1}{2}k(x - x_0)^2 + \tfrac{1}{6}k'(x - x_0)^3 + \cdots, \end{aligned} \qquad (12.47)$$

where we have set $k = (d^2E_p/dx^2)_0$, $k' = (d^3E_p/dx^3)_0$, etc.

The first term is constant and corresponds to a change in the zero of the potential energy. The second is just the quadratic term corresponding to a harmonic oscillator with $k = (d^2E_p/dx^2)_0$. The remaining terms are responsible for the anharmonicity, and are thus called *anharmonic terms.*

If the energy is not very high, the amplitude of the oscillations is small and, as a reasonable approximation, we may keep the first two terms only; that is, $E_p(x) = E_p(x_0) + \tfrac{1}{2}k(x - x_0)^2$. The motion is thus practically simple harmonic, with a frequency of oscillation having the approximate value

$$\omega = \sqrt{k/m} = \sqrt{(d^2E_p/dx^2)_0/m}. \qquad (12.48)$$

This approximation is acceptable in many instances. But for large energies, this value of ω is, in general, in great error as to the actual frequency, and the simple harmonic approximation is not adequate. Then the effect of the anharmonic terms must be taken into account.

The force acting on the particle corresponding to the potential energy given by Eq. (12.47) is

$$F = -\frac{dE_p}{dx} = -k(x - x_0) - \tfrac{1}{2}k'(x - x_0)^2 - \cdots \qquad (12.49)$$

The first is the simple harmonic force and the others are the anharmonic terms.

EXAMPLE 12.10. Obtain the frequency of oscillation corresponding to the intermolecular potential given in Example 8.11.

Solution: The intermolecular potential is

$$E_p = -E_{p,0}\left[2\left(\frac{r_0}{r}\right)^6 - \left(\frac{r_0}{r}\right)^{12}\right],$$

---

* See G. B. Thomas, *Calculus and Analytic Geometry*, third edition. Reading, Mass.: Addison-Wesley, 1962, page 787.

where r_0 is the equilibrium separation. Thus

$$\frac{d^2E_p}{dr^2} = -E_{p,0}\left(84\frac{r_0^6}{r^8} - 156\frac{r_0^{12}}{r^{14}}\right).$$

Setting $r = r_0$, we obtain

$$\left(\frac{d^2E_p}{dr^2}\right)_{r_0} = 72\frac{E_{p,0}}{r_0^2}.$$

Therefore, using Eq. (12.48), we find that the frequency of the oscillations is approximately $\omega = \sqrt{72E_{p,0}/mr_0^2}$.

In this formula m is the reduced mass, since we are discussing the relative motion of the two molecules. If we calculate r_0 in some independent way and observe ω experimentally, we can determine the strength $E_{p,0}$ of the molecular interaction. In solving this problem we have assumed that the oscillator is linear, so that the centrifugal potential (Section 8.10) does not enter into the picture.

12.12 Damped Oscillations

The discussion of simple harmonic motion in the previous sections indicates that the oscillations have constant amplitude. However, we know from experience that a vibrating body such as a spring or a pendulum oscillates with an amplitude that gradually decreases and eventually stops. That is, the oscillatory motion is damped.

To explain the damping dynamically, we may assume that, in addition to the elastic force $F = -kx$, another force, opposed to the velocity, acts. In Section 7.10 we considered a force of this kind, due to the viscosity of the medium in which the motion takes place. Following the logic of Section 7.10, we shall write this force as $F' = -\lambda v$, where λ is a constant and v is the velocity. The negative sign is due to the fact that F' is opposed to v. Note that other types of damping forces—proportional to higher powers of the velocity, or having other, different, physical relationships—may also be present in actual physical situations. The resultant force on the body is $F + F'$, and its equation of motion is

$$ma = -kx - \lambda v, \tag{12.50}$$

or, remembering that $v = dx/dt$ and $a = d^2x/dt^2$, we have

$$m\frac{d^2x}{dt^2} + \lambda\frac{dx}{dt} + kx = 0. \tag{12.51}$$

This equation is customarily written as

$$\frac{d^2x}{dt^2} + 2\gamma\frac{dx}{dt} + \omega_0^2x = 0, \tag{12.52}$$

where $2\gamma = \lambda/m$ and $\omega_0^2 = k/m$ is the natural angular frequency without damping. This is a differential equation that differs from Eq. (12.12) for simple harmonic motion in that it contains the additional term $2\gamma\, dx/dt$. Its solution can be obtained by the application of techniques to be learned in a calculus course.* Instead of attempting to obtain its solution in a formal way, let us just write it for the case of small damping, when $\gamma < \omega_0$. The solution then is

$$x = Ae^{-\gamma t} \sin(\omega t + \alpha), \tag{12.53}$$

where A and α are arbitrary constants determined by the initial conditions (as explained in Example 12.3 for the case of simple harmonic motion), and

$$\omega = \sqrt{\omega_0^2 - \gamma^2} = \sqrt{k/m - \lambda^2/4m^2}. \tag{12.54}$$

The student may verify by direct substitution that Eq. (12.53) is a solution of Eq. (12.52). Since it contains two arbitrary constants, it is the general solution of the differential equation. Equation (12.54) indicates that the effect of damping is to decrease the frequency of the oscillations.

The amplitude of the oscillations is no longer constant, and is given by $Ae^{-\gamma t}$. Because of the negative exponent, the amplitude decreases as t increases, resulting in a damped motion. Figure 12–34 shows how x changes with t.

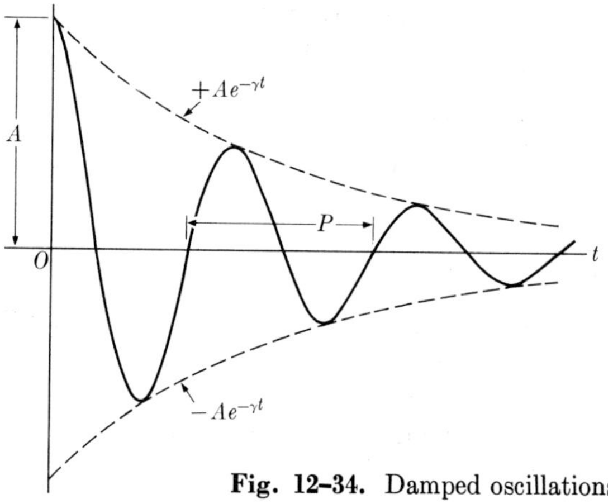

Fig. 12–34. Damped oscillations.

If the damping is very large, γ may become larger than ω_0 and ω, given by Eq. (12.54), becomes imaginary. In this case there are no oscillations and the particle, if displaced and released, gradually approaches the equilibrium position without crossing it, or, at most, crossing it once. The energy lost by the particle in damped oscillations is absorbed by the surrounding medium.

EXAMPLE 12.11. A pendulum consists of an aluminum sphere of radius 0.005 m suspended from a string 1 m long. Determine how the air viscosity affects its amplitude and its period.

---

* See, for example, *Calculus and Analytic Geometry*, third edition, by G. B. Thomas. Reading, Mass.: Addison-Wesley, 1962, Section 18.9.

Solution: From Section 7.10 we know that the viscous force acting on a sphere of radius R moving through a fluid with velocity v is $F = -6\pi\eta Rv$. Thus we can find the equation for the tangential motion of the pendulum by adding—to the force $F_T = -mg \sin\theta \approx -mg\theta$ obtained in Section 12.5 for small amplitude—the above viscous force, with $v = ds/dt = l\, d\theta/dt$, where l is the length of the pendulum. Therefore

$$ml\frac{d^2\theta}{dt^2} = -mg\theta - 6\pi\eta Rl\frac{d\theta}{dt} \quad \text{or} \quad \frac{d^2\theta}{dt^2} + \frac{6\pi\eta R}{m}\frac{d\theta}{dt} + \frac{g}{l}\theta = 0,$$

which is a differential equation mathematically identical to Eq. (12.52). Setting $m = (4\pi R^3/3)\rho$, where ρ is the density of the aluminum sphere, equal to 2.65×10^3 kg m^{-3}, we conclude that

$$\gamma = \frac{6\pi\eta R}{2(4\pi R^3/3)\rho} = \frac{9\eta}{4R^2\rho}.$$

The viscosity of air, assuming a temperature of 20°C, is 1.78×10^{-5} m^{-1} kg s^{-1}. Thus $\gamma = 6.43 \times 10^{-4}$ s^{-1}. The amplitude thus decreases according to the law $Ae^{-0.000643t}$. The time required for the amplitude to be reduced by 10% is obtained by equating the exponential to 0.9 or $-6.43 \times 10^{-4}t = \ln 0.9$. Thus $t = 1.64 \times 10^3$ s, or about 27 minutes.

To see how the frequency (or the period) of the oscillations is affected by the viscosity of the air, we use Eq. (12.54), noting that $\omega_0^2 = g/l$. Thus $\omega = \sqrt{g/l - \gamma^2}$. But $g/l = 9.8$ s^{-2}, while γ^2 in our case is of the order of 4×10^{-7} s^{-2} and therefore negligible compared with g/l. Accordingly, we conclude that the viscosity of the air practically does not affect the frequency or the period of the pendulum considered in this example, although it does affect its amplitude.

12.13 Forced Oscillations

Another problem of great practical importance is that of the forced vibrations of an oscillator; that is, the vibrations which result when we apply an external oscillatory force to a particle subject to an elastic force. This is the situation, for example, when we place a tuning fork on a resonating box, and force the walls of the box (and the air inside) to oscillate, or when electromagnetic waves, absorbed by an antenna, act on the electric circuit of our radio or television set, producing forced electric oscillations.

Let $F = F_0 \cos\omega_f t$ be the oscillating applied force, its angular frequency being given by ω_f. Assuming that the particle is subject also to an elastic force $-kx$ and a damping force $-\lambda v$, its equation of motion is $ma = -kx - \lambda v + F_0 \cos\omega_f t$. Or, making the substitutions $v = dx/dt$, $a = d^2x/dt^2$, we have

$$m\frac{d^2x}{dt^2} + \lambda\frac{dx}{dt} + kx = F_0\cos\omega_f t, \tag{12.55}$$

which, if we again make $2\gamma = \lambda/m$ and $\omega_0^2 = k/m$, may be written in the form

$$\frac{d^2x}{dt^2} + 2\gamma\frac{dx}{dt} + \omega_0^2 x = \frac{F_0}{m}\cos\omega_f t. \tag{12.56}$$

This is a differential equation similar to Eq. (12.52), differing only to the extent that the right-hand side is not zero. We could solve it by standard techniques; instead, let us use our physical intuition for guidance. It seems logical that in this case the particle will oscillate with neither its free undamped angular frequency ω_0 nor the damped angular frequency $\sqrt{\omega_0^2 - \gamma^2}$. Instead, the particle will be forced to oscillate with the angular frequency ω_f of the applied force. Thus we shall try, as a possible solution of Eq. (12.56), an expression of the form

$$x = A \sin(\omega_f t - \alpha), \tag{12.57}$$

where, for convenience, a negative sign has been given to the initial phase α. Direct substitution into the equation shows that it can be satisfied if the amplitude A is given by*

$$A = \frac{F_0/m}{\sqrt{(\omega_f^2 - \omega_0^2)^2 + 4\gamma^2\omega_f^2}} \tag{12.58}$$

and the initial phase of the displacement by

$$\tan \alpha = \frac{\omega_f^2 - \omega_0^2}{2\gamma\omega_f}. \tag{12.59}$$

Note that both the amplitude A and the initial phase α are no longer arbitrary quantities, but fixed quantities that depend on the frequency ω_f of the applied force. Mathematically, this means that we have obtained a "particular" solution of the differential equation.† Equation (12.57) indicates that the forced oscillations are not damped, but are of constant amplitude and have a frequency equal to that of the applied force. That means that the applied force overcomes the damping forces, and thus provides the energy necessary to maintain the oscillation.

In Fig. 12–35 the amplitude A is plotted against the frequency ω_f for a given value of λ. The amplitude has a pronounced maximum when the denominator in Eq. (12.58) has its minimum value. This occurs for the frequency ω_A, given by

$$\omega_A = \sqrt{\omega_0^2 - 2\gamma^2} = \sqrt{k/m - \lambda^2/2m^2}. \tag{12.60}$$

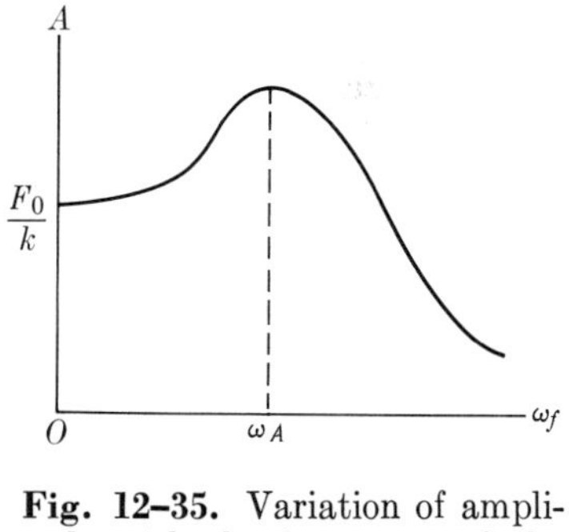

Fig. 12–35. Variation of amplitude with the frequency of the applied force.

* To verify this, first expand $\sin(\omega_f t - \alpha)$ and substitute the result in Eq. (12.56). Then equate the coefficients of $\sin \omega_f t$ and $\cos \omega_f t$, respectively, on both sides of the equation. From the two equations so obtained, Eqs. (12.58) and (12.59) follow immediately.

† It is proved in the theory of differential equations that the general solution of Eq. (12.56) is obtained by adding Eq. (12.53), the solution of Eq. (12.52), to Eq. (12.57). However, since Eq. (12.53) corresponds to a damped oscillation, it quickly becomes negligible and thus may be ignored. For that reason it is usually called the *transient* term.

When the frequency ω_f of the applied force is equal to ω_A, it is said that there is *amplitude resonance.* The smaller the damping, the more pronounced the resonance, and when λ is zero, the resonance amplitude is infinite and occurs at $\omega_A = \omega_0 = \sqrt{k/m}$. Figure 12–36 shows the variation of the amplitude A in terms of the frequency ω_f for different values of the damping λ.

The velocity of the forced oscillator is

$$v = \frac{dx}{dt} = \omega_f A \cos(\omega_f t - \alpha). \tag{12.61}$$

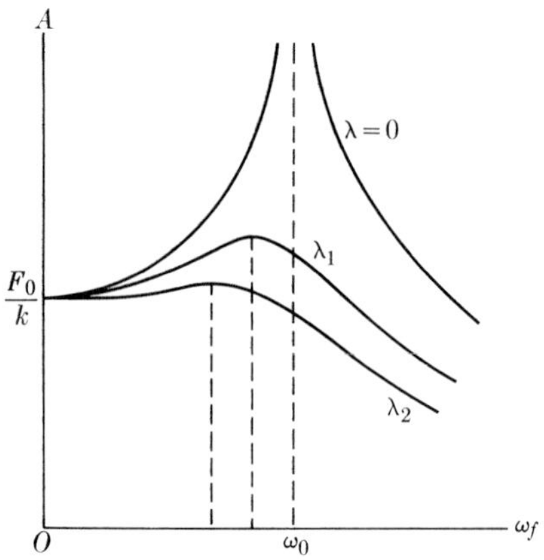

Fig. 12–36. Variation of the amplitude of the forced oscillations with the damping (in the figure, λ_2 is larger than λ_1).

Comparing this with the expression $F = F_0 \cos \omega_f t$ for the applied force, we see that α represents the phase shift of the velocity relative to the force. The velocity amplitude v_0 is

$$v_0 = \omega_f A = \frac{\omega_f F_0/m}{\sqrt{(\omega_f^2 - \omega_0^2)^2 + 4\gamma^2\omega_f^2}},$$

which can also be written in the form

$$v_0 = \frac{F_0}{\sqrt{(m\omega_f - k/\omega_f)^2 + \lambda^2}}. \tag{12.62}$$

The quantity v_0 varies with ω_f, as indicated in Fig. 12–37, and attains its maximum value when the quantity within the parentheses in the denominator is zero, $m\omega_f - k/\omega_f = 0$, or

$$\omega_f = \sqrt{k/m} = \omega_0. \tag{12.63}$$

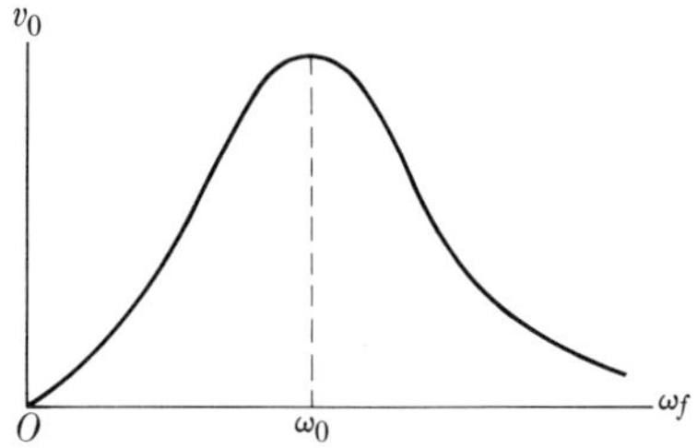

Fig. 12–37. Variation of velocity amplitude of forced oscillation with the frequency of the applied force.

At this frequency of the applied force, the velocity and also the kinetic energy of the oscillator are maximum, and it is said that there is *energy resonance.* Note that Eq. (12.63), when substituted into Eq. (12.59), gives $\alpha = 0$. Therefore energy resonance occurs when the frequency of the applied force is equal to the natural frequency of the oscillator without damping, and in this case the velocity is in phase with the applied force. These are the most favorable conditions for transfer of energy to the oscillator, since the rate of work done on the oscillator by the applied force is Fv, and this quantity is always positive when F and v are in phase. Therefore

> *at energy resonance the energy transfer from the applied force to the forced oscillator is at a maximum.*

When the damping is very small there is no great difference between the frequencies corresponding to amplitude resonance and to energy resonance.

Resonance can be illustrated with a very simple experiment. If, from the same string, we suspend several pendulums, as indicated in Fig. 12–38, and we set pendulum P in motion, the others will also start oscillating because of their coupling. However, of the five pendulums forced into oscillation, the one oscillating with greatest amplitude is number 3, which has the same length as P and therefore the same natural frequency, since the damping is negligible and there is no distinction between amplitude and energy resonance in this case.

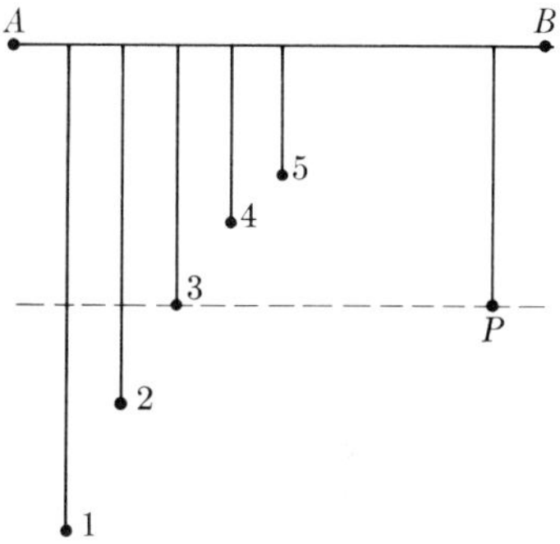

Fig. 12–38. Amplitude resonance in pendulum motion.

Resonance occurs in almost every branch of physics. It is found whenever a system is subject to an external action which varies periodically with time. For example, if a gas is placed in a region in which an oscillatory electric field exists (such as in an electromagnetic wave), forced oscillations will be induced in the atoms composing the molecules of the gas. Since, as we explained at the end of Section 12.10, the molecules have well-defined natural vibration frequencies, the energy absorption will be at a maximum when the frequency of the applied electric field coincides with one of the natural frequencies of the molecules. By means of this principle, we can obtain the *vibrational spectrum* of molecules. Similarly, we can consider the electrons in an atom as being oscillators which have certain natural frequencies. The energy which an atom absorbs from an oscillating electric field is maximum when the frequency of the field coincides with one of the natural frequencies of the atom. Some crystals, such as sodium chloride, are composed of positively and negatively charged particles (called *ions*). If the crystal is subject to an external oscillating electric field, the positive ions oscillate relative to the negative ions. The energy absorption by the crystal is at a maximum when the frequency of the electric field coincides with the natural frequency of relative oscillation of the ions, which in the case of sodium chloride crystals is approximately 5×10^{12} Hz.

Perhaps the most familiar example of resonance is what happens when we tune a radio to a broadcasting station. All broadcasting stations are producing forced oscillations on the circuit of the receiver at all times. But, to each setting of the tuner, there corresponds a natural frequency of oscillation of the electric circuit of the receiver. When this frequency coincides with that of a broadcasting station, the energy absorption is at a maximum, and hence this is the only station that we hear. If two stations have broadcast frequencies very close together, we sometimes hear both at the same time, which results in an interference effect.

We can extend the concept of resonance to many processes in which there are favorable conditions for transfer of energy from one system to another, even if we cannot describe the process in terms of forced oscillations. In this sense it is possible to talk about resonances in nuclear reactions and in processes which take place between fundamental particles. In this extended sense the concept of energy resonance plays an important role in the description of many phenomena.

12.14 Impedance of an Oscillator

A damped oscillator is characterized by three quantities: its mass m, the elastic constant k, and the damping constant λ. In the formulas in Section 12.13, these quantities always appear in special combinations with the frequency ω_f of the applied force.

The quantity appearing in the denominator of Eq. (12.62) is called the *impedance* of the oscillator, and is designated by Z. Then

$$Z = \sqrt{(m\omega_f - k/\omega_f)^2 + \lambda^2}. \tag{12.64}$$

Similarly, the *reactance* X and the *resistance* R are defined by

$$X = m\omega_f - k/\omega_f, \qquad R = \lambda. \tag{12.65}$$

Therefore

$$Z = \sqrt{X^2 + R^2}. \tag{12.66}$$

Substitution into Eq. (12.59) also yields

$$\tan \alpha = X/R. \tag{12.67}$$

The relationship between Z, X, and R is indicated in Fig. 12–39, which makes it easy to remember the above formulas.

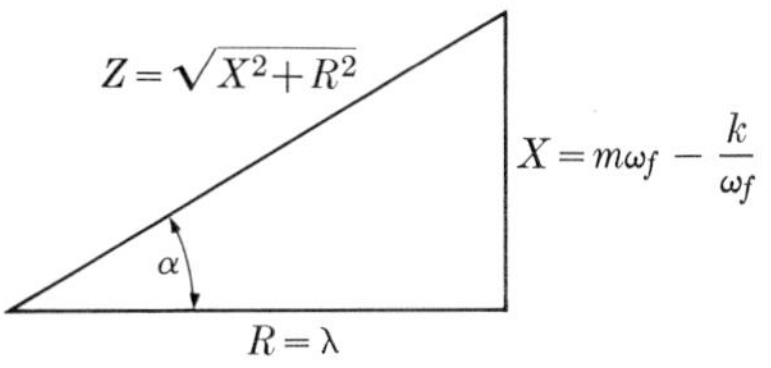

Fig. 12–39. Relation between impedance, resistance, and reactance in forced oscillations.

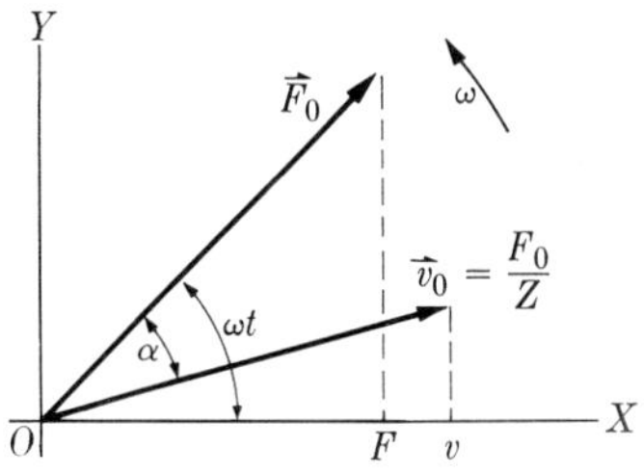

Fig. 12–40. Relation between the force and velocity rotating vectors in forced oscillators.

From Eq. (12.62) we see that $v_0 = F_0/Z$, and the velocity at any instant is

$$v = \frac{F_0}{Z} \cos (\omega_f t - \alpha). \tag{12.68}$$

This means that the force and the velocity may be represented by rotating vectors, as indicated in Fig. 12–40. Note that if α is positive, the rotating vector $\overrightarrow{v_0}$ *lags* the rotating vector $\overrightarrow{F_0}$, and if α is negative, rotating vector $\overrightarrow{v_0}$ *leads* $\overrightarrow{F_0}$. When there is energy resonance, $\alpha = 0$, and $\overrightarrow{v_0}$ and $\overrightarrow{F_0}$ have the same direction. The power transferred to the oscillator is

$$P = Fv = \frac{F_0^2}{Z} \cos \omega_f t \cos (\omega_f t - \alpha).$$

Expanding the second cosine and multiplying by the first, we have

$$P = \frac{F_0^2}{Z} (\cos^2 \omega_f t \cos \alpha - \cos \omega_f t \sin \omega_f t \sin \alpha). \tag{12.69}$$

We are more interested in the average power, P_{ave}, since this is what counts when we are computing the energy absorbed by the oscillator in a certain time. Now, according to Eqs. (M.13) and (M.14),

$$\cos^2 \omega_f t = \tfrac{1}{2}(1 + \cos 2\omega_f t) \qquad \text{and} \qquad \cos \omega_f t \sin \omega_f t = \tfrac{1}{2} \sin 2\omega_f t.$$

Also $(\cos 2\omega_f t)_{\text{ave}} = (\sin 2\omega_f t)_{\text{ave}} = 0$, since the sine and cosine curves are positive half the time and negative the other half, by the same amount. Therefore $(\cos^2 \omega_f t)_{\text{ave}} = \frac{1}{2}$ and $(\cos \omega_f t \sin \omega_f t)_{\text{ave}} = 0$, resulting finally in

$$P_{\text{ave}} = \frac{F_0^2}{2Z} \cos \alpha = \tfrac{1}{2} F_0 v_0 \cos \alpha = \frac{F_0^2 R}{2Z^2} = \tfrac{1}{2} R v_0^2. \tag{12.70}$$

This verifies that the maximum transfer of energy occurs when v_0 is a maximum, since R is fixed. At energy resonance, $\alpha = 0$ and $Z = R$, resulting in

$$(P_{\text{ave}})_{\text{res}} = \frac{F_0^2}{2R}. \tag{12.71}$$

The ratio between P_{ave} and $(P_{\text{ave}})_{\text{res}}$ is illustrated in Fig. 12–41.

The theory concerning damped and forced oscillators which we have formulated in the last three sections, although referred specifically to an oscillating particle, applies to any physical situation described by an equation such as Eq. (12.52) or Eq. (12.56). In particular, as we shall find in Chapter 17, this is precisely the case for electric circuits.

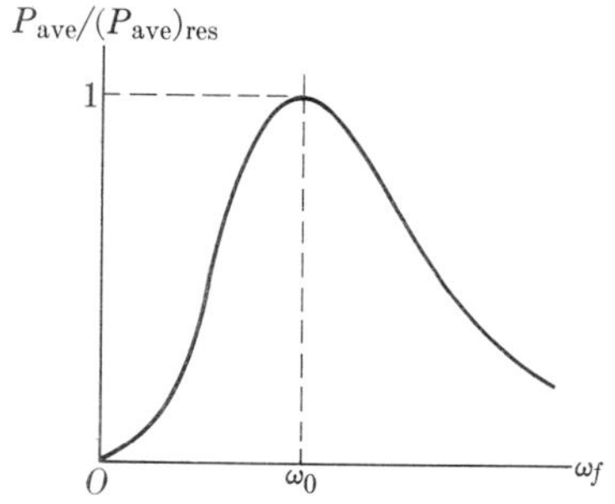

Fig. 12–41. Relation between P_{ave} and $(P_{\text{ave}})_{\text{res}}$.

12.15 Fourier Analysis of Periodic Motion

At the beginning of this chapter we explained that simple harmonic motion is just one specific case of periodic or oscillatory motion. But a general periodic motion of period P is described by

$$x = f(t), \tag{12.72}$$

where the function $f(t)$ is periodic and has the property that $f(t) = f(t + P)$, as shown in Fig. 12–42. The graph of $f(t)$ therefore repeats itself at intervals equal to P. This general oscillatory motion can be expressed as a combination of simple harmonic motions.

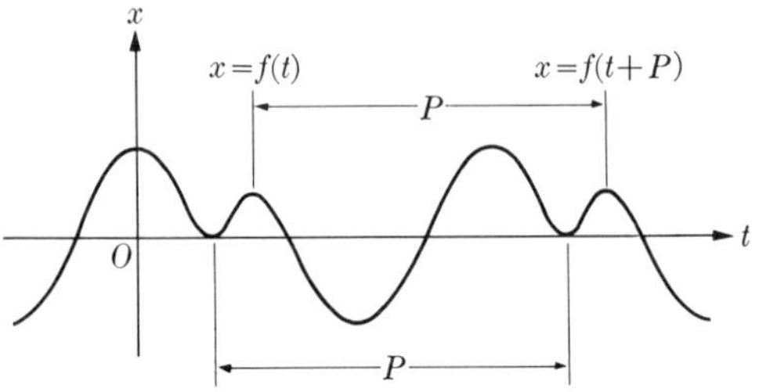

Fig. 12–42. A periodic function of time.

Let us first consider, as an example, the motion whose displacement is described by

$$x = A \sin \omega t + B \sin 2\omega t. \tag{12.73}$$

This represents the superposition of two simple harmonic motions of angular frequencies ω and 2ω or periods P and $\frac{1}{2}P$. Obviously x is also periodic, and its period will be P. This is seen in the graph of Fig. 12–43, in which curve (a) corresponds to $\sin \omega t$ and curve (b) to $\sin 2\omega t$. Although x is periodic, it is not simple harmonic.

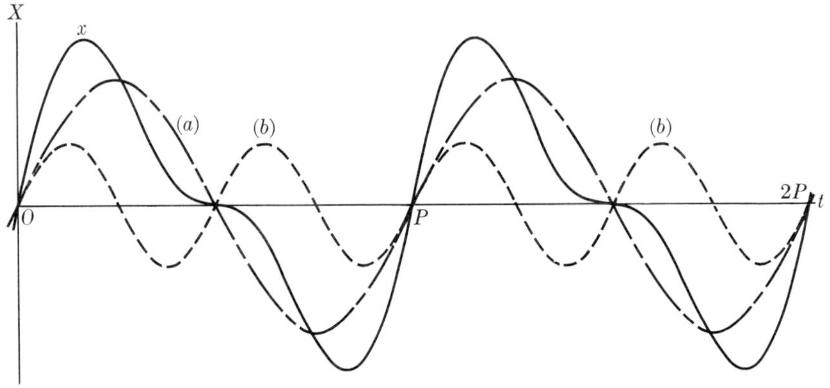

Fig. 12–43. Superposition of two SHM of frequencies ω and 2ω.

If we add to Eq. (12.73) terms of the form $\sin 3\omega t$, $\sin 4\omega t$, ..., $\sin n\omega t$, ... of angular frequencies 3ω, 4ω, ..., $n\omega$, ... and periods $P/3$, $P/4$, ..., P/n, ..., or if we add cosine functions of the same frequencies, we still get a displacement x that is periodic with period P. Its exact form depends on the number of sine and cosine functions we add, and on their relative amplitudes.

Thus we see that by adding simple harmonic motions whose frequencies are multiples of a fundamental frequency and whose amplitudes are properly selected, we may obtain almost any arbitrary periodic function. The reverse is also true, and constitutes *Fourier's theorem*, proved in mathematical texts. Fourier's theorem asserts that a periodic function $f(t)$ of period $P = 2\pi/\omega$ can be expressed as the sum

$$x = f(t) = a_0 + a_1 \cos \omega t + a_2 \cos 2\omega t + \cdots + a_n \cos n\omega t$$
$$+ \cdots + b_1 \sin \omega t + b_2 \sin 2\omega t + \cdots + b_n \sin n\omega t + \cdots \qquad (12.74)$$

This is known as a *Fourier series*. The frequency ω is called the *fundamental* and the frequencies 2ω, 3ω, ..., $n\omega$, ... are the *harmonics* or overtones.

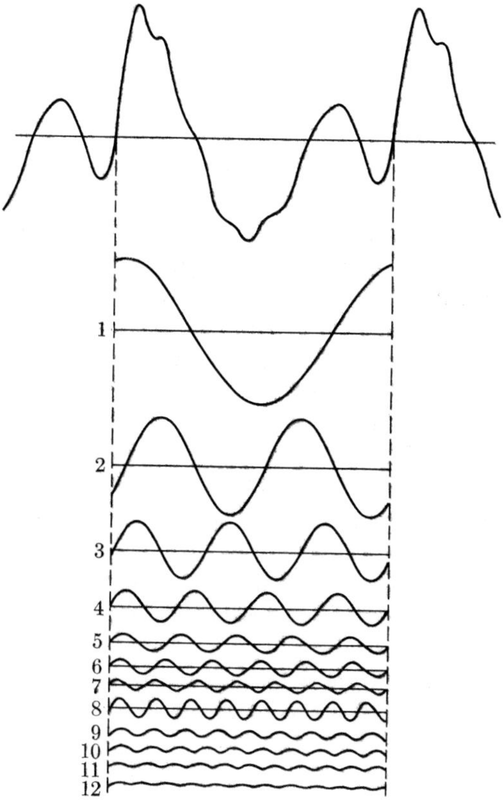

Fig. 12–44. Fourier analysis of a periodic function.

Note on Fourier coefficients: The coefficients a_n and b_n are obtained through the expressions

$$a_0 = \frac{1}{P}\int_0^P f(t)\,dt, \qquad a_n = \frac{2}{P}\int_0^P f(t)\cos n\omega t\,dt, \qquad b_n = \frac{2}{P}\int_0^P f(t)\sin n\omega t\,dt, \tag{12.75}$$

which are derived in mathematical texts but which the student can easily obtain by himself. For example, to obtain a_n, we multiply both sides of Eq. (12.74) by $\cos n\omega t$ and integrate. All terms except a_n give zero when integrated. For b_n, we use $\sin n\omega t$. (Consult G. B. Thomas, *Calculus and Analytic Geometry*, third edition. Reading, Mass.: Addison-Wesley, 1962, page 821.)

Fourier's theorem gives us yet another reason why simple harmonic motion is so important. By an application of Fourier's theorem, any kind of periodic motion can be considered as the superposition of simple harmonic motions. In Fig. 12–44 the periodic motion corresponding to the curve shown at the top is analyzed into its Fourier components. The first twelve harmonics are shown. Fourier's theorem also helps to explain the different *quality* of sound produced by different musical instruments. The same note or musical tone produced by a piano, a guitar, and an oboe sounds different to our ears, in spite of the fact that the tones have the same fundamental frequency. The difference is due to the presence of the harmonics or overtones with different relative amplitudes. In other words, the Fourier analysis of the sound is different for each instrument.

The Fourier method is useful not only for analyzing periodic curves, but also for analyzing nonperiodic ones. In a nonperiodic case, the curve extends from $-\infty$ to $+\infty$, and we may assume that this interval covers one period. The essential difference between this case and the one explained before is that instead of analyzing the curve in terms of a *discrete* frequency spectrum ω, 2ω, 3ω, . . . , $n\omega$, . . . , we must analyze it in terms of a *continuous* spectrum of frequencies. The amplitude corresponding to each frequency is given by a function of ω called the *Fourier transform* of the curve analyzed. We shall illustrate one example, without entering into the mathematical details.

Suppose that a curve is described by the equation $x = A \sin \omega_0 t$ in the time interval from t_1 to t_2, being zero everywhere else, as indicated in Fig. 12–45. Physically this corresponds to the situation in which a body is suddenly made to oscillate at $t = t_1$ and is as suddenly stopped at $t = t_2$. This is sometimes called a *pulse*.

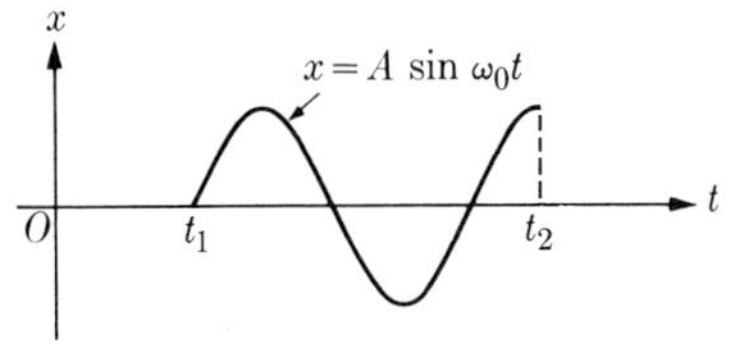

Fig. 12–45. Limited oscillatory pulse.

If the curve had extended from $-\infty$ to $+\infty$, we would not have had to make any Fourier analysis because then the curve would have been a harmonic function of frequency ω_0. But to annihilate the curve for $t < t_1$ or $t > t_2$, we have to add other frequencies, so that the resultant Fourier series in those regions is zero. Thus a finite pulse is the composite of many frequencies, even if the vibrating source has a well-defined frequency. It may be proved that the amplitude profile as a

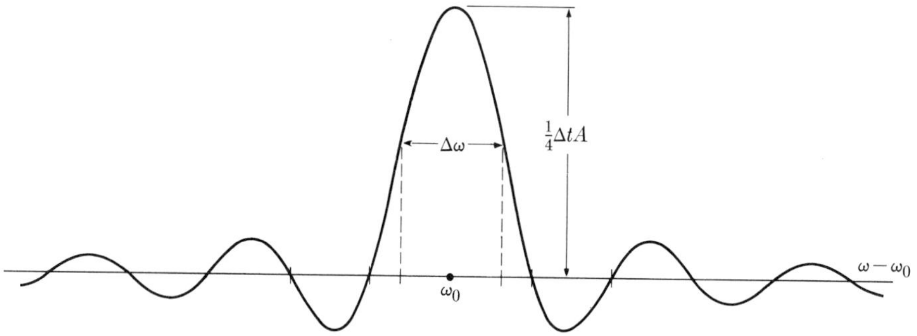

Fig. 12–46. Fourier analysis (or transform) of pulse of Fig. 12–45.

function of ω (or the Fourier transform) corresponding to the pulse is given by the function

$$F(\omega) = \tfrac{1}{4}\,\Delta t A \left[\frac{\sin \frac{1}{2}(\omega - \omega_0)\,\Delta t}{\frac{1}{2}(\omega - \omega_0)\,\Delta t}\right],$$

where $\Delta t = t_2 - t_1$. This amplitude profile is illustrated in Fig. 12–46. For $\omega = \omega_0$, we have $F(\omega_0) = \frac{1}{4}\,\Delta t A$. Because the numerator of the fraction inside the parentheses is never larger than one, when the difference $\omega - \omega_0$ increases in absolute value, the value of $F(\omega)$ decreases in an oscillatory form. The range of values of ω for which $F(\omega)$ is larger than 50% of its value for $\omega = \omega_0$ corresponds roughly to the condition

$$|\tfrac{1}{2}(\omega - \omega_0)\,\Delta t| < \frac{\pi}{2} \qquad \text{or} \qquad -\frac{\pi}{\Delta t} < \omega - \omega_0 < \frac{\pi}{\Delta t}.$$

Thus if we call $\Delta\omega = 2\pi/\Delta t$, we conclude that the only frequencies whose amplitudes are appreciable are those in the range $\Delta\omega$ around ω_0, given by

$$\Delta\omega\,\Delta t \sim 2\pi. \tag{12.76}$$

It indicates that the shorter the time interval, the larger the range of frequencies required to accurately represent the pulse.

References

1. "Restless Harmonic Oscillator," M. Hane; *Am. J. Phys.* **30,** 84 (1962)
2. "An Unusual Method of Solving the Harmonic Oscillator Problem," R. Weinstock; *Am. J. Phys.* **29,** 830 (1961)
3. "Precision Measurement of Period vs. Amplitude for a Pendulum," M. Smith; *Am. J. Phys.* **32,** 632 (1964)
4. "Exact Normal Modes of Oscillation of a Linear Chain of Identical Particles," J. Louch; *Am. J. Phys.* **30,** 585 (1962)
5. *Waves and Oscillations,* R. Waldron. Princeton, N.J.: Van Nostrand, Momentum Books, 1964

6. *Mechanics*, second edition, Keith R. Symon. Reading, Mass.: Addison-Wesley, 1960, Sections 2.7 through 2.11, 3.10, and 4.10
7. *Physical Mechanics*, third edition, by R. B. Lindsay. Princeton, N.J.: Van Nostrand, 1963, Chapter 9
8. *Introduction to Engineering Mechanics*, J. Huddleston. Reading, Mass.: Addison-Wesley, 1961, Chapter 14
9. *Vector Mechanics*, D. Christie. New York: McGraw-Hill, 1964, Chapters 8, 19, and 20
10. *The Feynman Lectures on Physics*, Volume I, R. Feynman, R. Leighton, and M. Sands. Reading, Mass.: Addison-Wesley, 1963, Chapters 21 through 25, 49, and 50
11. *Source Book in Physics*, W. F. Magie. Cambridge, Mass.: Harvard University Press, 1963, page 1, Galileo; page 93, Hooke; page 95, Young

Problems

12.1 A wheel of 30 cm radius is provided with a handle at its edge. The wheel is rotating at 0.5 rev s^{-1} with its axis in a horizontal position. Assuming that the sun's rays fall vertically on the earth, the shadow of the handle will describe simple harmonic motion. Find (a) the period of the motion of the shadow, (b) its frequency, and (c) its amplitude. (d) Write the equation expressing its displacement as a function of time. Assume zero initial phase.

12.2 A particle is moving with a simple harmonic motion of 0.10 m amplitude and a period of 2 s. Make a table indicating the values of the elongation, the velocity, and the acceleration at the following times: $t = 0, P/8, 3P/8, P/2, 5P/8, 3P/4, 7P/8$, and P. Plot the curves for elongation, velocity, and acceleration, each as a function of time.

12.3 A simple harmonic oscillator is described by the equation

$$x = 4 \sin (0.1t + 0.5),$$

where all quantities are expressed in MKS units. Find (a) the amplitude, period, frequency, and initial phase of the motion, (b) the velocity and acceleration, (c) the initial conditions, (d) the position, velocity, and acceleration for $t = 5$ s. Make a graph of position, velocity, and acceleration as functions of time.

12.4 A particle situated at the end of one arm of a tuning fork passes through its equilibrium position with a velocity of 2 m s^{-1}. The amplitude is 10^{-3} m. What is the frequency and period of the tuning fork? Write the equation expressing its displacement as a function of time.

12.5 A particle of mass 1 g is vibrating with a simple harmonic motion of 2 mm amplitude. Its acceleration at the end of the trajectory is 8.0×10^3 m s^{-2}. Calculate the frequency of the motion and the velocity of the particle when it passes through the equilibrium point and when the elongation is 1.2 mm. Write the equation expressing the force acting on the particle as a function of position and as a function of time.

12.6 A particle is vibrating with a frequency of 100 Hz and an amplitude of 3 mm. Calculate its velocity and acceleration at the middle and at the extremes of the trajectory. Write the equation expressing the elongation as a function of time. Assume zero initial phase.

12.7 A particle moving with a simple harmonic motion of 1.5 m amplitude is vibrating 100 times per second. What is its angular frequency? Calculate (a) its velocity, (b) its acceleration, and (c) its phase, when its displacement is 0.75 m.

12.8 The motion of the needle in a sewing machine is practically simple harmonic. If the amplitude is 0.3 cm and the frequency is 600 vib min^{-1}, what will be the elongation, velocity, and acceleration one-thirtieth of a second after the needle passes through the center of the trajectory (a) in the upward or positive sense, (b) in the downward or negative sense?

12.9 A particular simple harmonic motion has an amplitude of 8 cm and a period of 4 s. Calculate the velocity and acceleration 0.5 sec after the particle passes through the extreme of the trajectory.

12.10 In Problem 12.2, calculate the kinetic, potential, and total energy at each time, assuming the particle has a mass of 0.5 kg. Observe that the total energy remains constant. Plot the curves for kinetic and potential energy (a) as functions of time, (b) as functions of position. What is your conclusion?

12.11 A particle whose mass is 0.50 kg is moving with simple harmonic motion. Its period is 0.1 s and the amplitude of its motion is 10 cm. Calculate the acceleration, the force, the potential energy, and the kinetic energy when the particle is 5 cm away from the equilibrium position.

12.12 A particle of mass m is moving along the X-axis under the action of the force $F = -kx$. When $t = 2$ s the particle passes through the origin, and when $t = 4$ s its velocity is 4 m s^{-1}. Find the equation of the elongation and demonstrate that the amplitude of the motion will be $32\sqrt{2}/\pi$ m if the period of oscillation is 16 s.

12.13 A horizontal board is moving horizontally with simple harmonic motion with an amplitude of 1.5 m. If the board is oscillating at a rate of 15 osc min^{-1}, calculate the minimum value of the coefficient of friction in order that a body placed on the board will not slide when the board is moving.

12.14 When a man of mass 60 kg gets into a car, the center of gravity of the car lowers 0.3 cm. What is the elastic constant of the springs of the car? Given that the mass of the car is 500 kg, what is its period of vibration when it is empty and when the man is inside?

12.15 A wooden block whose density relative to water is ρ has dimensions a, b, and c. While it is floating in water with side a vertical, it is pushed down and released. Find the period of the resulting oscillation.

12.16 A particle moves so that its coordinates as functions of time are given by $x = v_0t$, $y = y_0 \sin \omega t$. (a) Plot x and y as functions of t. (b) Plot the path of the particle. (c) What force is required to produce this motion? (d) Find the magnitudes of its velocity and acceleration as functions of time.

12.17 Find, for simple harmonic motion, the values of $(x)_{\text{ave}}$ and $(x^2)_{\text{ave}}$, where the averages refer to time.

12.18 Find the average values of the kinetic and potential energies in simple harmonic motion relative to (a) time, (b) position.

12.19 The period of a pendulum is 3 s. What will be its period if its length is (a) increased, (b) decreased by 60%?

12.20 The pendulum of a clock has a period of 2 s when $g = 9.80$ m s^{-2}. If the length is increased by 1 mm, how slow will the clock be after 24 hours?

12.21 How slow will the clock in the previous problem be after 24 hr if it is moved to a place where $g = 9.75$ m s^{-2} without changing the length of its pendulum? What should the correct length of the pendulum be in order to maintain the correct time at the new position?

12.22 What should be the percentage change of length of a pendulum in order that a clock have the same period when moved from a place where $g = 9.80$ m s^{-2} to another where $g = 9.81$ m s^{-2}?

12.23 Find the value of the amplitude of a simple pendulum so that Eq. (12.15) for the period is correct within 2%.

12.24 A simple pendulum whose length is 2 m is in a place where $g = 9.80$ m s^{-2} The pendulum oscillates with an amplitude of 2°. Express, as a function of time, (a) its angular displacement, (b) its angular velocity, (c) its angular acceleration, (d) its linear velocity, (e) its centripetal acceleration, and (f) the tension on the string if the mass of the bob is 1 kg.

12.25 A pendulum 1.00 m long and having a bob of 0.60 kg mass is raised along an arc so that it is 4 cm above its equilibrium height. Express, as a function of the pendulum's height, the force tangent to its path, its tangential acceleration, its velocity, and its angular displacement when allowed to swing. Find the numerical values of these at the point of maximum amplitude and at the lowest point of the pendulum's path. Find its angular amplitude.

12.26 The pendulum in the previous problem is pulled aside until it makes a 30° angle with the vertical and is then released. Can its motion be considered simple harmonic? Calculate (a) the acceleration, (b) the velocity, and (c) the tension in the string when its angular displacement is 15° and when it is passing through the equilibrium point.

12.27 Estimate the relative order of magnitude of the first two corrective terms in the series for the period of a simple pendulum if the amplitude is (a) 10°, (b) 30°.

12.28 Referring to the pendulum of Example 12.7, find the maximum value of R/l so that the corrective term in the expression for the pendulum does not represent more than 1%.

12.29 A rod 1 m long is suspended from one of its ends in such a way that it constitutes a compound pendulum. Find the period and the length of the equivalent simple pendulum. Find the period of oscillation if the rod is hung from an axis at a distance from one of its ends equal to the length of the equivalent pendulum found previously.

12.30 A solid disk of radius R can be hung from a horizontal axis a distance h from its center. (a) Find the length of the equivalent simple pendulum. (b) Find the position of the axis for which the period is a minimum. (c) Plot the period as a function of h.

12.31 A rod of length L oscillates about a horizontal axis passing through an end. A body having the same mass as the rod can be clamped to the rod a distance h from the axis. (a) Obtain the period of the system as a function of h and L. (b) Is there a value of h for which the period is the same as if there were no mass?

12.32 A cubical solid, of side a, can oscillate around a horizontal axis coincident with an edge. Find its period.

12.33 A torsion pendulum consists of a rectangular wood block 8 cm × 12 cm × 3 cm and with a mass of 0.3 kg suspended by means of a wire passing through its center in such a way that the shortest side is vertical. The period of the torsional oscillations is 2.4 s. What is the torsion constant κ of the wire?

12.34 Referring to Fig. 12–11, prove that if K_C is the radius of gyration relative to a parallel axis through the center of mass of a compound pendulum, the length of the equivalent simple pendulum is $l = (K_C^2/b) + b$. [*Hint:* Use Steiner's theorem to refer the radius of gyration to the center of mass.]

12.35 Using the result of the preceding problem, prove that the length of the simple pendulum equivalent to a compound pendulum (Section 12.6) is the same as the distance between the center of percussion (Problem 10.28) and the point of suspension if the blow is applied at C.

12.36 Prove that if the compound pendulum oscillates around O' (Fig. 12–11) instead of O, its period is still the same and the length of the equivalent pendulum remains unchanged.

12.37 Find the equation of motion resulting from superposing two parallel simple harmonic motions whose equations are $x_1 = 6 \sin 2t$ and $x_2 = 8 \sin (2t + \alpha)$, if $\alpha = 0, \pi/2$, and π. Make a plot of each motion and of the resultant in each case.

12.38 Find the equation of motion resulting from superposing two parallel simple harmonic motions whose equations are

$$x_1 = 2 \sin (\omega t + \pi/3)$$

and

$$x_2 = 3 \sin (\omega t + \pi/2).$$

Make a plot of each motion and of the resultant. Plot their respective rotating vectors.

12.39 Find the equation of the path of the resulting motion of two perpendicular simple harmonic motions whose equations are: $x = 4 \sin \omega t$ and $y = 3 \sin (\omega t + \alpha)$, when $\alpha = 0, \pi/2$, and π. Make in each case a plot of the path of the particle and show the sense in which the particle traverses it.

12.40 By eliminating the time dependence between Eqs. (12.30) and (12.31), prove that the general expression for the equation of the path is

$$x^2/A^2 + y^2/B^2 - 2xy \cos \delta/AB = \sin^2 \delta.$$

Prove that this is the equation of an ellipse, with axes at an angle relative to the XY-axes. [*Hint:* Any equation of the type $ax^2 + bxy + cy^2 = k$ is an ellipse if $b^2 - 4ac < 0$. See Thomas, *Calculus and Analytic Geometry*, Section 9–10.]

12.41 Prove that the ellipse of Problem 12.40 is traversed clockwise or counterclockwise depending on whether $0 < \delta < \pi$ or $\pi < \delta < 2\pi$.

12.42 Find the equation of the path of a particle resulting from the application of two perpendicular simple harmonic motions, given that $\omega_1/\omega_2 = \frac{1}{2}$ and $\alpha = 0$, $\pi/3$, and $\pi/2$. In each case plot the path and show the sense in which it is traversed.

12.43 Prove by direct substitution in the equation of motion (12.37) that the expressions (12.38) are the normal oscillations, provided that $\omega = \sqrt{k_1/m_1}$. Prove the same for the normal oscillations (12.40) if $\omega = \sqrt{(2k_1 + k)/m_1}$.

12.44 The potential energy for the interaction between two atoms in a diatomic molecule can be expressed with good accuracy by the Morse potential $E(r) = D[1 - e^{-a(r-r_0)}]^2$, where D, a, and r_0 are constants characteristic of the molecule. (a) Make a schematic plot of the potential and find the position of equilibrium. (b) Make a series expansion in powers of $r - r_0$ and determine the ratio of the first anharmonic term to the harmonic term. (c) Find, in terms of D and a, the frequency of the relative vibration of two atoms at low energy. [*Hint:* Use Eq. (M.23) for expanding the exponential.]

12.45 Determine the values of A and α in terms of x_0 and v_0 for a damped oscillator. Apply to the case where $v_0 = 0$.

12.46 Verify, by direct substitution, that when $\gamma > \omega_0$, the solution of Eq. (12.52) for a damped oscillator is $x = Ae^{-(\gamma+\beta)t} + Be^{-(\gamma-\beta)t}$, where $\beta = \sqrt{\gamma^2 - \omega_0^2}$. Find the values of A and B if, for $t = 0$, $x = x_0$ and $v = 0$. Plot x as a function of t.

12.47 What happens to the solution of Eq. (12.54) when $\gamma = \omega_0$? Verify, by direct substitution, that in this case the general solution of Eq. (12.52) is $x = (A + Bt)e^{-\gamma t}$. It is then said that the oscillator is *critically damped*. Find A and B if, for $t = 0$, $x = x_0$ and $v = 0$. Plot x as a function of t. What differences do you see between this and the preceding problem?

12.48 Prove that in damped oscillatory motion the velocity is given by

$$v = A'e^{-\gamma t} \sin (\omega t + \alpha + \delta),$$

where $A' = A\omega_0$ and $\tan \delta = -\omega/\gamma$.

12.49 A simple pendulum has a period of 2 s and an amplitude of 2°. After 10 complete oscillations its amplitude has been reduced to 1.5°. Find the damping constant γ.

12.50 Find the limiting values of the amplitude and the phase of a forced damped oscillator when (a) ω_f is much smaller than ω_0, and (b) ω_f is much larger than ω_0. Determine the dominant factors in each case.

12.51 Prove that for the forced oscillations of a damped oscillator, the average power of the applied force is equal to the average power dissipated by the damping force.

12.52 Referring to the pendulum of Problem 12.49, calculate the power required to maintain the oscillations with constant amplitude. The mass of the pendulum is 1 kg.

12.53 In the case of a damped oscillator, the quantity $\tau = 1/2\gamma$ is called the *relaxation time*. (a) Verify that it is expressed in units of time. (b) How much has the amplitude of the oscillator changed after a time τ? (c) Express, as a function of τ, the time required for the amplitude to reduce to one-half its initial value. (d) What are the values of the amplitude after times equal to twice, three times, etc., the value obtained in (c)?

12.54 Assume that for a damped oscillator γ is very small compared with ω_0, so that the amplitude remains essentially constant during one oscillation. (a) Verify that the energy of the damped oscillator can be written in the form $E = \frac{1}{2}m\omega_0^2 A^2 e^{-2\gamma t}$. (b) The average power dissipation is defined by $P = -dE/dt$. Prove that $P = 2\gamma E = E/\tau$. (c) Prove that this power dissipation is equal to the average work done by the damping force per unit time.

12.55 Prove that for a forced oscillator $P_{\text{ave}} = \frac{1}{2}(P_{\text{ave}})_{\text{res}}$ when the reactance equals the resistance $X = \pm R$ or $\omega_f^2 - \omega_0^2 = \pm 2\gamma\omega_f$. The difference $(\Delta\omega)_{1/2}$ between the two values of ω_f for this situation is called the *bandwidth* of the oscillator and the ratio $Q = \omega/(\Delta\omega)_{1/2}$ is called the *Q-value* of the oscillator. Prove that for small damping $(\Delta\omega)_{1/2} = 2\gamma$ and thus $Q = \omega_0/2\gamma$. [*Hint:* Use Eqs. (12.70) and (12.71), with adequate values for R and Z.]

12.56 (a) Find the average values of the kinetic and potential energies of the forced oscillations of a damped oscillator. (b) Obtain the ratio of the sum of these two energies to the work done by the applied force in one period. This is a useful factor for indicating the performance of the oscillator. Prove that for small damping it is equal to $Q/2\tau$. (Remember Problem 12.55.)

12.57 Write the equation of motion of a simple harmonic undamped oscillator to which a force $F = F_0 \cos \omega_f t$ is applied. Verify that its solution is

$$x = [F_0/m(\omega_0^2 - \omega_f^2)] \cos \omega_f t.$$

Discuss the resonance in this case.

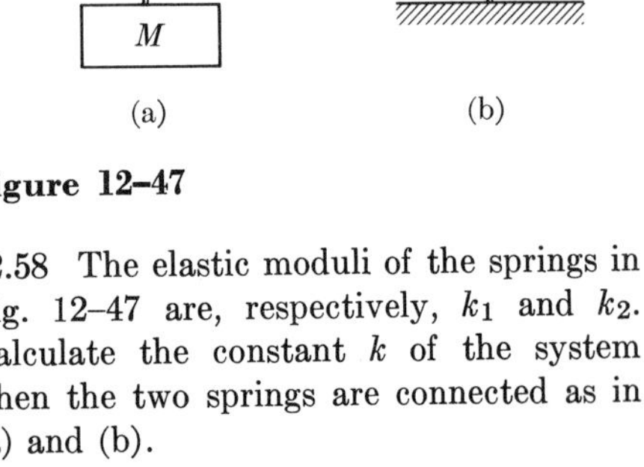

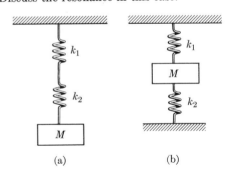

Figure 12–47

12.58 The elastic moduli of the springs in Fig. 12–47 are, respectively, k_1 and k_2. Calculate the constant k of the system when the two springs are connected as in (a) and (b).

12.59 A particle slides back and forth between two inclined frictionless planes (Fig. 12–48). (a) Find the period of the motion if h is the initial height. (b) Is the motion oscillatory? Is it simple harmonic?

Figure 12–48

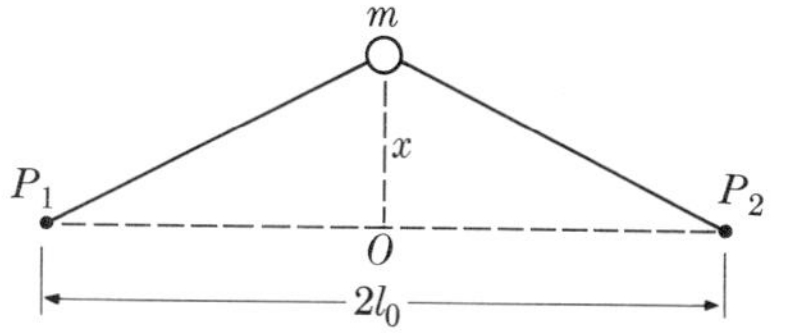

Figure 12–49

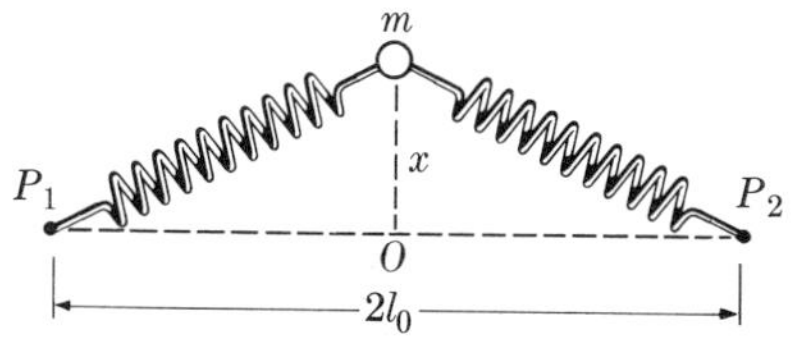

Figure 12–50

12.60 A particle of mass m placed on a horizontal frictionless table (Fig. 12–49) is held by two equal stretched wires of length l_0 whose other ends are fixed at points P_1 and P_2. The tension of the wires is T. If the particle is displaced sidewise an amount x_0 which is small compared with the length of the wires, and then released, determine its subsequent motion. Find its frequency of oscillation and write the equation of motion. Assume that the length of the wires and the tension remain unchanged.

12.61 The particle of Fig. 12–50 is under conditions similar to that of the preceding problem, but is held by two springs, each of elastic constant k and normal length l_0. Obtain the same information requested in the previous problem. Note that we must now take into account the lengthening of the springs.

12.62 Repeat the previous problem, assuming that the displacement of the particle is along the line P_1P_2, as in Fig. 12–51.

12.63 A particle of mass m is subject to the force shown in Fig. 12–52, called a *square wave*; i.e., the force is constant in magnitude but reverses direction at regular time intervals of π/ω. This force can be represented by the Fourier series:

$$F = F_0(4/\pi)(\sin \omega t + \tfrac{1}{3} \sin 3\omega t + \tfrac{1}{5} \sin 5\omega t + \cdots).$$

(a) Write the equation of motion of the particle. (b) Verify, by direct substitution, that its solution can be written as

$$x = a + bt + A \sin \omega t + B \sin 3\omega t + C \sin 5\omega t + \cdots,$$

where a and b are arbitrary constants, and determine the values of the coefficients A, B, C, ..., so that the equation of motion is satisfied.

12.64 A simple harmonic oscillator of natural frequency ω_0 is subject to the same driving force as in the preceding problem. (a) Write its equation of motion. (b) Verify, by direct substitution, that its solution can be written as $x = a \sin(\omega_0 t + \alpha) + A \sin \omega t + B \sin 3\omega t + C \sin 5\omega t + \cdots$, where a and α are arbitrary constants, and determine the values of the coefficients $A, B, C, \ldots$, so that the equation of motion is satisfied.

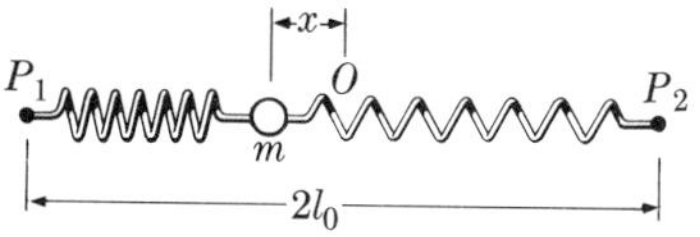

Figure 12–51

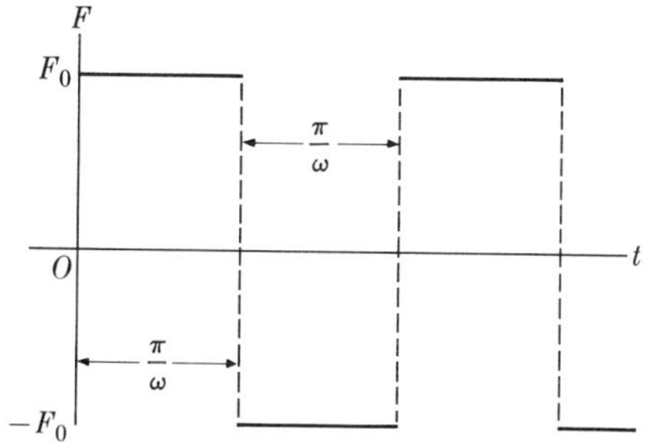

Figure 12–52

12.65 Prove that the potential energy of a pendulum can be written as $E_p = 2mgl \sin^2 \frac{1}{2}\theta$. Then, by application of Eq. (12.13), show that

$$P = 2\sqrt{l/g} \int_0^{\theta_0} d\theta/\sqrt{\sin^2 \tfrac{1}{2}\theta_0 - \sin^2 \tfrac{1}{2}\theta}.$$

This integral cannot be evaluated in terms of elementary functions. In the integral make the substitution $\sin \frac{1}{2}\theta = \sin \frac{1}{2}\theta_0 \sin \psi$, where ψ is a new variable going from 0 to $\pi/2$ when θ goes from 0 to θ_0. Next make a series expansion of the resulting radical, using Eq. (M.22), and integrate to obtain the series expression for P given in Section 12.5.

12.66 For simple harmonic motion, $E_p = \frac{1}{2}kx^2$. (a) Use Eq. (12.13) to obtain the period of motion for SHM and verify that the result agrees with Eq. (12.7). (b) Show that Eq. (8.34), with $x_0 = 0$, gives

$$\arcsin (x/A) = \omega t + \alpha,$$

where $A^2 = 2E/k$. Verify that this agrees with Eq. (12.1).

12.67 Consider a particle oscillating under the influence of the anharmonic potential $E_p(x) = \frac{1}{2}kx^2 - \frac{1}{3}ax^3$, where a is positive and much smaller than k. (a) Make a schematic plot of $E_p(x)$. Is the curve symmetric around the value $x = 0$? In view of your previous answer, in what direction is the center of oscillation displaced as the energy is increased? Do you expect x_{ave} to be zero? (b) Obtain the force as a function of x and make a schematic plot. What is the effect of the anharmonic term on the force?

12.68 Referring to the preceding problem, (a) write the equation of motion. (b) Try as a solution

$$x = A \cos \omega t + B \cos 2\omega t + x_1,$$

where the last two terms are the results of the anharmonic term. (c) Can this be an exact solution? (d) Neglecting all terms involving products of A and B or powers of B higher than the first, prove that $\omega = \omega_0$, $x_1 = \alpha A^2/2\omega_0^2$ and $B = -\alpha A^2/6\omega_0^2$, where $\omega_0^2 = k/m$ and $\alpha = a/m$. [*Hint:* Use the trigonometric relation $\cos^2 \omega t = \frac{1}{2}(1 + \cos 2\omega t)$.]

12.69 Repeat Problem 12.67, assuming that the potential energy is

$$E_p(x) = \tfrac{1}{2}kx^2 - \tfrac{1}{4}ax^4.$$

As before, a is much smaller than k.

12.70 Referring to the preceding problem, (a) write the equation of motion. (b) Try as a solution $x = A \sin \omega t + B \sin 3\omega t$, where the last term is the result of the anharmonic term. (c) Can this be an exact solution? (d) Neglecting all terms involving products of A and B or powers of B higher than the first, prove that $\omega^2 = \omega_0^2 - 3\alpha A^2/4$ and $B = \alpha A^3/4(9\omega^2 - \omega_0^2)$, where ω_0 and α have the same definitions as in Problem 12.68. [*Hint:* Use the trigonometric relation $\sin^3 \omega t = \frac{3}{4} \sin \omega t - \frac{1}{4} \sin 3\omega t$.]

12.71 Referring to Problems 12.68 and 12.70, find the values x_{ave} and $(x^2)_{\text{ave}}$, where the averages refer to time, and compare with the results for simple harmonic motion. (Recall Problem 12.17.)

12.72 Apply the results of Problem 12.70 to the motion of a simple pendulum by replacing $\sin \theta$ in the expression for F_T given at the beginning of Section 12.5 by its first two terms in its series expansion (M.25), obtaining $\omega \approx \omega_0(1 - \theta_0^2/16)$ and $\theta = \theta_0 \sin \omega t + (\theta_0^3/192) \sin 3\omega t$. From the value of ω, obtain directly the result for the period P given at the end of Section 12.5.

PART 2
INTERACTIONS AND FIELDS

A. Gravitation

Once we have grasped the general rules governing motion, the next step is to investigate the interactions responsible for such motions. There are several kinds of interactions. One is *gravitational interaction*, which manifests itself in planetary motion and in the motion of matter in bulk. Gravitation, in spite of the fact that it is the weakest of all known interactions, is the first interaction to be carefully studied, because of man's early interest in astronomy and because gravitation is responsible for many phenomena that affect our lives directly. Another is *electromagnetic interaction*, the best understood and perhaps the most important interaction from the point of view of daily life. Most of the phenomena we observe around us, including chemical and biological processes, are the result of electromagnetic interactions between atoms and molecules. A third kind is the *strong* or *nuclear interaction*, which is responsible for holding protons and neutrons (known as nucleons) within the atomic nucleus, and other related phenomena. In spite of intensive research our knowledge of this interaction is still incomplete. A fourth kind is the *weak interaction*, responsible for certain processes among the fundamental particles, such as beta decay. Our understanding of this interaction also is still very meager. The relative strength of the above interactions is: strong, taken as 1; electromagnetic $\sim 10^{-2}$; weak $\sim 10^{-5}$; gravitational $\sim 10^{-38}$. One of the as-yet-unsolved problems of physics is why there appear to be only four interactions, and why there is such a wide difference in their strength.

It is interesting to see what Isaac Newton, 200 years ago, said concerning interactions:

> Have not the small Particles of Bodies certain Powers, or Forces, by which they act . . . upon one another for producing a great Part of the Phaenomena of Nature? For it's well known, that Bodies act one upon another by the Attractions of Gravity, Magnetism, and Electricity; . . . and make it not improbable but that there may be more attractive Powers than these. . . . How these attractions may be perform'd, I do not here consider. . . . The Attractions of Gravity, Magnetism, and Electricity, reach to very sensible distances, . . . and there may be others which reach to so small distances as hitherto escape observation; . . . . (*Opticks*, Book III, Query 31)

To describe these interactions, we introduce the concept of *field*. By *field* we mean a physical property extended over a region of space and described by a function of position and time. For each interaction we assume that a particle produces around it a corresponding field. This field in turn acts on a second particle to produce the required interaction. The second particle produces its own field, which acts on the first particle, resulting in a mutual interaction.

Even though interactions can be described by means of fields, all fields do not necessarily correspond to interactions, a fact which is implicit in the definition of field. For example, a meteorologist may express the atmospheric pressure and temperature as a function of the latitude and longitude on the earth's surface and the height above it. We then have two scalar fields: the pressure field and the temperature field. In a fluid in motion, the velocity of the fluid at each point constitutes a vector field. The concept of field is thus of great and general usefulness in physics.

In Chapter 13 we shall discuss the gravitational interaction and field. In Chapters 14 through 17 (which appear in Volume II), we shall consider electromagnetic interactions. We shall talk about the other interactions in Volume III.

13 GRAVITATIONAL INTERACTION

13.1 Introduction

One of the fundamental problems of dynamics that has intrigued man since the dawn of civilization has been the motion of the heavenly bodies or, as we say today, planetary motion. Perhaps one of the most interesting processes in the history of science has been the evolution of our understanding of planetary motion.

The Greeks, who liked to consider man the center of the universe, assumed that the earth was at the geometric center of the universe and that the heavenly bodies moved around the earth. Those bodies known at that time were placed in the following order according to their average distance to the earth: moon, Mercury, Venus, sun, Mars, Jupiter and Saturn.

The first hypothesis about planetary motion was that the above planets described concentric circles, with the earth at the common center. This assumption, however, did not fit the observed motion of these bodies relative to the earth, and the geometry of planetary motion became more and more complex. In the second century A.D. the astronomer Ptolemy of Alexandria developed his theory of epicycles to explain this motion. In the simplest case the planet was assumed to describe, with uniform motion, a circle called an *epicycle*, whose center, in turn, moved on a larger circle, concentric with the earth and called the *deferent*. The resulting path of the planet is thus an *epicycloid* (Fig. 13–1). In some instances a more complicated arrangement was required in order to describe planetary motions. In our present language, what the Greeks did was to describe planetary motion relative to a frame of reference attached to the earth.

This description was accepted as correct until, in the sixteenth century, the Polish monk Nicolaus Copernicus (1473–1543), who was looking for a simpler solution, proposed to describe the motion of all planets, including the earth, relative to the sun, which would be at the center. The idea was not new; it had first been proposed by the Greek astronomer Aristarchus about the third century B.C. According to Copernicus, the orbits of the planets were placed in the following order with respect to the sun: Mercury, Venus, earth, Mars, Jupiter and Saturn, with the moon revolving around the earth. Essentially what Copernicus proposed was another frame of reference attached to the sun, in which the motion of the planets had a simpler description.

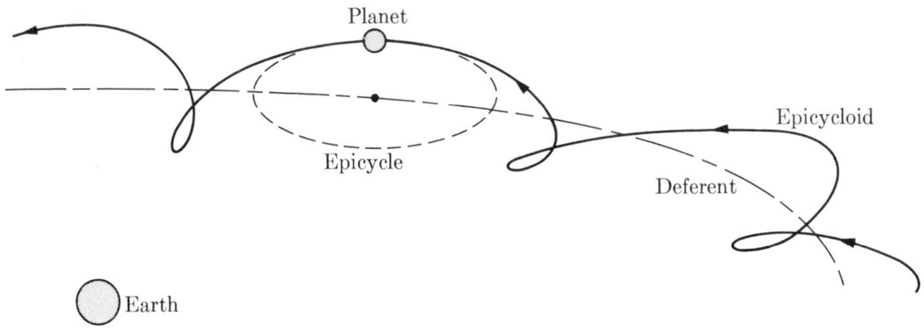

Fig. 13–1. Epicycle model for planetary motion referred to the earth.

TABLE 13-1 Basic Data about the Solar System*

Body	Mean radius, m	Mass, kg	Period of rotation, s	Mean radius of orbit, m	Period of orbital motion, s	Eccentricity of orbit
Sun	6.96×10^8	1.98×10^{30}	2.3×10^6	—	—	—
Mercury	2.34×10^6	3.28×10^{23}	5.03×10^6	5.79×10^{10}	7.60×10^6	0.206
Venus	6.26×10^6	4.83×10^{24}	(?)	1.08×10^{11}	1.94×10^7	0.007
Earth	6.37×10^6	5.98×10^{24}	8.62×10^4	1.49×10^{11}	3.16×10^7	0.017
Mars	3.32×10^6	6.40×10^{23}	8.86×10^4	2.28×10^{11}	5.94×10^7	0.093
Jupiter	6.98×10^7	1.90×10^{27}	3.54×10^4	7.78×10^{11}	3.74×10^8	0.049
Saturn	5.82×10^7	5.68×10^{26}	3.61×10^4	1.43×10^{12}	9.30×10^8	0.051
Uranus	2.37×10^7	8.67×10^{25}	3.85×10^4	2.87×10^{12}	2.66×10^9	0.046
Neptune	2.24×10^7	1.05×10^{26}	5.69×10^4	4.50×10^{12}	5.20×10^9	0.004
Pluto	(3.00×10^6)	(5.37×10^{24})	(?)	5.91×10^{12}	7.82×10^9	0.250
Moon	1.74×10^6	7.34×10^{22}	2.36×10^6	3.84×10^8	2.36×10^6	0.055

* Quantities in parentheses are uncertain. Orbital data of moon are relative to earth.

The sun, the largest body in our planetary system, is practically coincident with the center of mass of the system, and moves much more slowly than the other planets. This justifies its choice as center of reference, since it is, practically, an inertial frame. Copernicus' proposal assisted the astronomer Johannes Kepler (1571–1630) to discover the laws of planetary motion, as a result of his careful analysis of the astronomical measurements of Tycho Brahe (1546–1601). These laws, called *Kepler's laws*, are a kinematical description of planetary motion and are stated as:

I. *The planets describe elliptical orbits, with the sun at one focus.*

II. *The position vector of any planet relative to the sun sweeps out equal areas of its ellipse in equal times.* (This statement is called the *law of areas.*)

III. *The squares of the periods of revolution are proportional to the cubes of the average distances of the planets from the sun.* (This law may be stated by the equation $P^2 = kr^3_{\text{ave}}$, where k is a proportionality constant.)

The next step in the history of astronomy was a discussion of the dynamics of planetary motion and an attempt to determine the interaction responsible for such motion. Here is where Sir Isaac Newton (1642–1727) made his outstanding contribution, the *law of universal gravitation.* This law (to be discussed later in this chapter) was formulated by Newton in 1666, but it was not published until 1687, when it appeared as a chapter in his monumental work *Philosophiae Naturalis Principia Mathematica.*

The more important data about the solar system have been collected in Table 13–1.

13.2 The Law of Gravitation

Next to his statement of the laws of motion (Chapter 7), Newton's second, and perhaps greatest, contribution to the development of mechanics was the discovery of the law of gravitational interaction; that is, the interaction between two bodies, either planets or small particles, which produces a motion that can be described by Kepler's laws.

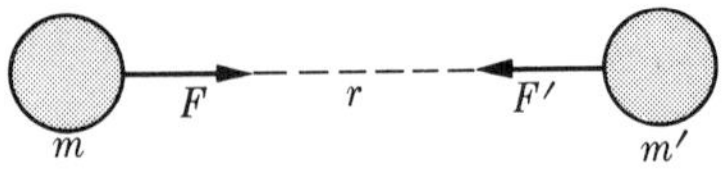

Fig. 13–2. Gravitational interaction between two masses.

In the first place, according to Section 7.14, the law of areas (or Kepler's second law) indicates that *the force associated with the gravitational interaction is central.* That is, the force acts along the line joining the two interacting bodies (Fig. 13–2), in this case a planet and the sun. Second, if we assume that gravitational interaction is a *universal* property of all matter, the force F associated with the interaction must be proportional to the "amount" of matter in each body; i.e., to their respective masses m and m'. Thus we may write $F = mm'f(r)$.

To determine the dependence of the force F on the distance r, expressed by $f(r)$, is a more difficult problem. We could determine this dependence experimentally by measuring the force between masses m and m' at several separations and deducting from our observations the relation between F and r. This has been done, but requires a very sensitive experimental setup because the gravitational interaction is extremely weak and the gravitational force is very small unless the two masses are very large (such as two planets), or unless the distance r is very small. But, in this second case, as we shall see later, other interactions stronger

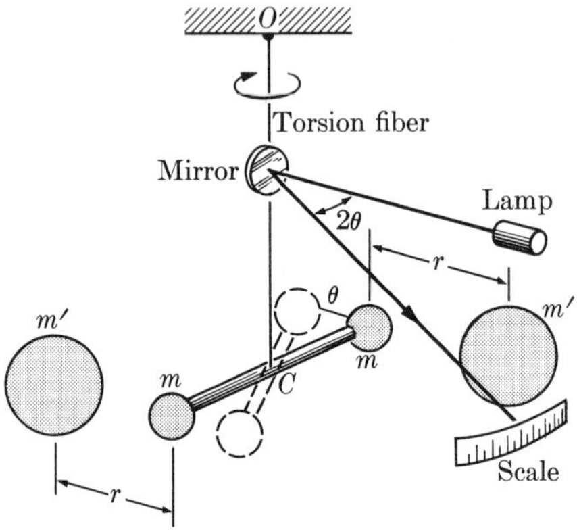

Fig. 13–3. Cavendish torsion balance. When masses m' are placed close to masses m, their gravitational attraction produces a torque on the horizontal rod that results in a torsion of the fiber OC. Equilibrium is established when the gravitational and torsional torques are equal. The torsional torque is proportional to the angle θ, which is measured by the deflection of a ray reflected from a mirror attached to the fiber. By repeating the experiment at several distances r, and using different masses m and m', we can verify law (13.1).

than the gravitational one enter into play, masking the gravitational effects. The results of these experiments allow us to conclude that *the gravitational interaction is attractive and varies inversely with the square of the distance between the two bodies;* that is, $f(r) \propto 1/r^2$.

Therefore we write for the force of gravitation the expression

$$F = \gamma \frac{mm'}{r^2}, \tag{13.1}$$

where the proportionality constant γ depends on the units used for the other quantities. Hence γ must be determined experimentally, by measuring the force F between two known masses m and m' at a known distance r (Fig. 13–3). The value of γ in MKSC units is

$$\gamma = 6.67 \times 10^{-11}\ \mathrm{N\ m^2\ kg^{-2}} \qquad (\mathrm{or\ m^3\ kg^{-1}\ s^{-2}}).$$

We may then state *Newton's law of universal gravitation* by saying that

> *the gravitational interaction between two bodies can be expressed by an attractive central force proportional to the masses of the bodies and inversely proportional to the square of the distance between them.*

In discussing Eq. (13.1) we have suggested that the gravitational interaction between two masses can be derived from experiments, but that does not necessarily imply that gravitational interaction is the force responsible for planetary motion according to Kepler's laws. In fact, Newton did not proceed in the way we have done, but in the reverse. Using Kepler's laws, he derived Eq. (13.1) for the required force between two planets and then generalized the result to apply to any two masses. We shall now give a simplified discussion of Newton's method, deferring a more general analysis until Section 13.5.

Kepler's first law states that the orbit of a planet is an ellipse. A particular case of an ellipse is the circle, where the two foci coincide with the center. In this case, according to the second law, the force F points toward the center of the circle. Thus, using Eq. (7.28) for the centripetal force in circular motion and referring the motion of m to a frame of reference attached to m' (Fig. 13–4), we may express the force as

$$F = \frac{mv^2}{r}.$$

Strictly speaking, we should use, instead of m, the reduced mass of the system composed of m and m', according to Eq. (9.15), but our simplification does not affect our conclusions. Remembering that $v = 2\pi r/P$, we have

$$F = \frac{4\pi^2 mr}{P^2}.$$

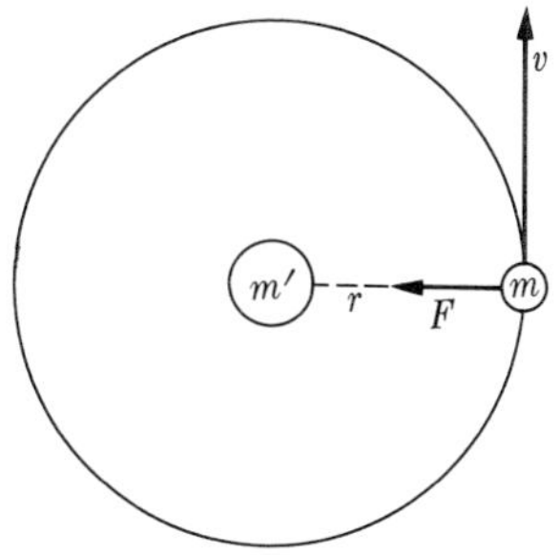

Fig. 13–4. Motion of particle m under its gravitational interaction with m'.

But the third law of Kepler, in the special case of a circular orbit when the average distance between m and m' is the radius of the circle, becomes $P^2 = kr^3$. Therefore

$$F = \frac{4\pi^2 m}{kr^2},$$

proving that to satisfy Kepler's laws the gravitational interaction must be central and inversely proportional to the square of the distance.

Newton himself checked the correctness of his assumption by comparing the centripetal acceleration of the moon with the acceleration of gravity $g = 9.80$ m s^{-2}. The centripetal acceleration of the moon is $a_c = v^2/r = 4\pi^2 r/P^2$, with $r = 3.84 \times 10^8$ m and $P = 2.36 \times 10^6$ s. Thus $a_c = 2.72 \times 10^{-3}$ m s^{-2}. Therefore

$$g/a_c = 3602 \approx (60)^2.$$

But, since the radius of the earth is $R = 6.37 \times 10^6$ m, we have that

$$\left(\frac{r}{R}\right)^2 = \left(\frac{384}{6.37}\right)^2 \approx (60)^2.$$

Therefore $g/a_c = (r/R)^2$ and, within the accuracy of our rough calculation, the two accelerations are in inverse proportion to the square of the distances of the points from the center of the earth.

EXAMPLE 13.1. Relate the acceleration of gravity to the mass of the earth. Using your answer, estimate the mass of the earth.

Solution: Consider a particle of mass m on the earth's surface. Its distance from the center of the earth is equal to the earth's radius R. Thus, if we denote the mass of the earth by M, expression (13.1) gives for the force on the body,

$$F = \gamma mM/R^2.$$

This force is what was defined in Eq. (7.16) as the *weight* of the body, and therefore must be equal to mg, where g is the acceleration of gravity. Therefore

$$mg = \gamma mM/R^2$$

or, canceling the common factor m, we have

$$g = \gamma M/R^2.$$

This result gives the acceleration of gravity in terms of the mass and the radius of the earth. Note that the mass of the body does not appear in this expression, and thus (if we neglect air resistance) all bodies should fall with the same acceleration, in agreement with observation.

Solving for the mass of the earth M, we obtain

$$M = gR^2/\gamma.$$

Introducing the proper numerical values $g = 9.8 \text{ m s}^{-2}$, $R = 6.37 \times 10^6$ m, and $\gamma = 6.67 \times 10^{-11} \text{ m}^3 \text{ kg}^{-1} \text{ s}^{-2}$, we get $M = 5.98 \times 10^{24}$ kg.

The student must note that in working this example we have used the distance of the mass m from the center of the earth. In other words, we are implicitly assuming that the force on m is the same as if all the mass of the earth were concentrated at its center, an assumption that will be justified in Section 13.7.

EXAMPLE 13.2. Compute the mass of a planet which has a satellite.

Solution: Suppose that a satellite of mass m describes, with a period P, a circular orbit of radius r around a planet of mass M. The force of attraction between the planet and the satellite is

$$F = \gamma m M / r^2.$$

This force must be equal to m times the centripetal acceleration $v^2/r = 4\pi^2 r/P^2$. Thus

$$\frac{4\pi^2 m r}{P^2} = \frac{\gamma m M}{r^2}.$$

Canceling the common factor m and solving for M, we get

$$M = 4\pi^2 r^3 / \gamma P^2.$$

We suggest that the student use this expression to reevaluate the mass of the earth, using the data for the moon ($r = 3.84 \times 10^8$ m and $P = 2.36 \times 10^6$ s). Agreement with the result of Example 13.1 is a proof of the consistency of the theory. This formula can also be used for obtaining the mass of the sun, using the data for the different planets.

13.3 Inertial and Gravitational Mass

In Chapter 7 we introduced the concept of mass in relation to the laws of motion. For that reason we called it *inertial mass*. We have also assumed that the laws of motion are of universal validity and are therefore the same for all kinds of matter, whether they are electrons, protons, neutrons, or groups of these particles. On the other hand, in this chapter we have been discussing a particular interaction called gravitation. To characterize its strength, we should have attached to each portion of matter a *gravitational charge* or *gravitational mass* m_g. We should then have written Eq. (13.1) in the form

$$F = \gamma m_g m_g' / r^2.$$

However, if we assume that gravitation is a universal property of all kinds of matter, we may consider that gravitational mass is proportional to inertial mass, and therefore the ratio

$$K = \frac{\text{gravitational mass, } m_g}{\text{inertial mass, } m}$$

must be the same for all bodies. By a proper choice of units for m_g, we can make this ratio equal to one, and therefore use the same number for the gravitational mass as for the inertial mass. This has implicitly been done in our selection of the value of the constant γ. The constancy of K, which is equivalent to the constancy of γ, has been verified experimentally for all kinds of bodies with great care, and can be considered as a sound hypothesis. The well-proven fact that all bodies near the earth fall with the same acceleration is an indication of the fact that inertial and gravitational mass are the same, since, under that assumption, the acceleration of gravity is $g = \gamma M/R^2$, as discussed in Example 13.1, and g is independent of the mass of the falling body. Therefore in what follows we shall use the term "mass" to refer to either the inertial or the gravitational mass, since the two are indistinguishable.

From Eq. (13.1) we may now define the unit of mass as that mass which, when placed at the unit of distance from an equal mass, attracts it with a force equal to γ units. By properly choosing the value of γ we may define any unit of mass. However, an arbitrary choice of γ may alter the structure of the equations in mechanics. Another drawback to this procedure for defining the unit of mass is that it requires a previous definition of the unit of force. Therefore this procedure is not used. Instead, as indicated previously, we follow the reverse method, and, after we have already chosen the units of mass and force, we determine the value of γ experimentally.

A way of measuring or comparing the masses of two bodies is by using a third body as reference. Consider two masses m and m' placed at the same distance r from a third reference mass M (Fig. 13–5). Then, according to Eq. (13.1), the forces on m and m' are

$$F = \frac{\gamma M m}{r^2}, \qquad F' = \frac{\gamma M m'}{r^2}.$$

The ratio of these two forces is $F/F' = m/m'$. Therefore, if we have a method of comparing forces without necessarily measuring each one, the preceding relation provides a method for comparing and measuring masses. The principle of the balance allows us to use this method when the reference body M is the earth. The balance achieves equilibrium when the two forces are equal, and therefore the masses are equal. We have now justified the method indicated in Section 2.3 for measuring mass by means of a balance.

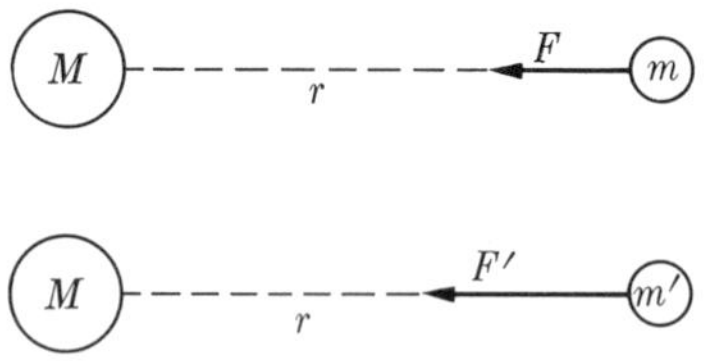

Fig. 13–5. Method for comparing two masses m and m' by means of their gravitational interaction with a third mass M.

13.4 Gravitational Potential Energy

Because the gravitational interaction given by Eq. (13.1) is central and depends only on the distance, it corresponds to a conservative force. We may therefore associate with it a *gravitational potential energy*. Taking the origin of coordinates at m' and considering only the force acting on m (Fig. 13–6), we note that $\boldsymbol{F}$, being an attractive force, is in the direction opposed to the vector $\boldsymbol{r} = \overrightarrow{OA} = r\boldsymbol{u}_r$, where $\boldsymbol{u}_r$ is the unit vector in the direction $\overrightarrow{OA}$, and therefore, instead of Eq. (13.1), we must write more properly the vector equation

$$\boldsymbol{F} = -\frac{\gamma m m'}{r^2}\boldsymbol{u}_r. \tag{13.2}$$

This force is equal to the negative of the gradient of the potential energy. In our case, since the force is central and acts along the radius, the potential energy depends only on r and it is sufficient to apply Eq. (8.25); that is, $F_r = -\partial E_p/\partial r$. Then $F_r = -\gamma m m'/r^2$ and

$$\frac{\partial E_p}{\partial r} = \frac{\gamma m m'}{r^2}.$$

Integrating, and assigning the value zero to the potential energy at a very large distance ($r = \infty$), we obtain

$$\int_0^{E_p} dE_p = \gamma m m' \int_\infty^r \frac{dr}{r^2},$$

giving for the gravitational potential energy of the system composed of masses m and m'

$$E_p = -\frac{\gamma m m'}{r}. \tag{13.3}$$

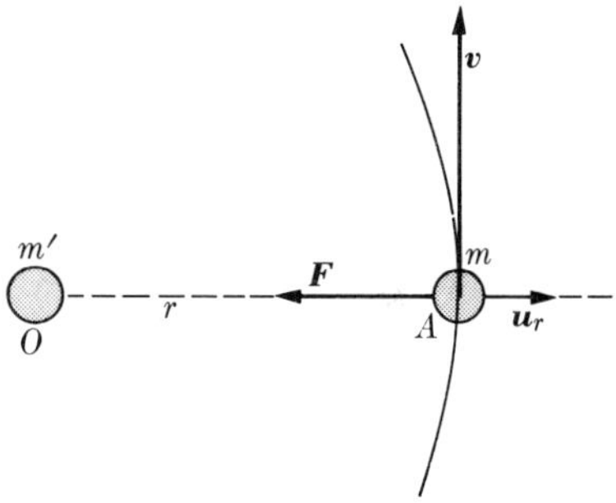

Fig. 13–6. The gravitational attraction of m' on m is opposed to the unit vector $\boldsymbol{u}_r$ directed away from m'.

The total energy of the system of two particles subject to their gravitational interaction is then

$$E = \tfrac{1}{2}mv^2 + \tfrac{1}{2}m'v'^2 - \frac{\gamma m m'}{r}. \tag{13.4}$$

For a system of more than two particles, subject to their gravitational interaction, the total energy is

$$E = \sum_{\substack{\text{All}\\ \text{particles}}} \tfrac{1}{2}m_i v_i^2 - \sum_{\substack{\text{All}\\ \text{pairs}}} \frac{\gamma m_i m_j}{r_{ij}}.$$

In the case of two particles, referring their motion to a frame of reference attached to the center of mass of the system, we may use the result of Example 9.9 to express the kinetic energy of the two particles as $E_k = \frac{1}{2}\mu v_{12}^2$, where μ is their reduced mass and v_{12} their relative velocity, so that the total energy in this frame is

$$E = \tfrac{1}{2}\mu v_{12}^2 - \gamma\frac{m m'}{r_{12}}.$$

In the special case where particle m' is very massive compared with m ($m' \gg m$), we have [recalling the definition of reduced mass, Eq. (9.15)] that $\mu \approx m$. In this case m' practically coincides with the center of mass of the system, and we may replace the relative velocity v_{12} by the velocity v of m relative to the center of mass, resulting in

$$E = \tfrac{1}{2}mv^2 - \frac{\gamma mm'}{r}. \tag{13.5}$$

If the particle moves in a circular orbit, the force acting on the mass is given by Eq. (7.28), $F_N = mv^2/r$ and, replacing F_N by the gravitational force of Eq. (13.1), we have

$$\frac{mv^2}{r} = \frac{\gamma mm'}{r^2}.$$

Therefore

$$\tfrac{1}{2}mv^2 = \frac{1}{2}\frac{\gamma mm'}{r}$$

and Eq. (13.5) reduces to

$$E = -\frac{\gamma mm'}{2r}, \tag{13.6}$$

indicating that the total energy is negative. This result is more general than our proof may suggest; all *elliptical* (or bound) orbits have a negative total energy ($E < 0$) when we define the potential energy as zero for infinite separation. The bound nature of the orbit means that the kinetic energy is not enough at any point in the orbit to take the particle to infinity, which would change its kinetic energy

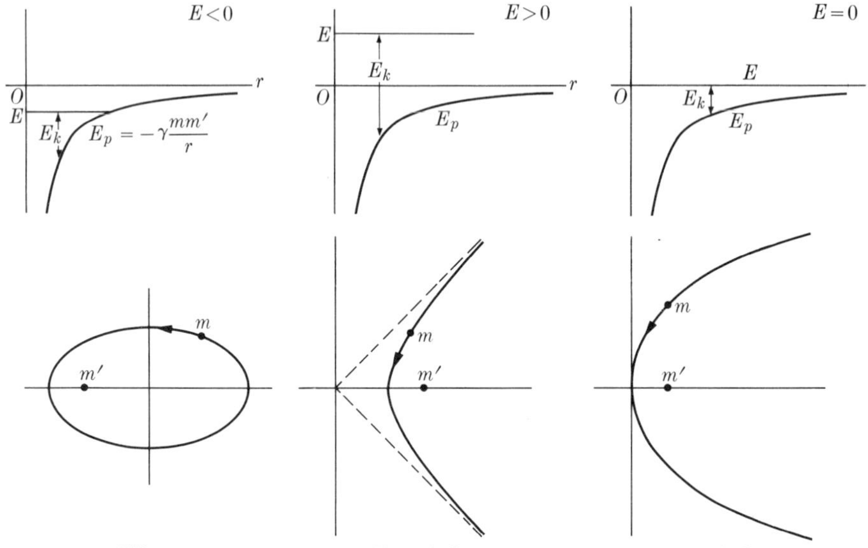

Fig. 13–7. Relation between total energy and path for motion under an inverse-square force.

into potential energy and overcome the gravitational attraction. This can be seen because, at infinite distance, the second term in Eq. (13.5) is zero, and we must have $E = \frac{1}{2}mv^2$, an equation impossible to satisfy if E is negative.

But if the energy is positive ($E > 0$), the particle can reach infinity and still have some kinetic energy left. From Eq. (13.5), if we set $r = \infty$, and designate the velocity at infinity by v_∞, the kinetic energy at infinity is

$$\tfrac{1}{2}mv_\infty^2 = E \qquad \text{or} \qquad v_\infty = \sqrt{2mE}. \tag{13.7}$$

This result may be interpreted in the following way. Suppose that the particle m is initially at a very large distance from m' and is thrown toward it with velocity v_∞, called the *velocity of approach*, so that the total energy is thus determined by Eq. (13.7). While the particle m is approaching m', its potential energy is decreasing (becoming more negative), and the kinetic energy increases until it reaches its maximum value at the point of closest approach, which depends on the angular momentum of the particle (remember Section 8.11 and Fig. 8–18). Then the particle begins to recede; it loses kinetic energy and eventually, at large distances, recovers the velocity v_∞. The path is an open curve, and it can be proved to be an *hyperbola* (Section 13.5).

The particular case of zero total energy ($E = 0$) is interesting because then the particle, according to Eq. (13.7), is at rest at infinity ($v_\infty = 0$). The orbit is still open but instead of being an hyperbola, it is now a *parabola*. Physically it corresponds to the situation in which particle m is released at a distance from m' with an initial velocity that makes its kinetic energy equal to its potential energy.

Figure 13–7 shows the three possible cases, indicating in each case the total energy, the potential energy, the kinetic energy, and the type of orbit.

These results are very important when scientists want to place an artificial satellite in orbit. Suppose that a satellite is launched from the earth. After reaching its maximum height h due to the launch, it receives a final thrust at point A, producing a horizontal velocity v_0 (Fig. 13–8). The total energy of the satellite at A is thus

$$E = \tfrac{1}{2}mv_0^2 - \frac{\gamma mM}{R+h}.$$

The orbit will be an ellipse, a parabola, or an hyperbola depending on whether E is negative, zero, or positive. In all cases the center of the earth is at one focus of the path. If the energy is too low, the elliptical orbit will intersect the earth and the satellite will fall back. Otherwise it will keep moving in a closed orbit, or escape from the earth, depending on the value of v_0.

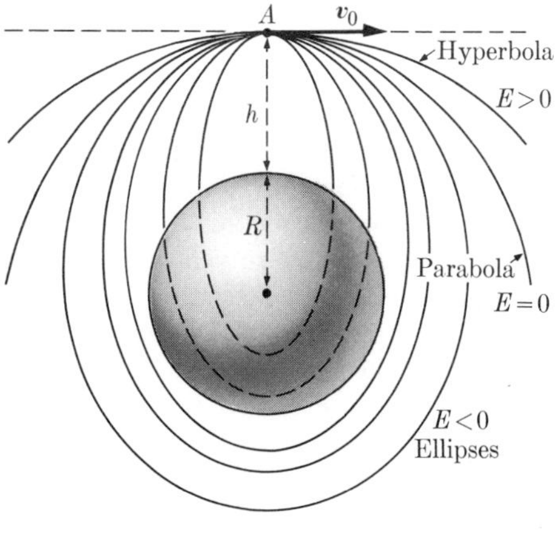

Fig. 13–8. Paths of a particle thrown horizontally from a height h above the earth's surface with a velocity $\boldsymbol{v}_0$.

The same logic applies to a natural satellite such as the moon. Obviously for interplanetary satellites an orbit with positive energy may be necessary. In any case, some guidance mechanism is generally required to adjust its path after launching.

EXAMPLE 13.3. The escape velocity is the minimum velocity with which a body must be fired from the earth if it is to reach infinity. Compute the escape velocity of a body from the earth.

Solution: In order for the particle to reach infinity, the total energy must be zero or positive, and obviously the minimum velocity will correspond to zero total energy. Therefore, from Eq. (13.5) with $E = 0$, and calling M the mass of the earth, R its radius, and v_e the escape velocity of the projectile, we have $\frac{1}{2}mv_e^2 - \gamma mM/R = 0$, which gives the proper relation between v_e and R at the launching station. Thus the escape velocity from the earth is

$$v_e = \sqrt{2\gamma M/R} = 1.13 \times 10^4 \text{ m s}^{-1}. \tag{13.8}$$

This is equal to 40,700 km/hr or about 25,280 mi/hr. Note that the escape velocity is independent of the mass of the body. However, the *thrust* required to accelerate a body until it reaches the escape velocity does depend on the mass of the body, and that is why heavier missiles and satellites require more powerful boosters.

A particle projected from the earth with a velocity v_e given by Eq. (13.8) will have zero velocity when it reaches infinity. If the velocity is greater than v_e, the particle will reach infinity with some velocity still left. If the launching velocity is less than v_e, the particle will fall back onto the earth, unless it is placed into a bound orbit by successive stages of the propelling rocket and the direction of the velocity is changed, as explained in connection with Fig. 13–8.

The concept of escape velocity is also useful in determining the escape of gases from the earth's atmosphere. If we assume that the gases composing the atmosphere are in thermal equilibrium, the rms velocity of their molecules is given by Eq. (9.59) as

$$v_{\text{rms}} = \sqrt{3kT/m}. \tag{13.9}$$

Root-mean-square velocities for gases found in the earth's atmosphere at its average temperature are: hydrogen, 1908 m s^{-1}; helium, 1350 m s^{-1}; nitrogen, 510 m s^{-1}; oxygen, 477 m s^{-1}; and carbon dioxide, 407 m s^{-1}. In all cases v_{rms} is much smaller than v_e, and thus we could conclude that no gas molecule can overcome the gravitational attraction and escape from the earth. But this would be a wrong conclusion.

The root-mean-square velocity v_{rms} is an average velocity, and that means that many molecules move with velocities either larger or smaller than v_{rms}. Even if v_{rms} is smaller than v_e, a certain number of molecules move with velocities which are equal to or larger than v_e, and these may escape from the earth, especially if they are in the upper layers of the atmosphere. From the above figures, we see that this effect is more important for the lighter gases than for the heavier, and this is one of the reasons why hydrogen and helium are relatively scarce in our atmosphere. It has been estimated that, due to this gravitational effect, hydrogen is escaping from the earth at the rate of about 1.3×10^{22} atoms per second, which is equivalent to about 600 kg per year. This does not represent the total loss of hydrogen from the earth's atmosphere, however, and the net loss may be different because of other processes.

For the planet Mercury, the escape velocity is much smaller than for the earth; most likely it has already lost its atmosphere completely. The same is true of the moon. Venus has an escape velocity almost the same as the earth's. Mars has an escape velocity about one-sixth that of the earth, and thus retains some atmosphere, but it has lost a proportionately larger fraction of its atmosphere. In fact, the atmospheric pressure on Mars is much less than that on the earth. For the other planets, the escape velocity is greater than that of the earth, and hence they still retain most of their original atmospheres. However, for other reasons, the composition of the atmospheres of these planets is different from that of the earth.

EXAMPLE 13.4. Determine the velocity which a body released at a distance r from the center of the earth has when it strikes the surface of the earth.

Solution: The body's initial velocity is zero and its total energy, according to Eq. (13.5), is therefore

$$E = -\frac{\gamma mM}{r},$$

where m is the mass of the body and M the mass of the earth. When it reaches the earth's surface, its velocity is v and its distance from the center of the earth is the earth's radius R. Thus

$$E = \tfrac{1}{2}mv^2 - \frac{\gamma mM}{R}.$$

Equating both values of E, since the energy has remained constant (we neglect air friction), we have

$$\tfrac{1}{2}mv^2 - \frac{\gamma mM}{R} = -\frac{\gamma mM}{r}.$$

Solving for v^2, we have

$$v^2 = 2\gamma M\left(\frac{1}{R} - \frac{1}{r}\right).$$

Or, remembering from Example 13.1 that $g = \gamma M/R^2$, we obtain

$$v^2 = 2R^2g\left(\frac{1}{R} - \frac{1}{r}\right). \tag{13.10}$$

This expression may also be used for finding the distance r reached by a body thrown vertically with velocity v from the earth's surface.

If the body is released at a great distance, so that $1/r$ is negligible compared with $1/R$, we get

$$v_\infty = \sqrt{2Rg} = \sqrt{2\gamma M/R} = 1.13 \times 10^4 \text{ m s}^{-1},$$

in agreement with the result given in Eq. (13.8) for the escape velocity. This is not surprising, since this problem is just the reverse of the problem of Example 13.3. The above result gives, for example, an estimate of the velocity with which a meteorite strikes the surface of the earth.

13.5 General Motion Under Gravitational Interaction

So far we have stated Kepler's laws only for elliptical orbits. In Section 13.2 we proved that, according to these laws, motion is produced, at least in the case of circular orbits, when the force is attractive and inversely proportional to the square of the distance. However, in Section 13.4, when we were discussing energy, we indicated that these laws also hold for hyperbolic and parabolic orbits, in addition to elliptical orbits. Let us now verify that assertion.

In Chapter 8 we developed a relation [Eq. (8.42)] between the polar coordinates of a particle in terms of the dynamical quantities of the motion. If we use Eq. (8.37) for the effective potential energy, we may write down that relation as

$$\left(\frac{dr}{d\theta}\right)^2 = \frac{m^2r^4}{L^2}\left\{\frac{2[E - E_p(r)]}{m} - \frac{L^2}{m^2r^2}\right\}, \tag{13.11}$$

where L is the angular momentum of the particle. Now the equation of a conic section in polar coordinates with the origin at a focus (see the note at the end of this section) is

$$\frac{\epsilon d}{r} = 1 + \epsilon \cos\theta, \tag{13.12}$$

where ϵ is the eccentricity and d the distance from the focus to the directrix. Taking the derivative with respect to θ, we have

$$-\frac{\epsilon d}{r^2}\frac{dr}{d\theta} = -\epsilon \sin\theta,$$

and thus

$$\left(\frac{dr}{d\theta}\right)^2 = \frac{r^4 \sin^2\theta}{d^2}.$$

Substituting into Eq. (13.11) and canceling r^4 on both sides, we may write

$$\sin^2\theta = \frac{d^2m^2}{L^2}\left\{\frac{2[E - E_p(r)]}{m} - \frac{L^2}{m^2r^2}\right\}.$$

Now, from Eq. (13.12), $\cos\theta = d/r - 1/\epsilon$. Therefore

$$\sin^2\theta = 1 - \cos^2\theta = 1 - \left(\frac{d}{r} - \frac{1}{\epsilon}\right)^2 = 1 - \frac{d^2}{r^2} + \frac{2d}{\epsilon r} - \frac{1}{\epsilon^2}.$$

Substitution into the previous equation yields

$$1 - \frac{d^2}{r^2} + \frac{2d}{\epsilon r} - \frac{1}{\epsilon^2} = \frac{2\,d^2mE}{L^2} - \frac{2\,d^2mE_p(r)}{L^2} - \frac{d^2}{r^2}.$$

Canceling the d^2/r^2 term on both sides and equating those terms that are constant and those that are dependent on r, we obtain

$$\frac{2\,d^2mE}{L^2} = 1 - \frac{1}{\epsilon^2} \quad \text{or} \quad E = \frac{L^2}{2\,d^2m}\left(1 - \frac{1}{\epsilon^2}\right) \tag{13.13}$$

and
$$-\frac{2\,d^2 mE_p(r)}{L^2} = \frac{2d}{\epsilon r} \quad \text{or} \quad E_p(r) = -\frac{L^2}{m\,d\epsilon r}. \tag{13.14}$$

Equation (13.14) indicates that, to describe a conic section with the center of force at one focus, the potential energy $E_p(r)$ must vary with the distance as $1/r$, and therefore the force, which is $F_r = -\partial E_p/\partial r$, must vary as $1/r^2$. This generalizes Kepler's first law to include the hyperbola and the parabola in addition to the ellipse as possible orbits.

The orbit will be an ellipse, parabola, or hyperbola depending on whether the eccentricity ϵ is less than, equal to, or greater than, one. From Eq. (13.13) we see that this relationship corresponds to a total energy E being negative, zero, or positive, thus verifying our discussion of Section 13.4.

We must note that an hyperbola has two branches, and under an inverse-square attractive force only the branch around the center of attraction is described (right branch in Fig. 13-9). If the force is repulsive, that is, if $F = +C/r^2$, the orbit corresponds to the branch on the left in Fig. 13-9. In this case, i.e., for a repulsive force, the potential energy is $E_p = +C/r$, and is positive. Therefore the total energy $E = \frac{1}{2}mv^2 + C/r$ is always positive, and there are no bound orbits. We have already considered motion under a repulsive inverse-square force when we discussed scattering in Example 7.16.

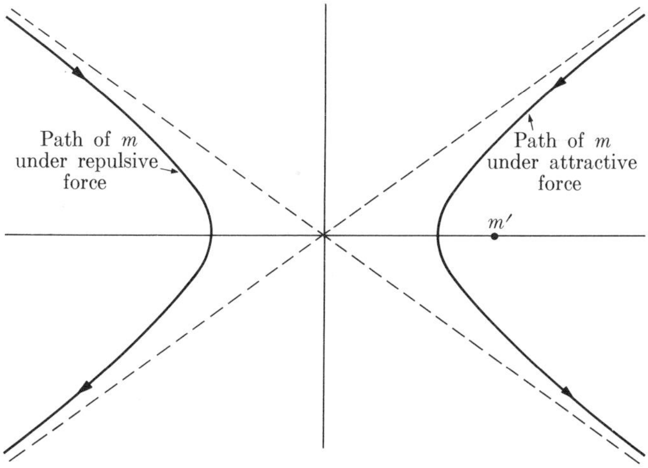

Fig. 13-9. Hyperbolic paths under attractive and repulsive inverse-square forces.

The preceding considerations would be enough to provide a complete analysis of planetary motion if we were to assume that the motion of a planet around the sun were not affected by the other planets and heavenly bodies. In other words, the orbit of the earth (and of all other planets) would be a perfect ellipse if there were no forces other than the sun's acting on the earth. However, the presence of other planets introduces perturbations in a planet's orbit. These perturbations can be calculated with great accuracy by means of special techniques that con-

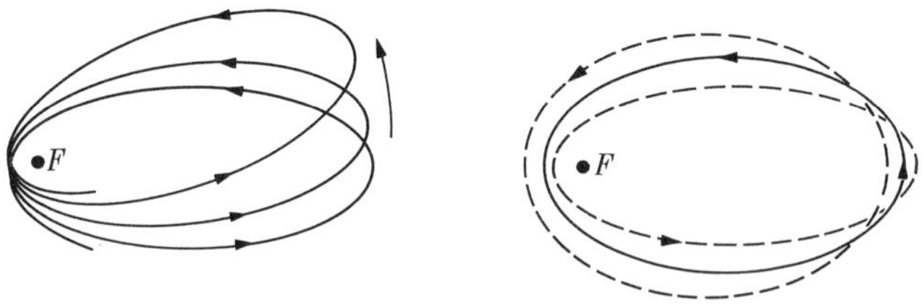

Fig. 13–10. Perturbation effects on planetary motion. (a) Rotation of the axis of the ellipse. (b) Oscillation in the eccentricity of the ellipse. The two effects have been greatly exaggerated.

stitute the science called celestial mechanics. They can be analyzed, essentially, as two effects. One effect is that the elliptical path of a planet is not closed, but the major axis of the ellipse rotates very slowly around the focus where the sun is located, an effect called the advance of the perihelion (Fig. 13–10a). The other effect is a periodic variation of the eccentricity of the ellipse about its average value, as indicated in Fig. 13–10(b). These changes occur very slowly. In the case of the earth they have a period of the order of 10^5 years (about 21′ of arc per century for the motion of the perihelion). Even so, they have produced noticeable effects, especially in the slowly changing climatic conditions of the earth. These changes have been identified by geophysicists who have studied the different layers of the earth's crust.

In discussing motion in a gravitational field we have assumed that the newtonian mechanics of Chapters 7 and 8 can be used. However, a more precise analysis requires the use of Einstein's general theory of relativity (see Section 13.8). One of the main relativistic effects is an *additional* rotation of the major axis of the orbit of a planet. This relativistic effect is greatest for the orbit of Mercury, the planet which is closest to the sun and which has one of the most eccentric orbits. The observed rate of advance of the perihelion of Mercury exceeds, by about 42″ of arc per century, the effect calculated by means of Newtonian mechanics which takes into account the perturbation of the other planets. Einstein's general theory of relativity predicts precisely this additional rate of advance of the perihelion. This relativistic effect is much less for other planets, and has not yet been observed.

Note on conic sections: An important family of plane curves are the *conic sections.* A conic section is defined as a curve generated by a point moving in a way such that the ratio of its distance to a point, called the *focus,* and to a line, called the *directrix,* is constant. There are three kinds of conic sections, called ellipse, parabola, and hyperbola, depending on whether this constant (called the *eccentricity*) is smaller than, equal to, or larger than one. Designating the eccentricity by ϵ, the focus by F, and the directrix by HQD (Fig. 13–11), we have

$$\epsilon = PF/PQ.$$

Now $PF = r$, and if we say that $FD = d$, then $PQ = FD - FB = d - r\cos\theta$. Therefore $\epsilon = r/(d - r\cos\theta)$. Or, solving for r, we find that

$$\frac{\epsilon d}{r} = 1 + \epsilon\cos\theta.$$

This is the form in which the equation of a conic section has been used in the text (Eq. 13.12). (In some texts, the equation for the conic section is derived using the angle $\pi - \theta$, and thus the equation appears in the form $\epsilon d/r = 1 - \epsilon\cos\theta$.) In the case of an ellipse, which is a closed curve, point A corresponds to $\theta = 0$ and point A' to $\theta = \pi$. Thus, according to the polar equation, we have

$$r_1 = \frac{\epsilon d}{1+\epsilon} \quad \text{and} \quad r_2 = \frac{\epsilon d}{1-\epsilon}.$$

Then, since $r_1 + r_2 = 2a$, the semimajor axis is given by

$$a = \tfrac{1}{2}(r_1 + r_2) = \frac{\epsilon d}{1-\epsilon^2}.$$

The semiminor axis T is $b = a\sqrt{1-\epsilon^2}$ and the area of the ellipse is

$$S = \pi ab = \pi a^2\sqrt{1-\epsilon^2}.$$

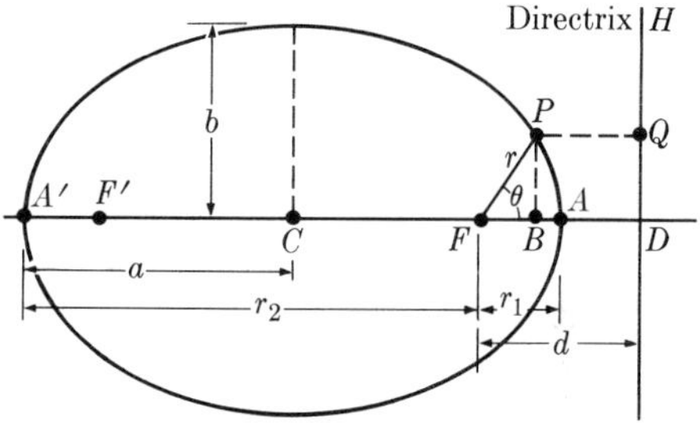

Fig. 13–11. Geometrical elements of the ellipse.

A circle is a special case of an ellipse, when $\epsilon = 0$. (For more details about conic sections, and in particular the ellipse, see G. B. Thomas, *Calculus and Analytic Geometry*, third edition. Reading, Mass.: Addison-Wesley, 1962, page 473.)

EXAMPLE 13.5. Relate the total energy and the angular momentum in the case of elliptical motion to the semimajor axis a and the eccentricity ϵ of the ellipse.

Solution: From the preceding note on conic sections, we have that the semimajor axis of an ellipse is expressed in terms of the eccentricity ϵ and the distance d according to

$$a = \frac{\epsilon d}{1-\epsilon^2}.$$

Therefore, from Eq. (13.13), we have

$$E = \frac{L^2}{2\,d^2m}\cdot\frac{\epsilon^2 - 1}{\epsilon^2} = -\frac{L^2}{2\epsilon\, dma}.$$

But from Eq. (13.14) with $E_p = -\gamma mm'/r$, we have

$$-\frac{\gamma mm'}{r} = -\frac{L^2}{m\epsilon\, dr} \quad \text{or} \quad \frac{L^2}{m\epsilon d} = \gamma mm'.$$

Thus, making the corresponding substitution in the expression for E, we obtain

$$E = -\frac{\gamma mm'}{2a}.$$

Comparing this result with Eq. (13.6), which we derived for circular orbits, we see that they are essentially identical, since $a = r$ for a circular orbit. This result also confirms the fact that the total energy is negative and depends only on the semimajor axis a. So all the elliptical orbits having the same semimajor axis as that illustrated in Fig. 13–12 have the same total energy, although they have different eccentricities. By using the expression $\epsilon d = a(1 - \epsilon^2)$, we may write another useful relation:

$$L^2 = \gamma m^2 m' \epsilon d = \gamma m^2 m' a(1 - \epsilon^2).$$

Eliminating the semimajor axis a by using the previous expression for the energy E, we obtain the eccentricity of the orbit,

$$\epsilon^2 = 1 + \frac{2E}{m}\left(\frac{L}{\gamma mm'}\right)^2.$$

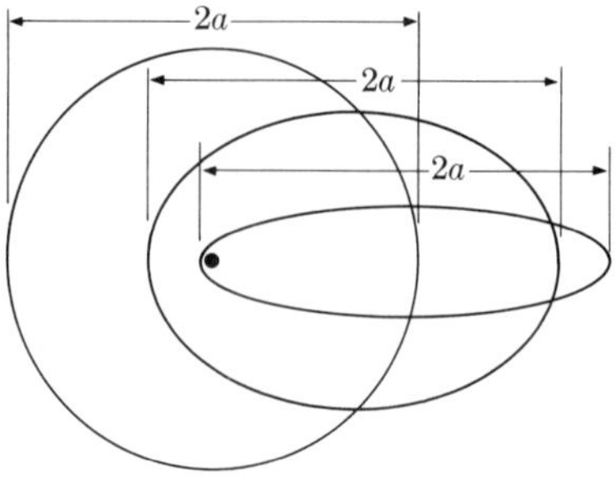

Fig. 13–12. Elliptical orbits for different values of angular momentum but the same energy. All orbits have the same focus and major axis, but differ in eccentricity.

Thus we see that the eccentricity depends on the energy and the angular momentum. The orbits illustrated in Fig. 13–12 all have the same energy, but differ in angular momentum and have different eccentricities. In other words, *in an inverse-square field, to a given total energy there may correspond many different angular momentum states.* This is of great importance in the discussion of atomic structure, because in an atom there may be several electrons which have the same energy but which differ in angular momentum.

We may summarize the preceding results by saying that *the "size" of the orbit* (as given by the semimajor axis) *is determined by the energy,* and that *for a given energy, the "shape" of the orbit* (as given by the eccentricity) *is determined by the angular momentum.*

EXAMPLE 13.6. Verify that Kepler's third law holds true for elliptical orbits.

Solution: Let us recall that in Section 13.2 we used Kepler's third law to verify the inverse-square law of force in the case of circular orbits. Now we shall verify that this law also holds for any elliptical orbit. The proof is a straightforward algebraic manipulation based on the properties of the ellipse.

From Eq. (7.35), which expresses the constancy of angular momentum, we have that

$$r^2 \frac{d\theta}{dt} = \frac{L}{m} \quad \text{or} \quad r^2\, d\theta = \frac{L}{m}\, dt.$$

In a period P the radius vector sweeps the whole area of the ellipse and θ goes from 0 to 2π. Thus we would obtain the area of the ellipse by writing

$$\text{Area} = \tfrac{1}{2}\int_0^{2\pi} r^2\, d\theta = \frac{L}{2m}\int_0^P dt = \frac{LP}{2m}.$$

But the area of the ellipse is $\pi a^2(1 - \epsilon^2)^{1/2}$ (see note at the end of Section 13.5). Therefore

$$\pi^2 a^4(1 - \epsilon^2) = L^2P^2/4m^2.$$

But from Example 13.5 we have that $L^2 = \gamma m^2 m' a(1 - \epsilon^2)$. Thus

$$\pi^2 a^3 = \tfrac{1}{4}\gamma m' P^2 \qquad \text{or} \qquad P^2 = \frac{4\pi^2}{\gamma m'} a^3,$$

which is Kepler's third law, since the average value of r is obviously proportional to the semimajor axis a.

13.6 Gravitational Field

We shall now introduce a very important concept in physics, that of the *gravitational field*. Suppose that we have a mass m and that we place, at different positions around m, another mass m' (Fig. 13–13). At each position the mass m' experiences a force due to its gravitational interaction with m given by Eq. (13.2),

$$\boldsymbol{F} = -\frac{\gamma m m'}{r^2} \boldsymbol{u}_r.$$

Of course, at each position m', the mass m experiences an equal but opposite force. However, at the moment we are interested only in what happens to m'.

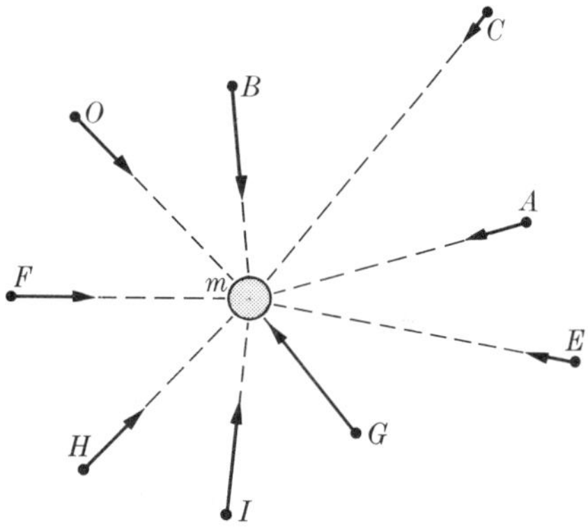

Fig. 13–13. Gravitational field produced by a point mass at several points.

We may then conveniently say that the mass m produces, in the space around it, a physical situation that we call a gravitational field, and that is recognized by the force that m exerts on another mass, such as m', brought into that region. Whether something exists in the free space around m, even if we do not use a test mass m' to probe the field, is something that we can only speculate on, and is to a certain extent an irrelevant question, since we notice the gravitational field only when we bring in a second mass.

The *gravitational field strength* $\mathcal{G}$ produced by the mass m at a point P is defined as the force exerted on the unit of mass placed at P. Then

$$\mathcal{G} = \frac{\boldsymbol{F}}{m'} = -\frac{\gamma m}{r^2} \boldsymbol{u}_r. \tag{13.15}$$

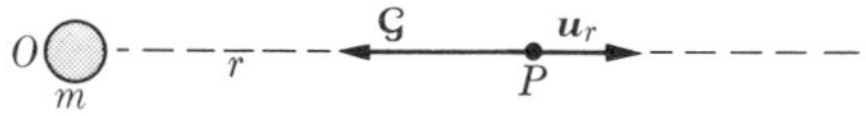

Fig. 13–14. The gravitational field at P, produced by the point mass m, is opposed to the unit vector $\boldsymbol{u}_r$.

Thus the gravitational field $\mathcal{G}$ has the direction opposite to that of the unit vector $\boldsymbol{u}_r$, which goes from the mass producing the field to the point where the field is computed. In other words, *the gravitational field always points toward the mass producing it.*

Expression (13.15) gives the gravitational field at a distance r from a particle of mass m placed at O. We may then associate with each point in the space around m (Fig. 13–14) a vector $\mathcal{G}$ given by Eq. (13.15), and such that the gravitational force exerted on any mass placed in that region is obtained by multiplying the mass by the corresponding $\mathcal{G}$. That is, $\boldsymbol{F}$ = (mass of particle) $\times\ \mathcal{G}$.

From its definition we see that the gravitational field strength is measured in $\mathrm{N\ kg^{-1}}$ or $\mathrm{m\ s^{-2}}$, and it is dimensionally equivalent to an acceleration. Comparing Eq. (13.15) with Eq. (7.16), we note that the acceleration of gravity may be considered as the gravitational field strength at the surface of the earth.

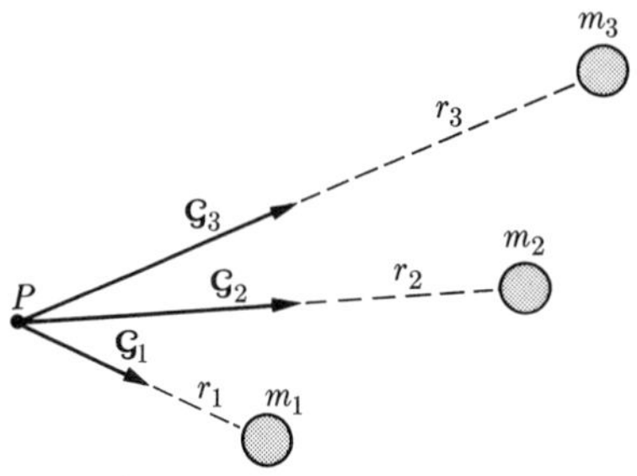

Fig. 13–15. Resultant gravitational field of several masses.

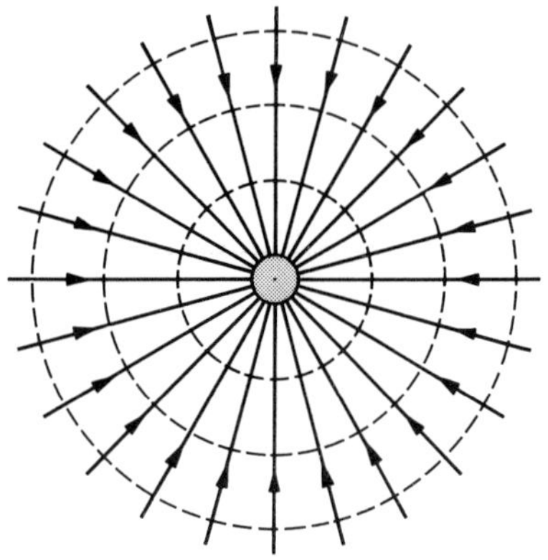

Fig. 13–16. Lines of force and equipotential surfaces of the gravitational field of a point mass.

Suppose now that we have several masses, m_1, m_2, m_3, ... (Fig. 13–15), each one producing its own gravitational field. The total force on a particle of mass m at P is obviously

$$\begin{aligned} \boldsymbol{F} &= m\mathcal{G}_1 + m\mathcal{G}_2 + m\mathcal{G}_3 + \cdots \\ &= m(\mathcal{G}_1 + \mathcal{G}_2 + \mathcal{G}_3 + \cdots) = m\mathcal{G}, \end{aligned} \tag{13.16}$$

where $\mathcal{G}_1$, $\mathcal{G}_2$, $\mathcal{G}_3$, ... are the gravitational fields produced by each mass at point P, and are computed according to Eq. (13.15). The resultant gravitational field at point P is then the vector sum

$$\mathcal{G} = \mathcal{G}_1 + \mathcal{G}_2 + \mathcal{G}_3 + \cdots = -\gamma \textstyle\sum_i \dfrac{m_i}{r_i^2}\, \boldsymbol{u}_{ri}. \tag{13.17}$$

A gravitational field can be represented pictorially by *lines of force.* A line of force is drawn such that at each point the *direction* of the field is tangent to the line that passes through the point. The lines of force are drawn so that their density is proportional to the *strength* of the field. Figure 13–16 depicts the field about a single mass; all the lines of force are radial and the field strength is greater nearer the mass. Figure 13–17 shows the fields about two unequal masses, namely, the earth and the moon. Here the lines are not radial and in the vicinity of point A the field strength is very weak (at A it is zero).

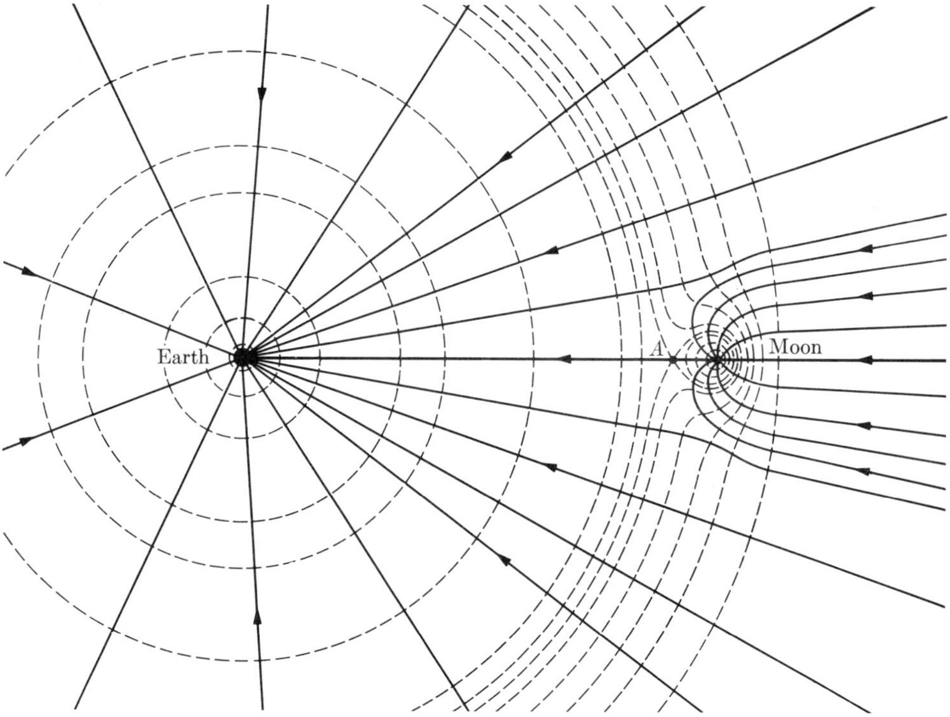

Fig. 13–17. Lines of force and equipotential surfaces of the resultant gravitational field, produced by the earth and the moon. At A the resultant gravitational field is zero. [After W. T. Scott, *Am. J. Phys.* **33,** 712 (1965)]

Another important concept is that of *gravitational potential,* defined as the potential energy per unit mass placed in the gravitational field. Thus if, at a certain point in a gravitational field, a mass m' has a potential energy E_p, the gravitational potential at that point is $V = E_p/m'$. The gravitational potential is thus expressed in the units J kg^{-1} or $\text{m}^2\ \text{s}^{-2}$.

From Eq. (13.3), dividing by m', we see that the gravitational potential at a distance r from a mass m is

$$V = -\gamma m/r. \tag{13.18}$$

If, instead of one particle, we have several masses, as in Fig. 13–15, the gravitational potential at P is the scalar sum $V = V_1 + V_2 + V_3 + \cdots$, or

$$V = -\gamma\left(\frac{m_1}{r_1} + \frac{m_2}{r_2} + \frac{m_3}{r_3} + \cdots\right) = -\gamma \textstyle\sum_i \dfrac{m_i}{r_i}. \tag{13.19}$$

Comparing Eq. (13.18) with Eq. (13.15), we note that the magnitude of the gravitational field is

$$\mathcal{G} = -\partial V/\partial r, \tag{13.20}$$

and in general, from $\boldsymbol{F} = -\text{grad } E_p$, we obtain

$$\mathcal{G} = -\text{grad } V, \tag{13.21}$$

where "grad" stands for gradient, as indicated in Section 8.7. Therefore *the gravitational field is the negative of the gradient of the gravitational potential.* In rectangular coordinates we may write

$$\mathcal{G}_x = -\frac{\partial V}{\partial x}, \qquad \mathcal{G}_y = -\frac{\partial V}{\partial y}, \qquad \mathcal{G}_z = -\frac{\partial V}{\partial z}.$$

The concept of gravitational potential is very useful because, since it is a scalar quantity, it can be computed very easily, as indicated by Eq. (13.19), and afterward the gravitational field strength $\mathcal{G}$ can be obtained by applying Eq. (13.21).

By joining the points at which the gravitational potential has the same value, we may obtain a series of surfaces called *equipotential surfaces.* For example, in the case of a single particle, when the potential is given by Eq. (13.18), the equipotential surfaces correspond to the spheres $r = \text{const}$, indicated by the dashed lines in Fig. 13–16. In Fig. 13–17 the equipotential surfaces have also been indicated by dashed lines. Note that in each case the equipotential surfaces are perpendicular to the lines of force. This can be verified, in general, in the following way. Let us take two points, very close to each other, on the same equipotential surface. When we move a particle from one of these points to the other, the work done by the gravitational field acting on the particle is zero. This results from the fact that the work done is equal to the change in potential energy. In this case there is no change in the potential energy because the two points have the same gravitational potential. The fact that this work is zero implies that the force is perpendicular to the displacement. Therefore *the direction of the gravitational field is perpendicular to the equipotential surfaces.* This means that if we know the lines of force we can easily plot the equipotential surfaces, and conversely.*

EXAMPLE 13.7. Discuss the gravitational field produced by two equal masses separated the distance $2a$.

Solution: Placing our coordinate axes as indicated in Fig. 13–18 and applying Eq. (13.19) for two equal masses, we have that the gravitational potential at a point $P(x, y)$ is

$$V = -\gamma m \left(\frac{1}{r_1} + \frac{1}{r_2}\right).$$

Now, from Fig. 13–18, we can see that

$$r_1 = [(x - a)^2 + y^2]^{1/2},$$

$$r_2 = [(x + a)^2 + y^2]^{1/2}.$$

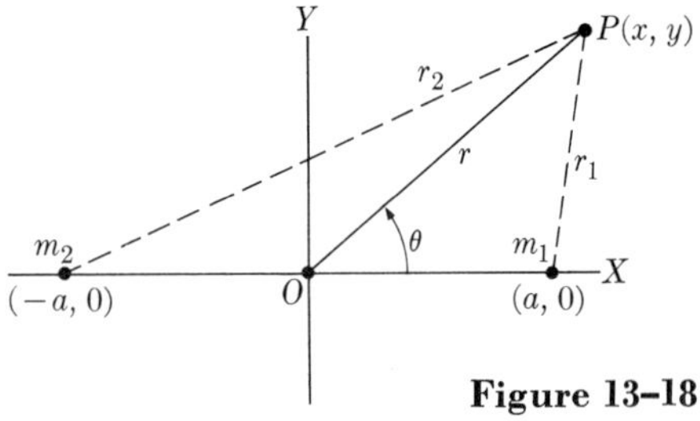

Figure 13–18

* The student is reminded of the note after Section 8.7 regarding the gradient, where it was shown that the vector grad E_p is perpendicular to the surfaces $E_p = \text{const}$. This is equivalent to the above statement, since $\mathcal{G} = -\text{grad } V$.

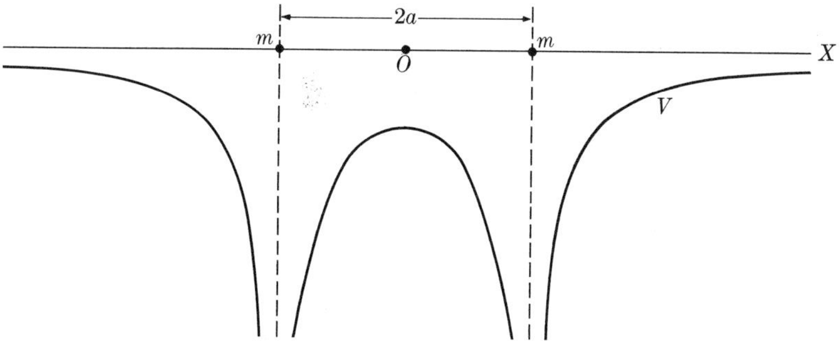

Fig. 13–19. Variation of the gravitational potential produced by two equal masses along the line joining them.

Thus

$$V = -\gamma m \left\{ \frac{1}{[(x-a)^2 + y^2]^{1/2}} + \frac{1}{[(x+a)^2 + y^2]^{1/2}} \right\}.$$

The change in the gravitational potential produced by the two masses as we move from $-\infty$ to $+\infty$ along the X-axis is illustrated in Fig. 13–19. We suggest that the student make a similar plot for the potential produced by four equal masses, all spaced the same amount along a straight line.

To obtain the gravitational field, we apply Eq. (13.21), using rectangular coordinates, to obtain

$$\mathcal{G}_x = -\frac{\partial V}{\partial x} = -\gamma m \left\{ \frac{x-a}{[(x-a)^2 + y^2]^{3/2}} + \frac{x+a}{[(x+a)^2 + y^2]^{3/2}} \right\},$$

$$\mathcal{G}_y = -\frac{\partial V}{\partial y} = -\gamma m \left\{ \frac{y}{[(x-a)^2 + y^2]^{3/2}} + \frac{y}{[(x+a)^2 + y^2]^{3/2}} \right\}.$$

The field has symmetry of revolution around the X-axis. We suggest that the student investigate the field along the Y- and Z-axes and that he plot the lines of force; these must be symmetric relative to O. We also suggest that he repeat the problem, using the polar coordinates r, θ of P, and finding $\mathcal{G}_r$ and $\mathcal{G}_\theta$.

EXAMPLE 13.8. Obtain the gravitational field produced by a thin layer of matter spread over an infinite plane.

Solution: Let us proceed by dividing the plane into a series of rings, all concentric, with the projection O of P on the plane (Fig. 13–20). Each ring has a radius R and a width dR. Therefore the area is $(2\pi R)\,dR$. If σ is the mass per unit area on the plane, the mass of the ring is $dm = \sigma(2\pi R\,dR) = 2\pi\sigma R\,dR$. All points of the ring are at the same distance r from P, and therefore the potential it produces at P is

$$dV = -\frac{\gamma\,dm}{r} = -\frac{2\pi\gamma\sigma R\,dR}{(z^2 + R^2)^{1/2}},$$

since $r = (z^2 + R^2)^{1/2}$. To obtain the total potential we have to add the contributions of all the rings. That is, we have to integrate the above expression from $R = 0$ to $R = \infty$.

The result is

$$V = -2\pi\gamma\sigma \int_0^\infty \frac{R\,dR}{(z^2 + R^2)^{1/2}}$$

$$= -2\pi\gamma\sigma(\infty - z).$$

We thus obtain an infinite but constant contribution from the upper limit. Since we are interested only in the potential *difference* between the plane and the point, which is what we actually measure experimentally, we must subtract from the above expression the value for $z = 0$; that is, $-2\pi\gamma\sigma(\infty)$. Thus we finally obtain

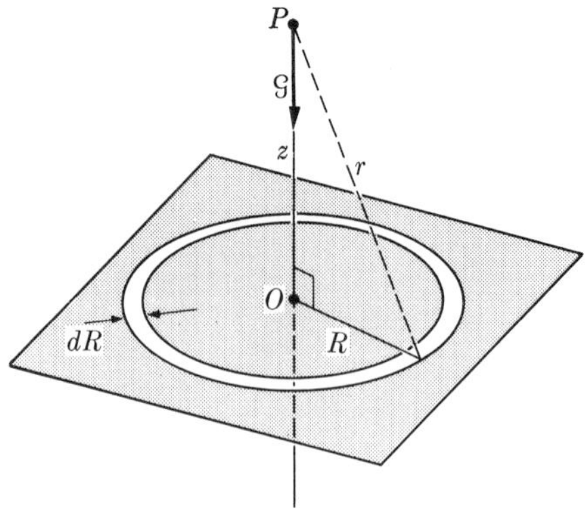

Fig. 13–20. Gravitational field of a plane.

$$V = 2\pi\gamma\sigma z.$$

What we have actually done is to perform a process called *renormalization*, in which we assign the value of zero to the potential of the plane, and we are therefore required to subtract an infinite quantity. This situation is illustrative of similar cases in other physical applications in which the result obtained is infinite or divergent but, because we are interested only in the difference between two infinite results, this difference may be expressed by a finite or convergent expression.

We obtain the field at P (since z is the coordinate of the point) by applying Eq. (13.20), which gives us

$$\mathcal{G} = -\frac{\partial V}{\partial z} = -2\pi\gamma\sigma.$$

The minus sign indicates that $\mathcal{G}$ is pointing toward the plane. Note that our process of renormalization does not affect the field, since the derivative of a constant, no matter how large the constant, is always zero. The gravitational field is thus constant or independent of the position of the point. We say then that the field is *uniform*. Actually, the expressions we have derived for V and $\mathcal{G}$ are valid only for $z > 0$. But the symmetry of the problem indicates that the field for $z < 0$ must be the mirror image of the results for $z > 0$. Thus, for $z < 0$, we must write $V = -2\pi\gamma\sigma z$ and $\mathcal{G} = +2\pi\gamma\sigma$. These results are perfectly compatible with our calculation, because the expression we used to compute V depends on z^2 and, in writing the solution, we should have expressed it in the form $V = 2\pi\gamma\sigma|z|$, which is now valid for $z \lessgtr 0$.

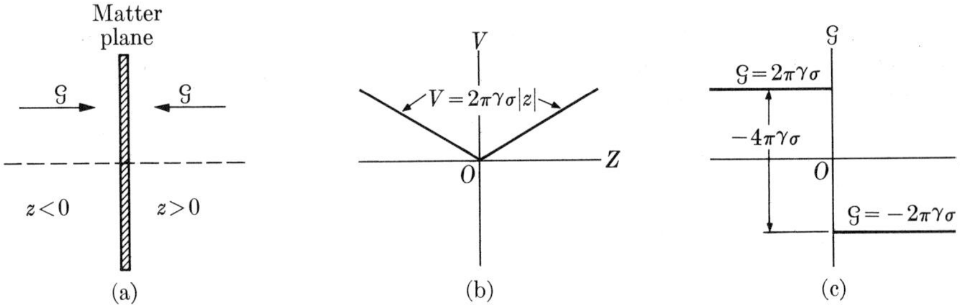

Fig. 13–21. Variation of $\mathcal{G}$ and V for matter on a plane.

The potential and the field on both sides of the matter plane have been illustrated in Fig. 13–21. We may note that, in moving from left to right across the plane, the potential does not change in value (but changes in slope discontinuously) and the field suffers a sudden change of $-4\pi\gamma\sigma$. It can be proved that this is a general result valid for any surface distribution of matter, irrespective of its shape.

13.7 Gravitational Field Due to a Spherical Body

All the formulas stated so far in this chapter are strictly valid only for point masses. When we applied them to the motion of the planets around the sun, it was under the assumption that their sizes are small compared with their separation. Even if this is true, their finite sizes may possibly introduce some geometrical factor in Eq. (13.1). Similarly, when we were relating the acceleration of gravity g to the mass and the radius of the earth in Example 13.1, we used Eq. (13.1), in spite of the fact that the above reasoning of relatively small size is not applicable in this case. Newton himself was worried by this geometrical problem, and delayed the publication of his law of gravitation for about 20 years until he found a correct explanation. In this section we are going to compute the gravitational field produced by a spherical body. We shall start by computing the gravitational field of a spherical shell; that is, of a mass uniformly distributed over the surface of a sphere which is empty inside.

Let us call a the radius of the sphere and r the distance of an arbitrary point P from the center C of the sphere. We are interested in obtaining the strength of the gravitational field at P. Consider first the case when P is outside the sphere (Fig. 13–22). We may divide the surface of the sphere into narrow circular strips, all with centers on the line AB. The radius of each strip is $a \sin\theta$ and the width is $a\,d\theta$. Therefore the area of the strip is

$$\text{Area} = \text{length} \times \text{width} = (2\pi a \sin\theta)(a\,d\theta) = 2\pi a^2 \sin\theta\,d\theta.$$

If m is the total mass uniformly distributed over the surface of the sphere, the mass per unit area is $m/4\pi a^2$ and the mass of the circular strip is

$$\frac{m}{4\pi a^2}(2\pi a^2 \sin\theta\,d\theta) = \tfrac{1}{2}m \sin\theta\,d\theta.$$

All points of the strip are at the same distance R from P. Therefore, applying Eq. (13.19), we find that the potential produced by the strip at P is

$$dV = -\frac{\gamma(\frac{1}{2}m\sin\theta\,d\theta)}{R} = -\frac{\gamma m}{2R}\sin\theta\,d\theta.$$

From Fig. 13–22, using the law of cosines, Eq. (M.16), we note that

$$R^2 = a^2 + r^2 - 2ar\cos\theta.$$

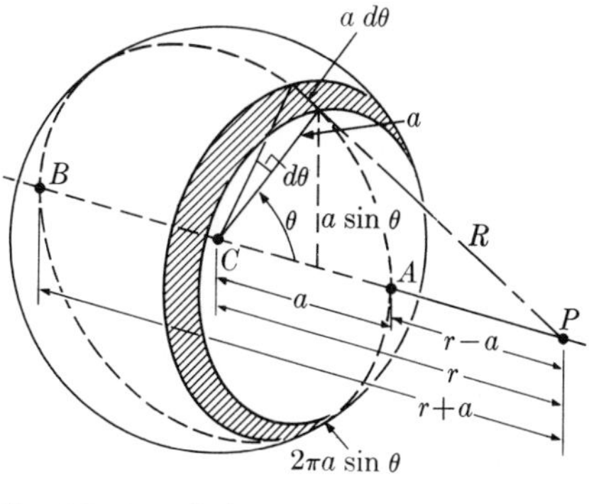

Fig. 13–22. Calculation of the gravitational field at a point outside a mass distributed uniformly over a spherical shell.

Differentiating, since a and r are constant, we obtain

$$2R\,dR = 2ar \sin\theta\,d\theta \qquad \text{or} \qquad \sin\theta\,d\theta = \frac{R\,dR}{ar}.$$

Substituting in the expression for dV, we get

$$dV = -\frac{\gamma m}{2ar}\,dR. \tag{13.22}$$

To obtain the total gravitational potential we must integrate over all the surface of the sphere. The limits for R, when the point P is outside the sphere, are $r + a$ and $r - a$. Therefore

$$V = -\frac{\gamma m}{2ar}\int_{r-a}^{r+a} dR = -\frac{\gamma m}{2ar}(2a) = -\frac{\gamma m}{r}, \qquad r > a, \tag{13.23}$$

is the potential at a point outside a homogeneous spherical shell. If the point P is inside the sphere (Fig. 13–23), the limits for R are $a + r$ and $a - r$, resulting in

$$V = -\frac{\gamma m}{2ar}\int_{a-r}^{a+r} dR = -\frac{\gamma m}{2ar}(2r) = -\frac{\gamma m}{a}, \qquad r < a, \tag{13.24}$$

which yields a gravitational potential that is a constant, independent of the position of P.

Applying Eq. (13.21), we find that the gravitational field at points outside the homogeneous spherical shell is

$$\mathcal{G} = -\frac{\gamma m}{r^2}\,\boldsymbol{u}_r, \qquad r > a, \tag{13.25}$$

and at points inside the spherical shell it is

$$\mathcal{G} = 0, \qquad r < a. \tag{13.26}$$

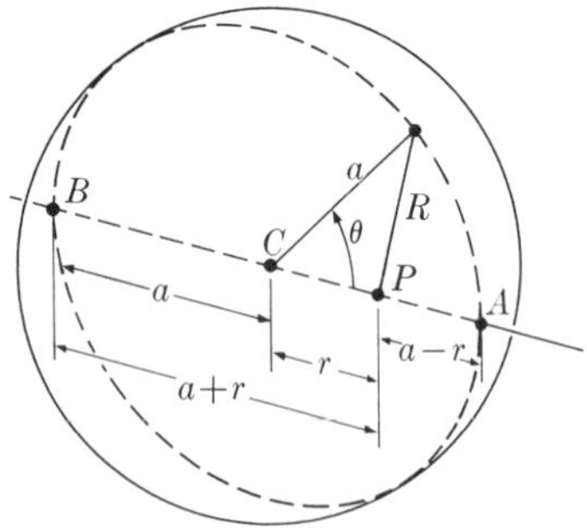

Fig. 13–23. Calculation of the gravitational field at a point inside a mass distributed uniformly over a spherical shell.

By comparing Eqs. (13.23) and (13.25) with Eqs. (13.18) and (13.15), we reach the following conclusion: *The gravitational field and potential at points outside a mass uniformly distributed over a spherical shell is identical to the gravitational field and potential of a particle of the same mass located at the center of the sphere. At all points inside the spherical shell, the field is zero and the potential is constant.*

Figure 13–24 shows the variation of $\mathcal{G}$ and V with distance from the center of the sphere. It may be seen that in moving from the center toward infinity, the potential at the spherical shell does not change in value (but the slope does change discontinuously). The field, however, suffers a sudden change of $-\gamma m/a^2$. Recalling that if σ is the surface mass density of the shell, $m = 4\pi a^2\sigma$, we see that the sudden change in the field is $-4\pi\gamma\sigma$. We thus obtain the same results as in Example 13.8 for a plane.

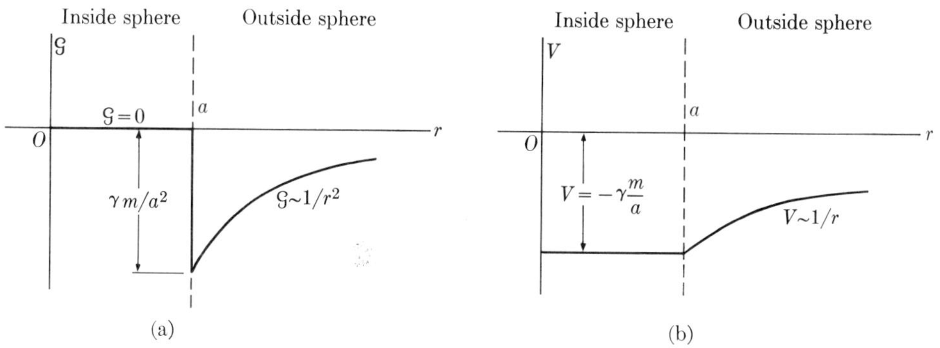

Fig. 13–24. Variation of $\mathcal{G}$ and V, as a function of the distance from the center, for a mass distributed uniformly over a spherical shell.

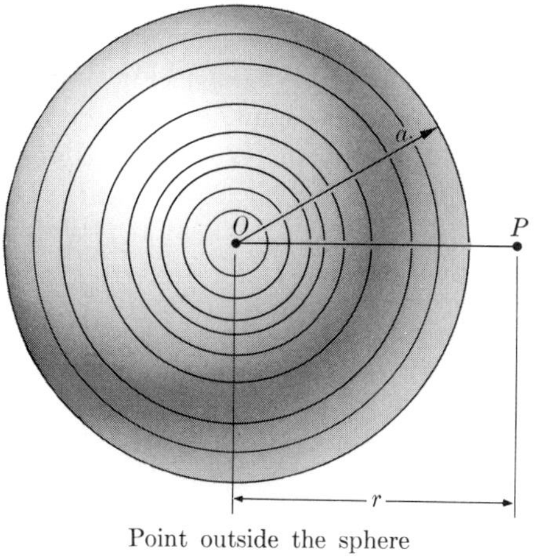

Fig. 13–25. Calculation of the gravitational field at a point outside a solid sphere.

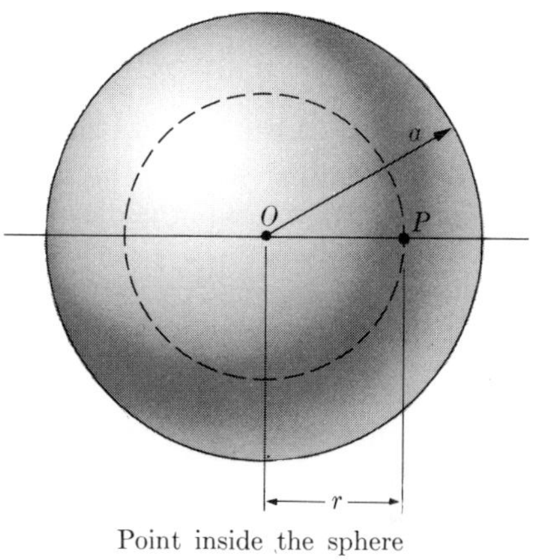

Fig. 13–26. Calculation of the gravitational field at a point inside a solid sphere.

Now suppose that the mass is uniformly distributed throughout all the volume of the sphere; i.e., the sphere is solid. We may then consider the sphere to be built in an onionlike fashion, as the superposition of a series of thin spherical layers or shells. Each layer produces a field given by Eqs. (13.25) or (13.26). For a point outside the sphere (Fig. 13–25), since the distance r from the center to P is the same for all layers, the masses add, again giving the result (13.25). Therefore *a solid homogeneous sphere produces, on outside points, a gravitational field and potential identical to those of a particle of the same mass located at the center of the sphere.**

---

* This result still holds true when the sphere, instead of being homogeneous, has its mass distributed with spherical symmetry; i.e., when its density is a function of the distance from the center only. But it does not hold if the mass is distributed in a manner that depends on the direction.

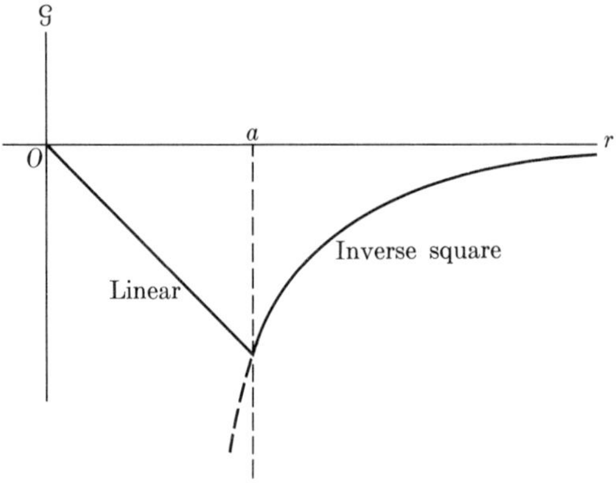

Fig. 13–27. Variation of $\mathcal{G}$ for a solid homogeneous sphere as a function of the distance from the center.

To obtain the field inside the homogeneous sphere, let us consider a point P a distance r from the center, with $r < a$. We draw a sphere of radius r (Fig. 13–26), and observe that those shells with radius larger than r do not contribute to the field at P, according to Eq. (13.26), since P is inside them, and the resultant field of all shells with a radius smaller than r produces a field similar to Eq. (13.25). Let us call m' the mass inside the dashed sphere. By Eq. (13.25), the field at P will be

$$\mathcal{G} = -\frac{\gamma m'}{r^2}\boldsymbol{u}_r. \tag{13.27}$$

The volume of the whole sphere is $\frac{4}{3}\pi a^3$ and, since the sphere is homogeneous, the mass per unit volume is $m/\frac{4}{3}\pi a^3$. The mass m' contained in the sphere of radius r is then

$$m' = \frac{m}{\frac{4}{3}\pi a^3}\left(\tfrac{4}{3}\pi r^3\right) = \frac{mr^3}{a^3}.$$

Substituting this result in Eq. (13.27), we finally obtain for the field at a point inside the homogeneous sphere

$$\mathcal{G} = -\frac{\gamma mr}{a^3}\boldsymbol{u}_r. \tag{13.28}$$

Therefore the gravitational field at a given point inside the homogeneous sphere is proportional to the distance r from the center. The reason why the field increases inside the sphere when the point moves away from the center is that the decrease due to the inverse-square law is overcompensated for by the increase in mass, which is proportional to the cube of the distance. Figure 13–27 depicts the variation of $\mathcal{G}$ in terms of r for a solid homogeneous sphere. This figure gives, for example, the variation which the weight of a body would have when it moved from the center of the earth to a point a great distance from it, if the earth were homogeneous.

We shall leave it to the student to verify that the gravitational potential at a point outside the homogeneous sphere is still given by Eq. (13.23), but at a point inside the sphere, the gravitational potential is

$$V = \frac{\gamma m}{2a^3}(r^2 - 3a^2), \qquad r < a.$$

Note that in the spherical problem we have considered in this section, the gravitational field at a point depends only on the distance from the point to the center, but not on the direction of the line joining the center to the point. This result was to be expected on the basis of the symmetry of the problem. If we were to consider, instead of a homogeneous sphere, a body with a different geometry or symmetry, or a nonhomogeneous sphere (with the mass distributed without spherical symmetry), we should expect the angles to appear in the formula. But for problems of spherical symmetry the properties depend on the distance from the point to the center only. The application of symmetry considerations greatly simplifies the solution of many problems in physics.

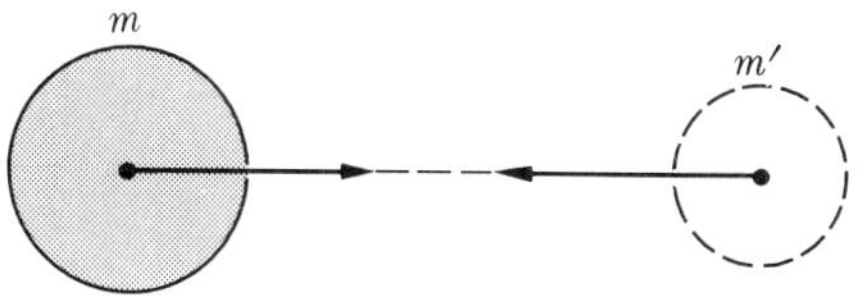

Fig. 13–28. The gravitational interaction between two homogeneous spherical bodies depends only on the distance between their centers.

We are now in a position to verify that Eq. (13.1) for the gravitational attraction between two point masses also holds for two homogeneous spherical bodies. Assume that we place a point mass m' at a distance r from the center of a spherical mass m (Fig. 13–28). The field it experiences is $\mathcal{G} = \gamma m/r^2$, and the force on m' is $m'\mathcal{G} = \gamma mm'/r^2$. By the law of action and reaction, m' must exert an equal and opposite force on m. This force is interpreted as being due to the field created by m' in the region occupied by m. Now, if we replace m' by a homogeneous spherical body of the same mass, the field around m does not change, because of the theorem we have just proved, and therefore the force on m remains the same. Again we invoke the principle of action and reaction, and conclude that the force on the spherical mass m' is still the same. Consequently, two homogeneous spherical masses attract each other according to the law (13.1), where r is the distance between their centers. If the masses are neither spherical nor homogeneous, some geometrical factors, including angles defining their relative orientation, will appear in the expression for their interaction.

EXAMPLE 13.9. Discuss the variation of the acceleration of gravity which occurs when one moves a small distance upward or downward from the earth's surface.

Solution: Let us call h the height of the body above the earth's surface. Its distance to the center is $r = R + h$. The intensity of the gravitational field, according to Eq. (13.25), is

$$\mathcal{G} = \frac{\gamma M}{(R+h)^2},$$

where the mass m has been replaced by the earth's mass M. Considering that h is small compared with R and using the binomial approximation (M.28) and the result of Example 13.1, we have

$$\mathcal{G} = \frac{\gamma M}{R^2(1+h/R)^2} = g\left(1+\frac{h}{R}\right)^{-2} \approx g\left(1-\frac{2h}{R}\right).$$

Introducing the values for g and R, we get

$$\mathcal{G} = 9.81 - 3.06 \times 10^{-6}h \text{ m s}^{-2}.$$

This expression gives, approximately, the variation in the acceleration of gravity and in the weight of a body when one moves *up* from the earth a small distance h.

If instead, we move into the interior of the earth a distance h, we have $r = R - h$. Using Eq. (13.28), with m replaced by M and a by R, we obtain

$$\mathcal{G} = \frac{\gamma M(R-h)}{R^3} = \frac{\gamma M}{R^2}\left(1-\frac{h}{R}\right) = g\left(1-\frac{h}{R}\right),$$

or, introducing the proper values,

$$\mathcal{G} = 9.81 - 1.53 \times 10^{-6}h \text{ m s}^{-2}.$$

So in both cases gravity decreases, but it decreases at a faster rate for points above the surface than below. (Recall Fig. 13–27.)

13.8 Principle of Equivalence

The fact that the inertial and the gravitational masses are the same for all bodies gives rise to an important result:

> *All bodies at the same place in a gravitational field experience the same acceleration.*

An example of this fact is Galileo's discovery that all bodies fall to earth with the same acceleration. This discovery, as we have already mentioned, is in turn an indirect proof of the identity of inertial and gravitational mass.

To prove the above statement, we note that in a place where the gravitational field is $\boldsymbol{\mathcal{G}}$, the force on a body of mass m is $\boldsymbol{F} = m\boldsymbol{\mathcal{G}}$, and its acceleration is

$$\boldsymbol{a} = \frac{\boldsymbol{F}}{m} = \boldsymbol{\mathcal{G}},$$

which is independent of the mass m of the body subject to the action of the gravitational field. Note that the acceleration of the body is equal to the field strength, which is consistent with our previous result that the gravitational field is measured in m s^{-2}.

If an experimenter's laboratory is placed in a gravitational field, he will observe that all bodies with which he is experimenting, and which are subject to no other forces, experience a common acceleration. The experimenter, by observing this common acceleration, may conclude that his laboratory is in a gravitational field.

However, this conclusion is not the only possible explanation for the observation of a common acceleration. In Section 6.2, when we discussed relative motion, we indicated that when a moving observer has an acceleration $\boldsymbol{a}_0$ relative to an inertial observer, and $\boldsymbol{a}$ is the acceleration of a body as measured by the inertial observer, the acceleration measured by the moving observer is expressed by

$$\boldsymbol{a}' = \boldsymbol{a} - \boldsymbol{a}_0.$$

If the body is free, the acceleration $\boldsymbol{a}$ measured by the inertial observer is zero. Therefore, the acceleration measured by the accelerated observer is $\boldsymbol{a}' = -\boldsymbol{a}_0$. Thus all free objects appear to the accelerated observer to have a common acceleration $-\boldsymbol{a}_0$, a situation identical to that found in a gravitational field of strength $\mathcal{G} = -\boldsymbol{a}_0$. Thus we may conclude that

> *an observer has no means of distinguishing whether his laboratory is in a uniform gravitational field or in an accelerated frame of reference.*

This statement is known as the *principle of equivalence*, since it shows an equivalence, insofar as the description of motion is concerned, between a gravitational field and an accelerated frame of reference. Gravitation and inertia thus appear to be not two different properties of matter, but only two different aspects of a more fundamental and universal characteristic of all matter.

Suppose, for example, that an observer has a laboratory in a railroad car moving along a straight horizontal track with constant velocity, and that the windows are blackened so that the observer has no access to the outside world. He experiments with some billiard balls by dropping them, and notes that all of them fall with the same acceleration. He may then conclude that he is surrounded by a vertical gravitational field in the downward direction, which is the normal interpretation. But he could equally well assume that what is happening is that his car is being lifted with a vertical acceleration, equal and opposite to that of the balls, and that the balls are free and not subject to a gravitational field.

Suppose now that the observer places the balls on a billiard table located in the car. When the observer notes that the balls on the table roll toward the rear of the car with a common acceleration, he may conclude that his laboratory either is acted on by a new horizontal gravitational field directed toward the rear of the car or that his laboratory is being accelerated horizontally in the forward direction. The second assumption is the usual one, associated with a decision by the train engineer to speed up the train. However, the train could instead be going up a grade, which is equivalent to producing a gravitational field parallel to the car's floor, with the same result to the motion of the billiard balls.

Because of the principle of equivalence,

> *the laws of nature must be written in such a way that it is impossible to distinguish between a uniform gravitational field and an accelerated frame of reference,*

a statement which constitutes the basis of the *general principle of relativity*, proposed by Einstein in 1915. This principle requires that physical laws be written in a form independent of the state of motion of the frame of reference. As we can see, the fundamental idea of the general principle of relativity is very simple. However, its mathematical formulation is rather complex, and will not be discussed here.

Let us now examine the case of an accelerated observer in a gravitational field $\mathcal{G}$. The acceleration of bodies subject only to the gravitational field as measured by our observer is expressed as $\boldsymbol{a}' = \mathcal{G} - \boldsymbol{a}_0$. As a concrete illustration, let us consider the case of a rocket accelerated upward from the earth. We have then that $\mathcal{G} = \boldsymbol{g}$. Let us write $\boldsymbol{a}_0 = -n\boldsymbol{g}$ for the rocket's acceleration relative to the earth, where n gives the value of $\boldsymbol{a}_0$ relative to $\boldsymbol{g}$. (The minus sign is due to the fact that the rocket is accelerated in the upward direction.) Then $\boldsymbol{a}' = (n + 1)\boldsymbol{g}$ is the acceleration, relative to the rocket, of a free body inside the rocket. For example, in a rocket accelerated upward with an acceleration four times that of gravity ($n = 4$), the weight of all bodies inside the rocket is five times their normal weight. This apparent increase in weight is particularly important at the launching stage when the rocket's acceleration is largest.

Now consider, as another example, an orbiting satellite. Here $\boldsymbol{a}_0 = \mathcal{G}$, because the satellite is moving under the gravitational action of the earth. In this case $\boldsymbol{a}' = 0$, and all bodies within the satellite appear to be weightless, since their acceleration relative to the satellite is zero. This is only a relative weightlessness because both the satellite and its contents are moving in the same gravitational field and have the same acceleration. Relative to the satellite, the bodies inside appear as free bodies unless other forces act on them; but, relative to a terrestrial observer, they are accelerated and subject to the gravitational field.

A man inside an elevator which is falling with the acceleration of gravity (due to a broken cable) would experience the same weightlessness relative to the elevator. In such a case (as in the satellite), $\boldsymbol{a}_0 = \boldsymbol{g}$, and again $\boldsymbol{a}' = 0$. Weightlessness, we insist, does not mean that the gravitational force has ceased to act. It means that all bodies, including the one serving as frame of reference, are acted on by one and the same field, which produces a common acceleration, and therefore there are no relative accelerations unless other forces act on the bodies. In other words, a gravitational field $\mathcal{G}$ can be "washed off" if the observer moves through it with an acceleration $\boldsymbol{a}_0 = \mathcal{G}$ relative to an inertial frame.

13.9 Gravitation and Intermolecular Forces

In the previous sections of this chapter we have seen how gravitational forces adequately describe planetary motion and the motion of bodies near the surface of the earth. It is interesting now to see if we can find out whether the same kind of interaction is responsible for keeping molecules together in a piece of matter or keeping atoms together in a molecule.

Let us first consider a simple molecule such as a hydrogen molecule, composed of two hydrogen atoms separated the distance $r = 0.745 \times 10^{-10}$ m. The mass of each hydrogen atom is $m = 1.673 \times 10^{-27}$ kg. Therefore the gravitational interaction of the two atoms corresponds to a potential energy

$$E_p = -\frac{\gamma m m'}{r} = 2.22 \times 10^{-54}\,\mathrm{J} = 1.39 \times 10^{-35}\,\mathrm{eV}.$$

However, the experimental value for the dissociation energy of a molecule of hydrogen is 7.18×10^{-19} J (= 4.48 eV), or 10^{35} times larger than the gravitational energy. Therefore we conclude that the gravitational interaction *cannot* be responsible for the formation of a molecule of hydrogen. Similar results are obtained for more complex molecules.

In the case of a liquid, the energy required to vaporize one mole of water (18 g or 6.23×10^{23} molecules) is 4.06×10^3 J, corresponding to a separation energy per molecule of the order of 6×10^{-21} J. The average separation of the molecules of water is of the order of 3×10^{-10} m, and the mass of a molecule is 3×10^{-26} kg, corresponding to a gravitational potential energy of 2×10^{-52} J, again far too small to explain the existence of liquid water.

Therefore we conclude that the forces giving rise to the association of atoms to form molecules or of molecules to form matter in bulk cannot be gravitational. In the next four chapters, which appear in Volume II, we shall discuss other forces that seem to be responsible for these associations: *electromagnetic interactions.*

However, gravitational interaction, being a mass effect, is very important in the presence of massive bodies that are electrically neutral, such as planets, and for that reason gravitation is the strongest force we feel on the earth's surface, in spite of the fact that it is the weakest of all forces known in nature. It is responsible for a large number of common phenomena affecting our daily lives. Tides, for example, are entirely due to the gravitational interaction of the moon and the sun with the earth.

References

1. "The Homocentric Spheres of Eudoxus," H. Swenson; *Am. J. Phys.* **31,** 456 (1963)
2. "The Celestial Palace of Tycho Brahe," J. Christianson; *Sci. Am.*, February 1961, page 118
3. "Johannes Kepler's Universe: Its Physics and Metaphysics," G. Holton; *Am. J. Phys.* **24,** 340 (1956)
4. "Newton and the Cause of Gravity," M. Evans; *Am. J. Phys.* **26,** 619 (1958)
5. "Gravity," G. Gamow; *Sci. Am.*, March 1961, page 94
6. "The Eötvös Experiment," R. Dicke; *Sci. Am.*, December 1961, page 84
7. "Gravitational and Inertial Mass," G. B. Bronson; *Am. J. Phys.* **28,** 475 (1960)
8. "Guidelines to Antigravity," R. Forward; *Am. J. Phys.* **31,** 166 (1963)
9. *Mechanics* (second edition), by K. Symon. Reading, Mass.: Addison-Wesley, 1964, Chapter 6
10. *Introduction to Engineering Mechanics,* by J. Huddleston. Reading, Mass.: Addison-Wesley, 1961, Section 6.8

11. *Vector Mechanics*, by D. Christie. New York: McGraw-Hill, 1964, Chapter 17
12. *The Feynman Lectures on Physics*, Volume I, by R. Feynman, R. Leighton, and M. Sands. Reading, Mass.: Addison-Wesley, 1963, Chapter 7
13. *Source Book in Physics*, by W. F. Magie. Cambridge, Mass.: Harvard University Press, 1963; page 92, Newton; page 105, Cavendish

Problems

13.1 Calculate the gravitational attractive force between the earth and (a) the moon, (b) the sun. Obtain the ratio between these two forces.

13.2 Calculate the gravitational attraction between the two protons in a hydrogen molecule. Their separation is 0.74×10^{-10} m.

13.3. Determine the gravitational attractive force between the proton and the electron in a hydrogen atom, assuming that the electron describes a circular orbit with a radius of 0.53×10^{-10} m.

13.4 Estimate the average distance between two helium atoms in one mole at STP. From this distance, obtain the gravitational attraction between two neighboring helium atoms. The mass of a helium atom may be considered as 4.0 amu.

13.5 Estimate the average distance between two water molecules in the liquid phase. From this distance, obtain the gravitational attraction between two neighboring water molecules. A water molecule is composed of an oxygen atom and two hydrogen atoms.

13.6 Two iron balls, each having a mass of 10 kg, are touching each other. Find their gravitational attraction. Compare it with the gravitational attraction of the earth on each ball. If one tried to separate the two balls, would one "feel" the attraction between them? [*Hint:* You may need to know the density of iron. It is listed in Table 2–2.]

13.7 Compare the gravitational attraction produced on a body of mass m at the earth's surface (a) by the moon, and (b) by the sun, with the attraction of the earth on the same body. What do you conclude about the possibility of observing a change in the weight of a body during the daily rotation of the earth?

13.8 A sphere of mass 5.0 kg is located in one pan of an equal-arm balance in equilibrium. A larger spherical mass (5.8×10^3 kg) is then rolled until it is directly underneath the first mass, the distance between the centers being 0.50 m. What mass must be placed in the other pan of the balance in order to restore equilibrium to the system? Assume $g = 9.80$ m s^{-2}. This method was used by G. von Jolly, in the last century, to determine the value of γ.

13.9 A man weighs 70 kgf. Supposing that the radius of the earth were doubled, how much would he weigh (a) if the mass of the earth remained constant, (b) if the average density of the earth remained constant?

13.10 Calculate the acceleration of gravity at the sun's surface. Its radius is 110 times the radius of the earth and its mass is 330,000 times the mass of the earth. Repeat for Venus, Jupiter, and the moon.

13.11 A man weighs 110 kgf. Calculate how much he would weigh at the surface of the sun and at the surface of the moon. What would be his mass at both places?

13.12 A man weighs 80 kgf at sea level. Calculate his mass and weight at 8000 m above sea level.

13.13 From the data in Table 13–1 for the radii and the periods of orbital motion of the planets, compute the mass of the sun.

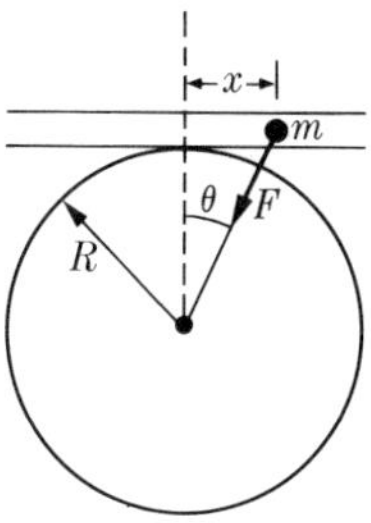

Figure 13–29

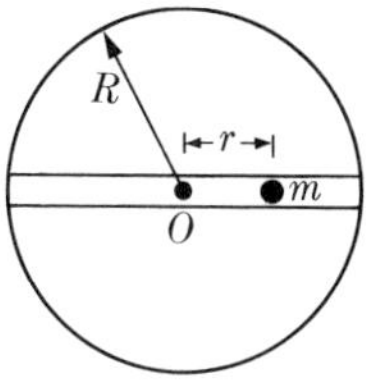

Figure 13–30

Use only three planets (Venus, earth, and Jupiter).

13.14 In a Cavendish experiment (Fig. 13–3), the two small masses are equal to 10.0 gm and the rod (of negligible mass) is 0.50 m long. The period of torsional oscillations of this system is 770 s. The two large masses are 10.0 kg each and are so placed that the distance between the centers of the large and small spheres is 0.10 m. Find the angular deflection of the rod.

13.15 How high must one go above the earth's surface for the acceleration of gravity to change by 1%? How deep should one penetrate into the earth to observe the same change?

13.16 Find the height and velocity of a satellite (in circular orbit in the equatorial plane) that remains over the same point on the earth at all times.

13.17 An earth satellite moves in a circular orbit at a height of 300 km above the earth's surface. Find (a) its velocity, (b) its period of revolution, and (c) its centripetal acceleration.

13.18 Compare the result of part (c) of the preceding problem with the value of g at that height, as computed directly by the method of Example 13.9.

13.19 What would be the period of a satellite revolving about the earth in an orbit whose radius is one-fourth the radius of the moon's orbit? The period of the moon is about 28 days. What would be the ratio of the velocity of the satellite to that of the moon?

13.20 A particle of mass m can move in a horizontal frictionless pipe (Fig. 13–29) under the action of the earth's gravitational attraction. Assuming that x is very small compared with R, prove that the particle has simple harmonic motion and that its period is $P = 2\pi\sqrt{R/g}$. Find the value of P. This is the longest period of a pendulum on the earth's surface. Can you prove it?

13.21 Suppose that a hole were drilled completely through the earth along a diameter (Fig. 13–30). (a) Show that the force on a mass m at a distance r from the center of the earth is $F = -mgr/R$, if we assume that the density is uniform. (b) Show that the motion of m would be simple harmonic, with a period of about 90 min. (c) Write the equations for position, velocity, and acceleration as functions of time, with numerical values of the constants.

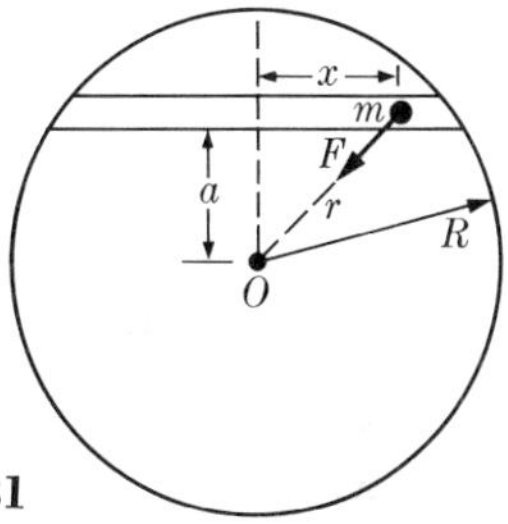

Figure 13–31

13.22 Show that the frictionless motion of a mass in a hole drilled as a chord through the earth (Fig. 13–31) would be simple harmonic. Calculate the period.

13.23 A mass m is dropped from a great height h above the hole in the earth in Fig. 13–32. (a) With what velocity would m pass the center of the earth? (b) Would the motion be simple harmonic? (c) Would

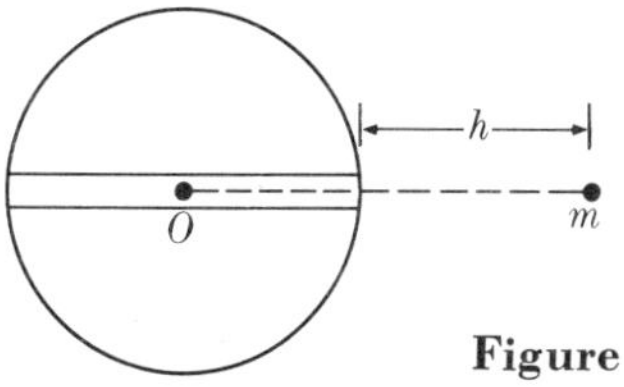

Figure 13–32

the motion be periodic? Give reasons for your answers.

13.24 From the data for the motion of the sun in the galaxy (Fig. 7–1), and assuming that the galaxy is a spherical aggregate of stars, estimate its total mass. Assuming that the stars have, on the average, the same mass as the sun (1.98×10^{30} kg), estimate their number and their average separation.

13.25 Write an equation which expresses algebraically the total energy of the system (a) earth–moon, (b) sun–earth–moon.

13.26 Estimate the kinetic energy, the potential energy, and the total energy of the earth in its motion around the sun. (Consider only the gravitational potential energy with the sun.)

13.27 Obtain the expression for the total energy of a circular orbit under gravitational forces (Eq. 13.6) using the virial theorem (Section 8.13).

13.28 One of the Pioneer moon rockets reached an altitude of about 125,000 km. Neglecting the effect of the moon, estimate the velocity with which this rocket struck the atmosphere of the earth on its return. Assume that the rocket was fired straight up and that the atmosphere begins 130 km above the earth's surface.

13.29 Given that h is the distance of a body *above* the earth's surface, then $r = R + h$. Verify, using the binomial expansion (M.21), that when h is very small compared with R, Eq. (13.10) reduces to $v^2 = 2gh$.

13.30 Compute the escape velocity for Mercury, Venus, Mars, and Jupiter. [*Hint:* To simplify the calculation, first compute the factor $\sqrt{2\gamma}$. Then you only have to multiply it by $\sqrt{M/R}$ for each planet.]

13.31 (a) Compute the escape velocity from the solar system for a particle at a distance from the sun equal to that of the earth. (b) Use this result to obtain the minimum escape velocity for a body launched from the earth, taking into account the earth's velocity but not its gravitational field.

13.32 A particle is at rest on the earth's surface. (a) Compute its total kinetic and potential energy relative to the sun, including the gravitational attraction of the earth and of the sun. (b) Obtain the escape velocity from the solar system. Compare with Problem 13.31.

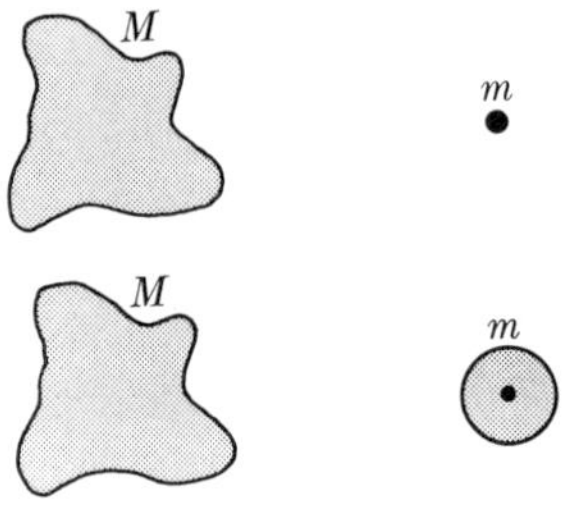

Figure 13–33

13.33 Using the results of Section 13.7, prove that the gravitational interaction between a mass M (Fig. 13–33) of arbitrary shape and a point mass or between M and a homogeneous spherical body having the same mass m is the same, provided that the center of the spherical body coincides with the position of the point mass.

13.34 Determine the potential energy between the planet Saturn and its rings. Assume that the rings have a mass of 3.5×10^{18} kg and are concentrated at an average distance of 1.1×10^8 m from the center of Saturn.

13.35 Determine the internal gravitational potential energy of 8 bodies, each of mass m, located at the vertices of a cube of side a. Apply it to a case in which the masses are of the same order as our sun and the side of the cube is one parsec. (See Problem 2.16.)

13.36 Prove that the energy required to build up a spherical body of radius R by adding successive layers of matter in an onionlike fashion until the final radius is attained (keeping the density constant) is $E_p = -3\gamma M^2/5R$.

13.37 Estimate the value of the gravitational potential energy of our galaxy. Assume that all the bodies composing the galaxy are roughly of the same mass as the sun and are separated by a distance of the order of 10^{21} m. [*Hint:* Consider that the galaxy is spherical, and use the result of Problem 13.36.]

13.38 Using the virial theorem and the results of the preceding problem, estimate the total kinetic energy of the galaxy (excluding the internal energy of the stars).

13.39 A meteorite is initially at rest at a distance from the center of the earth equal to six times the earth's radius. Calculate what its velocity would be when it reached the earth's surface.

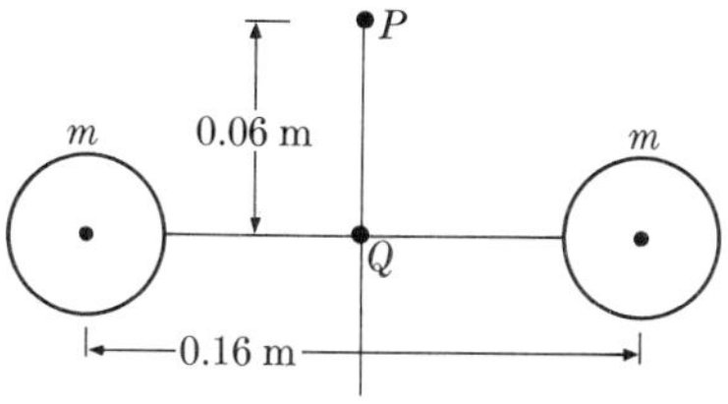

Figure 13–34

13.40 Two equal masses of 6.40 kg are separated by a distance of 0.16 m (Fig. 13–34). A third mass is released from a point P equidistant from the two masses and at a distance 0.06 m from the line joining them. Determine the velocity of this third mass when it passes through Q. Given that the mass is 0.1 kg, calculate its acceleration at P and at Q.

13.41 A rocket is fired vertically from the earth toward the moon, the fuel being consumed in a relatively short time after the firing. (a) At what point in its path toward the moon is its acceleration zero? (b) What would the minimum initial velocity of the rocket need to be in order to reach this point and fall on the moon by the action of lunar attraction? (c) In this case, what would the velocity of the rocket be when it hit the moon?

13.42 Prove that the time required for a body to fall from a distance r from the center of the earth down to the surface of the earth is

$$t = (r^{3/2}/R\sqrt{2g})[-\sqrt{(R/r)(1 - R/r)} + \sin^{-1}\sqrt{R/r}].$$

Verify that if r is very large compared with R, the result is $t = \frac{1}{2}\sqrt{R/2g}$. [*Hint:* Use Eq. (13.10); set $v = dr/dt$, solve for dt, and integrate.]

13.43 A satellite having a mass of 5000 kg describes a circular path around the earth of radius 8000 km. Find its angular momentum and its kinetic, potential, and total energies.

13.44 A 5000-kg satellite is describing a circular orbit at an altitude of 8000 km above the earth's surface. After several days, as a result of atmospheric friction, the orbit shrinks to an altitude of 650 km. Compute the changes in (a) velocity, (b) angular velocity, (c) kinetic energy, (d) potential energy, and (e) total energy. Assume that the orbits are essentially circular at each moment because the shrinking is very slow.

13.45 Referring to the previous problem, assume that the air resistance can be represented by an average force of 1.75×10^1 N. (a) Calculate the torque due to this force and, using this result, estimate the time required for the abovementioned drop in height. (b) Determine the rate of energy dissipation and, from it, also estimate the time computed in (a). (c) Using average period of revolution, obtain the total number of revolutions in that time.

13.46 Adapt the results of Section 13.5 to take into account the reduced mass.

13.47 In a double star, one of the stars has a mass of 3×10^{33} kg and the other a mass of 4×10^{33} kg. Find their angular velocity around their center of mass, given that their separation is 10^{17} m. Also find their total internal angular momentum and energy.

13.48 Using polar graph paper, plot Eq. (13.12) for $d = 1$ and (a) $\epsilon = 0.5$, (b) $\epsilon = 1$, (c) $\epsilon = 2$. Because of the symmetry of the curve you only have to compute r for θ between 0° and 180°, and repeat the curve below the X-axis. Identify the most important features of each curve. [*Hint:* Use values of θ in multiples of 20°.]

13.49 Prove that the ratio between the velocity of an orbiting body at *perigee* (distance of closest approach to the force center) and at *apogee* (farthest separation from it) is $(1 + \epsilon)/(1 - \epsilon)$. [*Hint:* Note that at both positions the velocity is perpendicular to the radius.]

13.50 A comet moves in an ellipse which has an eccentricity of $\epsilon = 0.8$. Find the ratio between (a) the distance to the sun, (b) linear velocities, and (c) angular velocities at aphelion and at perihelion.

13.51 The eccentricity ϵ and semimajor axis a of the orbits of certain planets are listed in the following table. (Bear in mind that 1 AU $= 1.495 \times 10^{11}$ m.)

	Mercury	Earth	Mars
ϵ	0.206	0.017	0.093
a (AU)	0.387	1.000	1.524

Compute for each of these planets: (a) the distance of closest approach to the sun, (b) the distance of farthest separation from the sun, (c) the total energy of translational motion, (d) the angular momentum, (e) the period of revolution, (f) the velocity at aphelion and at perihelion.

13.52 A satellite is put into an elliptical orbit at a distance above the earth's surface equal to the earth's radius by giving it an initial horizontal velocity equal to 1.2 times the velocity required to make it assume a circular orbit at that distance. Find (a) the angular momentum of the satellite, (b) its total energy, (c) the eccentricity of its orbit, (d) its maximum and minimum distances from the earth's surface, (e) the semimajor axis of its orbit, and (f) its period of revolution. (Let $m = 50$ kg.)

13.53 Repeat Problem 13.52, assuming that the satellite's initial velocity is 0.9 that of a similar satellite in circular orbit.

13.54 On the Gemini V flight (August 21 through August 29, 1965), the apogee and perigee heights above the earth's surface were 352 km and 107 km, respectively. Determine the eccentricity of the orbit, the maximum and minimum speeds of the spacecraft, and the variation in the gravitational field between apogee and perigee.

13.55 An artificial satellite moves in an orbit whose perigee is 640 km and apogee 4000 km above the earth's surface. Calculate (a) its semimajor axis, (b) its eccentricity, (c) the equation of its orbit, (d) its velocity at the perigee and at the apogee, (e) its period of revolution, (f) its total energy if its mass is 100 kg. (g) Using polar graph paper, plot the satellite's path.

13.56 The United States satellite Explorer III had an elliptical orbit with perigee at 109 mi above the earth's surface and a velocity at perigee of 27,000 ft s^{-1}. Determine (a) the eccentricity of its orbit, (b) its semimajor axis, (c) its period of revolution, and (d) its velocity and height at apogee.

13.57 A comet of mass m is observed at a distance of 10^{11} m from the sun traveling toward the sun with a velocity 5.16×10^4 m s^{-1} at an angle of 45° with the radius vector from the sun. Obtain for the comet (a) its total energy and angular momentum, (b) the equation of its orbit, (c) the distance of its closest approach to the sun. Note which results depend on the mass of

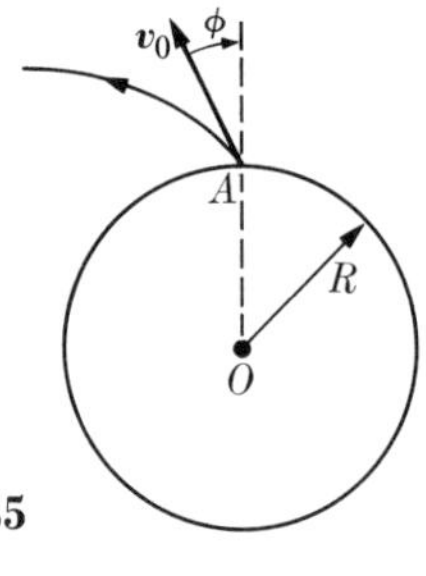

Figure 13–35

the comet, and which do not. Using polar graph paper, plot the comet's path.

13.58 A ballistic missile (Fig. 13–35) of mass m is fired at a point A with an initial velocity v_0, making an angle ϕ with the vertical or radial direction. Find (a) its angular momentum, (b) its total energy. (c) Prove that the eccentricity of its orbit is given by

$$\epsilon^2 = 1 + (R^2 v_0^2 \sin^2 \phi/\gamma^2 M^2)(v_0^2 - 2\gamma M/R).$$

[*Hint:* For (c), use the last result in Example 13.5.]

13.59 Referring to the preceding problem, show that the equation of the path is

$$r = R^2 v_0^2 \sin^2 \phi_0/\gamma M(1 + \epsilon \cos \theta).$$

[*Hint:* Remember from Example 13.5 that $L^2 = \gamma mm'\epsilon d$.]

13.60 Referring to Problems 13.58 and 13.59, assume that $v_0 = \sqrt{\gamma M/R}$ and that $\phi = 30°$. (a) Determine the missile's eccentricity. (b) Write the equation of its orbit. (c) Prove that the missile will fall back to earth at a point at a distance from A equal to $\pi R/3$ measured along the earth's surface. Using polar graph paper, plot the missile's path. [*Hint:* After computing ϵ, determine the values of θ for which $r = R$. One value corresponds to the firing point and the other to the point of return. The difference between the two angles gives the angular displacement of the two points.]

13.61 Referring to Problem 13.60, prove that the maximum height of the missile above the earth's surface is about $0.92R$. (It is suggested that the student compare the results of Problems 13.60 and 13.61 with those obtained using the methods of Section 5.7.)

13.62 Referring to Problem 13.58, prove that if the missile's launching velocity is equal to its escape velocity the path will be a parabola and, according to Problem 13.59, no matter how the missile is directed, its trajectory will be open and it will never return.

13.63 A ballistic missile is launched with a velocity equal to its escape velocity, so that its path is a parabola. Find the equation of its path when $\phi = 45°$ and $\phi = 90°$. Using polar graph paper, make a sketch of the path in each case.

13.64 A comet at a large distance from the sun has a velocity $\sqrt{2gR}$ and an impact parameter of $\sqrt{2}\,R$ (recall Example 7.16), where R is the radius of the sun. How close to the sun will the comet come?

13.65 A particle of mass m moves under an attractive force of magnitude k/r^2. Its velocity at one of the extreme positions is $\sqrt{k/2mr_1}$, where r_1 is the distance from the center of force. Calculate the distance r_2 corresponding to the other extreme position, the semimajor axis of the orbit, and the eccentricity.

13.66 A particle moves under a repulsive central force of magnitude $F = k/r^2$. It is thrown from a point a very large distance from the center of force with a velocity v_0 and an impact parameter b (remember Example 7.16). Determine (a) the equation of its path, (b) the distance of its closest approach to the force center, (c) the angle that the direction in which it recedes makes with the initial direction. Compare your answers with the results of Example 7.16. [*Hint:* Note that the formulas in this chapter can be applied if $-\gamma mm'$ is replaced by k.]

13.67 Calculate the strength of the gravitational field and the potential at the earth's surface due to the earth itself.

13.68 Estimate the value of the earth's gravitational field and the acceleration toward the center of a body at a point at a distance (a) $\frac{3}{2}R$, (b) $\frac{1}{2}R$ from the center of the earth. Assume that the earth is homogeneous.

13.69 Compute the magnitude of the gravitational field and the potential produced by the sun along the earth's orbit. Compare these values with the gravitational field and the potential produced by the moon on the earth.

13.70 Two bodies of masses m and $3m$ are separated a distance a. Find the points where (a) the resultant gravitational field is zero, (b) the two masses produce gravitational fields which are the same in magnitude and direction, (c) the two masses produce gravitational potentials which are identical.

13.71 Two bodies of masses m and $3m$ are separated a distance $13a$. Find the resultant gravitational field and potential at a point P at a distance $5a$ from the first mass, given that the lines joining P with the two masses are at right angles.

13.72 Two bodies of masses m and $2m$ are at the vertices of an equilateral triangle of side a. Find the gravitational field and the potential at (a) the midpoint between them, and (b) the third vertex of the triangle.

13.73 Three equal masses are located at the vertices of an equilateral triangle. Make a sketch of the equipotential surfaces (actually their intersection with the plane of the triangle) and of the lines of force of the gravitational field. Is there any point where the gravitational field is zero?

13.74 Obtain the gravitational field and the potential produced by a ring of mass m and radius R at points along the axis perpendicular to the ring through its center.

13.75 Referring to the preceding problem, a particle is released from a point on the axis at a distance h from the center. (a) What will be its velocity when it passes through the center? (b) How far will it go on the other side? (c) Is the resulting motion periodic? Under what conditions is the motion practically simple harmonic? Determine the corresponding frequency in this last case.

13.76 Two identical thin slabs of material are separated a distance a. Calculate the gravitational field they produce in the region between them and on either side.

13.77 Prove that the gravitational field and the potential of a thin filament having a mass λ per unit length are

$$\mathcal{G} = -(2\gamma\lambda/R)\boldsymbol{u}_R$$

and $V = 2\gamma\lambda \ln R$, respectively, where R is the distance from the point to the filament. [*Hint:* First determine, in view of the symmetry, what the direction of the field should be, and the variables determining it. Next divide the wire into small portions, each of length dx, and compute the component of its field in the final direction. Once you have obtained the resultant field by integration, you can obtain the gravitational potential from it by using Eq. (13.21).]

13.78 Determine the velocity and the total energy of a particle which is describing a circular orbit around the filament of Problem 13.77, and which is under its gravitational attraction.

13.79 Reconsider Example 13.8 for a case in which the thin layer of matter is replaced by a homogeneous slab of matter of thickness D.

13.80 Assume that a mass m is a distance ρ from a certain point O, used as a reference

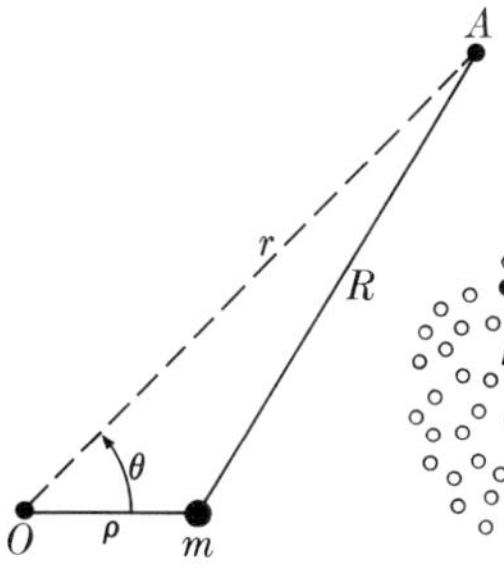

Figure 13–36

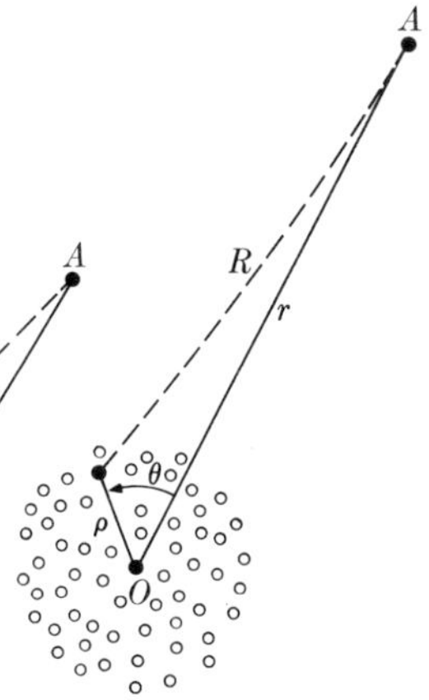

Figure 13–37

(Fig. 13–36). Show that the gravitational potential at A, at a distance R from m (R larger than ρ), can be expressed, in terms of the distance $OA = r$ and the angle θ, by the series

$$V = -(\gamma m/r)\,[1 + \rho\cos\theta/r + \rho^2(3\cos^2\theta - 1)/2r^2 + \cdots].$$

[*Hint:* Express R in terms of ρ, r, and θ by the law of cosines, and evaluate $1/R$ by means of the binomial expansion.]

13.81 Consider a cluster of masses m_1, m_2, $m_3, \ldots$ (Fig. 13–37). Show that the gravitational potential at a point A, at a distance large compared with the dimensions of the cluster, may be expressed as

$$V = -\gamma[M/r + P/r^2 + Q/r^3 + \cdots],$$

where $M = \sum_i m_i$ is the total mass, $P = \sum_i \rho_i \cos\theta_i$ is called the *dipole moment* of the mass distribution relative to OA, and $Q = \sum_i \frac{1}{2}\rho_i^2(3\cos^2\theta_i - 1)$ is called the *quadrupole moment* of the mass distribution, and so on. [*Hint:* Use the results of Problem 13.80 for each mass, and add.] The terms "dipole" and "quadrupole" will be explained in Chapter 14 (Volume II).

APPENDIX: MATHEMATICAL RELATIONS AND TABLES

ANSWERS TO ODD-NUMBERED PROBLEMS

INDEX

APPENDIX

MATHEMATICAL RELATIONS

This appendix, in which we present certain mathematical formulas that are frequently used in the text, is intended as a quickly available reference for the student. In a few cases we have inserted some mathematical notes in the text proper. Proofs and a discussion of most of the formulas may be found in any standard calculus text; e.g., *Calculus and Analytic Geometry*, third edition, by G. B. Thomas (Addison-Wesley, 1963). A short introduction to the basic concepts of the calculus, in a programmed format, may be found in *Quick Calculus: A Short Manual of Self Instruction*, by D. Kelpner and N. Ramsey (John Wiley & Sons, New York, 1963). The student will also have to refer to a number of tables which are in book form. Among these are the *C.R.C. Standard Mathematical Tables* (Chemical Rubber Company, Cleveland, Ohio, 1963), and *Tables of Integrals and Other Mathematical Data*, fourth edition, by H. B. Dwight (Macmillan Company, New York, 1961). We recommend that the student have at his disposal the *Handbook of Chemistry and Physics*, yearly editions of which are issued by the Chemical Rubber Company, Cleveland, Ohio. This handbook also contains a wealth of mathematical, chemical, and physical data.

1. Trigonometric Relations

Referring to Fig. M–1, we can define the following relations:

$$\sin\alpha = y/r, \qquad \cos\alpha = x/r, \qquad \tan\alpha = y/x; \tag{M.1}$$

$$\csc\alpha = r/y, \qquad \sec\alpha = r/x, \qquad \cot\alpha = x/y; \tag{M.2}$$

$$\tan\alpha = \sin\alpha/\cos\alpha; \tag{M.3}$$

$$\sin^2\alpha + \cos^2\alpha = 1, \qquad \sec^2\alpha + 1 = \tan^2\alpha; \tag{M.4}$$

$$\sin(\alpha \pm \beta) = \sin\alpha\cos\beta \pm \cos\alpha\sin\beta; \tag{M.5}$$

$$\cos(\alpha \pm \beta) = \cos\alpha\cos\beta \mp \sin\alpha\sin\beta; \tag{M.6}$$

$$\sin\alpha \pm \sin\beta = 2\sin\tfrac{1}{2}(\alpha \pm \beta)\cos\tfrac{1}{2}(\alpha \mp \beta); \tag{M.7}$$

$$\cos\alpha + \cos\beta = 2\cos\tfrac{1}{2}(\alpha + \beta)\cos\tfrac{1}{2}(\alpha - \beta); \tag{M.8}$$

$$\cos\alpha - \cos\beta = -2\sin\tfrac{1}{2}(\alpha + \beta)\sin\tfrac{1}{2}(\alpha - \beta); \tag{M.9}$$

$$\sin\alpha\sin\beta = \tfrac{1}{2}[\cos(\alpha-\beta) - \cos(\alpha+\beta)]; \tag{M.10}$$

$$\cos\alpha\cos\beta = \tfrac{1}{2}[\cos(\alpha-\beta) + \cos(\alpha+\beta)]; \tag{M.11}$$

$$\sin\alpha\cos\beta = \tfrac{1}{2}[\sin(\alpha-\beta) + \sin(\alpha+\beta)]; \tag{M.12}$$

$$\sin 2\alpha = 2\sin\alpha\cos\alpha, \qquad \cos 2\alpha = \cos^2\alpha - \sin^2\alpha; \tag{M.13}$$

$$\sin^2\tfrac{1}{2}\alpha = \tfrac{1}{2}(1-\cos\alpha), \qquad \cos^2\tfrac{1}{2}\alpha = \tfrac{1}{2}(1+\cos\alpha). \tag{M.14}$$

Referring to Fig. M–2, we can formulate, for any arbitrary triangle:

$$\text{Law of sines:}\quad \frac{a}{\sin A} = \frac{b}{\sin B} = \frac{c}{\sin C}, \tag{M.15}$$

$$\text{Law of cosines:}\quad a^2 = b^2 + c^2 - 2bc\cos A. \tag{M.16}$$

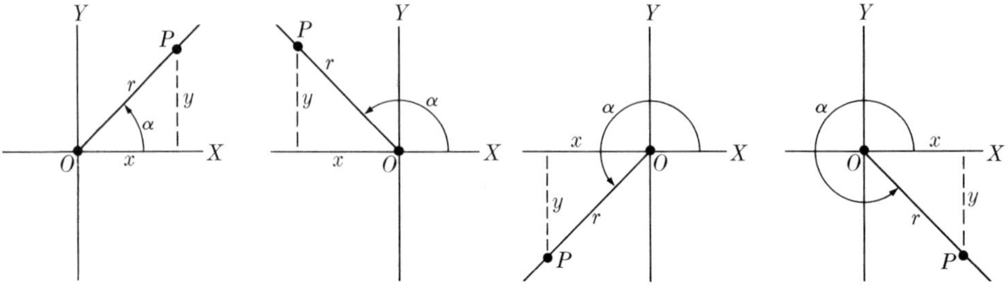

Figure M–1

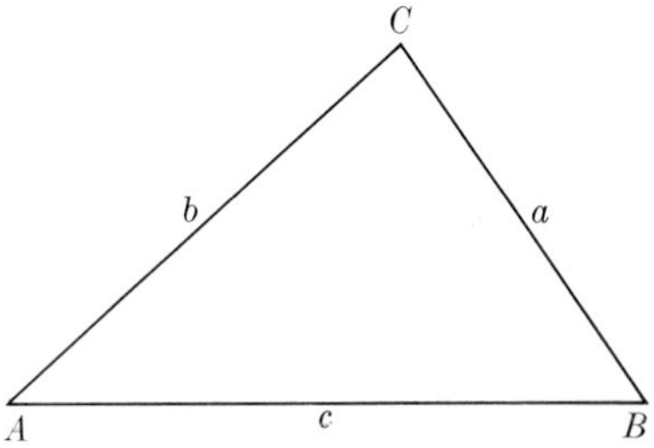

Figure M–2

2. *Logarithms*

(i) Definition of e:

$$e = \lim_{n\to\infty}\left(1+\frac{1}{n}\right)^n = 2.7182818\ldots \tag{M.17}$$

The exponential functions $y = e^x$ and $y = e^{-x}$ are plotted in Fig. M–3.

(ii) Natural logarithm, base e (see Fig. M–4):

$$y = \ln x \qquad \text{if } x = e^y. \tag{M.18}$$

Common logarithm, base 10:

$$y = \log x \qquad \text{if } x = 10^y. \tag{M.19}$$

The natural and common logarithms are related by

$$\ln x = 2.303\log x, \qquad \log x = 0.434\ln x. \tag{M.20}$$

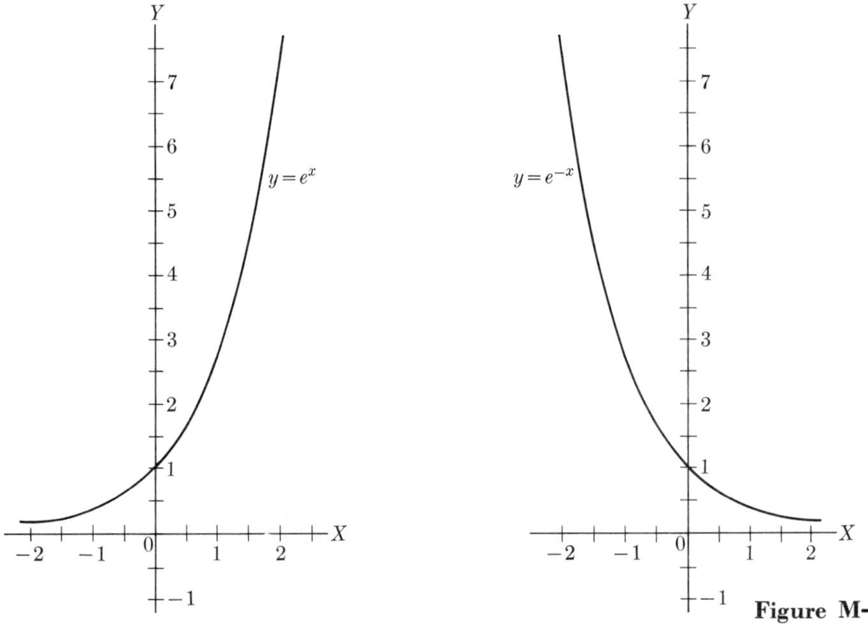

Figure M–3

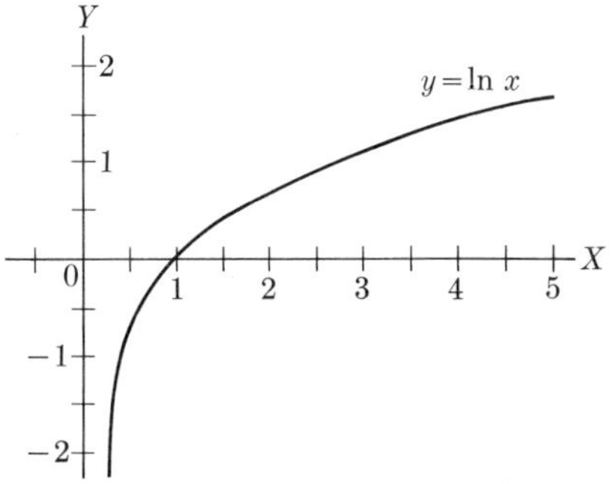

Figure M–4

3. Power Expansions

(i) The binomial expansion:

$$(a + b)^n = a^n + na^{n-1}b + \frac{n(n-1)}{2!}a^{n-2}b^2 + \frac{n(n-1)(n-2)}{3!}a^{n-3}b^3 + \cdots + \frac{n(n-1)(n-2)\cdots(n-p+1)}{p!}a^{n-p}b^p + \cdots \tag{M.21}$$

When n is a positive integer, the expansion has $n + 1$ terms. In all other cases, the expansion has an infinite number of terms. The case for which a is 1 and b is a quantity x is used numerous times in the text. Therefore the binomial expansion of $(1 + x)^n$ is written

$$(1 + x)^n = 1 + nx + \frac{n(n-1)}{2!}x^2 + \frac{n(n-1)(n-2)}{3!}x^3 + \cdots \tag{M.22}$$

(ii) Other useful series expansions:

$$e^x = 1 + x + \frac{1}{2!}x^2 + \frac{1}{3!}x^3 + \cdots \tag{M.23}$$

$$\ln(1 + x) = x - \frac{x^2}{2} + \frac{x^3}{3} - \cdots \tag{M.24}$$

$$\sin x = x - \frac{1}{3!}x^3 + \frac{1}{5!}x^5 - \cdots \tag{M.25}$$

$$\cos x = 1 - \frac{1}{2!}x^2 + \frac{1}{4!}x^4 - \cdots \tag{M.26}$$

$$\tan x = x + \frac{1}{3}x^3 + \frac{2}{15}x^5 + \cdots \tag{M.27}$$

For $x \ll 1$, the following approximations are satisfactory:

$$(1 + x)^n \approx 1 + nx, \tag{M.28}$$

$$e^x \approx 1 + x, \qquad \ln(1 + x) \approx x, \tag{M.29}$$

$$\sin x \approx x, \qquad \cos x \approx 1, \qquad \tan x \approx x. \tag{M.30}$$

Note that in Eqs. (M.25), (M.26), (M.27), and (M.30), x must be expressed in radians.

(iii) Taylor series expansion:

$$f(x) = f(x_0) + (x - x_0)\left(\frac{df}{dx}\right)_0 + \frac{1}{2!}(x - x_0)^2\left(\frac{d^2f}{dx^2}\right)_0 + \cdots + \frac{1}{n!}(x - x_0)^n\left(\frac{d^nf}{dx^n}\right)_0 + \cdots \tag{M.31}$$

If $x - x_0 \ll 1$, a useful approximation is

$$f(x) \approx f(x_0) + (x - x_0)\left(\frac{df}{dx}\right)_0. \tag{M.32}$$

4. Complex Numbers

With the definition $i^2 = -1$ or $i = \sqrt{-1}$,

$$e^{i\theta} = \cos\theta + i\sin\theta, \tag{M.33}$$

$$\cos\theta = \tfrac{1}{2}(e^{i\theta} + e^{-i\theta}), \tag{M.34}$$

$$\sin\theta = \frac{1}{2i}(e^{i\theta} - e^{-i\theta}). \tag{M.35}$$

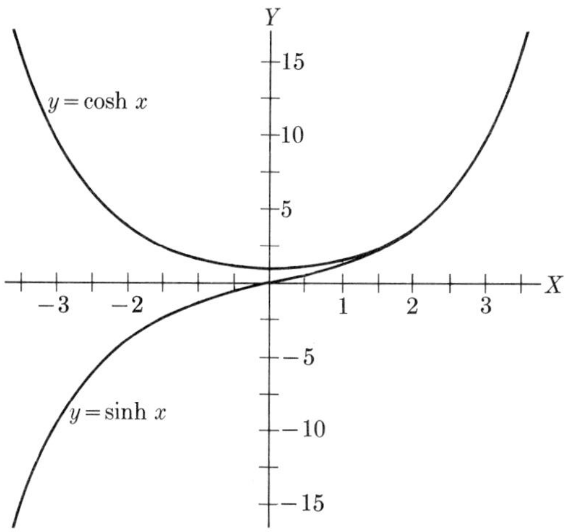

Figure M–5

5. Hyperbolic Functions

In order to visualize the following relations, see Fig. M–5.

$$\cosh\theta = \tfrac{1}{2}(e^{\theta} + e^{-\theta}), \tag{M.36}$$

$$\sinh\theta = \tfrac{1}{2}(e^{\theta} - e^{-\theta}), \tag{M.37}$$

$$\cosh^2\theta - \sinh^2\theta = 1, \tag{M.38}$$

$$\sinh\theta = -i\sin(i\theta), \qquad \cosh\theta = \cos(i\theta), \tag{M.39}$$

$$\sin\theta = -i\sinh(i\theta), \qquad \cos\theta = \cosh(i\theta). \tag{M.40}$$

6. Basic Derivatives and Integrals

$f(u)$	df/dx	$\int f(u)\,du$
u^n	$nu^{n-1}\,du/dx$	$u^{n+1}/(n+1)+C \;(n \neq -1)$
u^{-1}	$-(1/u^2)\,du/dx$	$\ln u + C$
$\ln u$	$(1/u)\,du/dx$	$u\ln u - u + C$
e^u	$e^u\,du/dx$	$e^u + C$
$\sin u$	$\cos u\,du/dx$	$-\cos u + C$
$\cos u$	$-\sin u\,du/dx$	$\sin u + C$
$\tan u$	$\sec^2 u\,du/dx$	$-\ln\cos u + C$
$\cot u$	$-\csc^2 u\,du/dx$	$\ln\sin u + C$
$\arcsin u$	$(du/dx)/\sqrt{1-u^2}$	$u\sin^{-1}u + \sqrt{1-u^2} + C$
$\sinh u$	$\cosh u\,du/dx$	$\cosh u + C$
$\cosh u$	$\sinh u\,du/dx$	$\sinh u + C$

A useful rule for integration, called *integration by parts*, is

$$\int u\,dv = uv - \int v\,du. \tag{M.41}$$

This method is most frequently used to evaluate the integral on the left by using the integral on the right.

7. Average Value of a Function

The *mean* or *average value* of a function $y = f(x)$ in the interval (a, b) is defined by

$$y_{\text{ave}} = \frac{1}{b - a} \int_a^b y \, dx. \tag{M.42}$$

Similarly, the average value of y^2 is defined by

$$(y^2)_{\text{ave}} = \frac{1}{b - a} \int_a^b y^2 \, dx. \tag{M.43}$$

The quantity $\sqrt{(y^2)_{\text{ave}}}$ is called the *root mean square* value of $y = f(x)$ in the interval (a, b), and in general is different from y_{ave}. It is designated y_{rms}.

NATURAL TRIGONOMETRIC FUNCTIONS

Angle					Angle				
Degree	Radian	Sine	Cosine	Tangent	Degree	Radian	Sine	Cosine	Tangent
0°	.000	0.000	1.000	0.000					
1°	.017	.018	1.000	.018	46°	0.803	0.719	0.695	1.036
2°	.035	.035	0.999	.035	47°	.820	.731	.682	1.072
3°	.052	.052	.999	.052	48°	.838	.743	.669	1.111
4°	.070	.070	.998	.070	49°	.855	.755	.656	1.150
5°	.087	.087	.996	.088	50°	.873	.766	.643	1.192
6°	.105	.105	.995	.105	51°	.890	.777	.629	1.235
7°	.122	.122	.993	.123	52°	.908	.788	.616	1.280
8°	.140	.139	.990	.141	53°	.925	.799	.602	1.327
9°	.157	.156	.988	.158	54°	.942	.809	.588	1.376
10°	.175	.174	.985	.176	55°	.960	.819	.574	1.428
11°	.192	.191	.982	.194	56°	.977	.829	.559	1.483
12°	.209	.208	.978	.213	57°	.995	.839	.545	1.540
13°	.227	.225	.974	.231	58°	1.012	.848	.530	1.600
14°	.244	.242	.970	.249	59°	1.030	.857	.515	1.664
15°	.262	.259	.966	.268	60°	1.047	.866	.500	1.732
16°	.279	.276	.961	.287	61°	1.065	.875	.485	1.804
17°	.297	.292	.956	.306	62°	1.082	.883	.470	1.881
18°	.314	.309	.951	.325	63°	1.100	.891	.454	1.963
19°	.332	.326	.946	.344	64°	1.117	.899	.438	2.050
20°	.349	.342	.940	.364	65°	1.134	.906	.423	2.145
21°	.367	.358	.934	.384	66°	1.152	.914	.407	2.246
22°	.384	.375	.927	.404	67°	1.169	.921	.391	2.356
23°	.401	.391	.921	.425	68°	1.187	.927	.375	2.475
24°	.419	.407	.914	.445	69°	1.204	.934	.358	2.605
25°	.436	.423	.906	.466	70°	1.222	.940	.342	2.747
26°	.454	.438	.899	.488	71°	1.239	.946	.326	2.904
27°	.471	.454	.891	.510	72°	1.257	.951	.309	3.078
28°	.489	.470	.883	.532	73°	1.274	.956	.292	3.271
29°	.506	.485	.875	.554	74°	1.292	.961	.276	3.487
30°	.524	.500	.866	.577	75°	1.309	.966	.259	3.732
31°	.541	.515	.857	.601	76°	1.326	.970	.242	4.011
32°	.559	.530	.848	.625	77°	1.344	.974	.225	4.331
33°	.576	.545	.839	.649	78°	1.361	.978	.208	4.705
34°	.593	.559	.829	.675	79°	1.379	.982	.191	5.145
35°	.611	.574	.819	.700	80°	1.396	.985	.174	5.671
36°	.628	.588	.809	.727	81°	1.414	.988	.156	6.314
37°	.646	.602	.799	.754	82°	1.431	.990	.139	7.115
38°	.663	.616	.788	.781	83°	1.449	.993	.122	8.144
39°	.681	.629	.777	.810	84°	1.466	.995	.105	9.514
40°	.698	.643	.766	.839	85°	1.484	.996	.087	11.43
41°	.716	.658	.755	.869	86°	1.501	.998	.070	14.30
42°	.733	.669	.743	.900	87°	1.518	.999	.052	19.08
43°	.751	.682	.731	.933	88°	1.536	.999	.035	28.64
44°	.768	.695	.719	.966	89°	1.553	1.000	.018	57.29
45°	.785	.707	.707	1.000	90°	1.571	1.000	.000	∞

COMMON LOGARITHMS

N	0	1	2	3	4	5	6	7	8	9
0	....	0000	3010	4771	6021	6990	7782	8451	9031	9542
1	0000	0414	0792	1139	1461	1761	2041	2304	2553	2788
2	3010	3222	3424	3617	3802	3979	4150	4314	4472	4624
3	4771	4914	5051	5185	5315	5441	5563	5682	5798	5911
4	6021	6128	6232	6335	6435	6532	6628	6721	6812	6902
5	6990	7076	7160	7243	7324	7404	7482	7559	7634	7709
6	7782	7853	7924	7993	8062	8129	8195	8261	8325	8388
7	8451	8513	8573	8633	8692	8751	8808	8865	8921	8976
8	9031	9085	9138	9191	9243	9294	9345	9395	9445	9494
9	9542	9590	9638	9685	9731	9777	9823	9868	9912	9956
10	0000	0043	0086	0128	0170	0212	0253	0294	0334	0374
11	0414	0453	0492	0531	0569	0607	0645	0682	0719	0755
12	0792	0828	0864	0899	0934	0969	1004	1038	1072	1106
13	1139	1173	1206	1239	1271	1303	1335	1367	1399	1430
14	1461	1492	1523	1553	1584	1614	1644	1673	1703	1732
15	1761	1790	1818	1847	1875	1903	1931	1959	1987	2014
16	2041	2068	2095	2122	2148	2175	2201	2227	2253	2279
17	2304	2330	2355	2380	2405	2430	2455	2480	2504	2529
18	2553	2577	2601	2625	2648	2672	2695	2718	2742	2765
19	2788	2810	2833	2856	2878	2900	2923	2945	2967	2989
20	3010	3032	3054	3075	3096	3118	3139	3160	3181	3201
21	3222	3243	3263	3284	3304	3324	3345	3365	3385	3404
22	3424	3444	3464	3483	3502	3522	3541	3560	3579	3598
23	3617	3636	3655	3674	3692	3711	3729	3747	3766	3784
24	3802	3820	3838	3856	3874	3892	3909	3927	3945	3962
25	3979	3997	4014	4031	4048	4065	4082	4099	4116	4133
26	4150	4166	4183	4200	4216	4232	4249	4265	4281	4298
27	4314	4330	4346	4362	4378	4393	4409	4425	4440	4456
28	4472	4487	4502	4518	4533	4548	4564	4579	4594	4609
29	4624	4639	4654	4669	4683	4698	4713	4728	4742	4757
30	4771	4786	4800	4814	4829	4843	4857	4871	4886	4900
31	4914	4928	4942	4955	4969	4983	4997	5011	5024	5038
32	5051	5065	5079	5092	5105	5119	5132	5145	5159	5172
33	5185	5198	5211	5224	5237	5250	5263	5276	5289	5302
34	5315	5328	5340	5353	5366	5378	5391	5403	5416	5428
35	5441	5453	5465	5478	5490	5502	5514	5527	5539	5551
36	5563	5575	5587	5599	5611	5623	5635	5647	5658	5670
37	5682	5694	5705	5717	5729	5740	5752	5763	5775	5786
38	5798	5809	5821	5832	5843	5855	5866	5877	5888	5899
39	5911	5922	5933	5944	5955	5966	5977	5988	5999	6010
40	6021	6031	6042	6053	6064	6075	6085	6096	6107	6117
41	6128	6138	6149	6160	6170	6180	6191	6201	6212	6222
42	6232	6243	6253	6263	6274	6284	6294	6304	6314	6325
43	6335	6345	6355	6365	6375	6385	6395	6405	6415	6425
44	6435	6444	6454	6464	6474	6484	6493	6503	6513	6522
45	6532	6542	6551	6561	6571	6580	6590	6599	6609	6618
46	6628	6637	6646	6656	6665	6675	6684	6693	6702	6712
47	6721	6730	6739	6749	6758	6767	6776	6785	6794	6803
48	6812	6821	6830	6839	6848	6857	6866	6875	6884	6893
49	6902	6911	6920	6928	6937	6946	6955	6964	6972	6981
50	6990	6998	7007	7016	7024	7033	7042	7050	7059	7067
N	0	1	2	3	4	5	6	7	8	9

COMMON LOGARITHMS (*continued*)

N	0	1	2	3	4	5	6	7	8	9
50	6990	6998	7007	7016	7024	7033	7042	7050	7059	7067
51	7076	7084	7093	7101	7110	7118	7126	7135	7143	7152
52	7160	7168	7177	7185	7193	7202	7210	7218	7226	7235
53	7243	7251	7259	7267	7275	7284	7292	7300	7308	7316
54	7324	7332	7340	7348	7356	7364	7372	7380	7388	7396
55	7404	7412	7419	7427	7435	7443	7451	7459	7466	7474
56	7482	7490	7497	7505	7513	7520	7528	7536	7543	7551
57	7559	7566	7574	7582	7589	7597	7604	7612	7619	7627
58	7634	7642	7649	7657	7664	7672	7679	7686	7694	7701
59	7709	7716	7723	7731	7738	7745	7752	7760	7767	7774
60	7782	7789	7796	7803	7810	7818	7825	7832	7839	7846
61	7853	7860	7868	7875	7882	7889	7896	7903	7910	7917
62	7924	7931	7938	7945	7952	7959	7966	7973	7980	7987
63	7993	8000	8007	8014	8021	8028	8035	8041	8048	8055
64	8062	8069	8075	8082	8089	8096	8102	8109	8116	8122
65	8129	8136	8142	8149	8156	8162	8169	8176	8182	8189
66	8195	8202	8209	8215	8222	8228	8235	8241	8248	8254
67	8261	8267	8274	8280	8287	8293	8299	8306	8312	8319
68	8325	8331	8338	8344	8351	8357	8363	8370	8376	8382
69	8388	8395	8401	8407	8414	8420	8426	8432	8439	8445
70	8451	8457	8463	8470	8476	8482	8488	8494	8500	8506
71	8513	8519	8525	8531	8537	8543	8549	8555	8561	8567
72	8573	8579	8585	8591	8597	8603	8609	8615	8621	8627
73	8633	8639	8645	8651	8657	8663	8669	8675	8681	8686
74	8692	8698	8704	8710	8716	8722	8727	8733	8739	8745
75	8751	8756	8762	8768	8774	8779	8785	8791	8797	8802
76	8808	8814	8820	8825	8831	8837	8842	8848	8854	8859
77	8865	8871	8876	8882	8887	8893	8899	8904	8910	8915
78	8921	8927	8932	8938	8943	8949	8954	8960	8965	8971
79	8976	8982	8987	8993	8998	9004	9009	9015	9020	9025
80	9031	9036	9042	9047	9053	9058	9063	9069	9074	9079
81	9085	9090	9096	9101	9106	9112	9117	9122	9128	9133
82	9138	9143	9149	9154	9159	9165	9170	9175	9180	9186
83	9191	9196	9201	9206	9212	9217	9222	9227	9232	9238
84	9243	9248	9253	9258	9263	9269	9274	9279	9284	9289
85	9294	9299	9304	9309	9315	9320	9325	9330	9335	9340
86	9345	9350	9355	9360	9365	9370	9375	9380	9385	9390
87	9395	9400	9405	9410	9415	9420	9425	9430	9435	9440
88	9445	9450	9455	9460	9465	9469	9474	9479	9484	9489
89	9494	9499	9504	9509	9513	9518	9523	9528	9533	9538
90	9542	9547	9552	9557	9562	9566	9571	9576	9581	9586
91	9590	9595	9600	9605	9609	9614	9619	9624	9628	9633
92	9638	9643	9647	9652	9657	9661	9666	9671	9675	9680
93	9685	8689	9694	9699	9703	9708	9713	9717	9722	9727
94	9731	9736	9741	9745	9750	9754	9759	9763	9768	9773
95	9777	9782	9786	9791	9795	9800	9805	9809	9814	9818
96	9823	9827	9832	9836	9841	9845	9850	9854	9859	9863
97	9868	9872	9877	9881	9886	9890	9894	9899	9903	9908
98	9912	9917	9921	9926	9930	9934	9939	9943	9948	9952
99	9956	9961	9965	9969	9974	9978	9983	9987	9991	9996
100	0000	0004	0009	0013	0017	0022	0026	0030	0035	0039
N	0	1	2	3	4	5	6	7	8	9

EXPONENTIAL FUNCTIONS

x	e^x	e^{-x}	x	e^x	e^{-x}
0.00	1.0000	1.0000	2.5	12.182	0.0821
0.05	1.0513	0.9512	2.6	13.464	0.0743
0.10	1.1052	0.9048	2.7	14.880	0.0672
0.15	1.1618	0.8607	2.8	16.445	0.0608
0.20	1.2214	0.8187	2.9	18.174	0.0550
0.25	1.2840	0.7788	3.0	20.086	0.0498
0.30	1.3499	0.7408	3.1	22.198	0.0450
0.35	1.4191	0.7047	3.2	24.533	0.0408
0.40	1.4918	0.6703	3.3	27.113	0.0369
0.45	1.5683	0.6376	3.4	29.964	0.0334
0.50	1.6487	0.6065	3.5	33.115	0.0302
0.55	1.7333	0.5769	3.6	36.598	0.0273
0.60	1.8221	0.5488	3.7	40.447	0.0247
0.65	1.9155	0.5220	3.8	44.701	0.0224
0.70	2.0138	0.4966	3.9	49.402	0.0202
0.75	2.1170	0.4724	4.0	54.598	0.0183
0.80	2.2255	0.4493	4.1	60.340	0.0166
0.85	2.3396	0.4274	4.2	66.686	0.0150
0.90	2.4596	0.4066	4.3	73.700	0.0136
0.95	2.5857	0.3867	4.4	81.451	0.0123
1.0	2.7183	0.3679	4.5	90.017	0.0111
1.1	3.0042	0.3329	4.6	99.484	0.0101
1.2	3.3201	0.3012	4.7	109.95	0.0091
1.3	3.6693	0.2725	4.8	121.51	0.0082
1.4	4.0552	0.2466	4.9	134.29	0.0074
1.5	4.4817	0.2231	5	148.41	0.0067
1.6	4.9530	0.2019	6	403.43	0.0025
1.7	5.4739	0.1827	7	1096.6	0.0009
1.8	6.0496	0.1653	8	2981.0	0.0003
1.9	6.6859	0.1496	9	8103.1	0.0001
2.0	7.3891	0.1353	10	22026	0.00005
2.1	8.1662	0.1225			
2.2	9.0250	0.1108			
2.3	9.9742	0.1003			
2.4	11.023	0.0907			

ANSWERS TO ODD-NUMBERED PROBLEMS

CHAPTER 2

2.1 (a) 1.6736×10^{-27} kg; (b) 26.565×10^{-27} kg

2.5 28.8 amu = 4.788×10^{-26} kg; 2.70×10^{19} molecules cm^{-3}; 5.4×10^{18} molecules cm^{-3}; 2.16×10^{19} molecules cm^{-3}

2.7 $1.26g$ hr^{-1}; 9.28×10^{17} molecules cm^{-2} s^{-1}

2.9 For a cubical model: 3.34×10^{-9} m; 3.10×10^{-10} m; 2.28×10^{-10} m. For a spherical model: 2.07×10^{-9} m; 1.92×10^{-10} m; 1.41×10^{-10} m.

2.11 5.5×10^3 kg m^{-3}; 1.4×10^3 kg m^{-3}

2.13 6.71×10^8 mi hr^{-1}; 7.5 trips per second; 9.46×10^{15} m or 5.88×10^{12} mi

2.15 4.05×10^{16} m, 4.3 light years, 2.72×10^5 AU

2.17 37.2°

2.19 (a) ~26°, ~45°, ~30°; (b) ~10°, 15°, 9.8°; (c) ~4°, 5.4°, 3.2°

CHAPTER 3

3.1 (a) 15 units, 0°; (b) 13.1 units, 35°27′; (c) 10.8 units, 56°6′; (d) 4.9 units, 104°6′; (e) 3 units, 180°

3.3 13.7 units; 20 units

3.5 124°48′; 8.67 units

3.7 (a) 9.2 units, 49°; (b) 12.8 units, 38°40′; (c) 15.6 units, 20°20′

3.9 13.2 units, 58°30′

3.17 $\boldsymbol{R} = \boldsymbol{u}_x(6) + \boldsymbol{u}_y(6) + \boldsymbol{u}_z(0)$; $R = 8.48$, $\alpha = 45°$, $\beta = 45°$, $\gamma = 90°$

3.21 20.3 units

3.25 $(x - 4)/-5 = (y - 5)/5 = (z + 7)/5$; $(x - 6)/-5 = y/5 = (z + 8/5)/5$

3.37 (a) Using the points given cyclicly to define the planes: $\boldsymbol{S}_1 = \boldsymbol{u}_z(-2)$, $\boldsymbol{S}_2 = \boldsymbol{u}_x(1) + \boldsymbol{u}_y(1)$, $\boldsymbol{S}_3 = \boldsymbol{u}_x(-1) + \boldsymbol{u}_z(1)$, $\boldsymbol{S}_4 = \boldsymbol{u}_y(-1) + \boldsymbol{u}_z(1)$; (b) $\boldsymbol{S} = 0$; (c) 6.24

3.39 60°; $(\sqrt{5}/3)a$

CHAPTER 4

4.1 410 lbf, 385 lbf

4.3 (a) 9.16 kgf; (b) 4 kgf

4.5 84.6 N, 75°45′

4.7 $\boldsymbol{\tau}_1 = \boldsymbol{u}_x(0) + \boldsymbol{u}_y(7500) + \boldsymbol{u}_z(1500)$ lbf ft;
$\boldsymbol{\tau}_2 = \boldsymbol{u}_x(2700) + \boldsymbol{u}_y(-400) + \boldsymbol{u}_z(-800)$ lbf ft;
$\boldsymbol{\tau}_3 = \boldsymbol{u}_x(450) + \boldsymbol{u}_y(100) + \boldsymbol{u}_z(-100)$ lbf ft

4.9 $24\sqrt{5}$ N m; $y = \frac{1}{2}x + 5$

4.11 With the origin at A, $\boldsymbol{R} = \boldsymbol{u}_x(2.33) + \boldsymbol{u}_y(3.17)$ N; $\boldsymbol{\tau}_A = \boldsymbol{u}_z(-1.4)$ N m; $\boldsymbol{\tau}_B = \boldsymbol{u}_z(-0.47)$ N m; $\boldsymbol{\tau}_c = \boldsymbol{u}_z(-1.9)$ N m

4.13 2 m

4.15 Along major diagonal, 1.77 ft from near corner; 2 lbf

4.17 25.7 lbf, line of action makes an angle of 61°40′ with the horizontal axis

4.19 Zero; but because the resultant torque with respect to the origin is $\tau = 55$ kgf cm, the system is replaced by a couple whose torque is 55 kgf cm

4.21 6600 dyn (6.7 gmf), 77.3 cm

4.23 $R_A = 1143$ N, $R_B = 1797$ N

4.25 30 kgf, 50 kgf

4.27 (a) 60 lbf; (b) 69 lbf

4.29 73.3 kgf; 156.3 kgf

4.31 25.9 kgf; 36.7 kgf

4.33 $W \sec \alpha$; $W \tan \alpha$

4.35 (a) 70.7 kgf, 50 kgf, 10 kgf; (b) 86.1 kgf, 43 kgf, 15 kgf; (c) 38.9 kgf, 29.8 kgf, 15 kgf

4.39 4170 N at 196 cm to the right of A

4.41 6690 kgf, 7010 kgf

4.43 $F_A = 110 - 12.5x$ kgf (x measured from A); $F_B = 10 + 12.5x$ kgf

4.45 58.6 kgf; 81.5 kgf

4.47 $W \cos \alpha$, $W \sin \alpha$; $\tan \phi = \cot 2\alpha$

4.49 $F_1 = F_3 = 9.84$ lbf, $F_2 = 37.05$ lbf

4.51 (a) From center of square $x_c = 2.07$ in., $y_c = 0$; (b) $x_c = 0.565$ in., $y_c = -0.251$ in.; (c) along the symmetry axis 5.89 in. up from the base

4.53 $x_c = 1.77$ cm, $y_c = 4.23$ cm

4.55 $(\sqrt{5}/12)a$ up altitude from the base

CHAPTER 5

5.1 1.125×10^{14} m s^{-2}

5.3 288 km hr^{-1}; 5.33 m s^{-2}

5.5 9.25 m

5.9 18 s; 180 m

5.13 (a) 10 m; (b) 0, 2.7 s; (c) 4 m s^{-1}; (d) $16 - 12t_0 - 6\,\Delta t$; (e) $16 - 12t$; (f) 16 m s^{-1}; (g) 1.33 s, 10.7 m; (h) -12 m s^{-2}; (i) -12 m s^{-2}; (j) never; (l) motion is retarded until $t = 1.33$ s, motion is accelerated thereafter

5.15 $v = 4t - t^3 - 1$; $x = 2t^2 - t^4/12 - t + \frac{3}{4}$

5.17 $v = v_0/(1 + Kv_0t)$; $x = x_0 + (1/K) \ln (1 + Kv_0t)$; $v = v_0e^{-K(x-x_0)}$

5.19 (a) Motion is in the positive direction except for 2.2 s $< t <$ 2.8 s; (b) the body is instantaneously retarded at 0.8 s and 2.2 s; it is instantaneously accelerated at 1.8 s and 2.8 s; (c) 0.28 s, 2.65 s, and 3.0 s; (d) between 0.8 s and 1.8 s. From the graph, the average velocities are: (a) -2.25 m s^{-1}; (b) 1.25 m s^{-1}; (c) 0

5.21 1.43 s; 2.65 s; 18.6 m

5.23 119 ft; 25 ft; 96 ft s^{-1}

5.27 12.2 s

5.29 574 ft

5.31 (a) 6.2 s; (b) 34.3 s

5.33 2.6×10^{-6} rad s^{-1}; 991 m s^{-1}; 2.6×10^{-4} m s^{-2}

5.35 2.4×10^5 m s^{-1}; 2.4×10^{-10} m s^{-2}

5.37 2 rad s^{-2}; 125 rad

5.39 5.33×10^{10} m s^{-2}

5.41 1.13 ft

5.43 15.6 min

5.45 $20t$ rad s^{-1}; 20 rad s^{-2}

5.47 10 s

5.49 20 m

5.51 38.4 ft s^{-1}, 48 ft

5.53 $v = A\omega \cos \omega t$; $a = -A\omega^2 \sin \omega t = -\omega^2 x$; $v = \omega\sqrt{A^2 - x^2}$

5.55 (a) $x^{1/2} - y^{1/2} = 1$; (b) the path is a parabola; (c) $t = 0.5$ s; (d) (16, 9), (9, 16); (e) $a_T = (4t - 2)/\sqrt{2t^2 - 2t + 1}$ ft s^{-2}, $a_N = 2/\sqrt{2t^2 - 2t + 1}$ ft s^{-2}; (f) $a_T = 2$ ft s^{-2}, $a_N = 2$ ft s^{-2}

5.57 (a) $x^2 + y^2 = 4$; (b) 2ω cm s^{-1}; (c) $a_T = 0$, $a_N = 2$ cm s^{-2}

5.59 $y^2 = 4x$

5.61 (a) 31.8 km; (b) 27.5 km; (c) 375 m s^{-1}, 11.2 km; (d) 405 m s^{-1}, 25 s, 79 s

5.63 (a) 204 m s^{-1}; (b) 23.9 s; (c) 700 m; (d) 171 m s^{-1}

5.65 $(2v_0^2/g) \cos \alpha \sec^2 \phi \sin (\alpha - \phi)$

5.67 3°10′ and 89°

CHAPTER 6

6.1 20 km hr^{-1}; 160 km hr^{-1}

6.3 3:11 P.M., 318 km; 8:40 P.M., 867 km

6.5 100 km hr^{-1}, N 53°8′ W; 100 km hr^{-1}, N 53°8′ E

6.7 (a) S 41°19′ E; (b) 1 hr 34 min

6.9 Man in boat, 40 min; man walking, 30 min

6.11 Man across and back, 34.64 min; man up and down, 40 min

6.13 (a) Constant horizontal velocity of 100 ft s^{-1}, constant vertical acceleration g; (b) as in (a), but horizontal velocity is 800 ft s^{-1}; (c) 29° above or below the horizontal

6.15 (a) 15 m s^{-1}; (b) 45 m s^{-1}; (c) 36.6 m s^{-1}

6.17 3.27 cm

6.19 6.56×10^{-3} m s^{-2}

6.23 For noncoincident origins $\boldsymbol{V} = \boldsymbol{v}_{OO'} + \boldsymbol{\omega} \times \boldsymbol{r}' + \boldsymbol{V}'$,
$\boldsymbol{a} = \boldsymbol{a}_{OO'} + \boldsymbol{\omega} \times (\boldsymbol{\omega} \times \boldsymbol{r}') + \boldsymbol{\alpha} \times \boldsymbol{r}' + 2\boldsymbol{\omega} \times \boldsymbol{V}' + \boldsymbol{a}'$

6.25 $0.866c$

6.27 (a) 1.6 s; (b) 2.3×10^8 m; (c) 0.96 s

6.29 (a) 4.588×10^{-6} s; (b) 4305 m

6.31 7.5 years; 6.25 years; 1.25 years

6.33 6×10^{10} m; $0.9c$

6.35 8.04 hr

6.43 0.82 m, 59°5′, in the direction of motion

CHAPTER 7

7.1 (a) 14.4 m s^{-1}, W 0°47′ S; (b) $\boldsymbol{p} = \boldsymbol{u}_{\text{west}}(19.2) + \boldsymbol{u}_{\text{north}}(8)$ kg m s^{-1}; (c) $\Delta\boldsymbol{p}_1 = \boldsymbol{u}_{\text{west}}(-24) + \boldsymbol{u}_{\text{north}}(8.4)$ kg m s^{-1}, $\Delta\boldsymbol{p}_2 = \boldsymbol{u}_{\text{west}}(24) + \boldsymbol{u}_{\text{north}}(-8.4)$ kg m s^{-1}; (d) $\Delta\boldsymbol{v}_1 = \boldsymbol{u}_{\text{west}}(-7.5) + \boldsymbol{u}_{\text{north}}(2.6)$ m s^{-1}, $\Delta\boldsymbol{v}_2 = \boldsymbol{u}_{\text{west}}(15) + \boldsymbol{u}_{\text{north}}(-5.2)$ m s^{-1}; (e) $\Delta v_1 = 7.9$ m s^{-1}, $\Delta v_2 = 15.9$ m s^{-1}

7.3 3.33×10^4 m s^{-1}, 82°30′ with respect to original direction of H atom

7.5 (a) 0.186 m s^{-1}, 27°30′ below the $+X$-axis; (b) $\Delta\boldsymbol{p}_1 = \Delta\boldsymbol{p}_2 = \boldsymbol{u}_x(-0.049) + \boldsymbol{u}_y(0.026)$ kg m s^{-1}, $\Delta\boldsymbol{v}_1 = \boldsymbol{u}_x(-0.0247) + \boldsymbol{u}_y(0.0128)$ m s^{-1}, $\Delta\boldsymbol{v}_2 = \boldsymbol{u}_x(0.164) + \boldsymbol{u}_y(-0.0857)$ m s^{-1}

7.7 $m_A = 1$ kg, $m_B = 2$ kg

7.9 (a) bt; (b) $-p_0 + bt$

7.11 9 km s^{-1}

7.13 (a) -0.3 kg m s^{-1}, -3 N; (b) -0.45 kg m s^{-1}, -4.5 N; momentum of cart is not conserved because an external force acts

7.15 347 N

7.17 $10^3 g$ dyn

7.19 (a) 14° forward; (b) 20° backward

7.21 116.3 kgf (1139 N)

7.23 75 kgf (735 N)

7.25 (a) 882 N; (b) 882 N; (c) 1152 N; (d) 612 N; (e) 0 N

7.27 $F = -m\omega^2 x$; (a) in negative X-direction; (b) in positive X-direction

7.31 (a) A braking force of 3350 N; (b) a braking force of 3150 N

7.33 (a) $\Delta\boldsymbol{p} = \boldsymbol{u}_N(-9.87 \times 10^3) + \boldsymbol{u}_E(14.1 \times 10^3)$ kg m s^{-1};
(b) 8.6×10^2 N, S 55° E

7.35 (a) $a = (F - m_2 g)/(m_1 + m_2)$, $T = m_2(a + g)$; 166 cm s^{-2}, 9.17×10^4 dyn; (b) $a = [F + (m_1 - m_2)g]/(m_1 + m_2)$, $T = m_2(a + g)$; 543 cm s^{-2}, 1.22×10^5 dyn

7.37 (a) $a = g(m_1 \sin\alpha - m_2)/(m_1 + m_2)$, $T = m_2(a + g)$; -206 m s^{-2}, 1.39×10^5 dyn; (b) $a = g(m_1 \sin\alpha - m_2 \sin\beta)/(m_1 + m_2)$, $T = m_2(a + g \sin\beta)$; -144 cm s^{-2}, 1.50×10^5 dyn

7.39 (b) $[m_1(m_2 + m_3) + 4m_2m_3]g/(m_2 + m_3)$

7.43 15 kg, $g/5$

7.45 0.27 m, $1/\sqrt{3}$

7.47 48.9 lbf T^{-1}

7.49 (a) 1.6 kgf (15.7 N); (b) $0.2g$; (c) relative to the lower block, the upper block will have an acceleration of $0.1g$ toward the rear in the first case and toward the front in the second

7.51 $(v_0/g)(1 - \frac{1}{3} \times 10^{-3}) \cong 6.1$ s, $(v_0^2/2g)(1 - 2.7 \times 10^{-4}) \cong 183.6$ m

7.53 $\tau \ln 2 = 8.66$ s; $\tau = 12.5$ s; 138 m

7.55 8.81×10^{-8} N

7.57 (a) 13.9 N; (b) 33.5 N; (c) 23.7 N; (d) 2.42 m s^{-1}

7.59 2 ft

7.61 (a) 13.6 ft s^{-1}; (b) 247 lbf; (c) 340 lbf; (d) 2.06 rad s^{-1} (777 rev/min)

7.63 125.2 N, 20°10′

7.67 (a) $\boldsymbol{u}_y 15$ kg m s^{-1}; (b) $\boldsymbol{u}_z(105)$ kg m^2 s^{-1}

7.69 Tangent of the angle of the direction of motion with the X-axis is Ft/mv_0 at any time t; $FL^2/2mv_0^2$

7.71 (a) $\boldsymbol{u}_x + \boldsymbol{u}_y(-4t)$ N; (b) $\boldsymbol{u}_x(12t^2 + 8t) + \boldsymbol{u}_y(3t + 2) + \boldsymbol{u}_z(-8t^3 + 24t^2)$ N m; (c) $\boldsymbol{u}_x(36t - 36) + \boldsymbol{u}_y(-72t^2) + \boldsymbol{u}_z(18)$ kg m s^{-1}, $\boldsymbol{u}_x(144t^3 + 144t^2) + \boldsymbol{u}_y(54t^2 + 72t - 72) + \boldsymbol{u}_z(-72t^4 + 288t^3)$ kg m^2 s^{-1};

7.75 3.03×10^4 m s^{-1}; 1.93×10^{-7} rad s^{-1} at aphelion and 2.06×10^{-7} rad s^{-1} at perihelion

7.77 3.37×10^3 m s^{-1}, 14.8 km

CHAPTER 8

8.1 (a) 250 m kg s^{-1}; (b) 25 N

8.3 2927.75 J, 24.4 W

8.5 3300 J, 2000 J, 1500 J, −200 J

8.7 98 N

8.9 23.54 W

8.11 10,258.6 W, 1.03×10^5 J

8.13 There is no maximum velocity if the resistance of the wind remains constant.

8.15 (a) 2.592×10^4 erg; (b) 4.392×10^4 erg; (c) 2,160 erg s^{-1}; (d) 2.592×10^4 erg

8.17 7200 J; 19.6 J, 0.8 rad s^{-1}

8.19 284.2 eV, 5.22 Mev

8.21 7.61×10^6 m s^{-1}

8.23 (a) $\boldsymbol{u}_x(56)$ m kg s^{-1}; (b) 10 s. Results are the same for both cases.

8.25 (a) $\boldsymbol{u}_x(4200)$ N s; (b) $\boldsymbol{u}_x(4260)$ m kg s^{-1}; (d) 590,360 J; (e) 591,260 J

8.27 (a) 50.6 J; (b) 29.4 J; (c) 64 J; (d) 42 J

8.29 (a) −45 J; (b) 75 W, 0.1 hp; (c) −45 J

8.35 (a) 7.2 J; (b) 470.40 J; (c) 477.60 J; (d) 48.8 m s^{-1}

8.37 81.2 m s^{-1}; 13.9 m

8.39 $h = 2R/3$

8.41 7.2×10^{-2} m

8.43 2.45×10^{-2} m; (a) 9.8 m s^{-2}; (b) 5.8 m s^{-2}, 0; −2.2 m s^{-2}, 0.395 m s^{-1}; 0.490 m s^{-2}, 0.477 m s^{-1}; (c) 4.90×10^{-2} m

8.47 1360 J

8.49 $F = W/200$, W = weight of train

8.55 $x = 2$, stable; $x = 0$

CHAPTER 9

9.1 3.417 m s^{-1}, 215°55′

9.3 (a) $x = 1.50 + 0.25t^2$ m, $y = 1.87 + 0.19t^2$ m;
(b) $\boldsymbol{P} = \boldsymbol{u}_x(8t) + \boldsymbol{u}_y(6t)$ N s

9.5 $p = \rho v^2 \cos^2 \theta$

9.7 (a) $\boldsymbol{v}_1 = \boldsymbol{u}_x 10$ m s^{-1}, $\boldsymbol{v}_2 = \boldsymbol{u}_x(-4.00) + \boldsymbol{u}_y(6.96)$ m s^{-1};
(b) $\boldsymbol{v}_{CM} = \boldsymbol{u}_x(1.6) + \boldsymbol{u}_y(4.17)$ m s^{-1};
(c) $\boldsymbol{v}_1' = \boldsymbol{u}_x(8.4) + \boldsymbol{u}_y(-4.17)$ m s^{-1}, $\boldsymbol{v}_2' = \boldsymbol{u}_x(-5.60) + \boldsymbol{u}_y(2.79)$ m s^{-1};
(d) $\boldsymbol{p}_1' = -\boldsymbol{p}_2' = \boldsymbol{u}_x(16.8) + \boldsymbol{u}_y(-8.34)$ m kg s^{-1};
(e) $\boldsymbol{v}_{12} = \boldsymbol{u}_x(14) + \boldsymbol{u}_y(-6.96)$ m s^{-1}; (f) 1.2 kg

9.9 (a) (−0.6, 0.4, 1.6) m; (b) $\boldsymbol{u}_x(-8.35) + \boldsymbol{u}_y(-16.8) + \boldsymbol{u}_z(25.15)$ m^2 kg s^{-1};
(d) $\boldsymbol{u}_x(-13.92) + \boldsymbol{u}_y(28) + \boldsymbol{u}_z(-26.96)$ m^2 kg s^{-1}

9.11 (a) 4.11 MeV, 0.07 MeV; (b) 9.35×10^{-23} m kg s^{-1};
(c) 1.41×10^4 m s^{-1}, 2.41×10^2 m s^{-1}

9.15 $x = [v_0\sqrt{v_0^2 + 2gh} - v_0^2]/g$ on either side

9.17 (a) 0.54 m s^{-1}, 1.13 m s^{-1}; (b) −2.64 kg m s^{-1}, +2.65 kg m s^{-1}

9.19 (a) 0.866 m s^{-1}, 0.2 m s^{-1}; (b) ±1.333 kg m s^{-1}, ±4.0 kg m s^{-1}

9.23 (a) 0.46 m s^{-1}, 1.54 m s^{-1}; (b) 1.57 m s^{-1} and 0.979 m s^{-1} at −50°33′

9.25 (c) $e = 1$

9.27 When m_1 is raised: (a) 0.022 m, 0.089 m; (b) 0.0142 m, 0.0802 m; (c) 0.022 m.
When m_2 is raised: (a) 0.022 m, 0.355 m; (b) 0.025 m, 0.321 m; (c) 0.022 m.

9.29 $v_1' = -ev_1$, $v_2' = 0$, $Q = -\frac{1}{2}(1 - e^2)m_1 v_1^2$, $h' = e^2 h$

9.33 (a) 8; (b) 52; carbon

9.35 $\pi/2$

9.37 About 4

9.39 (a) 48 m^2 kg s^{-1}, 14.4 m^2 kg s^{-1}; (b) 35 J, 15.6 J

9.41 $\boldsymbol{u}_x(0.167) + \boldsymbol{u}_y(-0.083)$ m s^{-1}

9.49 6.17×10^{-21} J or 3.8×10^{-2} eV; (a) 2.73×10^3 m s^{-1}; (b) 0.482×10^3 m s^{-1};
(c) 0.515×10^3 m s^{-1}; He: 1.37×10^3 m s^{-1}; CO_2: 0.413×10^3 m s^{-1}

9.51 12.95×10^2 J

9.53 8.31×10^2 J; 21.26×10^2 J

9.59 45 J or 188.3 cal

9.61 (a) 10 m s^{-1}, 2.37×10^5 N m^{-2}; (b) 0.3 m^3 min^{-1}; (c) 2.5×10^2 J kg^{-1}

CHAPTER 10

10.1 (a) 1.875 m^2 kg, 0.61 m; (b) 0.9375 m^2 kg, 0.434 m; (c) 0.625 m^2 kg, 0.354 m

10.3 (a) 0.040 m^2 kg, 0.028 m; (b) 0.025 m^2 kg, 0.0204 m;
(c) 0.020 m^2 kg s^{-1}, 0.0183 m

10.5 6.80×10^{-46} m^2 kg

10.7 X_0: 5.604×10^{-47} m^2 kg; Y_0: 7.196×10^{-47} m^2 kg; Z_0: 5.527×10^{-47} m^2 kg

10.9 1.34 rad s^{-2}

10.11 325 s; 452 rev

10.13 (a) 0.436 rad s^{-2}; (b) 21.80 rad; (c) 176.58 m^2 kg s^{-1}; (d) 192.49 J

10.15 334.4 N m; 63,104 J

10.17 63.6 m^2 kg s^{-1}, 5997 J; 12.72 N m, 1199.4 W

10.19 $h = 2.7R$

10.21 226,551 J

10.23 (a) $3g \sin\alpha/2L$; (b) $\sqrt{3g \cos\alpha/L}$; (c) $\frac{5}{2}Mg\cos\alpha$ parallel to the radius and $-\frac{1}{4}Mg\cos\alpha$ perpendicular to the radius

10.25 (a) acc. $= 50g\cos\alpha/(2.18 + 10\sin 2\alpha)$;
(b) $a_x = (-\frac{3}{8}L\cos\alpha) \times$ acc., $a_y = (-\frac{5}{8}L\sin\alpha) \times$ acc.

10.27 (a) mva; (b) mv, before; $mv(1 + ML/2ma)/(1 + ML^2/3ma^2)$ after;
(d) $-(\frac{1}{2}mv^2)ML^2/(ML^2 + 3ma^2)$

10.29 (a) 8.702 rad s^{-2}; (b) 4.351 m s^{-2}; (c) 54.49 N

10.31 $a = \frac{2}{3}F(1 - r/R)$ m

10.33 $\alpha = [m - m'(r/R)]g/[\frac{1}{2}M + m + m'(r/R)^2]R$, $a = R\alpha$, $a' = r\alpha$

10.35 (a) 120.05 J; (b) 35.32 N on the left and 32.37 N on the right

10.37 7.84 rad s^{-1}

10.43 (a) $1.40 \times 10^{-2} \times (4\pi)^2$ N m; (b) $\pi/2$

CHAPTER 11

11.3 $c/\sqrt{2}$; $\sqrt{2}\, m_0c^2$; $(\sqrt{2} - 1)m_0c^2$

11.5 (a) $m_0/0.916$; (b) $m_0/0.60$; $\rho_{\text{class}}/\rho_{\text{rel}} = 0.36$

11.7 1.65×10^{-17} m kg s^{-1}; 0.99945c

11.9 $c/1386$; $c/37.2$

11.13 $\Delta E/m_0c^2 = 0.153, 1.141, 0.891, 3.807$

11.15 0.115c; 3.40 keV, 6.28 MeV

11.19 5.34×10^{-22} m kg s^{-1}; 4.97 MeV/c; 2×10^3 MeV/c

11.21 10^{14} m s^{-2}, 0.512×10^{14} m s^{-2}

11.23 (a) 10^{14} m s^{-2}, 0.512×10^{14} m s^{-2}; (b) 1.25×10^{14} m s^{-2}, 0.8×10^{14} m s^{-2}

11.25 (a) 0.918c; (b) 11.876×10^9 eV, 10.898×10^9 eV/c; (d) 1.31×10^9 eV

11.27 (a) 56 GeV; (b) 1780 GeV

11.33 (a) $c^2p_1/(E_1 + m_2c^2)$; (b) $Q = 0$

11.35 (a) $E_4 = (E'^2 - m_3^2c^4)/2E'$, where E' is given by Eq. (11.47). (b) In the L-frame the energy depends on the direction of motion of the resulting particles.

CHAPTER 12

12.1 (a) 2 s; (b) 0.5 Hz; (c) 0.30 m; (d) $x = 0.3\sin(\pi t)$ m

12.3 (a) 4 m, 20π s, $0.05/\pi$ Hz, 0.5 rad;
(b) $v = 0.4\cos(0.1t + 0.5)$ m s^{-1}, $a = -0.04\sin(0.1t + 0.5)$ m s^{-2};
(c) 1.85 m, 0.18 m s^{-1}, -0.02 m s^{-2}; (d) 3.36 m, 0.34 m s^{-1}, -0.03 m s^{-2}

12.5 $10^3/\pi$ Hz, 4 m s^{-1}, 3.2 m s^{-1}; $F = -4 \times 10^3 x$ N, $F = 8 \sin(2 \times 10^3 t + \alpha)$ N

12.7 $2 \times 10^2 \pi$ Hz; (a) $2.6 \times 10^2 \pi$ m s^{-1}; (b) $3 \times 10^4 \pi^2$ m s^{-2}; (c) 30°

12.9 $2.8\pi \times 10^{-2}$ m s^{-1} and $1.4\pi^2 \times 10^{-2}$ m s^{-2}, both toward the center

12.11 $20\pi^2$ m s^{-2}, $10\pi^2$ N, $\frac{1}{4}\pi^2$ J, $\frac{3}{4}\pi^2$ J

12.13 0.24

12.15 $2\pi\sqrt{\rho a}$

12.17 0, $\frac{1}{2}A^2$, where A is the displacement amplitude

12.19 3.80 s; 1.90 s

12.21 18.6 min; 0.988 m

12.23 32°10′

12.25 $5.88y\sqrt{1 + 2/y}$ N, $9.8y\sqrt{1 + 2/y}$ m s^{-2}, $4.43\sqrt{4 \times 10^{-2} - y}$ m s^{-1}, arccos $(1 - y)$, where y is the vertical height of the bob in m; 1.68 N, 2.8 m s^{-2}, 0 m s^{-1}, 16°15′; 0 N, 0 m s^{-2}, 0.886 m s^{-1}, 0°; 16°15′

12.27 (a) 1.9×10^{-3}, 8.12×10^{-6}; (b) 1.68×10^{-2}, 6.31×10^{-4}

12.29 1.71 s, $\frac{2}{3}$ m; 1.71 s

12.31 (a) $4\pi[(h^2 + \frac{1}{3}L^2)/(2h + L)]^{1/2}$; (b) no

12.33 3.565×10^{-3} N m (per rad)

12.37 14 sin $2t$; 10 cos $2t$; −2 sin $2t$

12.39 $y = \frac{3}{4}x$; $x^2/16 + y^2/9 = 1$; $y = -\frac{3}{4}x$

12.45 $A = x_0/\sin\alpha$; $\alpha = \arctan[\omega x_0/(v_0 + x_0\Upsilon)]$; if $v_0 = 0$, $A = x_0\omega_0/\omega$ and $\alpha = \arctan(\omega/\Upsilon)$

12.47 $\omega = 0$; $A = x_0$, $B = \Upsilon x_0$

12.49 1.44 s^{-1}

12.53 (b) approx. 0.6 of the original amplitude; (c) 1.386τ; (d) $(\frac{1}{2})^n A_0$, where n is an integer and A_0 is the original amplitude

12.57 $d^2x/dt^2 + \omega_0^2 x = (F_0/m)\cos\omega_f t$

12.59 (a) $(4/\sin\alpha)\sqrt{2h/g}$; (b) yes, no

12.61 $\omega \cong \omega_0(\sqrt{3}\, x_0/2l_0)$; $d^2x/dt^2 + (k/l_0^2)x^3 - (k/2ml_0^4)x^5 = 0$

12.63 (a) $d^2x/dt^2 = F/m = (4F_0/\pi m)(\sin\omega t + \frac{1}{3}\sin 3\omega t + \cdots)$; (b) $A = -4F_0/\pi m\omega^2$, $B = A/27$, $C = A/125$

12.67 (a) No; away from the equilibrium point; no; (b) $F = -kx + ax^2$

12.69 (a) Yes; does not move; yes; (b) $F = -kx + ax^3$

12.71 x_1, $\frac{1}{2}(A^2 + B^2)$; 0, $\frac{1}{2}(A^2 + B^2)$

CHAPTER 13

13.1 (a) 3.557×10^{22} N; (b) 1.985×10^{20} N; 1.79×10^2

13.3 3.62×10^{-48} N

13.5 Approx. 2×10^{-10} m (*cf.* Problem 2.9); 1.49×10^{-42} N

13.7 (a) $2.96 \times 10^5:1$; (b) $1.65 \times 10^3:1$

13.9 (a) 17.5 kgf; (b) 140 kgf

13.11 3.06×10^4 kgf; 18.8 kgf; 110 kg

13.13 $(1.976 \pm 0.012) \times 10^{30}$ kg

13.15 32.1 km; 64.1 km

13.17 (a) 7.73×10^3 m s^{-1}; (b) 3.42×10^3 s; (c) 8.965 m s^{-2}

13.19 3.5 days; 2:1

13.21 (c) $r = 6.37 \times 10^6 \cos(1.24 \times 10^{-3}t)$ m;
$v = 7.90 \times 10^3 \sin(1.24 \times 10^{-3}t)$ m s^{-1};
$a = -9.80 \cos(1.24 \times 10^{-3}t)$ m s^{-2}

13.23 (a) $\sqrt{2\Upsilon m_e/h + R_e}$; (b) no; (c) yes

13.31 (a) 4.31×10^4 m s^{-1}; (b) 1.23×10^4 m s^{-1}

13.35 $-(8\Upsilon m^2/a)[3(1 + 1/\sqrt{2}) + 1/\sqrt{3}]$; -4.03×10^{35} J

13.37 -1.09×10^{48} J, based on a density of 1.6×10^{-32} kg m^{-3}

13.39 1.02×10^4 m s^{-1}

13.41 (a) 3.45×10^8 m from the earth; (b) almost escape velocity;
(c) 2.37×10^3 m s^{-1}

13.43 2.82×10^{14} m^2 kg s^{-1}; 1.25×10^{11} J; -2.50×10^{11} J; -1.25×10^{11} J

13.45 (a) 1.78×10^8 N m, 4.16 days; (b) 0.112 MW, 7.5 days; (c) 30 revolutions

13.47 2.16×10^{-14} rad s^{-1}; 3.70×10^{53} m^2 kg s^{-1}; -4.0×10^{39} J

13.51 Mercury: (a) 4.59×10^{10} m; (b) 6.98×10^{10} m; (c) -3.74×10^{31} J;
(d) 9.955×10^{38} m^2 kg s^{-1}; (e) 7.60×10^6 s; (f) 4.35×10^4 m s^{-1};
6.61×10^4 m s^{-1}.
Earth: (a) 1.47×10^{11} m; (b) 1.52×10^{11} m; (c) -2.64×10^{32} J;
(d) 2.718×10^{40} m^2 kg s^{-1}; (e) 3.16×10^7 s; (f) 2.92×10^4 m s^{-1};
3.02×10^4 m s^{-1}.
Mars: (a) 2.07×10^{12} m; (b) 2.49×10^{12} m; (c) -1.85×10^{31} J;
(d) 3.445×10^{39} m^2 kg s^{-1}; (e) 5.94×10^7 s; (f) 2.19×10^3 m s^{-1};
2.64×10^3 m s^{-1}

13.53 (a) 3.21×10^{12} m^2 kg s^{-1}; (b) -9.31×10^8 J; (c) 0.191;
(d) 6.37×10^6 m, 2.29×10^6 m; (e) 1.071×10^7 m; (f) 1.10×10^4 s

13.55 (a) 8.69×10^6 m; (b) 0.193; (c) $8.36 \times 10^6/r = 1 + 0.193 \cos\theta$;
(d) 1.62×10^3 m s^{-1}, 1.10×10^3 m s^{-1}; (e) 8.06×10^3 s; (f) -2.295×10^9 J

13.57 (a) $m(1.06 \times 10^7)$ J, $m(3.65 \times 10^{15})$ m^2 kg s^{-1};
(b) $1.009 \times 10^{11}/r = 1 + 24.5 \cos\theta$; (c) 5.0×10^{10} m

13.63 $r = R(1 + \cos\theta)$; $r = 2R(1 + \cos\theta)$

13.65 $r_2 = \frac{1}{3}r_1$, or r_1; $\frac{2}{3}r_1$, or r_1; $\frac{1}{2}$ or 0

13.67 9.8 m s^{-2}, 6.26×10^7 m^2 s^{-2}

13.69 For the sun: 5.9×10^{-3} m s^{-2}, 1.22×10^9 m^2 s^{-2};
for the moon: 3.32×10^{-5} m s^{-2}, 1.28×10^4 m^2 s^{-2}

13.71 $-3.01 \times 10^{-12} m/a^2$; $3.0 \times 10^{-11} m/a$

13.75 (a) $v^2 = (2\Upsilon m/R)(1 - 1/\sqrt{1 + h^2/R^2})$; (b) $-h$; (c) yes; when the value of h is small compared with R; $2\pi\sqrt{\Upsilon m/R^3}$.

INDEX

ABCDE69876

Table A–3 Units and Symbols

Quantity	Symbol	Name of unit	Relation to fundamental units	
			MKSC	MKSA
Length	l, s	meter	m	
Mass	m	kilogram	kg	
Time	t	second	s	
Velocity	v		$m\ s^{-1}$	
Acceleration	a		$m\ s^{-2}$	
Angular velocity	ω		s^{-1}	
Angular frequency	ω		s^{-1}	
Frequency	ν	hertz (Hz)	s^{-1}	
Momentum	p		$m\ kg\ s^{-1}$	
Force	F	newton (N)	$m\ kg\ s^{-2}$	
Angular momentum	L		$m^2\ kg\ s^{-1}$	
Torque	τ		$m^2\ kg\ s^{-2}$	
Work	W	joule (J)	$m^2\ kg\ s^{-2}$	
Power	P	watt (W)	$m^2\ kg\ s^{-3}$	
Energy	E_k, E_p, U, E	joule (J)	$m^2\ kg\ s^{-2}$	
Temperature	T	°K	$m^2\ kg\ s^{-2}$/particle	
Coefficient of diffusion	D		$m^2\ s^{-1}$	
Coefficient of thermal conductivity	K		$m\ kg\ s^{-3}\ °K^{-1}$	
Coefficient of viscosity	η		$m^{-1}\ kg\ s^{-1}$	
Young's modulus	Y		$m^{-1}\ kg\ s^{-2}$	
Bulk modulus	κ		$m^{-1}\ kg\ s^{-2}$	
Shear modulus	G		$m^{-1}\ kg\ s^{-2}$	
Moment of inertia	I		$m^2\ kg$	
Gravitational field	$\mathcal{G}$		$m\ s^{-2}$	
Gravitational potential	$V_{\mathcal{G}}$		$m^2\ s^{-2}$	
Charge	q, Q	coulomb	C	A s
Electric current	I	ampere	$s^{-1}\ C$	A
Electric field	$\mathcal{E}$		$m\ kg\ s^{-2}\ C^{-1}$	$m\ kg\ s^{-3}\ A^{-1}$
Electric potential	V	volt (V)	$m^2\ kg\ s^{-2}\ C^{-1}$	$m^2\ kg\ s^{-3}\ A^{-1}$
Current density	j		$m^{-2}\ s^{-1}\ C$	$m^{-2}\ A$
Electric resistance	R	ohm (Ω)	$m^2\ kg\ s^{-1}\ C^{-2}$	$m^2\ kg\ s^{-3}\ A^{-2}$
Inductance	L	henry (H)	$m^2\ kg\ C^{-2}$	$m^2\ kg\ s^{-2}\ A^{-2}$
Electric permittivity	ϵ_0		$m^{-3}\ kg^{-1}\ s^2\ C^2$	$m^{-3}\ kg^{-1}\ s\ A^2$
Polarization	$\mathcal{P}$		$m^{-2}\ C$	$m^{-2}\ s\ A$
Dielectric displacement	$\mathcal{D}$		$m^{-2}\ C$	$m^{-2}\ s\ A$
Magnetic field	$\mathcal{B}$	tesla (T)	$kg\ s^{-1}\ C^{-1}$	$kg\ s^{-2}\ A^{-1}$
Magnetic permeability	μ_0		$m\ kg\ C^{-2}$	$m\ kg\ s^{-2}\ A^{-2}$
Magnetization	$\mathcal{M}$		$m^{-1}\ s^{-1}\ C$	$m^{-1}\ A$
Magnetizing field	$\mathcal{H}$		$m^{-1}\ s^{-1}\ C$	$m^{-1}\ A$
Magnetic flux	$\Phi_{\mathcal{B}}$	weber (Wb)	$m^2\ kg\ s^{-1}\ C^{-1}$	$m^2\ kg\ s^{-2}\ A^{-1}$
Electric dipole moment	p		m C	m s A
Electric quadrupole moment	Q		$m^2\ C$	$m^2\ s\ A$
Magnetic dipole moment	M		$m^2\ s^{-1}\ C$	$m^2\ A$
Magnetic quadrupole moment	Q		$m^3\ s^{-1}\ C$	$m^3\ A$
Capacity	C	farad (F)	$m^{-2}\ kg^{-1}\ s^2\ C^2$	$m^{-2}\ kg^{-1}\ s^4\ A^2$